THE HISTORICAL ATLAS OF BREEDING BIRDS IN
BRITAIN AND IRELAND: 1875–1900

First published in 1996
by T. & A. D. Poyser Ltd.
24–28 Oval Road, London NW1 7DX

United States Edition published by
ACADEMIC PRESS INC.
San Diego, CA 92101

A catalogue record for this book is available from the British Library

Text set in 9/10pt Bembo
Typeset by P & R Typesetters Ltd, Salisbury
Printed and bound in Great Britain by Butler and Tanner, Frome, Somerset

This book is printed on acid-free paper

ISBN 0-85661-094-1

Contents

Abbreviations used in the text

BOC	British Ornithologists' Club
BOU	British Ornithologists' Union
BSBI	Botanical Society of the British Isles
CBC	Common Birds Census (British Trust for Ornithology)
E	East
FC	Forestry Commission
FLS	Fellow of the Linnean Society
FRSE	Fellow of the Royal Society of Edinburgh
FZS	Fellow of the Zoological Society
FZS (Scotland)	FZS of Scotland
ha	hectare
km	kilometre
MBOU	Member of the BOU
m	metre
N	north
RBBP	Rare Breeding Birds Panel
RSPB	Royal Society for the Protection of Birds
S	South
10-km square	10km x 10km square of the British or Irish National Grids
W	West

Frequently cited references

88–91 Atlas. GIBBONS, D.W., J.B. REID and R.A. CHAPMAN, 1993. *The New Atlas of Breeding Birds in Britain and Ireland: 1988–91.* T. & A.D. Poyser, London.

68–72 Atlas. SHARROCK, J.T.R., 1976. *The Atlas of Breeding Birds in Britain and Ireland.* T. & A.D. Poyser, Berkhamsted.

The present volume is referred to as the *1875–1900 Atlas.*

Introduction

Historical Background

Several historical reviews of the birds of Britain and Ireland have been undertaken this century, and in each case the extensive ornithological literature of the 19th century has been examined. The focus of these reviews has, in the main, been an interpretation of the modern status of birds in the light of the changes that have occurred since the 19th century. This is, of course, an important avenue of research and the changes that have occurred over the last 100–150 years have had an enormous impact on the avifauna of today. This volume focuses on the status of breeding birds of the period 1875–1900. This was an important period during which the environment and the habitats of plants and animals in Britain and Ireland were changing rapidly. It followed immense changes in the landscape as a consequence of the development of agriculture, was coincident with the industrial revolution during which rapid widespread, wholesale changes to the environment were made, and occurred at a time when the persecution of birds and mammals was at its most thoughtless height. The same period, however, saw the beginning of the Sentimentalist backlash, the belief of some Victorians that the new Humanitarianism movement should encompass animals and that cruelty to animals corrupted those who indulged in it.

Any survey of the birds of this period is assisted by the enormous increase in the number of published works that started in about 1840. For instance the number of papers and books concerned with the ornithology of Devonshire rose from a maximum of four per decade up to the 1820s to 99 during the 1870s (Table 1).

The rise of the leisured clergy and gentry and the post-Darwinian interest in the science of the natural world made this a respectable area of study for second sons and for returning soldiers from the Napoleonic wars (in this case, however, running parallel with the interest in sporting expeditions), and created a huge interest in the field of scientific discovery. In 1866 the first of the modern county avifaunas were published. These were the *Birds of Middlesex* (Harting 1866) and the *Birds of Norfolk* (Stevenson 1866–90). The attachment that many people felt towards their place of origin or residence, coupled with the contemporary growth in ornithological knowledge, was probably the stimulus for the series of county avifaunas that followed those of 1866 and has not been matched since. By the early part of the 20th century all but a very few English and Welsh counties had their own account of the birds of the area and, albeit stretched across many shelves, an almost complete survey of the birds of Britain and Ireland was in existence.

The 20th century saw a change in emphasis in ornithological research and the details of the distribution of bird populations took a back seat to the investigation of their biology. From the 1950s, however, new attempts were made to map the distribution of birds. Research by J. L. F. Parslow for *The Status of Birds in Britain and Ireland* (1973) built on the earlier, rather sketchy, work of Alexander and Lack (1944) and provided information on status and distribution that was used widely around that time by several other publications. In 1960, however, C. A. Norris published a paper containing the results of a new approach in ornithology. This was a survey in 1952 of the distribution of 30 species based on the 25-km square. Eventually, a similar grid based approach was adopted during field work for *The Atlas of Breeding Birds in Britain and Ireland* (Sharrock 1976). This was the result of a national survey during 1968–1972 based on the 10-km square and forms the basis on which many future distributional studies will be based.

The present work aims, with the aid of the published literature of the time, to provide a benchmark survey of the distributions of birds in Britain and Ireland during 1875–1900, to allow comparison with the *68–72 Atlas*. It is the first attempt to map the historical distribution of all birds breeding in Britain and Ireland at county level and to determine the geographical differences in abundance between each county.

Counties and faunal regions

The Watsonian vice-counties
Hewett Cottrell Watson (1804–81), a noted English amateur botanist of the 19th century, devoted much of his life to recording and studying the distribution of vascular plants in Great Britain; his name is commemorated in *Watsonia*, the title of the current scientific journal of the Botanical Society of the British Isles (BSBI). The phytogeographical work which he initiated in 1832 by the publication of his *Outlines of the Geographical Distribution of British Plants*, and afterwards elaborated in his *Cybele Britannica* (1847–59) and *Topographical Botany* (1873–74), led eventually to the production in 1962 of the modern *Atlas of the British Flora*, edited by F. H. Perring and S. M. Walters for the BSBI. The cartographic unit used in this atlas was the 10-km square of the Ordnance Survey National Grid—a much smaller unit than any used by

Table 1. *The published literature on the birds of Devonshire, 1790–1909.*

Decade	1790	1800	1810	1820	1830	1840	1850	1860	1870	1880	1890	1900
No.	2	4	1	4	10	22	54	87	99	69	73	54

Source: Mullens and Swann (1919–20)

Watson, but a logical continuation of his wish to present accurate information about the range of plants in Britain. He himself progressively refined the geographical definition in his work until he reached the concept of the vice-county, adapted from the traditional division of Britain into administrative counties. Despite the current modern use of grid-squares for mapping purposes, the Watsonian Vice-county System is still useful especially when maps are not the only means of expression, and when old records are to be taken into account.

Origins of the Vice-county System

The Watsonian Vice-county System dates from 1852 when Watson, at the end of the third volume of his *Cybele Britannica*, gave a list of 38 sub-provinces and 112 vice-counties into which he proposed to divide the country. As he explained in the fourth volume of the *Cybele*, the object of the Vice-county System was to provide a set of unit areas more equal in their dimensions than the counties whose 'extreme inequality of size' was 'most inconvenient and objectionable'. In this fourth volume Watson elaborated the scheme and provided definitions of the vice-counties (Table 2 and Fig. 1) although it was in his classic *Topographical Botany* (1873–74) that the system was really used on a full scale. With the publication of this work the Vice-county System secured general adoption by British botanists.

The Watsonian Vice-county System was developed to encompass all of 19th century Britain. However, the study of the ornithology of Scotland was based not on vice-counties but, rather, on a system of faunal regions (see later). Table 2 and Fig. 1 only describe the vice-counties of England and Wales.

The sub-divisions of England and Wales used in the 19th century avifaunas

The distributions of all breeding birds in Britain have never been investigated or mapped by vice-county. This volume is the first to attempt to do this. Information concerning the distribution of birds in the late 19th century was published, in the main, by political county, a practice that continues today. The political boundaries chosen were the same as those used by Watson though he frequently sub-divided the political county to form two or more vice-counties and, less often, amalgamated small political counties with their neighbours (i.e. Table 2). Some of these distinctions were not recognised by the writers of the county avifaunas or, at least, were not recognisable as such. On the other hand, although not generally expressed as such, distinctions were made in the county accounts between the birds of different parts of the political county and, in some cases, these areas coincided with Watsonian county sub-divisions; thus the vice-county sub-divisions have been used for the purposes of the present study. In other counties, however, the writer(s) of the avifauna(s) clearly differentiated parts of their area by topographical, altitudinal, vegetation type or other criteria and described the different bird populations in those areas. Though they did not necessarily follow Watsonian vice-county boundaries, the

Table 2. *The Watsonian Vice–counties of England and Wales.*

	Name	Comments
V.C.1	West Cornwall	Western Cornwall; includes the Isles of Scilly
V.C.2	East Cornwall	Eastern Cornwall; includes the Eddystone Rocks
V.C.3	South Devon	Southern Devonshire
V.C.4	North Devon	Northern Devonshire; includes Lundy Island
V.C.5	South Somerset	Southern Somersetshire
V.C.6	North Somerset	Northern Somersetshire; includes Steep Holm Island
V.C.7	North Wilts	Northern Wiltshire
V.C.8	South Wilts	Southern Wiltshire
V.C.9	Dorset	Dorsetshire
V.C.10	Isle of Wight	Isle of Wight
V.C.11	South Hants	Southern Hampshire excluding the Isle of Wight
V.C.12	North Hants	Northern Hampshire
V.C.13	West Sussex	Western Sussex
V.C.14	East Sussex	Eastern Sussex
V.C.15	East Kent	Eastern Kent

Table 2. *Continued.*

	Name	Comments
V.C.16	West Kent	Western Kent; includes the southeastern part of the administrative county of Greater London
V.C.17	Surrey	Surrey; includes the southwestern part of the administrative county of Greater London
V.C.18	South Essex	Southern Essex; includes the northeastern part of the administrative county of Greater London
V.C.19	North Essex	Northern Essex
V.C.20	Herts	Hertfordshire; includes part of Barnet, part of the administrative county of Greater London
V.C.21	Middlesex	Middlesex; mainly the northwestern part of the administrative county of Greater London
V.C.22	Berks	Berkshire
V.C.23	Oxford	Oxfordshire
V.C.24	Bucks	Buckinghamshire
V.C.25	East Suffolk	Eastern Suffolk
V.C.26	West Suffolk	Western Suffolk
V.C.27	East Norfolk	Eastern Norfolk
V.C.28	West Norfolk	Western Norfolk
V.C.29	Cambridge	Cambridgeshire
V.C.30	Bedford	Bedfordshire; includes the detached part (Tetworth enclave) of Huntingdonshire
V.C.31	Hunts	Huntingdonshire; the detached part is excluded (see Bedfordshire)
V.C.32	Northampton	Northamptonshire; includes the Soke of Peterborough
V.C.33	East Gloucester	Eastern Gloucestershire
V.C.34	West Gloucester	Western Gloucestershire
V.C.35	Monmouth	Monmouthshire
V.C.36	Hereford	Herefordshire
V.C.37	Worcester	Worcestershire; the detached part is excluded (see Stafford)
V.C.38	Warwick	Warwickshire
V.C.39	Stafford	Staffordshire; includes the detached part (Dudley enclave) of Worcestershire
V.C.40	Salop	Shropshire
V.C.41	Glamorgan	Glamorganshire; includes the island of Flat Holm

Table 2. *Continued.*

	Name	Comments
V.C.42	Brecon	Brecknockshire
V.C.43	Radnor	Radnorshire
V.C.44	Carmarthen	Carmarthenshire
V.C.45	Pembroke	Pembrokeshire; includes Grassholm Island
V.C.46	Cardigan	Cardiganshire
V.C.47	Montgomery	Montgomeryshire
V.C.48	Merioneth	Merionethshire
V.C.49	Caernarvon	Caernarvonshire
V.C.50	Denbigh	Denbighshire; includes the detached parts (Marford and Overton enclaves) of Flintshire
V.C.51	Flint	Flintshire; excludes the detached parts (see Denbigh)
V.C.52	Anglesey	Anglesey
V.C.53	South Lincoln	Southern Lincolnshire
V.C.54	North Lincoln	Northern Lincolnshire
V.C.55	Leicester	Leicestershire; includes Rutland
V.C.56	Notts	Nottinghamshire
V.C.57	Derby	Derbyshire
V.C.58	Chester	Cheshire
V.C.59	South Lancaster	Southern Lancashire
V.C.60	West Lancaster	Northern Lancashire; excludes Furness (see Westmorland)
V.C.61	Southeast York	Southeast Yorkshire
V.C.62	Northeast York	Northeast Yorkshire
V.C.63	Southwest York	Southwest Yorkshire
V.C.64	Mid west York	Mid west Yorkshire
V.C.65	Northwest York	Northwest Yorkshire
V.C.66	Durham	Durham
V.C.67	Northumberland South	Southern Northumberland
V.C.68	Cheviotland	Northern Northumberland
V.C.69	Westmorland	Westmorland; includes Furness
V.C.70	Cumberland	Cumberland
V.C.71	Isle of Man	Isle of Man

opportunity has been taken here to sub-divide these counties and thus produce finer resolution distribution maps. The manner in which counties and Watsonian vice-counties have been retained, lumped or split for the present work is outlined in Table 3 and Fig. 2. In total, slightly more sub-divisions in England and Wales (80) are recognised here than were recognised by Watson (71).

The majority of sub-divisions used here coincide exactly with a Watsonian vice-county. The counties or regions for which this is the case are Somersetshire, Dorsetshire, Isle of Wight, Surrey, Hertfordshire, Middlesex, Berkshire, Buckinghamshire, Suffolk, Norfolk, Cambridgeshire, Bedfordshire, Huntingdonshire, Northamptonshire, Monmouthshire, Herefordshire, Worcestershire, Warwickshire, Staffordshire, Glamorganshire, Breconshire, Radnorshire, Carmarthenshire, Pembrokeshire, Cardiganshire, Montgomeryshire, Merionethshire, Denbighshire, Flintshire, Lincolnshire, Nottinghamshire, Lancashire, Yorkshire, Durham, Westmorland, Cumberland, Isle of Man.

In some cases Watson sub-divided a political county to create two vice-counties but the account of the avifauna of the area did not provide sufficient detail to follow the division and so the political boundary only is used here. The counties for which this is the case are Cornwall, Wiltshire, Sussex, Kent, Essex, Northumberland.

The information contained in the avifaunas of a few counties has allowed here the division of the county into regions that do not coincide with the Watsonian sub-division. The counties for which this is the case are Devonshire, Hampshire, Gloucestershire.

In some cases, authors of the avifauna divided their county into distinctive areas even though Watson had not done so. These divisions are followed here for the following counties: Oxfordshire, Shropshire, Caernarvonshire, Anglesey, Derbyshire, Cheshire.

Finally, Leicestershire and Rutland, 'lumped' by Watson, have been split during this study; Northamptonshire and Huntingdonshire have been 'lumped' here because there is insufficient detail concerning the birds of the latter county to treat them separately and in one case it is possible to distinguish a discrete area not recognised at all by Watson— the London division has been created from small parts of neighbouring counties.

Changes in county boundaries
The county boundaries accepted by Watson, and used by the writers of the county avifaunas of the 19th century were, of course, of their time. As a means of determining the distribution of plants and animals then they were adequate but neither Watson nor writers on the distribution of other organisms foresaw the immense changes in the numbers and distribution of the human population that would take place in the wake of the Industrial Revolution. Before the end of the 19th century Local Government Acts made many boundary changes (among other things the County of London and the first of the County Boroughs were formed), and the process has been going on steadily

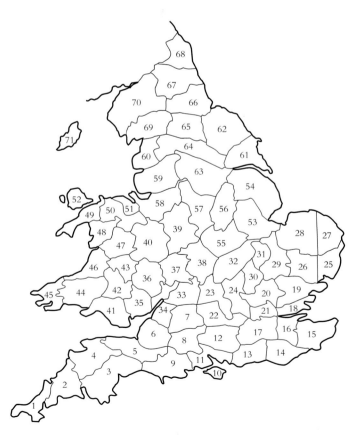

Fig. 1 The Watsonian Vice-counties of England and Wales.

5

Table 3. *The counties and sub-divisions of the 19th century avifaunas of England and Wales.*

Name	Vice–counties included	Sub–divisions	
Cornwall	V.C. 1 and 2	1	The Isles of Scilly
		2	Cornwall
Devon	V.C. 3 and 4	3	Northern Devonshire
		4	Southern Devonshire; includes Dartmoor
Somerset	V.C. 5 and 6	5	Southern Somersetshire
		6	Northern Somersetshire
Wilts	V.C. 7 and 8	7	Wiltshire
Dorset	V.C. 9	8	Dorsetshire
Isle of Wight	V.C. 10	9	Isle of Wight
Hants	V.C. 11 and 12	10	The Hampshire New Forest
		11	Northern Hampshire
Sussex	V.C. 13 and 14	12	Sussex
Kent	V.C. 15 and 16	13	Kent
Surrey	V.C. 17	14	Surrey
Essex	V.C. 18 and 19	15	Essex
London		16	The administrative county of Greater London
Herts	V.C. 20	17	Hertfordshire
Middlesex	V.C. 21	18	Middlesex
Berks	V.C. 22	19	Berkshire
Oxford	V.C. 23	20	Northern Oxfordshire
		21	Mid Oxfordshire
		22	Southern Oxfordshire
Bucks	V.C. 24	23	Buckinghamshire
Suffolk	V.C. 25	24	Eastern Suffolk
	V.C. 26	25	Western Suffolk
Norfolk	V.C. 27	26	Eastern Norfolk
	V.C. 28	27	Western Norfolk
Cambridge	V.C. 29	28	Cambridgeshire
Bedford	V.C. 30	29	Bedfordshire; includes the detached part (Tetworth enclave) of Huntingdonshire
Hunts	V.C. 31	30	Huntingdonshire; the detached part is excluded (see Bedfordshire)

Table 3. *Continued.*

Name	Vice–counties included		Sub–divisions
Northampton	V.C. 32	31	Northamptonshire; includes the Soke of Peterborough
Gloucester	V.C. 33 and 34	32	The Cotswolds, Gloucestershire
		33	The northwest district, Gloucestershire
		34	The Severn, Gloucestershire
		35	The Vale, Gloucestershire
Monmouth	V.C. 35	36	Monmouthshire
Hereford	V.C. 36	37	Herefordshire
Worcester	V.C. 37	38	Worcestershire; the detached part is excluded (see Stafford)
Warwick	V.C. 38	39	Warwickshire
Stafford	V.C. 39	40	Staffordshire; includes the detached part (Dudley enclave) of Worcestershire
Salop	V.C. 40	41	Lowland Shropshire
		42	The southwestern hills, Shropshire
		43	The Oswestry uplands, Shropshire
Glamorgan	V.C. 41	44	Glamorganshire; includes the island of Flat Holm
Brecon	V.C. 42	45	Brecknockshire
Radnor	V.C. 43	46	Radnorshire
Carmarthen	V.C. 44	47	Carmarthenshire
Pembroke	V.C. 45	48	Pembrokeshire; includes all Pembrokeshire islands
Cardigan	V.C. 46	49	Cardiganshire
North Wales	V.C. 47	50	Montgomeryshire
	V.C. 48	51	Merionethshire
	V.C. 49	52	Eastern Caernarvonshire
		53	Lleyn Peninsula, Caernarvonshire; includes Bardsey
	V.C. 50	54	Denbighshire; includes the detached parts (Marford and Overton enclaves) of Flintshire
	V.C. 51	55	Flintshire; excludes the detached parts (see Denbigh)
	V.C. 52	56	Southeastern Anglesey
		57	Northwestern Anglesey

Table 3. *Continued.*

Name	Vice–counties	Sub–divisions	
Lincoln	V.C. 53	58	Southern Lincolnshire
	V.C. 54	59	Northern Lincolnshire
Leicester	Part of V.C. 55	60	Leicestershire
Rutland	Part of V.C. 55	61	Rutland
Notts	V.C. 56	62	Nottinghamshire
Derby	V.C. 57	63	Southern plains, Derbyshire
		64	Central or hilly region, Derbyshire
		65	Northern division, Derbyshire
Chester	V.C. 58	66	The Wirral and Dee Marshes, Cheshire
		67	The Central plain, Cheshire
		68	The Eastern hills, Cheshire
Lancaster	V.C. 59	69	Southern Lancashire
	V.C. 60	70	Northern Lancashire; excludes Furness (see Westmorland)
York	V.C. 61	71	Southeast Yorkshire
	V.C. 62	72	Northeast Yorkshire
	V.C. 63	73	Southwest Yorkshire
	V.C. 64	74	Mid west Yorkshire
	V.C. 65	75	Northwest Yorkshire
Durham	V.C. 66	76	Durham
Northumberland	V.C. 67 and 68	77	Northumberland
Lakeland	V.C. 69	78	Westmorland; includes Furness
	V.C. 70	79	Cumberland
Isle of Man	V.C. 71	80	Isle of Man

ever since. This is especially the case in the neighbourhood of expanding cities like Birmingham, Bristol, Manchester and Sheffield which are situated near the edge of their original counties and have gradually absorbed territory from adjoining ones. Later on large boundary changes made in the Greater London area involved the complete disappearance of Middlesex as an administrative county and, in 1974, many 'old' counties were discarded in favour of a number of slimmed-down 'super-counties' These changes create considerable difficulties when attempting to record population and distributional changes over an extended period, but give further support to Buchanan White and Harvie-Brown's efforts to ignore the political boundaries of Scotland in favour of topographical and geological divisions (see below).

The Buchanan White faunal districts of Scotland.
Francis Buchanan White (1842–94) graduated as an M.D. but, having no desire to follow that profession and being of independent means, was able to devote himself almost entirely to the advancement of 'the knowledge of the Natural History of Scotland'. The direction of his interest was apparent from early days and was demonstrated in his graduation thesis which bore the title 'On the relations, Analogies, and Similitudes of Insects and Plants'. He became a noted authority on insects and plants, especially so on the classification of willows and

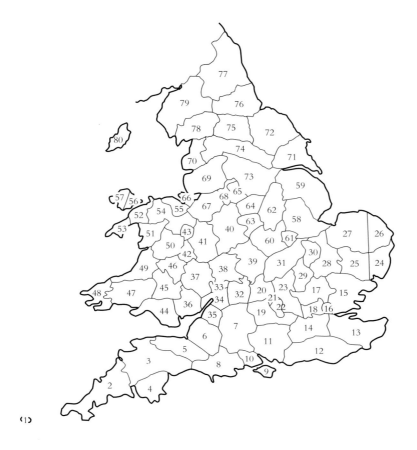

Fig. 2 The counties and sub–divisions of the 19th century county avifaunas of England and Wales.
Each numeral refers to a separate county or sub–division. See Table 3 for a complete listing.

Hemiptera and the structure and habits of Lepidoptera. In 1872 he commenced one of his most noted projects—an attempt to catalogue and record the distribution of insects in Scotland. This was his *Insecta Scotica,* but only the Lepidoptera was completed and was published in the *Scottish Naturalist* between 1872 and 1879. It was prefaced by a short introduction, which included a map, laying out his plan to divide Scotland into a series of districts that followed topographical features. He described his aim thus:

> In publishing lists of the Scottish Insects, it will be advisable to indicate, so far as is practicable, the distribution of each species throughout the country. For this purpose Scotland has been divided into thirteen districts. In selecting these, an attempt has been made to obtain natural divisions (such as those afforded by the basins of the larger rivers), instead of the arbitrary sections heretofore used for similar purposes.

He then went on to describe the districts and these are reproduced in Table 4 and Figure 3.

The Fauna of Scotland Series
Harvie-Brown was a friend of Buchanan White and familiar with the latter's work on the distribution of insects in Scotland. Harvie-Brown developed a desire to record

the distribution of the animals in the country and, from the outset, was convinced that this should be completed in areas delineated by natural features rather than the artificial polititical boundaries used in the past, and prevalent in England and Wales. He determined to produce his *Fauna of Scotland Series* based largely on Buchanan White's faunal districts although he refined the boundaries slightly in some areas and described them in far more detail later (Harvie-Brown and Bartholomew 1893). His conviction that the distribution of birds and mammals was influenced by topographical features was demonstrated in a paper that he contributed to the *Annals of Scottish Natural History* in 1898 titled 'On the Minor Faunal Areas' in which he gave examples of several species whose current and former distribution, or their decline and increase, had been shaped by the presence of water courses, watersheds, mountain ranges and other features in the Scottish landscape. For the purposes of the present study information contained in the pages of the Series and from other sources has allowed the sub-division of the Scottish faunal districts. These are described in Table 4.

The counties of Ireland
The sub-divisions of Ireland (Table 5 and Fig. 4) used during the present study are, in the main, the political counties of the 19th century. In two cases the political counties have been divided. The 19th century Tipperary accounts often

Table 4. *The Faunal Districts of Scotland.*

The Buchanan White Faunal Districts	Main counties included	The modified Faunal Districts
Tweed – the part drained by the Tweed and other rivers entering the sea between Berwick and Cockburnspath	Peeblesshire, Selkirkshire, Roxburghshire, Berwickshire	E1
Forth – the part drained by the Forth and other rivers between Cockburnspath and Fife Ness	East Lothian, Midlothian, West Lothian, Fife, Kinross, Stirling, South Perthshire, Clackmannan	E2
Tay – the part drained by the Tay and other rivers between Fifeness and Crawton	Mid Perthshire, North Perthshire, Forfar (Angus), Kincardineshire	E3
Dee – the part drained by the Dee and other rivers between Crawton and Pitsligo	Aberdeenshire	E4
Moray – the part drained by rivers between Pitsligo and Ord of Caithness, and by the Caledonian Canal as far west as Loch Oich	Banff, Moray (Elgin), East Inverness, Nairn	E5S
	Easter Ross, East Sutherlandshire	E5N
Sutherland – the part drained by the rivers between Ord of Caithness and Cape Wrath	Caithness	E6E
	West Sutherland	E6W
Orkney	Orkney	E7
Zetland	Shetland	E8
Solway – the part drained by the rivers between the Liddel and Culzean Castle and includes parts of Roxburghshire.	Dumfriesshire	W1D
	Kirkcudbrightshire	W1K
	Wigtownshire	W1W
Clyde – the part drained by the Clyde and other rivers between Culzean Castle and Loch Awe; includes Arran (White included Islay and west Kintyre in Clyde but Harvie-Brown divided Kintyre along its central ridge and included Islay and west Kintyre in the Argyll District)	Ayrshire	W2Ay
	Lanark, east Dumbarton	W2L
	Renfrewshire	W2R
	South Argyllshire, west Dumbarton, Buteshire, Arran	W2Ar
Argyll – the part drained by rivers between Lochs Awe and Ailort: includes west Kintyre, Islay, Mull, Tiree and adjacent islands	South Argyllshire	W3S
	North Argyllshire	W3N
West Ross – the part drained by rivers between Loch Ailort and Cape Wrath; includes Skye	West Ross-shire	W4S
		W4C
	West Sutherlandshire	W4N
	Skye	W4Sk
Outer Hebrides – includes St Kilda, the Flannans, Sula Sgeir, North Rona	Lewis and Harris	W5N
	North and South Uist	W5S

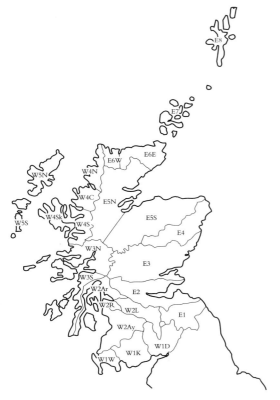

Fig. 3 The Buchanan White faunal districts of Scotland. Each letter/numeral refers to a separate district. See Table 4 for a complete listing.

Fig. 4 The counties of 19th century Ireland. Each numeral refers to separate county. See Table 5 for a complete listing.

distinguished between the north and south of the county and, in Galway, the bird communities of the east, along the coast, and of the west were clearly separated; these subdivisions have been followed here.

Since the 19th century, and the partition of Ulster, some changes in county names have taken place.

Table 5. *The 19th century counties of Ireland.*

	Name	Comments
1	Kerry	Includes the Blaskets
2	Cork	
3	Waterford	
4	Clare	Includes the Aran Islands
5	Limerick	
6N	Tipperary	Northern Tipperary
6S		Southern Tipperary
7	Kilkenney	
8	Carlow	
9	Wexford	Includes the Saltees
10	Wicklow	
11	Dublin	Includes Lambay
12	Kildare	
13	Queen's County	Now Leix

Table 5. *Continued.*

	Name	Comments
14	King's County	Now Offaly
15	Longford	
16	Westmeath	
17	Meath	
18	Louth	
19E	Galway	Eastern Galway
19W		Western Galway
20	Roscommon	
21	Mayo	Include Achill
22	Sligo	
23	Leitrim	
24	Cavan	
25	Fermanagh	
26	Monaghan	
27	Armagh	
28	Down	
29	Antrim	Includes Antrim Island
30	Londonderry	
31	Tyrone	
32	Donegal	

Data Sources

General

Information for this atlas has been gleaned from a wide variety of sources as no single, detailed contemporary overview of the 1875–1900 period was ever produced for Britain; More's (1865) review was out of date. Fortunately a contemporary review for the period had been produced for Ireland (Ussher and Warren 1900). The primary sources were the county and regional avifaunas. These varied in their completeness, thoroughness and style but, although most parts of Britain were covered by such accounts, there were gaps for some counties. Many of these were served by bird lists. These were published in various forms, sometimes as discrete lists, as chapters in general accounts of the natural history of the counties, as contributions to local natural history society journals and the larger journals, or as chapters to such publications as the Victoria County Histories or British Association Handbooks. Single species studies or short notes proliferated in the natural history journals and of these the most important were *Transactions of the Cardiff Naturalists' Society*, *Transactions of the Norfolk and Norwich Naturalists' Society*, *Transactions of the Royal Physical Society of Edinburgh*, *Transactions of the Royal Society of Edinburgh*, *Transactions of the Natural History Society of Glasgow*, *Annals of Scottish Natural History*, *Scottish Naturalist*, *British Birds*, *The Ibis* and *The Zoologist*.

The main accounts consulted to determine pre-1875 status

Four works in particular gave an overall view, between them, of the status of birds in Britain and Ireland during the first 75 years of the 19th century and were regarded by contemporary writers as the most accurate and influential of their time. As such they were consulted regularly during the preparation of the present work. These works, along with an annotated bibliography of their authors, are as follows.

YARRELL, William. 1837–43. *A History of British Birds*. Van Voorst, London.

YARRELL, William. 1871–85. *A History of British Birds*. 4th edition, revised and enlarged by A. Newton (vols. i, ii) and Howard Saunders (vols. iii, iv). Van Voorst, London.

Yarrell was born on 3rd June 1784, in Great Ryder Street in the parish of St James's, London. His father carried on the trade of a newspaper agent in Duke Street and to this business Yarrell succeeded in due course. He was educated at Ealing and in 1802 joined the banker Herries, Farquhar and Co. as a clerk, but left soon after to join his father in business. Yarrell developed his interest in ornithology whilst on the hunting and shooting trips with which he varied the monotony of business. His love for natural history slowly increased and he gradually abandoned his fishing and hunting expeditions in favour of the systematic study of zoology. In 1823 he commenced his notebooks and was said to have aided Bewick by sending him rare birds. He became a FLS in 1825 and was one of the original members of the Zoological Society.

In 1836 he completed *A History of British Fishes* and in 1837 published the first part of *A History of British Birds*. It immediately proved a great success. Yarrell, besides being an accomplished ornithologist, was said to know exactly what the public wanted in the form of a popular textbook and possessed the skill of presenting his knowledge in a concise and easy manner. The information the, originally three, volumes contained was regarded as of a high degree of accuracy and the illustrations, executed by Alexander Fussell and John Thompson and his sons, were highly acclaimed. *A History of British Birds* appeared in three editions, later ones with the addition of supplements, and, in 1871 a fourth edition was commenced and was almost entirely rewritten by Newton and Saunders.

A set of 'Yarrell' formed the basis of every naturalist's library and made ornithology accessible to many people. For the purposes of the present study *A History of British Birds* provides the earliest overall view of the distribution of birds in Britain, the accuracy of which was little criticised by contemporary naturalists and hence provides valuable early information.

Yarrell died after a sudden illness in Yarmouth in 1856 and was buried at Bayford in Hertfordshire.

THOMPSON, William. 1849–56. *The Natural History of Ireland*. Reeve, Benham and Reeve, London.

This well-known Irish ornithologist of his day was born the son of a Belfast linen merchant in that city in 1805 and apprenticed to the linen trade in 1820. He ultimately took over his father's business but apparently with little success and so eventually abandoned it and devoted himself to science. He published his first ornithological paper in 1827, following a four-month tour of the continent, but it was his 1840 'Report on the Fauna of Ireland' to the British Association in Glasgow that brought him to the notice of his peers. In 1841 he began his valuable papers on the birds of Ireland in the *Annals and Magazine of Natural History*. His *The Natural History of Ireland* is an important landmark in the study of the Irish fauna and was regarded as an accurate and faithful work. He died in 1852 whilst on a visit to London.

MORE, Alexander Goodman. 1865. On the Distribution of Birds in Great Britain during the Nesting Season. *The Ibis* New Series I:*1–27, 119–142, 425–458*.

Alexander More was born in London in 1830. He was educated at Rugby and Cambridge but left in 1857, in which year he was elected a Fellow of the Ray Society. He first visited Ireland in 1850 and became Curator of the Natural History Department of the Dublin Museum in 1882. He died in Ireland in 1895.

More's 'On the Distribution…' was envisaged as a partner to Watson's geographical distribution of British plants, the *Cybele Britannica*. It was based on Watson's original 18 Provinces and 38 Subprovinces and was carried out by correspondence with naturalists and sportsmen in each Subprovince (although there were a number of gaps and More felt that Wales, NW England and most of Scotland were not adequately covered). It was the first attempt to determine the distribution of birds in Britain as a subject in itself, and is immensely valuable as a contribution to the ornithology of the mid 19th century. Some of his records, however, were questioned by later 19th century writers.

There were a number of works dealing with the birds of Britain and Ireland during the early part of the 19th century. Several of these works, though of a high reputation, have been consulted occasionally in order to confirm some early records. In general, however, they have not been widely used, either because of their local nature, reputation for inaccuracy or simply because they were superseded. Some examples are:

LOW, Rev. George. 1813. *Fauna Orcadensis: or The Natural History etc. of Orkney and Shetland*. Constable, Edinburgh.

EYTON, Thomas Campbell. 1838–39. An attempt to ascertain the fauna of Shropshire and North Wales. *Annals Nat. Hist.* I: 285–292, II: 52–56.

LUBBOCK, Rev. Richard. 1845. *Observations on the Fauna of Norfolk*. Longmans, London.

KNOX, Arthur Edward. 1849. *Ornithological Rambles in Sussex*. London.

MORRIS, Francis Orpen. 1851-57. *A History of British Birds*. Groombridge and Son, London.

MACGILLIVRAY, William. 1855. *The Natural History of Deeside and Braemar*. London.

The main county and regional accounts for 1875–1900
More than 100 county and regional avifaunas have been consulted during the preparation of this volume. The main accounts, along with an annotated bibliography of their authors, are as follows.

Cornwall and the Isles of Scilly V.C.1 & 2.
RODD, Edward Hearle. 1880. *The Birds of Cornwall and the Scilly Islands*. Trübner & Co., London.
Born in 1810, Rodd settled in Penzance in 1833 after training for the law and, until he retired in 1878, held many official posts in the town. He was a well-known Cornish ornithologist and contributed a number of papers concerning his study of local birds to the *The Zoologist* from its first year of publication in 1843. He announced the forthcoming publication of the *Birds of Cornwall and the Scilly Islands* in 1877 but unfortunately died in 1880 a short time before it was published. His papers were passed to his nephew, F. R. Rodd (he contributed the notes concerning the birds of Scilly), who arranged for publication to carry on under the editorship of J. E. Harting, an eminent naturalist of his day and the author of *The Birds of Middlesex*.
BIDWELL, Edward. 1886. A Visit to the Isles of Scilly during the Nesting Season. *Trans. Norfolk and Norwich Nat. Soc.* IV, pt. II: 201–214.
Bidwell made a yachting trip to the islands during the spring of 1885 to collect seabirds' eggs.

Devonshire V.C. 3 & 4.
PIDSLEY, William E. Helman. 1891. *The Birds of Devonshire*. Gibbings, London.
Pidsley was a resident of Exeter whilst he wrote this, his main work.
D'URBAN, William Stewart Mitchell and the Rev. Murray Alexander MATHEW. 1892. *The Birds of Devon*. Porter, London.
D'URBAN, W. S. M. and M. A. MATHEW, 1895. *A Supplement to The Birds of Devon*. Porter, London.
D'Urban was born in Ireland in 1836, the son of a British officer stationed there. He returned to England in 1861 and took up the post of curator and librarian to the Albert Memorial Museum in Exeter in 1862 which he held for 22 years. He then moved to California until 1888 when he returned to Exeter and continued to study the fauna of Devonshire. He contributed many papers on birds and other animals to several periodicals from 1853 until his death.
Mathew was born in Middlesex in 1838 but was moved to Barnstaple, Devonshire when an infant. He was educated at Barnstaple and then Oxford before taking up his first curacy at the age of 22 at Taunton, Somerset. Other posts

followed in Somerset before he took up a Pembrokeshire curacy in 1880, moving there on account of his poor health, the clean Pembrokeshire air apparently noted for its curative powers. In 1888 he returned to Somerset and held a curacy near Frome until his death in 1908. Mathew was a well-known ornithologist and contributed many ornithological papers, mainly to *The Zoologist* from 1857. He was a MBOU and a FLS and was also the author of *The Birds of Pembrokeshire and its Islands*.

Somerset V.C. 5 & 6.
SMITH, Cecil. 1869. *The Birds of Somersetshire*. Van Voorst, London.
Smith was born at Bishop's Lydiard in 1826 and obtained his B.A. at Cambridge in 1849. He was a MBOU and a FZS and a contributor to *The Zoologist* of ornithological notes from Somerset and the Channel Islands, to which he made summer visits for many years. Whilst at Lydiard he made frequent shooting trips to the Exe estuary and provided many contributions to D'Urban and Mathew's *Birds of Devonshire*. He also wrote *The Birds of Guernsey*.
BLATHWAYT, Rev. Francis Linley. 1906. [Birds in] *Victoria History of the County of Somerset*. Dawsons of Pall Mall, London.
Born in India in 1875, Blathwayt completed his education at Hertford College, Oxford. He was a leisured naturalist of his time and wrote notes on many of his field trips in a number of periodicals. Following his appointment as Rector of Doddington, Lincolnshire, he contributed several papers on the ornithology of that county, useful additions to the avifauna of an area with limited published material at the time.

Wiltshire V.C. 7 & 8.
SMITH, Rev. Alfred Charles. 1887. *The Birds of Wiltshire*. R. H. Porter, London.
Smith spent all of his life in Wiltshire and studied the local ornithology in some detail. His series of articles in the *Wiltshire Archaeological and Natural History Magazine* between 1857 and 1869 formed the basis of *The Birds of Wiltshire*. His observations of birds were detailed; his work was particularly scholarly and included the etymological basis to many of the names attributed to the species.

Dorsetshire V.C. 9.
MANSELL-PLEYDELL, John Clavell. 1888. *The Birds of Dorsetshire*. R. H. Porter, London.
Mansell-Pleydell was born in 1817 at Smedmore in Dorset and completed his education at Cambridge in 1839. He was admitted as a student of Lincoln's Inn in 1840 but was not called to the Bar. He succeeded to his mother's estate and some property and in 1876 was made High Sheriff of Dorset. He was a well-known antiquary and naturalist and founded the Dorset Natural History and Antiquarian Field Club in 1875. He held the Presidency of the Club from its inception until his death in 1902. His best-known work was the *Flora of Dorsetshire* (1874) a partner volume to the *Birds of Dorsetshire*. The *Birds of Dorsetshire* was a well written and detailed account and contained, according to *Country Life*, the first reproduction in a book of a photograph of wild birds—of the Swannery at Abbotsbury.

Isle of Wight V.C. 10.
FOX, Reginald Henry. 1909. Birds. In Morey, F. (ed.), *A Guide to the Natural History of the Isle of Wight*. The Country

Press, Newport.

Fox was born in 1860 and educated in Dorsetshire. He wrote almost nothing else ornithological apart from this contribution.

KELSALL, Rev. John Edward and Philip Winchester MUNN. 1905. *The Birds of Hampshire and the Isle of Wight.* Witherby, London.

See under Hampshire.

Hampshire V.C. 11 & 12.

KELSALL, Rev. John Edward and Philip Winchester MUNN. 1905. *The Birds of Hampshire and the Isle of Wight.* Witherby, London.

After his education at Rugby and Oxford, Kelsall took up the post as Rector of Milton in Hampshire. He remained there for the rest of his life and became a well-known authority on the vertebrate fauna of his county.

Munn was born in 1865 in Laverstoke, Hampshire, and was the manager of Laverstoke Bank after completing his education in Germany. Apart from contributions to *The Ibis* and other periodicals this work was his only publication.

Sussex V.C. 13 & 14.

BORRER, William. 1891. *The Birds of Sussex.* R. H. Porter, London.

Borrer was born in Henfield in Sussex in 1814 the son of a Sussex botanist who was a friend of Sir Joseph Banks. His father is said to have instilled in him his love of natural history. Following the completion of his education at Cambridge he married in 1840 and settled near Cowfield where he resided for the rest of his life. His collection of British birds and mammals was accumulated throughout his life and, upon his death in 1898, the birds were presented to the famous Booth Museum in Brighton by his nephew. He was a long-time contributor to *The Zoologist*, his first paper being published in 1845, and he was a MBOU.

Kent V.C. 15 & 16.

BALSTON, Richard James, Rev. Charles William SHEP-HERD and Edward BARTLETT. 1907. *Notes on the Birds of Kent.* R. H. Porter, London.

Balston was born in Maidstone in Kent in 1839 and, after completing his education at Eton, took over the family paper manufacturing business. He was a MBOU from 1889 and a FLS.

Shepherd was the Rector of Trottiscliffe near Maidstone, was a MBOU from 1865 and a FZS.

Bartlett spent many years in Sarawak and his most important works concern the mammalian fauna of that country. He held the posts of Curator at the Maidstone and Sarawak Museums.

TICEHURST, Norman Frederick. 1909. *A History of the Birds of Kent.* Witherby, London.

Ticehurst entered medicine after his education at Cambridge. He became a MBOU at the age of 20 in 1893, and was a member of its Committee between 1911 and 1914. He was one of the originating members of the BOC Migration Committee as he was of the *British Birds* magazine, for which he acted as assistant editor for many years. He was a FZS and had published papers in a number of periodicals concerning many aspects of ornithology. His *Birds of Kent* was greeted as a valuable addition to the ornithology of Britain and is a detailed and accurate account that took him 16 years to complete.

Surrey V.C. 17.

BUCKNILL, Sir John Alexander Strachey. 1900. *The Birds of Surrey.* R. H. Porter, London.

This work was compiled whilst Bucknill resided at the family home in Epsom. He was then 27 and shortly before had entered the Inner Temple, becoming barrister-at-law. He subsequently became King's Advocate at Nicosia, Cyprus and contributed several papers on the ornithology of that island to *The Ibis* from 1909.

Essex V.C. 18 & 19.

CHRISTY, Robert Miller. 1890. *The Birds of Essex.* Simkin Marshall Hamilton, Chelmsford.

Christy was born of old Quaker stock in 1861 and lived in Chelmsford for much of his life. From his childhood he had a remarkable interest in natural history, collected many conchological and ornithological specimens and, even at that time, started to write on these subjects for local publications. After he left school he spent over a year camping and exploring in Manitoba with the celebrated naturalist Ernest Thompson Seton who was to become a lifelong friend. On his return he became a partner in the family printing firm. His list of papers is long and the subject matter very wide—he wrote on subjects as diverse as Manitoba, the history of banking in Essex, oven clocks and the trade signs of Essex, besides a number of ornithological works.

Hertfordshire V.C. 20.

CROSSMAN, Alan Fairfax. 1902. [Birds in] *Victoria County History of Hertfordshire.* I. Dawsons of Pall Mall, London.

Crossman was the county Recorder in Ornithology between 1896 and 1901 but, soon after, moved to Australia. His account of the birds of Hertfordshire is little more than a simple list and is supported in the present review by earlier papers by Crossman (1896–1901) and Littleboy (1880) and by B. L. Sage's *A History of the Birds of Hertfordshire* (1959) all of which provide detail around this core list.

Middlesex and London V.C. 21.

HARTING, James Edmund. 1866. *The Birds of Middlesex.* Van Voorst, London.

Harting was born in London in 1841, the eldest son of James Vincent Harting. He completed his education at London University and spent a few years travelling extensively on the continent, spending some time studying the zoological collections in the museums of Paris and Leyden. Soon after his marriage in 1868 he gained the first of his editorships. In 1871 he became Natural History Editor of *The Field*, a post that he held for almost 50 years, whilst, between 1877 and 1896, he very successfully edited *The Zoologist*. For many years, until his retirement in 1902, he was Assistant Secretary and Librarian to the Linnaean Society of London and, after he was elected a FLS in 1868, became a member of its Council. Amongst membership of other august 19th century organisations he was a life member of the Zoological Society and the BOU. His *Birds of Middlesex* (with the first volume of Stevenson's *Birds of Norfolk*) was regarded as having begun the series of county avifaunas that has continued to the present day. His list of ornithological and falconry writings is vast and he was also the editor of Rodd's *The Birds of Cornwall and the Scilly Isles*.

SWANN, Harry Kirke. 1893. *The Birds of London*. Swan Sonnenschein, London.

Swann was 22 when he wrote this work after observing London's birds for six or seven years. His many publications began a year or so earlier with the first two volumes of the *Naturalists' Journal* and continued with a number of important late 19th and early 20th century general ornithological works (including the 1896 reissue of Seebohm's *British Birds*) and other works and papers. This chapter owes a great deal to his *A Bibliography of British Ornithology*, compiled with W. H. Mullens in 1917 (Mullens and Swann 1917). Around the turn of the century he became a partner in Wheldon and Wesley Limited, a firm of booksellers, still one of the world's most important dealers in natural history books.

Berkshire V.C. 22.
KENNEDY, Capt. Alexander William Maxwell Clark. 1868. *The Birds of Berkshire and Buckinghamshire*. Private publication, Eton.

This book was written when Kennedy was 16 and a pupil at Eton. Despite his age this early work is reasonably complete, owing, in no small part, to the advice, assistance and notes he received from many, more senior, local naturalists. These included the eminent Richard Bowdler-Sharpe and J. E. Harting (see under Middlesex). The book also includes what are reputedly the earliest colour photographs of birds, but what are, in fact, hand-coloured photographs of stuffed specimens. He contributed a few ornithological notes to a number of natural history journals through his life, but this avifauna was his only notable work. He was a FZS, FLS and a MBOU.

NOBLE, Heatley. 1906. [Birds in] *Victoria History of the County of Berkshire*. Dawsons of Pall Mall, London.

Noble was born in 1862 in London. He was a well-known zoologist and contributed a few papers to *The Zoologist British Birds*, but little else.

Oxfordshire V.C. 23.
APLIN, Oliver Vernon. 1889. *The Birds of Oxfordshire*. Oxford University Press, Oxford.

Aplin, and his brothers, were well-known Oxfordshire ornithologists. Oliver was sent, in 1892, by Dr Sclater, to Uruguay to investigate the ornithology of that country, the results being published in *The Ibis* in 1894. He was a prodigious writer of ornithological papers; his studies of the distribution of Spotted Crake and Cirl Bunting and his account of a visit to Bardsey were particularly valuable in the preparation of the present volume. *The Birds of Oxfordshire* is one of the most detailed and accurate of the county avifaunas of the period.

Buckinghamshire V.C. 24.
KENNEDY, Capt. Alexander William Maxwell Clark. 1868. *The Birds of Berkshire and Buckinghamshire*. Eton & London.

See under Berkshire.

HARTERT, Dr Ernest J. O. and Hon. Walter ROTHSCHILD. 1905. [Birds in] *Victoria History of the County of Buckinghamshire*. Dawsons of Pall Mall, London.

Hartert was born in Hamburg in 1859. He was a prolific writer of entomological and ornithological papers and travelled widely. His most important works were on South American ornithology although he had also written on the birds of Africa and India. He was a lifelong friend of Lord

Rothschild and in 1892 became the Director of the (Rothschild) Zoological Museum at Tring, Hertfordshire.

Lord Rothschild was born in 1868 and completed his education at Magdalene College, Cambridge. His major achievement was his involvement with the Zoological Museum at Tring and his co-editorship, with Hartert, of the Museum journal, the *Novitiates Zoologicæ*. He published the first description of the British Willow Tit in the first volume of *British Birds* in 1907.

Suffolk V.C. 25 & 26.
BABINGTON, Rev. Churchill. 1884–86. *Catalogue of the Birds of Suffolk*. Van Voorst, London.

Babington was born in 1821, the son of Matthew Babington, himself a cousin of a noted botanist, Charles Babington. He was better known as a classical scholar and archaeologist than an ornithologist, but in later years he also achieved a reputation as a botanist and towards the end of his life became interested in conchology. His *Birds of Suffolk* was reprinted from the *Proceedings of the Suffolk Institute of Archæology and Natural History* and was considered an accurate and full account by Ticehurst (1932).

Norfolk V.C. 27 & 28.
STEVENSON, Henry. 1866–90. *The Birds of Norfolk*. Van Voorst, London.

Stevenson was born in 1833 to the proprietors of the *Norfolk Chronicle*. After completing his education in London he was elected, in 1855, to the post of honorary secretary to the Norfolk and Norwich Museum which he held until his death in 1888. In 1864 he was elected a member of the BOU being one of the first additions to the founding members of the society. Stevenson had a very retiring personality and took little part in public life, apart from his brief spell as Sheriff of Norwich in 1875, and felt incapable of reading his own paper on the Great Bustard in Norfolk at a meeting of the British Association. He was a prolific contributor to many natural history journals and his *Birds of Norfolk* was, with the *Birds of Middlesex*, the first of the modern series of county avifaunas and one of the most detailed. He died before seeing the publication of the third volume, this being accomplished following its completion by Thomas Southwell (see below).

GURNEY, John Henry (Jr.) and Thomas SOUTHWELL. 1886–1904. Fauna and Flora of Norfolk, part XI. List of Norfolk Birds. *Trans. Norfolk and Norwich Nat. Soc.* Parts IV, V and VII.

Gurney could be said to have been born an ornithologist in 1848 as he was the son of John Henry Gurney (senior), a noted Norfolk naturalist. He was educated at Harrow and from the age of 18 was a regular, and prolific, contributor to many natural history journals. He spent his life fostering his father's projects, most notably the Norfolk and Norwich Naturalists' Society and the collection of 'Raptorial Birds' in the Norfolk and Norwich Museum. Probably his most important work was his *The Gannet* published in 1913, a monograph that has stood the test of time and is still a reliable source of reference.

Southwell was born in 1831 in King's Lynn and spent much of his youth developing an interest in ornithology through egg collecting whilst skipping school. In 1846 he joined the King's Lynn branch of Gurney's (now Barclays) Bank and here met his life-long friend, J. H. Gurney. He spent much of his life in the bank and was a prolific contributor to many journals, particularly the transactions of the Norfolk and Norwich Naturalists' Society.

Cambridgeshire V.C. 29.
EVANS, Arthur Humble. 1904. The Birds of Cambridgeshire. In Marr, J. E. and A. E. Shipley (eds), *Handbook to the Natural History of Cambridgeshire*. Cambridge University Press, Cambridge.
Evans was born in Northumberland in 1855, the son of the Rev. Hugh Evans, a noted horticulturalist. He was educated at Durham School and Clare College, Cambridge. He completed an M.A. at Cambridge and spent the rest of his life there, partly working for the university and partly in his own scientific pursuits. He formed a close friendship with Howard Saunders, a noted ornithologist, and undertook a number of expeditions throughout Britain with him. He became joint editor with Sclater of *The Ibis* in 1901. His other, important works included two volumes of the Fauna of Scotland series, the volume on birds in the 1899 *Cambridge Natural History* and the *Aves Hawaiienses* 1890–99.

Bedfordshire V.C. 30.
STEELE-ELLIOTT, Jannion. 1897–1901. *The Vertebrate Fauna of Bedfordshire*. Privately published, Birmingham.
Born in 1871, Steele-Elliott developed his interest in birds during his schooldays. In pursuit of his egg-collecting hobby he became a keen walker—he once walked from London to Bedford in a day for a bet. He took over a foundry business in Dudley in 1896 with his brother, and moved away from Bedford. Whilst there he remained in touch with Bedfordshire sportsmen, taxidermists and naturalists and accumulated a large amount of information on the mammals and birds of the county. His account of the vertebrates of Bedfordshire was discontinued after the 5th part, though he completed the birds section.

Huntingdonshire V.C. 31.
There is no complete account of Huntingdonshire's birds. Records of its avifauna are accumulated from the pages of *The Field, The Zoologist* and, especially, Lord Lilford's various works on the birds of Northamptonshire. See under Northamptonshire.

Northamptonshire V.C. 32.
LILFORD, Lord. 1895. *Notes on the Birds of Northamptonshire and Neighbourhood*. R. H. Porter, London.
Thomas Lyttleton Powys, fourth Baron Lilford, was born in 1833. Even as a schoolboy at Harrow he contributed notes to *The Zoologist,* a practice that he continued throughout his life. He travelled widely in southern Europe and contributed many notes on the birds he found there whilst also adding to his famous collection of birds of prey. He will always be linked to the fortunes of the Little Owl, a species that he introduced into Britain. Illness forced him to curtail his foreign trips during the 1880s and he devoted most of the rest of his life to several famous works, the greatest of which was his beautiful *Coloured Figures of the Birds of the British Islands*. He was a founder MBOU and subsequently became its President, a post he held for many years. He died in 1896 and was buried at Lilford Hall, Northamptonshire.

Gloucestershire V.C. 33 & 34.
MELLERSH, William Lock. 1902. *A Treatise on the Birds of Gloucestershire*. Bellows, Gloucester.
Little is known of Mellersh's life. He was apparently a school-teacher based in Cheltenham and wrote only a handful of other ornithological notes. His Treatise,

however, although not written in the classic style of a listed account, was very complete and detailed and a valuable contribution to Gloucestershire ornithology.

Monmouthshire V.C. 35.
INGRAM, Geoffrey C. S. and H. MORREY SALMON. 1939. The Birds of Monmouthshire. *Trans. Cardiff Nat. Soc.* **LXX**, 93–127.
This account drew, in part, from information on the avifauna of 19th century Monmouthshire published in journals and from the accounts of birds of the adjacent counties of that time. The birdlife of Monmouthshire during the 19th century remains, however, poorly understood.
Ingram was a MBOU (1923–1953) and became a Life Member in 1962. He was a member of the Court of Governors and of the Council (1943–1958) of the National Museum of Wales, and was a past President of the Cardiff Naturalists' Society.
Morrey Salmon was the Treasurer of the National Museum of Wales and a Member of the Court of Governors of the University College of South Wales and Monmouthshire. He was a Member of the Nature Conservancy (1957–1960), of the Committee for Wales (1951–1966) and of the BOU and was a past President of the Cardiff Naturalists' Society and Vice-President of the Glamorgan County Naturalists' Trust.

Hertfordshire V.C. 36.
BULL, Henry Graves. 1888. *Notes on the Birds of Herefordshire*. Jakeman and Carver, London.
Henry Bull was born in 1818. He was an M.D. and a Fellow of the Botanical Society, Edinburgh. His greatest work, in collaboration with Hogg, was the famous *Herefordshire Pomona*, an inventory of the Herefordshire cider apple varieties and one of the finest works on fruit culture published in Britain at the time. His *Notes* was published after his death in 1885, and was an edited work of contributions from the members of the Woolhope Naturalists' Club, but was not regarded as having any great ornithological significance.
HUTCHINSON, T. 1900. Birds of Herefordshire. *Trans. Woolhope Nat. Field Club*, 1899, 190–243.
This is an annotated list and, once again, was edited from the contributions of the club members. Its main merit is the authentification of Bull's and others' works.

Worcestershire V.C. 37
BUND, John William Willis. 1891. *A List of the Birds of Worcestershire and the Adjoining Counties*. Private publication, Worcester.
Bund was educated at Cambridge and became a member of the Linnean Society in 1886. He was best known as a writer on fishing subjects and this was his only ornithological work. It is an extremely scarce and eccentric publication and little more than an annotated list but it does provide the only full account of Worcestershire birds of the 19th century.
TOMES, Robert Fisher. 1901. [Birds in] *Victoria History of the County of Worcestershire*. Dawsons of Pall Mall, London.
Tomes was born in Evesham and developed an interest in zoology from an early age. His interest in ornithology waned, however (he resigned his membership of the BOU in 1866), and he concentrated far more on the study of mammals. His contributions on the birds of Worcestershire

and Warwickshire to the Victoria County History series were his only ornithological works.

Warwickshire V.C. 38.
NORRIS, C.A. 1947. *Notes on the Birds of Warwickshire.* Cornish Brothers Ltd, Birmingham.
Norris drew heavily on the amount of information published on Warwickshire ornithology to provide a history of the birds of that county.
TOMES, Robert Fisher. 1904. [Birds in] *Victoria County History of the County of Warwickshire.* Dawsons of Pall Mall, London.
See under Worcestershire
This was the first account of the whole county.

Staffordshire V.C. 39.
McALDOWIE, Alexander Morison. 1893. *The Birds of Staffordshire.* Stoke-on-Trent.
Born in Scotland, McAldowie completed his medical training at Aberdeen University in 1879. He was a FRSE and a member of the North Staffordshire Naturalists' Field Club. His *Birds of Staffordshire* was reprinted from the *Transactions* of the latter society but contained a number of records that Smith (1930–38) felt were doubtful; however, these did not include any of breeding species.

Shropshire V.C. 40.
BECKWITH, William Edmund. 1879. Birds of Shropshire. *Trans. Shropshire Archæol. Nat. Hist. Soc.* 2: 365–395.
BECKWITH, William Edmund. 1881. Birds of Shropshire continued. *Trans. Shropshire Archæol. Nat. Hist. Soc.* 4: 326–328.
BECKWITH, William Edmund. 1887–93. Notes on Shropshire Birds. *Trans. Shropshire Archæol. Nat. Hist. Soc.* 10: 383–98; 11: 223–38, 387–402. Second series 1: 201–16; 2: 1–16, 3: 313–28; 4: 183–98; 5: 31–48
Beckwith was born at Eaton Constantine, Shropshire, in 1844, the son of the local rector. He was educated at Bridgnorth and King's College, London. He lived at Eaton Constantine until his father's death in 1888. The family moved to Radbrook House in Shrewsbury and William died there in 1892. He was a very active and enthusiastic observer of birds and 'always used a good field glass, a practice that he firmly recommended to others'. His *Notes* was unfinished, but is the most detailed account of Shropshire birds in the 19th century.
FORREST, Herbert Edward. 1899. *The Fauna of Shropshire.* Wilding, Shrewsbury.
Forrest was born in Wolverhampton in 1858 and in the same year was moved to Shrewsbury where his father opened a pianoforte and music business in Castle Street. After receiving an elementary education from his mother he entered Shrewsbury School in 1870 and four years later became a clerk in Lloyds Bank at Aston, Birmingham. He remained there for five years and was then transferred to the branch at Welshpool. Two years later, on the destruction of his mother's business by fire (his father had died in 1880) he left the bank and returned to Shrewsbury to help his brother rebuild the family business. On his brother's retirement in 1919 Herbert became the sole proprietor.

In 1888 Forrest married Harriette Kate of Hereford and had five children. During his sojourn in Birmingham he developed an interest in natural history and published his first paper in the *Midland Naturalist* in 1879, a note on

microscopic primitive pond-dwellers known as Vorticellidae. In 1893 he became the first local and then later the honorary Secretary and Treasurer of the Caradoc and Severn Valley Field Club, a post that he held until 1929 when he relinquished it to become president. His most important work was the later *Vertebrate Fauna of North Wales* and he was a frequent contributor of Shropshire and Welsh ornithological notes to many journals. He published studies on many other diverse subjects, from the architectural study of the old houses of Shropshire, to the promulgation of his theory of the origin and cause of the Ice Age.

Glamorgan V. C. 41.
CARDIFF NATURALISTS' SOCIETY (A Committee of). 1900. *The Birds of Glamorgan.* Cardiff.
The Committee was set up in the early 1890s and consisted of R. Drane, T. W. Proger, T. H. Thomas, Dr Paterson and Mrs Paterson. Drane, Proger and Dr Paterson appear to have been the most active of the Glamorgan ornithologists and of the Committee. Between them they published other works concerning the birds of the county, including regular contributions to the *Transactions of the Cardiff Naturalists' Society* and a small account of 'The Rarer Birds of Cardiff and District' published in the *British Association Handbook for Cardiff and District.* The Patersons and Proger took part in the Committee that prepared the 1925 *Birds of Glamorgan.* The 1900 account, although devoid of unnecessary detail, was a clear, well laid out and researched account, benefiting from the experience of people familiar with different areas of the county.

Brecon V.C. 42.
PHILLIPS, Edward Cambridge. 1899. *The Birds of Breconshire.* Edwin Davies, Brecon.
This work arose out of a series of five papers originally contributed to *The Zoologist* in 1881 and 1882 and reprinted in the latter year. The 1899 work is often called the second edition and consists of the previous work together with supplementary information published in *The Zoologist* between 1884 and 1890. As one of the very few Welsh county avifaunas of the 19th century, it is an invaluable work notwithstanding Phillips' apparent preparedness to accept all records communicated to him with little further investigation. Phillips was born in Wiltshire in 1840, made his home in Breconshire and was, for over 60 years, the Justices' Clerk of the Devynock (Defynnog) and Talgarth petty sessional divisions. He had a great love of the country and, in 1866, married the daughter of a Carmarthenshire squire. He lived with his wife near Brecon for 40 years but then, finally, moved to Hay-on-Wye where he died in 1931. He was a frequent contributor to the *Transactions of the Woolhope Naturalists' Field Club* and the *Transactions of the Cardiff Naturalists, Field Club* and, in 1908, compiled the list of the birds for the *Victoria County History of Herefordshire.* He was a FLS and a MBOU and of the Permanent International Ornithological Committee. In 1892, he was made an honorary member of the Woolhope Naturalists' Field Club of which he was President in 1911.

Radnor V.C. 43.
INGRAM, Geoffrey C. S. and H. MORREY SALMON. 1955. *A Handlist of the Birds of Radnorshire.* Herefordshire Ornithological Club, Kington.

The older records in this account were drawn from submissions to *The Field, The Zoologist* and the *Transactions of the Woolhope Naturalists' Field Club*. In addition to these records, John Walpole-Bond's *Bird Life in Wild Wales* (1903) described in great detail his experiences in central Wales in 1902 and 1903. With the assistance of 'Jock' the authors of the *Birds of Radnorshire* were able to extract the relevant observations of birds and clearly form an important contribution to the knowledge of the birds of that time. Forrest (see under Shropshire) was also able to contribute some notes from his correspondents.

Carmarthenshire V.C. 44.
BARKER, T. W. 1905. *Handbook to the Natural History of Carmarthenshire.* Private publication, Carmarthen.
Little is known of Barker. His annotated list of the birds of the county included in this work appears to have been drawn from a small number of lists supplied to him by Carmarthenshire ornithologists, the avifaunas of neighbouring counties and his own observations. It is clear and concise and accepted with little question by later writers of the birds of the county.

Pembrokeshire V.C. 45.
MATHEW, Rev. Murray Alexander. 1894. *The Birds of Pembrokeshire and its Islands.* R. H. Porter, London.
Mathew's book contained some inaccuracies but is nevertheless invaluable as one of the few Welsh county avifaunas of the 19th century. Mathew had the curious and erroneous belief that the Prescelly Mountains prevented many small migrants (he lists the Redstart, Garden and Wood Warblers and Wryneck) entering southern Pembrokeshire. Later writers have omitted seven species claimed by Mathew to have been obtained in the county but none of these was claimed to have bred. For a brief biography of Mathew see under Devonshire.

Cardiganshire V.C. 46.
SALTER, John Henry. 1900. *List of the Birds of Aberystwyth and Neighbourhood.* University College of Wales Scientific Society, Aberystwyth.
Salter was the first occupant of the Chair of Botany at the University College, Aberystwyth between 1891 and 1908. He came to reside in Aberystwyth in 1891 and soon started a long series of communications of ornithological interest to *The Zoologist*, the first major one being his 'Observations on Birds in Mid-Wales' in 1895. His *List* was published for the Scientific Society of the College and has been supported, for the purposes of the present work, by his contributions to *The Zoologist* between 1895 and 1904.

Montgomeryshire V.C. 47.
FORREST, Herbert Edward. 1907. *The Vertebrate Fauna of North Wales.* Witherby, London.
This was a monumental work and one of the most important contributions to the avifauna of Britain at that time. It has stood as the basis to the study of the fauna of North Wales to the present day and has been almost universally accepted since it was published. A biography of Forrest is included in the section on Shropshire.

Merioneth V.C. 48.
See under Montgomeryshire.

Caernarvonshire V.C. 49.
See under Montgomeryshire.

Denbighshire V.C. 50.
See under Montgomeryshire.

Flintshire V.C. 51.
See under Montgomeryshire.

Anglesey V.C. 52.
See under Montgomeryshire.

Lincolnshire V.C. 53 & 54.
CORDEAUX, John. 1899. *A List of the British Birds belonging to the Humber District.* R. H. Porter, London.
Cordeaux was considered an outstanding ornithologist of his time. He was born in 1831 and from the 1840s lived at Great Cotes near Grimsby until his death in 1899, although his area of observation and recording covered the whole of the Humber district in Lincolnshire and Yorkshire. The first President of the Lincolnshire Naturalists' Union in 1893, he was also President of the Yorkshire Naturalists' Union in 1896. His chief interest was in migration and for many years—from 1864 to 1899—he contributed lengthy reports on bird migration on the northeast Lincolnshire coast to *The Zoologist*. This interest was developed during a visit to Heligoland in 1874 when he formed an acquaintance with Gatke. In 1879 he joined Harvie-Brown in a scheme for obtaining reports on the subject from the keepers of lighthouses and lightships and, at the Swansea meeting of the British Association for the Advancement of Science, was appointed secretary of a Committee to carry out this plan. He held the post for nearly 20 years and was largely responsible for conducting a vast enquiry into bird migration on the coasts of Britain and Ireland undertaken by the Committee from 1880 to 1887. The above *List* followed an earlier work published in 1872 and was much more concise, and brought up to date all his information about the status and distribution of birds in the district. It must be said, however, that Cordeaux did not always appear to demand of himself the highest standards of care and accuracy in identification and recording that he required from others. Some of his own sight records of rare species appear to have been made on quite inadequate evidence and he was too ready to accept similar records of others. For the purposes of the present account, however, this was far more a problem for rare, non-breeding migrants than for the breeding birds of the area.
BLATHWAYT, Rev. Francis Linley. 1915. The Birds of Lincolnshire. *Lincolnshire Nat. Union Trans. 1914,* 178–211.
Blathwayt was an ornithologist of a new era. Resident in the county from 1900 to 1916, first in Lincoln and then at nearby Doddington, from 1907 to 1919 he was Secretary of the Vertebrate Zoology Section of the Lincolnshire Naturalists' Union and in 1918 he became the Union's President. He was particularly interested in the numbers and distribution of birds and in the changes brought about by the activities of people and natural causes. He tried to encourage others to investigate some of the many problems of bird distribution in the county. He was the first to attempt a census of Great-crested Grebe, Heron and Black-headed Gull populations of the county.

Leicestershire and Rutland V.C. 55.
BROWNE, Montagu. 1889. *Vertebrate Animals of Leicestershire and Rutland.* Private publication, Birmingham.

Montagu Browne was, for a number of years, Curator of the Corporation Museum and Art Gallery at Leicester and in addition to 'Vertebrate Animals...' wrote *Artistic and Scientific Taxidermy and Modelling* (1896) which gives a clue to his favourite pastime. His 'Vertebrate Animals...' arose out of his series of papers on the vertebrates of Leicestershire in *The Zoologist* during 1885–86. He apparently obtained his information about Rutland's birds from the Earl of Gainsborough.

HAINES, Charles Reginald. 1907. *Notes on the Birds of Rutland*. R. H. Porter, London.

Haines taught at Uppingham School and resided in the village at the time that he wrote this work. He was a MBOU from 1898 until 1904.

Nottinghamshire V.C. 56.

WHITAKER, Joseph. 1907. *Notes on the Birds of Nottinghamshire*. Walter Black and Co., London.

Whitaker resided at Rainworth Lodge near Mansfield and was regarded as the most noted ornithologist of his county. He made the birds of Nottinghamshire his special study for over 40 years. He was born at Ramsdale in 1850, the son of Joseph, a noted all-round sportsman of his day. Joseph junior was educated at Uppingham, Rutland, was a JP for the county and borough of Mansfield and Vice-President of the Selbourne Society and a FZS.

Rainworth Lodge, which stands on ground that was formerly part of Sherwood Forest, was first built about the end of the 11th century for one of the King's Foresters. Whitaker junior strove for many years to turn Rainworth into a sanctuary for birds and evidently succeeded—the numbers of birds in the grounds were often commented upon and 158 species were recorded there; over 300 nest boxes were erected. The wildfowl on Rainworth Water was apparently a great feature of the place.

Derbyshire V.C. 57.

WHITLOCK, F. B. 1893. *The Birds of Derbyshire*. Bemrose and Sons, London.

Whitlock lived at Beeston and, as a young man, was a bank cashier at Basford near Nottingham. He did most of his bird watching in the Trent valley along the Derbyshire/Nottinghamshire border and was a most energetic ornithologist. He wrote a list of the birds for the *British Association Handbook for Nottinghamshire* published in 1893, and in 1896 he became an assistant editor with H. K. Swann of the *Ornithologist*. In the preparation of *The Birds of Derbyshire* he was greatly assisted by a local taxidermist, A. S. Hutchinson; however, this did not allay the criticism of the book, in *The Zoologist* in 1894, that the publication was hurried and did not cover the county as well as was claimed. The criticism was scathing, particularly in relation to the records of rarities, although accounts of the breeding birds of the county were generally sound and well written and not questioned during the review.

Cheshire V.C. 58.

COWARD, Thomas Alfred and Charles OLDHAM. 1900. *The Birds of Cheshire*. Sherratt and Hughes, Manchester.

Coward was born in 1867, a son to Thomas senior, a noted botanist and geologist, in Bowden, Cheshire, and spent most of his life there. He was educated at Brooklands School and Owens College, Manchester and was one of the founders of the Manchester Natural History Society whose museum has since grown into the Manchester Museum.

With Oldham he published a number of papers on the ornithology of Anglesey and other parts of North Wales and, eventually, in 1910, the thorough *The Vertebrate Fauna of Cheshire and Liverpool Bay*. Oldham's interest in mammals enabled him to contribute the bulk of the records for the non-ornithological parts of 'The Vertebrate Fauna...'. He was a MBOU and a FZS. He died in Berkhamsted in 1942.

Lancashire V. C. 59 & 60.

MITCHELL, Frederick Shaw. 1892. *The Birds of Lancashire*, 2nd edition revised and annotated by Howard Saunders. Gurney and Jackson, London.

Mitchell was born in 1850 and lived at Clitheroe. He published the first edition of *The Birds of Lancashire* in 1885 but it quickly sold out. Unfortunately he left for Vancouver Island, Canada, before he could complete the revision of the book for a second edition and, so, this task was undertaken by Saunders, an eminent ornithologist of the day. Both books attained a commendable degree of accuracy assisted in no small part by the wealth of information that was available to both writers concerning the birds of the county.

Yorkshire V. C. 61, 62, 63, 64 & 65.

NELSON, Thomas Hudson, William Eagle CLARKE and Frederick BOYES. 1907. *The Birds of Yorkshire*. Brown and Sons, London.

Nelson was born in 1856 in Bishop Auckland, County Durham and educated there and privately under Marquis de Kervan. He followed no profession and was interested in general natural history, but especially in ornithology. He was an assistant editor of *The Naturalist* and published a number of papers on the ornithology of Yorkshire. He was a JP for the North Riding and became a MBOU in 1882. Clarke was credited with persuading Nelson to undertake 'this stupendous task' and acted as an assistant writer of the work. Boyes, similarly, assisted in the production of the book, contributing much information on the birds of East Yorkshire. *The Birds of Yorkshire* was an immense undertaking and consisted of almost 900 pages and numerous photographic illustrations of birds and Yorkshire bird habitats in two large volumes. It was very detailed and thorough and stands as a major contribution to Yorkshire ornithology.

Clarke was born in Leeds in 1853, son of a local solicitor. He began his working life as a civil engineer and surveyor but later took up natural history as a profession, having all his life been keenly interested in it. He took a number of museum posts in Leeds and Edinburgh and was elected a member of the British Association Committee on Bird Migration in 1884. He was a FRSE and was President of the Yorkshire Naturalists' Union in 1905. During the early 20th century he was Editor of the *Scottish Naturalist* as he was of its predecessor, the *Annals of Scottish Natural History*. This interest in Scottish (and Arctic and Antarctic) zoology followed his early work in Yorkshire (many notes on which he contributed to various periodicals) which included, with W.D. Roebuck, *A Handbook of the Vertebrate Fauna of Yorkshire* published in 1881.

Durham V.C. 66.
See under Northumberland.

Northumberland V.C. 67 & 68.

HANCOCK, John. 1874. *A Catalogue of the Birds of Northumberland and Durham*. Williams and Norgate, London.

Hancock was born the son of a Newcastle-upon-Tyne tradesman in 1807. His father died whilst John was still a child and so he received a poor education, something that he was to regret for the rest of his life, and it was with only the greatest inducement that he committed his ornithological knowledge to paper. He was devoted to the study of natural history from boyhood and Bewick wrote of him as a friend in 1826. Hancock oversaw the production of the 8th, and acclaimed as the best, edition of Bewick's *British Birds*. In 1833 he accompanied Hewitson on a bird nesting expedition to Norway and Charles St John on a similar tour of Sutherland. His vast and detailed knowledge from the field of the birds of Northumberland and Durham was recorded in his 'Catalogue'.

BOLAM, George. 1912. *The Birds of Northumberland and the Eastern Borders*. Henry Hunter Blair, Alnwick.

Bolam was born at Barmoor, Northumberland, in 1859 and was educated at Northallerton and Uppingham Schools. He was encouraged to undertake his very detailed and complete work through his friendship of many of the older naturalists including Hancock, Adamson and Robert Gray. These naturalists, especially Hancock, placed at Bolam's disposal their notes on the ornithology of the region. He also published many papers and notes in *The Zoologist*, *The Naturalist* and the transactions of several local natural history societies. In 1932 he published an updated account of the birds of Northumberland.

Westmorland V.C. 69.
See under Cumberland.

Cumberland V.C. 70.

MACPHERSON, Rev. Hugh Alexander. 1892. *A Vertebrate Fauna of Lakeland*. David Douglas, Edinburgh.

This prolific writer was born in Calcutta in 1858. He was sent to Haileybury College in 1872 but never attained a very high standing in the school; apparently he was already distracted by his interest in natural history. In 1878 he went to Oriel College, Oxford, where he joined the Oxfordshire Natural History Society at its founding in 1880. Here he met Aplin with whom he corresponded for over 20 years. He developed an early interest in the trapping of birds that culminated in the publication, in 1895, of his *History of Fowling*. Birds were not the only animals that took his interest. During a holiday in France in 1881 his interest in reptiles led him to attempt the capture of a snake by hand—the resulting bite made him seriously ill for several days.

About this time, on the death of Sir John Macleod, Macpherson inherited the Glendale Estate on Skye. To other men this may have seemed like a mixed blessing as it did not produce a large income, but it made Macpherson very happy because of his interest in natural history. Having obtained his degree in 1881, he commenced his clerical duties at St James's, Carlisle, and immediately set about the task of investigating the birds of the district. This led him, in collaboration with William Duckworth, to publish the *Birds of Cumberland* in 1886. His visits to his property in Skye enabled him to collect enough information on the birds of the island to publish a paper 'The Birds of Skye' in 1886. These two accounts formed the basis of his two most

valuable works—*A Vertebrate Fauna of Lakeland* and, in collaboration with Harvie-Brown, *A Fauna of the North-West Highlands and Skye* (1904). This latter was the final publication in a long list, as Macpherson died in 1901.

Isle of Man V.C. 71.

RALFE, Pilcher George. 1906. *The Birds of the Isle of Man*. David Douglas, Edinburgh.

Ralfe, MBOU, of Castletown, Isle of Man, was born at Ellanbane near Ramsey on that island in 1861. In 1880 he entered the employment of the Isle of Man Bank, becoming its agent at Laxey in 1895 and, in 1897, agent at Castletown, a post he held until his retirement. Ralfe remained a bachelor all his life, he was an indefatigable walker, an intrepid sailor, a keen continental traveller, a capable linguist and, for over 40 years, the dominant figure of Manx ornithology. *The Birds of the Isle of Man* is a work of great scholarship and reflects meticulous research. The book introduced Manx birds to a widespread audience and led to the increasingly regular publication in *British Birds* of Manx ornithological notes. Publication began in 1905 and Ralfe's last report was in 1934. He died in 1936.

Channel Islands.

SMITH, Cecil. 1879. *The Birds of Guernsey and the Neighbouring Islands*. Van Voorst, London.

This book was unavailable during the preparation of the present study but use has been made of a later account (Dobson 1952) that includes many of Smith's records. For a biography of Smith see under Somerset.

Dumfriesshire W1D.

GLADSTONE, Hugh Steuart. 1910. *The Birds of Dumfriesshire*. Witherby, London.

Gladstone, of Capenoch, Thornhill, Dumfriesshire and 40, Lennox Gardens, London was born in London in 1877. He was educated at Eton and Trinity Hall, Cambridge, from where he gained his M.A. and, in 1897, became an officer in the King's Own Scottish Borderers. He served in the South African War between 1899 and 1902, was twice decorated and retired from the forces in 1903. He married in 1907 and fathered a son and two daughters.

He was always interested in birds and, after his return from South Africa, began to take photographs of birds, some of which were reproduced in *The Birds of Dumfriesshire*. He travelled widely to take his photographs—in India, East Africa and, on many occasions, in Europe. He was elected FZS, and MBOU in 1903, FRSE in 1909, FZS (Scotland) in 1912 and President of the Dumfriesshire and Galloway Natural History and Antiquarian Society in 1909.

Kirkcudbrightshire W1K.

SERVICE, Robert. 1902. The Vertebrate Zoology of Kirkcudbrightshire. [In Maxwell's] *Guide Book to the Stewartry of Kirkcudbright*. 7th edition, Castle Douglas.

Service, for many years considered the recognised authority on the avifauna of the Solway area, was born in 1854 at Nether Place near Mauchline, Ayrshire, where his father was gardener to Lord Justice Clerk Hope. He was educated in Maxwelltown in Dumfriesshire where his father had established a nursery business and which Robert entered on leaving school and continued to operate for the rest of his life. He was a very keen ornithologist, numbering Newton, Saunders, Macpherson, Harvie-Brown and other well-known writers among his correspondents. Gladstone was indebted for his assistance during the preparation of *The Birds of Dumfriesshire*. He was Secretary of the Dumfriesshire and Galloway Natural History Society from 1876 to 1882, a MBOU, a member of the British Association, Natural History Society of Glasgow and several other societies. He was a prolific contributor to natural history and other journals and local newspapers and his papers and notes numbered over 200. He died at his home, Janefield, Maxwelltown, in 1911 leaving a wife and five children.

Wigtownshire W1W.
GRAY, Robert and Thomas ANDERSON. 1869. *Birds of Ayrshire and Wigtownshire*. Murray, Glasgow.
Gray was born at Dunbar, East Lothian in 1825. As a boy he formed the usual collection of natural history specimens—birds' eggs and skins, fish, shells, crustacea and insects—and kept it in a 'museum' in the attic at his family's home. Gradually he concentrated more and more on ornithology and his appointment to the post of inspector of branches of the City of Glasgow Bank gave him the opportunity to travel frequently in Scotland. He systematically took the opportunity to settle his business early with the agent of the branch he was visiting and then to make contact with a local taxidermist or naturalist. In this way he gained both many ornithological contacts throughout the country and many stuffed specimens, and was able to make copious notes and sketches. *The Birds of Ayrshire and Wigtownshire* and, his most important work, *The Birds of the West of Scotland* (1871), owe their origin to these journeys and collected materials. Gray was Secretary of the Natural History Society of Glasgow from 1860, of the Royal Physical Society of Edinburgh from 1877 and Vice-President of the Royal Society of Edinburgh. He died in 1887.

Little is known of Anderson, he appears to have been a travelling companion of Gray.

Clyde Faunal Region W2Ay, W2L, W2R, W2Ar.
PATERSON, John. 1901. [Birds of the Clyde Area in] *Fauna, Flora and Geology of the Clyde Area, a Handbook Prepared for the Meeting of the British Association at Glasgow, 1901*. Glasgow.
Paterson was a member of the local Committee of the British Association and a resident of Glasgow. His main sources of reference in compiling the above scant list were Gray and Anderson's *The Birds of Ayrshire and Wigtownshire* (1869) and Gray's *The Birds of the West of Scotland* (1871). As these accounts were somewhat out of date by the turn of the century reference has also been made to the following later accounts in the present study.
McWILLIAM, Rev. J. M. 1927. *The Birds of the Island of Bute*. Witherby, London.
PATON, E. Richmond and Oliver G. PIKE. 1929. *The Birds of Ayrshire*. Witherby, London.
McWILLIAM, Rev. J. M. 1936. *The Birds of the Firth of Clyde*. Witherby, London.

Tweed Faunal Region E1.
EVANS, Arthur Humble. 1911. *A Fauna of the Tweed Area*. David Douglas, Edinburgh.
For a biography of Evans see Cambridgeshire.
This was the final volume in the Fauna of Scotland series; those planned for the Solway, Clyde and Forth

regions were never published. As with the others of the series it forms a cornerstone of Scottish ornithology and was extremely well researched, complete and thorough. The Tweed district had a large amount of previously published ornithological information, not the least of which was Muirhead's *The Birds of Berwickshire*, 1889–95, which Evans was able to draw upon.

Berwickshire part of E1.
MUIRHEAD, George. 1889–95. *The Birds of Berwickshire*. David Douglas, Edinburgh.
Muirhead was an inhabitant of the county when he wrote his remarkably detailed *The Birds of Berwickshire* but later moved to Moray. He became a FRS (Edinburgh) and MBOU in 1886. His library was evidently considerable and he was also a noted botanist.

Forth Faunal Region E2.
RINTOUL, Leonora Jeffrey and Evelyn V. BAXTER. 1935. *A Vertebrate Fauna of Forth*. Oliver and Boyd, Edinburgh.
Naturalists had looked forward to the completion of a Fauna of the Forth region for many years. It had been expected that William Evans, following his *An Annotated List of the Birds of the Forth Area* (1912), would write of the area that had been his life-long study. Though he wrote and published preliminary studies of the mammals, reptiles and batrachians, had published many papers and notes on different aspects of the Forth fauna and had prepared and delivered a resumé of 'Our Present Knowledge of the Fauna of the Forth Area' as his Presidential address to the Royal Physical Society in 1906, he died before he could write an avifauna. His *Annotated List of the Birds...* was published posthumously by his daughter. W. E. Clarke encouraged Rintoul and Baxter to take on the job of completing the task and they were able to draw heavily on William Evans' early work.

Tay Faunal Region E3.
HARVIE-BROWN, John Alexander. 1906. *A Fauna of the Tay Basin and Strathmore*. David Douglas, Edinburgh.
Harvie-Brown was born in 1844 and educated at Merchiston and at Edinburgh and Cambridge Universities. His family name was Harvie but when his father was left a property at Quarter, south of Glasgow, by a John Brown, the double-barrelled name was formed. His family, however, lived at Dunipace House, Larbert in Stirlingshire and it was here that Harvie-Brown made his base for his investigation of the Scottish fauna.

His contributions to Scottish ornithology were legion. His first contribution to *The Zoologist* seems to have been in 1862 (a note on his observation of a Sandpiper diving). Later contributions were numerous although his later papers were published, in the main, in the flourishing Scottish journals such as the *Proceedings of the Physical Society of Edinburgh*, the *Natural History Society of Glasgow*, the *Annals of Scottish Natural History* and the *Scottish Naturalist* (he was the editor of the latter for many years). His papers from the 1860s, 1870s and early 1880s show clearly his interest in, primarily, the distribution of the birds of Scotland. He attempted to record the avifauna of some of the Scottish islands and the distribution of single species (such as the Capercaillie and Dotterel). This interest led to the development of his plan to record the animals of Scotland in a series of volumes based on the faunal regions developed by Buchanan White in 1872. The first was published in 1887; the Fauna of the Tay was the 10th volume in the series. They remained the most important contribution to the ornithology of Scotland until Baxter and Rintoul's *The Birds of Scotland* (1953), and are still an important source of historical information.

Dee Faunal Region E4.
SIM, George. 1903. *The Vertebrate Fauna of Dee*. Wyllie and Son, Aberdeen.
Born in 1835, Sim was a taxidermist and naturalist from Castle Street, Aberdeen. His primary interest was ichthyology and he wrote *The Food of Fishes* (1884) along with other works on the subject. He contributed many articles and notes on fish and ornithology to the scientific journals of the day and was a correspondent of Harvie-Brown, particularly during the preparation of the Moray volume of the Fauna of Scotland series. His other main ornithological achievement was the publication, in 1889, of his account of the great invasion of the Pallas's Sandgrouse.
The Fauna of Dee was designed to fit into the Fauna of Scotland series and was even bound in a similar fashion. However, Sim's interest in fish is obvious as they are treated with clear thoroughness, whereas the ornithological section was far less thorough than those in Harvie-Brown's accounts.

Moray Faunal Region E5S, E5N.
HARVIE-BROWN, John Alexander and Thomas Edward BUCKLEY. 1895. *A Vertebrate Fauna of the Moray Basin*. David Douglas, Edinburgh.
For a biography of Harvie-Brown see under Tay Faunal Region.
Buckley was born in 1846 the son of the rector of St Thomas, Old Trafford, at that time just outside Manchester. He was educated at Rugby and by private tuition and spent a few years of his youth with his family in Old Trafford and then Beverley, Yorkshire, before he went to Cambridge University and took his degree in 1867 or 1868. He visited Scotland for the first time in 1869 as a guest of Donald Cameron of Glenbrittle, Skye. From 1866 he travelled widely on sporting and collecting trips—Lapland and Sweden in that year, Sweden again in 1867 and 1868, Turkey and Greece in 1869, the Gold Coast in 1872, Matabeleland in 1873, Amaswaziland in 1876, New Brunswick in 1882 and 1884, Kilimanjaro in 1888–89 and, finally, to the Rockies in 1893. His visit to Skye, however, clearly made a strong impression on him and he became determined to settle in Scotland. In 1870 he took the shooting rights of Gordonbush, Brora, in Sutherland and married in 1874. In 1885 he purchased the small Highland estate of Rossal on the River Cassley in Sutherland but, disliking it, sold it in 1887 and built a house in Inverness in which he resided until his death.
It is recorded that Buckley broke the record of salmon taken with a single rod in North Scotland—his record on the Helmsdale was 22 fish taken with a fly on a 12-foot trout-rod, and unaided by an attendant. It is also recorded that his greatest personal sorrow was the loss of his friend, Guy Dawnay, whom he met during his trip to Kilimanjaro, and who met his death 'from the treacherous charge of a wounded buffalo' in Canada.
The Moray volumes of the Fauna of Scotland series (the 6th and 7th) covered the largest area and were considered

to have been the best by contemporary reviewers.

Argyll Faunal Region W3S, W3N.
HARVIE-BROWN, John Alexander and Thomas Edward BUCKLEY. 1892. *A Vertebrate Fauna of Argyll and the Inner Hebrides*. David Douglas, Edinburgh.
For a biography of Harvie-Brown see under Tay Faunal Region, and for a biography of Buckley see under Moray Faunal Region.
The Argyll volume was the 5th of the Fauna of Scotland series and included many of the Inner Hebrides that Harvie-Brown and various friends toured in his motor yacht from the 1870s.

West Ross and Skye Faunal Region W4S, W4C, W4N, W4Sk.
HARVIE-BROWN, John Alexander and Rev. H. A. MACPHERSON. 1904. *A Fauna of the North-West Highlands and Skye*. David Douglas, Edinburgh.
For a biography of Harvie-Brown see under Tay Faunal Region and for a biography of Macpherson see under Cumberland.
The mainland portion of the *Fauna of North-West Highlands and Skye* was written by Harvie-Brown whilst Macpherson contributed notes made during his residence on Skye. This was the 9th volume in the Fauna of Scotland series.

Sutherland Faunal Region E6E, E6W.
HARVIE-BROWN, John Alexander and Thomas Edward BUCKLEY. 1887. *A Vertebrate Fauna of Sutherland, Caithness and West Cromarty*. David Douglas, Edinburgh.
For a biography of Harvie-Brown see under Tay Faunal Region and for a biography of Buckley see under Moray Faunal Region.
This was the first volume in the Fauna of Scotland series and, as such, was very much less refined than later volumes. Many records were published of observations made in parts of Sutherland that were outside the faunal region and thus were repeated in the Moray volume. The area was split between the co-authors; Harvie-Brown covered the north and west of the area, that is west of the high road between Lairg and Tongue.

Outer Hebrides Faunal Region W5N, W5S.
HARVIE-BROWN, John Alexander and Thomas Edward BUCKLEY. 1888. *A Vertebrate Fauna of the Outer Hebrides*. David Douglas, Edinburgh.
For a biography of Harvie-Brown see under Tay Faunal Region and for a biography of Buckley see under Moray Faunal Region.
This, the second volume in the Fauna of Scotland series, was based in large part upon visits that Harvie-Brown made to the islands from the 1870s. Much of the information from that source was a little out of date by the end of the century and so it has been supported, in the current work, by papers published in the Scottish natural history journals.

Orkney Faunal Region E7.
HARVIE-BROWN, John Alexander and Thomas Edward BUCKLEY. 1891. *A Vertebrate Fauna of the Orkney Islands*. David Douglas, Edinburgh.
For a biography of Harvie-Brown see under Tay Faunal Region and for a biography of Buckley see under Moray Faunal Region.

This was the 4th volume in the Fauna of Scotland series.

Zetland (Shetland) Faunal Region E8.
EVANS, Arthur Humble and Thomas Edward BUCKLEY. 1899. *A Vertebrate Fauna of the Shetland Islands*. David Douglas, Edinburgh.
For a biography of Evans see under Tweed Faunal Region and for a biography of Buckley see under Moray Faunal Region.
This was the 8th volume in the Fauna of Scotland series and it benefited in no small way from Saxby's earlier work (Saxby 1874).

Ireland.
USSHER, Richard John and Robert WARREN. 1900. *The Birds of Ireland*. Gurney and Jackson, London.
Ussher, of Cappagh House, Waterford, one of the most eminent of Irish ornithologists, was born in 1841 and at the age of 12 was sent to school at Portarlington and, subsequently, Chester. Afterwards, being delicate, he was educated by a tutor. He entered Trinity College, Dublin but, owing to ill health, never took his degree, and spent the next few winters travelling with his mother and a tutor in Spain, Italy, Corfu and other Mediterranean countries. When 25 he married and again travelled abroad for some years. On his return he devoted himself to public duties in his own county and became Deputy-Lieutenant and High Sheriff and took great interest in Church matters, being for many years a member of the General Synod.

His interest in egg collecting and ornithology dated from boyhood and was said to have developed further after his wife became an invalid in 1877. He spent his summers at Ardmore on the Waterford coast and became an expert climber during his raids on the seabird colonies on the cliffs there. Almost every part of Ireland was visited in his relentless search for the eggs of rare birds and, during these travels, he enlisted the help of innumerable correspondents all over the country and assembled a collection of eggs unique in Ireland for its size and completeness. After he presented the collection to the National Museum in Dublin he ceased taking eggs and concentrated even more on studying the birds. Ussher was also greatly interested in cave exploration and spent many hours working underground. He made many discoveries; amongst them was the remains of the Great Auk in a Waterford cave. He was described as 'a fairly big man, almost six feet high, well set-up, with reddish hair and beard. He had a rugged, but good-natured face, kindly blue eyes, and a quiet courteous manner'. He died, after a short illness, in 1913, aged 72 years.

Warren was born in Cork in 1829 and died at his Cork residence, Ardnaree, Monkstown, in 1915. About 1846 he assisted William Thompson with information for his *Natural History of Ireland* and it was through this contact that Warren developed his interest in gulls and terns. In 1851 he left Cork and settled on the shores of Killala Bay, his residence for the latter half of his life being Moyview, Ballina on the banks of the Moy in Mayo, for which county he was JP. He made the Moy estuary and other localities in Mayo and Sligo his special area of study and his notes in the zoological journals were remarkable for their number. He added many birds to the Irish list.

The Birds of Ireland was almost wholly written by Ussher, Warren only writing the chapters on the White Wagtail, Surf Scoter, Spotted Redshank, Greenshank, Bar-tailed Godwit and Sandwich Tern, although he placed much material at Ussher's disposal.

The main 20th century accounts
A number of references were consulted to provide a view of the changing status of birds from the 19th and through the 20th century. Many of these were local accounts and were useful to confirm some of the 19th century claims, but the following were used widely.
HARTERT, Ernst, F. C. R. JOURDAIN, N. F. TICEHURST and H. F. WITHERBY 1912. *A Hand-List of British Birds*. Witherby, London.
BAXTER, Evelyn V. and Leonora Jeffrey RINTOUL. 1928. *The Geographical Distribution and Status of Birds in Scotland*. Oliver and Boyd, Edinburgh.
(Note: despite its publication date this work was assembled from, mainly, late 19th century sources and therefore has been a valuable consolidated record of those earlier accounts.)
WITHERBY, H. F., Rev. F. C. R. JOURDAIN, Norman F. TICEHURST, and Bernard W TUCKER. 1938–41. *The Handbook of British Birds*. Witherby, London.
BAXTER, Evelyn V. and Leonora Jeffrey RINTOUL. 1953. *The Birds of Scotland*. Oliver and Boyd, Edinburgh.
BANNERMAN, David A. 1953–63. *The Birds of the British Isles*. Oliver and Boyd, Edinburgh.
KENNEDY, P. G., Robert F RUTTLEDGE. and C. F. SCROOPE. 1954. *The Birds of Ireland*. Oliver and Boyd, Edinburgh.
PARSLOW, John. 1973. *Breeding Birds of Britain and Ireland*. Poyser, Berkhamsted.
SHARROCK, J. T. R. 1976. *The Atlas of Breeding Birds in Britain and Ireland*. Poyser, Calton.
THOM, Valerie M. 1986. *Birds in Scotland*. Poyser, Calton.
HUTCHINSON, Clive D. 1989. *Birds in Ireland*. Poyser, Calton.
MARCHANT, John H., Robert HUDSON., Steve P. CARTER, and Phil WHITTINGTON. 1990. *Population Trends in British Breeding Birds*. BTO, Tring.
GIBBONS, David Wingfield, James B. REID, and CHAPMAN, Robert A. 1993. *The New Atlas of Breeding Birds in Britain and Ireland: 1988–1991*. Poyser, London.
LOVEGROVE, Roger, Graham WILLIAMS, and Iolo WILLIAMS. 1994. *Birds in Wales*. Poyser, London.

Genus and single species studies
Detailed accounts of families of birds or individual species have been a valuable source of historical information. The heyday of the monographs of whole families of birds was during the last quarter of the 19th century and the first decade of the 20th; these families were generally chosen for their beauty or sporting connections rather than for any interesting behavioural reasons. The monographs of single species are a much later development, and although a monograph of the Nightingale was published in France in 1751, the majority of such books have been published during the last 40 years. The development of ornithology is demonstrated by changes in the emphasis of ornithological publishing. The 19th century was an age of discovery, not only of aspects of behaviour or the details of distribution but regularly of new species. As more species were discovered, and families of birds were being worked out, it was natural that they should be described and illustrated.

Once the discovery of new bird species, and their relationship with other, known species, was complete, ornithologists had the time, and the physical aids, to enable them to make protracted studies of individual species of birds. Such single species monographs have attempted to bring together as much as possible of the life history, behaviour, distribution and relationships of the species concerned. This was made easier as more knowledge was accumulated by many observers working independently, and by gathering together this knowledge the authors had a foundation upon which to build their own studies.

The publications of the type considered under this heading and of use in determining the distribution of birds during the 19th century have come from a wide variety of sources.

Studies of birds with sporting links

Books about gamebirds (including the ducks, geese and swans, grouse, pheasants and partridges, rails, Crane, Bustard, pigeons and waders) made up many of the early special accounts. Their sporting, economic and aesthetic appeal ensured that the publications could be treated in the grand style of the time, and there were several published that included magnificent coloured plates. For the purposes of the present study they often provided information about the distribution of introduced species that was unobtainable from other sources. Shooting and hunting, in its various forms, were important activities during the 19th century and, as distasteful as it appears today, led to many new ornithological discoveries. Most of the new species that were added to the British list were shot by sportsmen and efforts to improve the success of their sporting forays led to many discoveries of aspects of their target's biology. An early example of the genre was *British Gamebirds and Wildfowl* (Morris 1855) which provided details of early efforts to naturalise some foreign species, and the later *The Game Birds and Wild Fowl of the British Islands* (Dixon 1893) which was a very thorough account that gave an overview of each species' distribution in Britain at that time. *Pheasants, their Natural History and Practical Management* (Tegetmeier 1911) was another invaluable book that has been consulted whilst trying to unravel the early history of the introduction of exotic game-bird species.

There was also another type of book on a loose sporting theme that provided detailed and important information of the birds of the late 19th century. These were written by sportsmen who had developed the thrill of discovery during their hunting expeditions and wrote wonderfully evocative accounts of birds in the wilder and remote parts of Britain Examples of this genre include *Rough Notes on Birds observed in the British Isles* (Booth 1881–87), *Bird-Life of the Borders* (Chapman 1889, 1907) and *The Birds of Iona and Mull* (Graham 1890).

Studies of other species or groups

The warblers were served by two important accounts. *The British Warblers* (Sweet 1823–32) was a behavioural account based mainly on the author's experiences of birds in captivity, but also of many years of observations in the wild. It provides a little distributional information as does the other monograph of the same name, *The British Warblers* (Howard 1907–14) which is a classic work. It is an elaborate (and was a very expensive) work furnished with beautifully delicate illustrations, although it was designed as a behavioural rather than a distributional account.
The Great Auk or Garefowl (Grieve 1885) was a painstaking piece of research and relates what accounts of its past

distribution the author could discover and any details of its behaviour and life history which contemporary observers were able to give on both sides of the Atlantic. The first monograph of a living seabird was *The Gannet, a Bird with a History* (Gurney 1913). This is a substantial account of a species that had an ancient economic value and whose population was very dynamic during the 19th century. The book's detail of the Gannet's historical and present distribution provides a benchmark that is still used today.

Other special distribution studies were undertaken during the 19th century. Some of the most important for the purposes of the present account were those concerning species that were undergoing substantial changes in range. Amongst many, those of the Capercaillie, Great Spotted Woodpecker, Starling and Tufted Duck were the subject of Harvie-Brown's interest in Scotland whilst, over Britain as a whole, Aplin published the results of his enquiries into the status of the Cirl Bunting and Spotted Crake.

Throughout the 20th century, monographs, particularly of single species, continued to be published. These have, in many cases, included a review of the historical distribution of the species studied but, more importantly, advances in the study of ornithology have allowed the determination of the reasons for the changes in status that have been recorded.

The diaries of egg collectors and nest finders

Although clearly the records of an unfortunate pastime, some of the accounts contain valuable records of the nesting sites of rare species. Pre-eminent amongst these was the substantial *Ootheca Wolleyana* (Wolley 1864–1907). This was a catalogue of the egg collection of John Wolley assembled during the second quarter of the 19th century in Britain and Scandinavia. The published record was begun by him and completed by Alfred Newton. It is clearly a book of its time but the records of the nesting sites of rare Scottish species such as the Golden Eagle and Osprey and of the last of the English Red Kites, particularly in the light of their detail (a necessity to establish provenance and therefore value amongst the egg-collecting fraternity), are not available from other sources. Another, different, type of publication was that exemplified by *Bird Life in Wild Wales* (Walpole-Bond 1903). Walpole-Bond was a nest-finder extraordinaire who, through his egg-collecting experience, developed an interest in bird biology that led him to contribute many observations of the ornithology of his time. *Bird Life in Wild Wales* is a wonderful account of a Welsh avifauna that hardly exists now and, when the localities are deciphered, provide a record of some of the few Red Kite's nests that remained in mid Wales just after the turn of the 19th century.

The illustrations accompanying the species' accounts

Thomas Bewick was credited with the revival and perfection of an 18th century printing technique called 'wood-engraving' towards the end of that century. This involved the cutting of blocks on the end grain of the wood (usually boxwood) with a graver, rather than on the surface of a plank of soft-wood. It had many advantages over the latter process (the blocks were more durable, they could be mounted with moveable type in a printing press and the engraver's hand was far less inhibited by the grain of the wood and hence could produce far finer illustrations) and was rapidly seized upon by the newspapers and magazines of the time who needed the types of illustrations that the rediscovered technique could provide. Bewick's most famous work was the *History of British Birds* (Bewick 1797–1804) and provided the first accessible illustrated book of birds. Contemporary works were very expensive containing fine, hand-coloured plates that were out of reach of all but the very rich and Bewick's volumes were undoubtedly responsible for introducing an interest in birds to the masses. Beswick was an illustrator, not an ornithologist, however, and his *History...* gave only the barest outline of the species with which he dealt. It was finally superseded by the similarly titled *A History of British Birds* (Yarrell 1837–43); the whole subject was updated and far more thoroughly dealt with than in Bewick's work and, once again, was liberally illustrated with wood-engravings. Many of the illustrations from Yarrell's *A History...* are reproduced here alongside the main accounts. Yarrell's work was also hugely influential in its day. It was reasonably cheap and accessible to many people and, in its four editions, was often noted as the first illustrated bird book that the writers of the county avifaunas were bought as children and remained their standard textbook.

Alexander Fussell was given credit in the preface in the first volume of Yarrell's *A History...* for the creation of 'nearly five hundred' of the 520 drawings reproduced in the volumes. Alexander was about 23 when he began his drawings for Yarrell and was the eldest of three sons of a Birmingham art teacher, Joseph. The paucity of information about Alexander in Yarrell's *A History...* can probably be explained by the fact that the Fussell family became very well known in London art circles during the first half of the 19th century as many of them exhibited regularly in the city and, occasionally, at the Royal Academy.

John Thompson and his sons were given the credit for transferring the drawings to the printing medium. As demand for cheap illustrations gathered pace so demand for, and numbers of, wood-engravers grew. Almost all of the busy engravers in London in the early 19th century were pupils of Bewick and amongst these were Charles Thompson and, a little later, his talented brother, John (1756–1866), Yarrell's engraver. Charles settled in Paris in 1816 and introduced there the Bewick technique of engraving. He introduced the talents of his brother to French publishers a little later and the reputation of both brothers grew. Much of John's work found its way back to Britain in the English translations of important works of the time and his business in his home country began to flourish. The new generation of French wood-engravers owes as much to the Thompsons as the wood-engravers of London did to Bewick.

Alexander Fussell and the Thompson family were probably entirely responsible for the illustrations in the first three editions of Yarrell's *A History...* The fourth, completely revised and almost entirely re-written edition, which was published in 1871–85, included a number of additional illustrations by various other artists. These artists were Charles Whymper, J. G. Keulemans and Edward Neale.

The Late 19th Century Environment

Habitats

The development of agriculture

The long process of the modernisation of British agriculture began before the 17th century. By then the practice of serfdom had long been abolished, much of farming was undertaken for profit and the feudal–type landlords had given way to a more commercial approach. After the early 17th century three periods of change can be discerned: from the 1620s to the 1870s, from the 1870s to the 1930s and from then to the present.

Between the early 1600s and the 1870s there were two major changes in agriculture, the institutional and the technical. Slowly, the open fields and common pastures were removed by the process of enclosure. Most of western and southeastern England was already enclosed in the early 17th century; later enclosure activities reduced the fragmentation of farms in the Midlands, and by the 1850s there was very little arable left in open fields although upland commons remained. At the same time farms grew slowly larger while the number of small land-owners declined, and by the 1870s 70% of English farmland was owned by only 13,000 landlords. Over most of this period, except for a brief interval in the early 1700s, the agricultural population steadily increased.

The major technical advance up to the 1870s was the integration of crop and livestock production so that each benefited from the other. Livestock was allowed to feed on part of the cropland, then a year under turnips allowed weeding, and another year under clover provided nitrogen for the soil as well as grazing for cattle and sheep; the rotation of crops also reduced disease. The maintenance of soil fertility was almost entirely a function of the number of livestock kept and the area of leguminous crops grown. As this type of farming was taken up between the 1620s and 1850s a steady, if unspectacular, rise in crop yields resulted. This rise was greater than the increase in the farm population so that the productivity of both land and labour rose.

Farmers were protected during this period against competition from overseas by the Corn Laws (a protectionist measure against imports), the difficulty in transporting fresh produce and the high cost of that transport. From 1845 this protection began to disintegrate with the abolition of import duties, the development of railway systems on the continent and elsewhere, the fall in shipping freight rates and the use of refrigeration. Despite the repeal of the Corn Laws farm prices remained stable until the 1860s but from then until the 1930s the price of most staple farm products fell. This had important consequences for Britain's farms, particularly those of the lowlands.

Products of relatively low perishability, especially wheat, wool and meat, were the first to be undercut by imports. Farmers turned to less-threatened products such as milk, vegetables and fruit as prices for mutton, wool and wheat fell. The practice of feeding livestock on cultivated crops (especially turnips), an essential part of the cycle of maintaining soil fertility, became uneconomic and so declined; farmers turned to feeding livestock on imported grains and oilseeds. These years of low prices (between about 1870 and the 1930s) became known as the agricultural depression and little attention was paid to increasing the productivity of the land. Drainage was neglected, the use of fertilisers fell behind that of mainland Europe and the rate of increase of crop yields slowed (indeed, in the case of some crops, yields actually declined). One development that was to have very long-term effects, however, did take place; the fast-rising cost of farm labour drove advances in the use of machinery, and the harvesting of cereal crops was transformed from the middle of the 19th century.

Up to the 1920s the output of British farms remained more or less static but, up to about 1940, knowledge was accumulated that allowed the post-1939–45 war explosion in agricultural productivity and output. The manufacture of nitrogen fertilisers was begun in the 1920s, pesticides were developed and the first British experiments with herbicides began in the 1920s and 1930s along with many other advances, particularly the invention of tractors and combine harvesters.

From the 1930s the rotation system of farming was finally rendered unnecessary with the remarkable increases in output and productivity allowed by the chemical control of disease and the provision of plant nutrients by fertilisers—specialisation could now replace diversification and the development of monoculture began. The spread of machinery to all types of crop led to a dramatic decline in the farming labour-force but, currently, the area of agricultural land, and of land under crops, in Britain is almost 0.5 million ha less than that in the 1850s and 1860s and the area under crops is less than it was in 1944 after the war-time plough-up (Table 6 and Fig. 5).

Man-made land

Currently about three-quarters of the total area of England and Wales is used for agriculture, 8% is wooded and the remainder is used for housing, industry and transport. The land under crops and grass occupies a little over 9 million ha and has taken centuries to develop. It was created not just by the removal of the woodland that once covered all but the highest land, but also by fundamental alterations to the environment.

A great proportion of the native woodland was destroyed in pre-Roman times; by the 17th century most of Britain's forest had gone. This was just the beginning of the modification of the countryside: the draining of fens, ploughing of the uplands and drainage of heavy clay soils continued the process (Table 7).

The term 'improved land' is used for land under crops and grass which is enclosed and cultivated. Improved land has taken centuries to produce. The term is an ancient one and is concerned with making good use of land to enable the (profitable) production of the foods and produce that the human population demands. The qualitative interpretation of the term improved land, in the sense that agricultural historians use it, is the conversion of 'waste-

Table 6. *Agricultural land-use in Britain, 1866–1984 (thousand ha).*

Date	Grass			Arable			Total
	England and Wales	Scotland	Britain	England and Wales	Scotland	Britain	
1866	4,154	362	4,516	5,778	1,322	7,100	11,616
1886	5,802	490	6,292	5,432	1,476	6,908	13,200
1906	6,401	583	6,984	4,694	1,390	6,084	13,068
1926	6,127	607	6,734	4,272	1,294	5,566	12,300
1946	4,029	452	4,481	5,820	1,339	7,159	11,640
1966	4,154	373	4,527	5,723	1,373	7,096	11,623
1980–84	4,034	362	4,396	5,539	1,258	6,797	11,193

Source: Ministry of Agriculture, Fisheries and Food, 1993

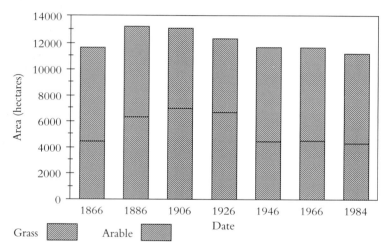

Fig. 5 Agricultural land use in Britain 1866–1986. Source: Grigg (1989) and Agricultural Statistics, Ministry of Agriculture.

Table 7. *Land-use in England and Wales (% of total area).*

Date	Agricultural land	Woodland	Urban land	Other land
1901	83.7	5.0	4.5	6.8
1939	81.3	6.2	8.0	4.5
1980	74.1	8.0	11.6	6.3

Source: Grigg (1989)

land' (another old and emotive term) to productive land—it is not, clearly, a term used to describe the land's usefulness to wildlife. We are living during a period where there is much criticism of farmers for continuing to drain marshland, ploughing uplands and cutting down the little woodland that remains and perhaps, whilst Europe holds food surpluses, this may seem unnecessary. This criticism is, of course, a recent phenomenon. In years past they were lauded for their efforts. It should be remembered that Britain is almost entirely a man-made landscape as farmland was created in the first instance by the destruction of the forests that once covered all but the highest hills.

The extent of improved land in Britain grew steadily until its zenith during the 1850s and 1870s; improved land probably occupied almost 12 million ha in 1870–74.

Since then the area under crops and grass has declined continuously. There are various reasons for this decline. Though afforestation has largely taken place in the unimproved uplands, some lowland has been lost to forest. In a few areas agricultural land was abandoned in the 1920s and 1930s and some land requisitioned by the Ministry of Defence during the wars has not been returned. However, the principle reason for the decline in extent of improved agricultural land has been the expansion of urbanisation. In England and Wales the urban area expanded by 178,000ha between 1901 and 1921 and since 1922 about 1 million ha of agricultural land have been lost to urban expansion with 240,000ha converted to woodland. No similar data exist for the 19th century but it has been estimated that the urban area increased by almost 1 million ha between 1801 and 1891. While not all of this expansion was on to improved land, much of it was. Since the 1930s the area of agricultural land lost to urbanisation is almost equal to the land reclaimed by farmers. Very little of this reclaimed land is newly improved; almost all of it is land improved during the 19th and earlier centuries and that fell into disuse during the agricultural depression.

However, I am bound to add that there are plenty of bird species that, without the conversion, the 'improvement' of Britain's scrub and forest to open fields, would not now be so common. This would include the Swallow and would also include species like Skylark, Partridges and Lapwing. The Corncrake, of course, probably experienced a dramatic increase in numbers and range in Britain during and following the forest clearances but, as agricultural practices continue to evolve, is not now provided with habitat suitable for its survival in much of the country.

I have felt that I should record here the status of Britain and Ireland's birds over the last century or so without making any emotional or qualitative judgements on human activities. I have tried to record just the apparent facts related to the birds' distribution, population and reason for change buried in past and recent literature. The reader will be the judge of the appropriateness of humankind's influence.

In fact the total area of land farmed in Britain at the end of the 20th century is little different to that of around the middle of the 19th century. Modern farming management practices, however, are having widespread, but largely underestimated, influences on bird populations on farmland. The kind of changes evident since the 1939–45 war are increased mechanisation, regional specialisation, the intensification of cereal farming, the change from spring to autumn sowing of cereals and the consequent loss of spring tillage, the increase of stocking rates on grassland and the shift from hay to silage (O'Connor and Shrubb 1986). A consequence of modern intensive agriculture has been a dramatic reduction of the total length of hedgerow, improved drainage of low-lying land and the increased use of chemicals that include fertilisers and pesticides. Changes of local importance have included the conversion of broadleaved woodland to arable and the reclamation of heath and scrub.

Intensification and specialisation have destroyed the pattern of many different types of field-use found within a small area—familiar to anyone walking the countryside between the wars. The technical development of the 19th century—the practice of rotation to maintain soil fertility—has become an impedence in the drive to increase farming outputs and rendered unnecessary by the use of chemicals to artificially improve productivity. Farmland 'mosaics' are recognised as being of value to a number of bird species and include the Lapwing, Rook and Skylark (Marchant et al. 1990).

The use of chemicals has not only allowed these changes in the agricultural landscape but there are cases where they have had direct influences on bird populations. A dramatic decline in Stock Dove numbers during the 1950s and 1960s has been directly attributed to the ingestion of aldrin and dieldrin pesticides applied as seed dressings whilst the high concentrations of pesticides that accumulate in species at the top of the food-chain caused severe declines in raptors, such as Peregrine and Sparrowhawk, and Grey Heron (Marchant et al. 1990). Although pesticides and herbicides have rarely been suspected of directly causing mortality in recent years there is much concern on their effect on reducing the diversity of the farmland ecosystem. Bird species that have suffered severe declines since the late 1970s, losses which are suspected to have been caused by reductions of food in farmland, include Grey Partridge, Skylark, Linnet, Reed Bunting, Corn Bunting and Tree Sparrow. Whether set aside and its attendant fallow land, the current moves to reduce chemical usage and the growth in organic farming are able to reverse these trends remains to be seen (Marchant et al. 1990).

Draining the marshlands
Since Roman times efforts have been made to drain and embank coastal marsh and inland fen but effective drainage did not begin until Dutch engineers cut drains in the Fens and in the Isle of Axholme in the mid 17th century. Attempts to drain the valley of the Hull were made at about the same time. Drainage of the Ancholme valley in N Lincolnshire and the Somerset Levels were not attempted until late in the 18th century and most of the drainage of the Lancashire and Cheshire mosses took place during the 19th. The effectiveness of many of the early drainage schemes was mixed. Initially, some areas were used immediately for arable crops but flooding occurred regularly and it was not until the age of mechanical pumping that the permanent conversion of summer grazing and fen to arable was complete. Windmills provided some improvement, but the use of steam powered pumps, the first in the Fens in 1817 followed by more widespread use in the 1830s, finally kept the waters at bay. With the help of modern methods the drainage of the Lancashire mosses was almost complete; 70% of their area was under arable crops by the 1870s.

Drained lands in England and Wales form an important proportion of the present improved land and over 0.5 million ha depend on artificial drainage, about 400,000 of that being arable. Although this is less than 10% of the total area of arable land most of it is of the highest quality agricultural land.

Draining heavy soils
Clay soils make up about 25% of the land area of England and Wales. They have long been favoured for growing arable crops, especially wheat, because of their natural fertility and, from the 17th century, methods were developed to make their cultivation more simple. Clay soils are more difficult to plough than lighter soils and their poor natural drainage inhibits plant growth during adverse weather.

The technique of ploughing the land into alternate ridges and furrows, thus providing surface drainage, was in use up to the late 17th century. Essex farmers then began to experiment with sub-surface drainage methods. They dug run-off trenches, partially filled them with stones or brush and then covered them again with soil. This method spread but was superseded by the development of drainage tiles in the early 19th century. In the 1840s a tile-making machine was developed and, in 1846, Peel introduced financial assistance for land drainage to placate landlords following the repeal of the Corn Laws. These changes gave a boost to land drainage and it has been estimated that between 1840 and 1880 1.2–5 million ha of heavy clay soils were drained.

The agricultural depression caused a halt to drainage schemes in the 1880s and many existing schemes were neglected until 1939 when grant-aid for the installation of field drainage was introduced. By 1968–69 about 700,000ha were drained under the grant schemes, mainly in eastern England, but it was estimated that a total of up to another 3 million ha were in need of drainage. Land drainage in the uplands allowed the sowing of grass where only rough grazing was possible before.

The improvement of light soils

Because of their poor fertility, limestone and chalk uplands and lowland sands were not highly valued by farmers up to the last decades of the 17th century. They were traditionally managed as sheepwalk and many held rabbit warrens and the resultant grazing developed downland grass and lowland heath habitats throughout England and the Scottish lowlands. From the late 17th century, however, the adoption of rotational farming systems and the integration of sheep into the arable system helped to increase soil fertility and led to the development of some of the best farming areas by the early 19th century. Gradually, the importance of rabbits declined and even in areas where these thin soils resisted the plough for many years enormous changes occurred in these habitats as trees and shrubs invaded. Huge areas of downland and lowland heath had disappeared by the middle of the 19th century but were allowed a brief respite during the agricultural depression. Agricultural reclamation was resumed with the 1939–45 war and much of the remaining southern chalk was ploughed then, although some of the light soils, such as those on the Bunter Sands in Sherwood Forest, were not improved until the 1950s.

In recent years, despite efforts to halt the losses, conifer plantations (especially in the Brecklands of the Norfolk/Suffolk border), mineral extraction, development and agricultural reclamation are still threatening the remaining sites.

The decline of Dorset heathland has been much quoted. At the time of the Domesday Book around 24,000ha of heath were recorded in the county. By the early 19th century over 30,000ha were in existence; by the end of the century this had declined to a little over 22,000ha and the decline accelerated, especially from the beginning of the 1939–45 war. In 1934 about 18,000ha remained, in 1960 about 10,000ha and by 1978 just 6,000ha of heathland were left. The rate of destruction has slowed during the 1980s and 1990s and the amount of heathland left is only slightly less than in the late 70s (Fuller 1982).

The reclamation of the uplands

More than a third of the total land area of England and Wales and the bulk of that of Scotland consists of land over 240m above sea-level where soils are thin and acid, rainfall is high and temperatures are low. These areas resisted the efforts of modern farming to improve them for many years even though settlements at over 300m were not abandoned until the 14th century. It was not until the 16th century that inflation began to hit prices of wool and wheat and farming gradually spread uphill. During the Napoleonic Wars land was ploughed for crops as high as 520m in parts of Wales. The montane habitat type (Fuller 1982) of Britain consists of areas above 611m and lies above the effective limit of tree-growth (the hills were covered with forest certainly up to about 520m and, possibly in some areas, to about 610m or even higher). Certainly, at least up to the end of the 19th century, these areas were some of the least modified in the country. Modern threats include overgrazing, building development and recreation but the latter two threats did not exist before the 20th century in these areas and, although overgrazing may have been a problem very locally prior to the present century, it certainly more or less disappeared in the wake of falling wool prices from the 1870s on.

The difficulties involved with farming the hills, on land over 240m, led to a marked lack of enthusiasm for it in the wake of the falling prices of the 1860s and 1870s. From then on cultivation in the uplands was abandoned; permanent grass was neglected and reverted to rough grazing, cropland turned to grass, and bracken began its relentless expansion in the hills of Britain. The outbreak of the 1939–45 war encouraged the cultivation of the hills again. After the war, subsidies on hill sheep and cattle were maintained and subsidies and grants on lime, fertilisers, under-drainage, reseeding and ploughing further encouraged a return by farmers to the uplands. It must be remembered, however, that most of the land reclaimed since 1940 is of improved land abandoned during the 1880s and subsequently. The greatest modern threat to the upland heaths, moorland, grasslands and mires is the afforestation of vast areas with non-native conifers. This is a 20th century problem but modification of some of the heather-dominated moorlands by management for grouse or for deer did take place during the 19th century. There is little indication, however, that overgrazing either by deer or sheep was ever a widespread threat then.

Farming in the uplands

During the 17th and 18th centuries, hills were farmed in ways similar to today. Sheep and cattle were reared there, although the ratio of cattle kept was higher than at present, and, because of their isolation from the lowlands, other products, such as cheese, were manufactured and oats and rye grown to make poor bread.

Until the 18th century, sheep were kept mainly for wool and only incidentally for meat. In the 18th and early 19th centuries the demand for mutton increased in order to feed the growing lowland human population, and the uplands supplied sheep to the lowland farms for fattening. During the 18th century the number of sheep doubled and the production of wool rose up until the 1870s. In the uplands the ratio of sheep to cattle increased substantially although the breeds reared there produced a coarse wool suitable only for blankets and carpets.

During the early 1900s large areas of Wales were enclosed to create new farms and the highest densities of sheep were found here and in the N Pennines. From the 1870s, in the wake of cheap wool from Australia and

Table 8. *The sheep population in England and Wales (millions).*

Region	1889	1949	1973
Upland counties	5.8	6.2	9.4
All counties	18.7	11.7	19.4

Source: Grigg (1989)

elsewhere, numbers of sheep in the lowlands decreased until about 1947 and, as a consequence, the proportion of sheep in the uplands increased from less than a third in 1889 to more than a half in 1949 and increased in real terms by about 7% (Table 8). Similarly, the total number of cows in the upland counties has increased steadily since the 1880s.

During the first half of the 20th century rough grazing land in the hills was lost to improved grassland and fodder crops. Much rough grazing has been ploughed up and reseeded with improved varieties of grass, other grassland has been limed to reduce acidity, the spreading bracken has been treated with herbicides and peat bogs have been drained.

Woodland

Britain's wildwoods had disappeared many centuries before the 19th. What was left was a pale shadow of the extensive natural woodlands and of a fundamentally different composition (Rackham 1986). The activities of the shipbuilders had denuded the maritime counties of their oaks and, in inland counties, mature woodlands along the banks of inland waterways were exploited. By the end of the Napoleonic wars England and Wales were among the least wooded countries in the world. Oaks planted during the wars would not have reached maturity when the era of wooden ships passed in the 1860s and many oaks survived in the Forest of Dean, the New Forest and other royal Forests in southern England. Although firewood had ceased to be the principal fuel in homes and furnaces, woods around towns and cities distant from the coalfields continued to be plundered. On the other hand, where charcoal was manufactured for iron-smelting, natural regeneration and coppice plantations restored some woodland cover.

Against this background of a broadly stable picture of Britain's woods is set the losses of woodland to agriculture that continued to take place until 1870. There is little detailed historical information about this period but it is unlikely that these further losses were very large although efforts by the Commissioners of Woods and Forests to promote the enclosure and sale of royal Forests caused local losses until the 1880s. Elsewhere there were some losses of woodland during the creation of the rail network in Britain, and it was said that the central moor of Rothiemurchus was denuded of timber to supply sleepers for the Highland Railway in 1864. After 1870, replanting of woodland began to exceed that cleared. Between 1870 and 1905 the extent of woodland in England increased from 500,000ha to almost 700,000ha. In the lowlands much cleared land was replanted with coppice and, by 1905, coppice-woods covered more than 200,000ha. In the uplands and on poor soils conifers were planted extensively—sometimes as windbreaks or to anchor drifting sands, but mainly to supply the increasing demand for softwoods for building timber, pit props and pulp. Commercial plantings were particularly a feature of some Scottish estates but other new woodland was created during the landscaping of large estates elsewhere.

Although the remaining woodland, by the 1914–18 war, was in a better state than is generally considered, the war encouraged the idea of reforestation. It used timber resources at an alarming rate and brought home the realisation that imports could not be relied upon. On the recommendation of a government committee the Forestry Commission (FC) was set up under the 1919 Forestry Act to undertake the reforestation of Britain. Its objective was to supply industrial timber for use in the mines as quickly and cheaply as possible. From the beginning non-native conifers have been chosen and planted in managed blocks to achieve this objective. By 1939 the FC had planted 150,000ha but as the memory of the 1914–18 war receded progress slowed. During and since the 1939–45 war, however, planting accelerated again. At the present day woodland cover in Britain is about double that in 1919, about 10% of the total area but still amongst the lowest in Europe.

The native pinewoods of Scotland are now a tiny proportion of their former extent. This habitat is vital for three of Scotland's special species: the Capercaillie, Scottish Crossbill and Crested Tit. In prehistory the pinewoods probably covered a quarter of the country but most had been cleared by the 17th century. Little overall change has taken place in the total area of these forests since then and, almost certainly, the present area of about 12,500ha (about 0.16% of Scotland's land area) existed during the last quarter of the 19th century.

Hedgerows

The hedgerow is an ancient feature of the British countryside and one that emerged as the native woodlands were felled and woodland strips were left to delineate boundaries of ownership and provide cattle enclosures. The change from the field strip system to large enclosed fields that came with the changes in the cultivation of cereals in the 18th century demanded new, stock-proof hedges to protect the crops from wandering animals. During that century 1770 individual Acts enclosed over 1.25 millionha, most of those during the second half, and this gives some indication of the length of hedges being planted then. As the enclosure of improved land and the improvement of new land gathered pace the amount of hedgerow increased and probably reached a maximum in the 1860s. Other new features of the countryside during the early 19th century demanded stock-proof barriers. By 1830 over 5000km of inland waterways had been constructed and stretched across open countryside, altering field shapes and demanding new hedges. The railway boom that began before the middle of the 19th century saw nearly every town and many villages served by a main or branch line by the end of that century.

All of this track had to be well fenced or hedged to keep livestock from straying into the path of the trains. The specification for the railway hedges was of a particularly high standard and density reflecting the safety concerns of both the farmer and the railway traveller.

After 1870 the decline in agriculture probably led to little overall change in the length of hedgerow in the country-side although a small amount of enclosure continued almost to the end of the century. Until 1940, through the recession to the start of the war-time plough-up, very little planting or removal of hedgerows took place although neglect in the countryside took its toll and many hedges fell

Table 9. *Length of linear features in England and Wales (thousand km).*

Date	Hedgerows	Fences	Banks	Open ditches	Walls	Woodland fringe
1947	796	185	151	122	117	241
1969	703	193	140	116	114	241
1980	653	199	132	111	111	243
1985	621	210	128	112	108	243

Source: Department of the Environment (1991)

Table 10. *Changes in hedge and fence features between 1984 and 1990.*

Feature	Change in length: thousand km	Change in length: percentage
Fence	+75	+12
Hedge	-67	-24
Hedge and fence	-64	-23
Relict hedge	+7	+24
Relict hedge and fence	+24	+83

Source: Department of the Environment (1991)

Table 11. *Numbers of people employed in agriculture in England and Wales, 1851–1991 (thousands).*

Date	Feature
1851	1706
1861	1640
1871	1438
1881	1273
1891	1198
1901	1117
1911	1183
1921	1137
1931	996
1951	966
1991	416

Source: Grigg (1889)

into decay. The beginning of the present period of hedgerow removal began during the 1939–45 war and, with the post-war rise in the numbers of tractors and combines of ever increasing horsepower and size, extensive grubbing up of hedgerows has taken place, especially in arable areas, to provide optimum field size and maximise the potential of the new machines. Since the end of the war over a fifth of Britain's hedgerows have disappeared and many of those that remain are falling into a state of disrepair (Tables 9 and 10).

In hedgerows, as in broad-leaved woodland, active policies to remove dead and dying trees have an impact on the amount of insect food available to birds that forage on bark and dead wood. Clearance of dead wood may also remove timber that provides suitable nest holes. The Dutch Elm disease epidemic that killed many elms from the 1970s resulted in an increase of rotting wood in the countryside for a few years whilst the trees were allowed to remain in situ. However, these trees have been gradually removed.

Changes in the numbers and distribution of the human population in the 19th century

The 19th century saw many social and economic changes in Britain; industrial growth, imperial expansion and domestic reform were most notable among them. It also saw a fundamental change in the way of life of the human population as it moved from a predominantly rural to an urban existence. Towns grew and the countryside shrank and the face of the country changed as fields and pastures succumbed to bricks and mortar. Great ports and industrial towns dominated the land. Liverpool grew from 300,000 inhabitants to nearly 700,000 during Queen Victoria's reign. During the same period Birmingham's population nearly trebled to over 500,000, Glasgow's similarly trebled to 762,000, the population of Nottingham increased nearly five-fold and that of the new Tees-side port of Middlesbrough rose by more than 15 times to 91,000. To cap all this London grew from an already enormous 2 million to 4.5 million people.

In 1851 the population of the countryside was at its peak. Farming, horticulture and forestry supported over 2 million people in England, over a fifth of the total population, but by the turn of the century this figure had fallen by about a quarter and represented only 1 in 11 of the employed population (Table 11).

The physical evidence of these changes was most evident in the Midlands and the north. The countryside was squeezed into thin green strips between the advancing fingers of the industrial centres whilst the connecting scars of railways and telegraph poles and wires marched through those parts of the country still left.

It should be added that there have been some positive effects of the industrial era. Nearly all of the lowland lakes in England are man-made. Some were built to provide water for the increasingly urbanised population, others as canal feeder reservoirs and most of the rest were the result of industrial workings. These reservoirs, lagoons and sand and gravel pits have undoubtably created new feeding and breeding habitats for a number of waterbirds that, before the creation of the new lakes, were restricted to the rivers. The networks of new canals also provided waterside habitat on some stretches where vegetation was allowed to develop while the new network of railways provided the only unimproved corridors of rough vegetation in an otherwise increasingly altered agricultural landscape.

The decline of the horse and growth of machinery in agriculture

The greater speed of the horse led to the gradual replacement of oxen on the farm between 1500 and 1800— oxen were not of any national significance after the late 18th century. With this change came some disadvantages. Horses required the cultivation of oats for feed whereas oxen fed on grass, horse tackle was more expensive and oxen could be sold for meat when too old for work. The total number of horses in Britain doubled between 1811 and the 1880s and reached a peak in the early 20th century (Table 12).

It was estimated that *ca* 2ha were needed to feed a horse and so it would have taken over a fifth of the arable land of Britain to provide fodder to sustain the horse population; the decline of the horse from the 1920s released a substantial amount of land for other uses.

The first machine to be used on British farms was the threshing machine in the late 1820s. It took many years for these, and other, new developments to be taken up widely and the reliability of the machines similarly took a long time to improve. Although the prime motivation for their development was economic, the main impediment to their widespread use was the cheap cost of labour in the 1820s. Only after the 1840s, when labour shortages became apparent, was the mechanical reaper more widely used.

The early tractors were similarly viewed with suspicion for they were unreliable, poorly serviced and dangerous to drive. It was not until the 1950s that the tractor replaced the horse despite the first commercial version being available in 1902.

The agricultural scene in Ireland in the 19th century

The widespread English reconquest and land confiscation during the 16th and 17th centuries effectively ended the ancient tribal system of land tenure and the field systems that had developed. In an attempt to achieve effective subjugation of the human population in Ireland, English and Scottish settlers were brought in to displace dispossessed Irish landowners and a policy of plantation by these settlers was introduced. Plantations differed in time and effectiveness, the most effective being in Ulster, but most of the country outside Connaught and W Munster was affected to some extent. In the mid 17th century there was much more general confiscation and only the counties of Mayo, Roscommon, Galway and Clare were reserved for dispossessed landowners from other parts of the country. By the late 18th century 95% of Irish land was owned by the settlers.

The new settlers regarded land as a source of profit rather than subsistence and a substantial commercial element developed in Irish agriculture from the 17th century. Exports to Britain, Europe and the American colonies developed and, with increasing demand and prices for grain in Britain along with the Corn Laws of 1758, a major expansion of cereal growing began. Cultivation of the potato, which was introduced to Ireland in about 1600, was greatly extended to improve the soil for cereals and to feed the rapidly expanding population. In the early 18th century there had been about 2.5 million people in Ireland; by 1800 there were 5 million.

Table 12. *Horses in Britain 1811-1924 (thousands).*

	1811	1851	1871	1881	1891	1901	1911	1924
Commercial	251	264	444	*ca* 650	858	1,166	995	374
Private	236	277	414	585	500	600	537	549
Agricultural	800	*ca* 870	940	987	1,087	1,089	1,087	753
Non-agricultural on farms	*ca* 190	*ca* 250	314	441	394	572	626	425
Total	*ca* 1,480	*ca* 1,660	2,112	*ca* 2,660	2,839	3,427	3,245	2,101

Source: Grigg (1989); (data is unavailable for some of the sample years)

33

Responding to the stimulus of the developing cash economy, landlords striving to improve their new estates and the more privileged tenants effected many changes in Irish agriculture during the 18th and early 19th centuries, especially in the east and south. Improvements included the adoption of new farming practices, better crop varieties and livestock breeds and the greater use of fertilisers, land reclamation and field enclosure. The rural landscape was transformed by the enclosure of the open fields and some of the common lands but the bulk of the human population, the tenants and landless labourers, remained very poor. The population, which remained largely rural, was increasing at about 2% per annum and reached nearly 8.5 million in the mid 1840s. As the population grew there was extensive sub-division of holdings, small farms multiplied and there was widespread reclamation of mountain, bog and other improved land. After 1815 agricultural prices collapsed and led to widespread unemployment in agriculture and little chance of employment outside of it. The plight of many was grave and conditions were worse in the highly congested west with a rural population density of 150 per km² of agricultural land.

Under the prevailing conditions, severe and prolonged failure of the potato crop resulted in the Great Famine of 1846–48. More than a million people died from starvation and disease and a further million emigrated so that by 1851 the population had been reduced to 6.5 million. Emigration and a diminishing population continued and by 1926 the population was 4.2 million, about half its pre-Famine level. The Famine resulted in the demise of many small holdings, those of under 2ha decreased from 440,000 to 125,000.

With diminishing population pressure in the post-Famine period, there was a trend towards farm enlargement. Yet land reclamation continued until the improved area reached a peak in the 1870s when an agrarian depression began. This was linked to the repeal of the Corn Laws in 1846 and with growing imports into Britain, Ireland's primary export customer, from foreign sources. Tillage area diminished by more than half by 1914 although the number of beef cattle continued to increase, doubling between the Famine and 1920 and exceeding the human population for the first time in the 1890s.

Changes in the British climate

Since the end of the last great ice age, about 10,000 years ago, the climate of Britain has undergone a series of fluctuations of both major and minor degree. The present so-called Post-glacial Period is now believed to be an inter-glacial period (generally referred to as the Flandrian Interglacial) that reached its climatic optimum around the boundary of the Middle Stone Age and Neolithic Era, about 7,000–6,000 years ago. Superimposed upon this major climatic change have been a number of minor swings since the ice sheets finally retreated with a number of identifiable warm phases interspersed with cooler periods. Britain has experienced an almost complete cycle over the past 200 years or so from a cold climate around the beginning of the 19th centuries through a warm period that reached its peak between 1920 and 1940, cooling again, anthropogenic effects excluded, to the present day.

The so-called Little Ice Age that lasted from the middle of the 13th century to around 1850 reached its height during the latter half of the 17th century. Indeed, the years

between 1550 and 1700 was the longest and coldest period in Britain in modern historical times and featured frequent cold winters (some of them very severe) and springs and a number of cool summers. Punctuated by a couple of warmer periods the 18th century remained very cold. Five or six severe winters were recorded per decade during the second half of the century and the River Thames froze over 10 times between 1700 and 1814 (Lamb 1963). Indeed, the latter year saw the most severe frost of that century and the last Frost Fair on the river.

The decade from 1825 appears to have been quite a warm one but a series of wet summers in the 1840s and the consequent crop failures led to the potato famine in Ireland and, at least in part, to the repeal of the Corn Laws in Britain. The Little Ice Age is generally accepted to have ended in around 1850 and a period of ameliorating climate ensued. Some set-backs took place as the 19th century progressed (such as a number of harsh winters around the 1880s) but the amelioration accelerated during the 1890s and reached its zenith in the 1930s and 1940s. At its height, this warm period was about 0.5°C warmer than 1880 and 1°C warmer than it was during the Little Ice Age.

Since about 1950 a return to climatic deterioration or cooling has taken place. Predictions based on ice core samples suggested that the mid 1970s should have reached a climate comparable with the early years of the 19th century with cooling continuing to become more severe as the 21st century opened (Broecker 1975). Clearly, this situation has not occurred perhaps providing evidence of the effects of man's activities (Burton 1995). Current research is tackling the problems associated with atmospheric pollution and its effect on climate. Recent estimates of the average rise in temperature that may be expected globally by 2050 in comparison with 1990 have ranged from 0.5°C to 2°C with most authorities agreeing on about 1.3°C for the UK (Hulme 1994).

The effects of these climatic swings on the flora and fauna of Britain have been marked. Burton (1995) suggests that the mammal fauna in the tundra-like landscapes of Britain south of Yorkshire was very similar to that of present-day Lapland at periods during the Last Ice Age. It may have included such species as elk, reindeer, Arctic Fox and Arctic Lemming as well as Snowy Owls, Snow Buntings and Ptarmigan. In addition, musk ox, woolly mammoth and woolly rhinoceros were also to be found. Relative to the changes in temperature, the climatic swings over the past few centuries will also have led to substantial range changes of European bird species. Burton (1995) presents evidence of range changes of a large number of temperate and northern bird species due to the effects of periods of both climatic warming and climatic cooling since 1850. Some of these claims are, as he admits, highly speculative, nevertheless, the changing climate may be involved as, either, a primary or secondary factor in some of the dramatic range shifts demonstrated by the maps presented later.

Persecution of birds in the 19th century

The rise of gamekeepers
Systematic destruction of birds and beasts of prey began with the rise of the organised management of small game. The creation of artificial populations of gamebirds began many years earlier but the active *preservation* of game really took off from

around the middle of the 19th century. The widespread rearing of Pheasants and the development of the breech-loaded shotgun in 1853 created the motivation and the tools with which to destroy the birds on the gamekeeper's list of targets, and as the number of gamekeepers grew so the population of avian predators fell. Primary targets were the Sparrowhawk, Kestrel and corvids, although mustelids and foxes and other birds of prey (e.g. Buzzards) were killed when they appeared. Many other species of birds were killed 'just in case'. The steady reply of the gamekeeper when remonstrated with by a Sentimentalist over the owl nailed to the side of his shed was 'Look at his beak and tell me that that there bill weren't made to tear a bird's breast to bits? Just see here—all crooked and pointed: why an owl have got a hooked beak like an eagle. It stands to reason as he must be in mischief' (D'Urban and Mathew 1892). He may have made the same observation of the Red-backed Shrike or Nightjar; both species were recorded regularly on the gamekeeper's gibbet. Shooting was not the only means of destruction—poisoned baits were laid out to kill corvids and foxes, gins and wires were used in the destruction of stoats and weasels and, when placed on the top of poles, raptors. Birds of prey were trapped in live bird baited traps and the nests of all species on the 'list' were located and destroyed. All of the methods used were indiscriminate and many other species of birds were killed incidentally, the worst method being the pole trap that killed many Cuckoos.

The national census returns showed that the number of gamekeepers in Britain reached 22,000 in 1911. The outbreak of the 1914–18 war sent many young men to the front and the number of gamekeepers employed fell to about 12,000 (Figure 6). This was effectively the beginning of a decline in numbers; few of the pre-war gamekeepers returned from the war. Though numbers increased slightly thereafter, the 1939–45 war saw a further decline and only 5000 were employed by the end of that war. Numbers have increased only slightly since. In Scotland the decline has been even more relentless as grouse moors have given way to forestry. The 1939–45 wartime decline in the number of gamekeepers demonstrates their influence on raptor numbers as the number of nestlings of the commoner raptor species ringed increased substantially at that time. Anecdotal evidence suggests that many species of raptor increased rapidly during both wars.

Moore (1957) discussed the decline of the Buzzard between 1800 and about 1915 and its subsequent recovery up to 1954. He published evidence that only one major factor could be correlated with the changes in the Buzzard population—game-preservation. A dramatic example of this correlation was provided by the maps showing the distribution of the breeding population of Buzzards in Britain in 1954 and the frequency of gamekeepers at the same time showing that where a high frequency of gamekeepers occurred Buzzards were scarce or absent and that the converse was also true. Studies of the histories of the White-tailed Eagle (Love 1983), the Sparrowhawk (Newton 1986) and the Hen Harrier (Watson 1977) also provided evidence of the correlation between 19th century declines of these species and the rise in game-preservation.

Persecution of seabirds and the Preservation of Sea Birds Act
In the 1860s the devastation of gulls and other cliff-nesting species by weekend sportsmen enormously increased the persecution suffered by these species. These, often urban, gunners shot huge numbers of seabirds as target practice and for many years the wings of seabirds were used for millinery decoration. Sailors and fishermen protested at this persecution as, when approaching the northeast coast of England in bad weather, they often used the cries of cliff-nesting birds to guide them, and as a consequence of their persecution moreships were running ashore off Flamborough Head. Gulls here were known as 'Flamborough Pilots' and fishermen were accustomed to follow flocks of them to shoals. Farmers also protested. They appreciated the flocks of gulls that followed the plough and picked up grubs, but a farmer in Filey wrote that he had not seen a gull all summer on his farm where, in previous years, he had seen many. Heavy destruction was recorded in Norfolk, Pembrokeshire, Devonshire and Cornwall. An Act for the Preservation of Sea Birds in 1869 silenced the guns during the breeding season but the demand for wings continued and, on 1st August each year as the closed season ended, boats would be sent out from Clovelly, Devonshire, to Lundy Island and many hundreds of Kittiwakes, both young and old, were shot (the barred wings of the young birds were particularly in demand), their wings torn off and the mangled remains thrown into the sea. Contemporary

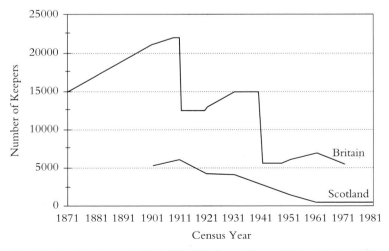

Fig. 6 Number of gamekeepers in Britain 1871–1981. Source: Newton (1986) and Hudson (1992).

accounts recorded the sea tinged pink by the process. Similarly the Flamborough Pilots were butchered as the breeding season officially ended.

Persecution of other bird species and the Wild Birds Protection Acts

Examples of the ways that birds were killed and the means to which they were put have been included in some of the species' accounts. Whether it was the trapping of male Skylarks for the cage or females for the pot, the collection of plovers' eggs to eat or the eggs of rare breeding species by avaricious Victorians for display, many species were considered to have suffered severely because of the numbers taken during the last half of the 19th century. Never before had birds been in greater need of protection. Their foes were many. There was an increasing number of sportsmen, whether gentry hunting for the pot, trap-pigeon shooters or the fast-increasing 'cockney' sportsmen. The demand for the resultant corpses included gourmets, whose meals were often accompanied by the carcasses of 30 songbirds, and fashion designers, whose creations were decorated by entire, or parts of, birds. Farmers blamed birds for numerous depredations amongst their crops, often on slender evidence, and covered up their poor farming practices by causing the destruction of many thousands of sparrows, pigeons and Starlings. Other persecutors included dealers in caged birds and their suppliers, the tribe of netters, fowlers and trappers who also caught birds for the table or sport, the self-styled naturalists who sought out rare birds and their eggs and almost every schoolboy who limed twigs, laid nets, robbed nests and stoned fledglings or caught birds to sell to dealers who sold them to other schoolboys.

The concern of some naturalists and the so-called 'Sentimentalists' led to a series of efforts by Parliament to restrict the slaughter and the destruction of nests. The 1869 Sea Birds Preservation Act was gradually expanded in 1872 and 1876 to include more species and led to the Wild Birds Protection Act of 1880, again extended in 1894, 1896 and 1898. These Acts provided for the protection of named species of birds during the breeding season, different for each county, but it was often said that it was 'nobody's business to put the Acts into motion against offenders' (Coward and Oldham 1900) and the Acts had only a limited effect on the fortunes of birds. A number of other abuses were legislated against during the early 20th century. In 1904 the pole trap was prohibited, in 1908 the practice of catching seabirds with baited hooks was outlawed and in 1921 an Act of Parliament prohibited the shooting of captive birds and thereby outlawed the 'game battue' (a particularly abhorrent sport practised by the leisured urban rich in which pigeons, and sometimes other species, were released from a basket at an instruction and shot as they escaped). During this period argument raged over the trade in cage birds. In 1925 some of the cruellest methods of catching wild birds (such as birdlime) were outlawed, but the measure that caused the biggest flutter was the Protection of Wild Birds Bill of 1933. Its opponents quickly realised that its aim was to wipe out the trade in British songbirds and in this it was partially successful. However, there were numerous loopholes in the Act that allowed, with some difficulty, the continuation of the trade. These loopholes were not finally plugged until the Act's substantial revision in 1953.

Instrumental in the development of legislation and species protection to halt the abuses of birds has been the Royal Society for the Protection of Birds. The embryonic society was formed in 1889 and became the Society for the Protection of Birds in 1891. The early work of the Society was mainly concerned with protest against the trade in plumage for fashion. Much of the trade concerned exotic species but Kittiwake wings, Kingfishers and even Robins were taken in their thousands in Britain to adorn ladies' hats. A major success was achieved in 1899 when Queen Victoria confirmed an Order that certain regiments should discontinue wearing Osprey plumes. The Society's first 'watcher' was employed in 1901. He was appointed to protect breeding Pintails from egg-collectors at Loch Leven in Scotland and the Watchers' Fund was started the following year to enable the appointment of further watchers at other sites to protect other rare species. In 1930, Cheyne Court, Romney Marsh in Kent was purchased, the RSPB's first reserve. The Society continued to campaign, lobby for legislation, purchase reserves and prosecute through the present century. At their centenary in 1989 membership broke the 500,000 barrier. Now with a membership of over 850,000 and as the largest owner of land in Europe by a voluntary conservation organisation, the RSPB is the most influential voice in species and habitat protection in Britain.

The Species Accounts

Scope

The species accounts are dealt with in three sections. Within each section the species are presented in taxonomic order, following that used in the *88–91 Atlas*. The main species accounts include all the species that bred (probable and confirmed) in Britain and Ireland during 1875–1900. The majority of these are given a full page of text, a table and an accompanying map. Records of some species in the old literature are incomplete. These are usually of introduced or domesticated species or those that were considered to derive largely from introductions or to survive only through human intervention. A map has been produced for these species and is complete, with the proviso that areas where no published information exists, and are therefore not shaded, may only indicate absence by omission. The status of the species in the 19th century, as far as can be determined, however, is recorded in the text accounts because of its bearing on modern populations. Brief species accounts are given for the remaining species. These species include those that have bred since 1800 but not during 1875–1900. Some of these became extinct before 1875 and have not bred since; a few became extinct before 1875 but have recolonised during the 20th century. Also included are those species that colonised in the 20th century but were never recorded breeding during the 19th century. Records of these species in Britain and Ireland as vagrants, on passage or as winter migrants during 1875–1900 are added, where they exist, to a brief account of their 20th century status.

The texts

The name of the species considered is given at the top of each text. The first name given is the currently used English name and follows that used in the *88-91 Atlas*. The second name or names that occasionally follow in parentheses are English names that were in use in the publications of the 19th century. The aim is to allow the 20th century reader to locate the species in the indexes of 19th century publications, not to give a comprehensive list of all of the colloquial and alternative names that many species were given. The third name given is the scientific name in current use and, once again, follows those used in the *88–91 Atlas*. The core of the majority of the texts is an account of the species' distribution and numbers during 1875-1900 and to this is added a brief overview of its status during the *68–72* and *88–91 Atlas* surveys. Where relevant or interesting the following may be given: a brief history of the species prior to 1875 and especially since 1800, contemporary accounts of the environment and human activities in Britain and Ireland in the 19th century, changes in status between 1900 and the *68–72 Atlas*, and aspects of the species' 19th century breeding biology. The accounts of distribution and abundance (see below) are based, mainly, on contemporary accounts and little interpretation of the published information has been made in this volume.

Where reinterpretation of old records has been made, either by later 19th century writers or following 20th century research of the status of birds in the 19th century, these have been used in preference to the original record or account. Where available, the most recent interpretations of changes in distribution and/or abundance since 1800 have been included. To ensure that the most up-to-date analyses of the old records and subsequent changes in distribution have been included, a panel of specialist referees has examined, and recommended changes to, the texts. Notwithstanding these efforts at accuracy, if any mistakes, omissions or inaccuracies exist in this work, they are those of the author.

There are almost no quantitive data on bird populations before the 20th century; consequently the interpretation of all of the 19th century records is a subjective exercise of what were mainly subjective records and interpretations. It has become clear with increasing ornithological knowledge that many of the 19th century records were flawed. Nevertheless, these published records are all that exist and deserve to be re-examined as they represent the first attempts to record bird populations scientifically in detail and, when treated with caution, give an overall picture of the avifauna of Britain and Ireland during a period of great change in the countryside and of the human population. The opinions expressed in the texts must be considered as only hypothetical.

At the foot of the majority of the main texts is a table that provides a quantitive comparison of the species' distribution between the periods 1875–1900 and 1968–72. Where the precise locations of the records of rare breeding birds were not revealed in the *68-72 Atlas* a comparison with 1875–1900 is not attempted. The number of counties in which the species bred during 1968–72 was calculated by overlaying the 1875–1900 county boundaries on to the maps in the *68–72 Atlas*. Provided a single probable or confirmed breeding record fell within a county's boundary, then that species was considered to have bred in that county during 1968–72. Occasionally, where a 1968–72 record fell on a county boundary, it was difficult to be sure whether it had bred within the historic county of 1875–1900. Such cases, however, were very rare indeed and were easily cleared up by reference to the relevant modern county avifauna or other published sources. Percentage change values have been calculated, for Britain and Ireland separately and for both combined, on the basis of the number of counties/regions in which breeding was recorded during 1875–1900 and 1968–72.

The maps

Distribution

The areas used to sub-divide Britain and Ireland are discussed in a previous section. In addition to these primary divisions, where it is clear that a species bred only along the coast, the maps document this with a shaded coastal strip. The width of these strips is entirely arbitrary and does not represent the extent of inland breeding.

Distributions are shown by shading the county or faunal region in which breeding was recorded during 1875–1900. No shading indicates that breeding was not recorded in that area during 1875–1900 or that the records were unsupported by sufficient evidence as judged by either the contemporary naturalists/writers or more recent, mainly 20th century, writers. 'Sufficient evidence', as accepted by 19th century and later writers and adopted for the purposes of the present account, includes two main types.

1. The unsupported assertions of regular breeding of species that were widely known to breed in the county at the time. An example of this type is the following entry in *The Birds of Glamorgan* (Cardiff Naturalists' Society 1900).

Whitethroat. *Sylvia cinerea*.
Welsh—*Llwydfron*.
Common. Summer visitor. Breeds regularly.
It is well distributed through the county.

Another example of this type of unsupported account and for which breeding has been presumed is the following from *The Birds of Dorsetshire* (Mansell-Pleydell 1888).

WHITE-THROAT. *Sylvia rufa* (Bodd).

Yarrell, i. p. 406; *Dresser*, ii. p. 377; Sylvia cinerea, *Harting*, p. 16; *Seebohm*, i. p. 405; T*his List*, p. 11; Motacilla cinerea, ß., *Pulteney's List*, p. 9.

This is one of our commonest summer visitants; it arrives towards the end of April, and may often be seen on the top spray of a hedgerow, or rising in the air sending forth its short, jerky song. It is very shy, taking every precaution for concealment, invariably keeping on the off-side of a hedge to elude the notice of the passer-by.

2. If breeding rarely or occasionally took place then to be included in the present account some supporting evidence is required; by necessity, some of this evidence was very scant. An example is the following in *The Fauna of Shropshire* (Forrest 1899).

Kite—*B. Milvus ictinus*. Old writers speak of the Kite as of quite common occurrence, but it must now be regarded as very rare. Mr. Beckwith wrote in 1879, that a few still tried to nest near Ludlow, and that the bird had also been seen on the Breidden. One was shot at Wallop, October 25th, 1887, and another at Bucknell, November 4th, 1895. Mr. Rocke says Kites used to build yearly in Stokes Wood, near Craven Arms, and two or three nests of live birds have been taken there.

In some cases there was insufficient evidence to satisfy either of these two criteria, though what evidence there was indicated that breeding probably took place.

Such records are attributed to a probable breeding category, though is necessarily arbitrary and has been based on many types of evidence. The following extract from *The Vertebrate Fauna of Bedfordshire* (Steele-Elliott 1897–1901) is an example of this type.

TUFTED DUCK
(*Fuligula cristata*)
Writing me in reference to this species, Mr. W. C. Thompson assured me that the Tufted Duck bred at Luton Hoo Park in 1894, but the water-keeper there could not confirm this; except that they remained there late on in the spring.

The scale of the maps does not allow clear shading of very small features, particularly the smaller islands. The avifaunas of these islands were often interesting as they included some of the most important seabird colonies and some nationally rare species, as well as having become an important area of modern ornithological research. Some of these islands have been treated separately in Appendix A.

Assessment of relative abundance
The authors of the county/regional avifaunas and lists of birds used subjective terms (for instance 'abundant', 'uncommon', 'can hardly be called uncommon', 'not as common as [another species]', 'rare', 'occasionally breeds') to describe the abundance of each species. The majority of writers, especially of the English and Welsh counties, had limited knowledge of bird populations in other areas and, of necessity, their assessment of relative abundance was compared to other species within the writer's own county. The present study requires assessment of relative abundance between counties/regions as well as between species. To achieve this the terms of abundance used by each writer of the avifaunas have been calibrated to the extremes of population density used by each author. The phrases used to describe these extremes were often clear—'abundant', 'the commonest species in the county' or 'very common' and 'very rare', 'hardly ever breeds' or 'occasionally breeds'. The terms used to describe the abundance of other birds in the county have been related to these 'calibration' species. Furthermore, a number of species were described as abundant or very common over almost all of Britain and Ireland and, so, have been considered as providing a universal benchmark of abundance from which inter-county conformity can be achieved.

Population size classes
The terms used to describe the abundance of bird species in the counties and regions of Britain and Ireland in the 19th century have been calibrated and attributed to one of seven abundance classes. On the maps, the different population classes are distinguished by differing levels of shading and hatching. A key is given alongside each map to enable the class for each county/region to be readily determined. The population classes are such that variation both within and between species can be determined. Thus, for any species it is possible to see where it was more or less abundant, and for each county/region it is possible to determine which was the most abundant, and which was the rarest, species. The population size classes are as follows.

Abundant—this class has generally been used to describe the abundance of those species that existed in the largest and most widespread populations. These species were familiar and very common in both rural and urban areas, covering a wide range of elevations and vegetation and landscape types.

Common—this class was used for species that were not regarded as the commonest in the region, were distributed more locally or were less common than the Abundant species but were, nevertheless, well known throughout the study area. Their populations remained reasonably stable from year to year and were not subject to large, short-term fluctuations.

Uncommon—species either common in locally suitable areas or thinly scattered throughout the county/region. The species may have undergone short–term (certainly within the 25-year period considered during this study) fluctuations in population size. They were species that were considered by the 19th century authors to have been less common than those in the previous class.

Rare—species that have been placed in this, and the following, population size classes were generally easily distinguished in the 19th century accounts by the special, detailed treatment they were given. The birds and their habits were often not well known at first hand and the authors took great care to describe encounters with the species, or specimens collected, in full detail. Each occurrence was usually recorded and skins and eggs were in great demand by collectors. In the area under consideration they bred more or less annually. It was often difficult to know whether to attribute a Rare classification to a species whose nests were rarely encountered owing to its secretive nature even though it may have been more common.

Occasional—rare species that did not breed in a county/region annually. This generally applied to species breeding at the edge of their normal range, in areas with little suitable breeding habitat, or to irruptive species.

Probable, not confirmed—species that were recorded in the breeding season in suitable breeding habitat and that displayed signs of breeding activity in a number of years during 1875–1900, but for which nests or eggs were not found. If the author at that time believed that a species was probably breeding and later authors agreed then the Probable class has been attributed. This class has been used freely if breeding had been proven prior to 1875–1900, or subsequently, and was suspected of having taken place during that period.

Not breeding—no classification of abundance has been attributed to species either not recorded breeding during 1875–1900, or to those for which the evidence was vague, unreliable, unproven, unlikely or undated, or whose provenance was not recorded. If breeding records were not accepted by later, generally 20th century, ornithologists then they are attributed to this class.

The sites of many seabird colonies are marked with a large, shaded dot. The shading conforms to the same population size classes as used elsewhere on the maps.

Extinctions

If a species was known to have bred regularly in a county/region between 1800 and 1875 but not during 1875–1900 then the maps carry the letter E in that county/region. Some of these species may have recolonised the county/region during the 20th century. Where possible, species that had only occasionally bred in the past are not identified on the maps, though these records are mentioned in the texts.

Referencing

When reference has been made to a particular county in the species account, yet no source has been given, it can be assumed that the record was published in the corresponding main county or regional avifauna (see Introduction). Otherwise, the source is identified by the author's name, and year of the publication.

Red-throated Diver

Gavia stellata

The Red-throated Diver was evidently decreasing in its Scottish range at the end of the 19th century. This decrease was mainly taking place in the more accessible parts of its distribution and was probably the result of the collection of eggs and specimens and persecution from fishermen.

Numbers of the Red-throated Diver in the southwest of its range (south of Ben Nevis) had decreased substantially by the 1880s. Prior to that it had bred frequently through S Argyll and in Kintyre but easy access for collectors from the south seriously depleted the population. After the 1880s, owing to ignorance of the precise extent of the decline and to the suppression of breeding records, information on the species' status is scant. It seems likely that until at least the end of the century it bred very infrequently in S Argyll and, indeed, in the early years of the 20th century it may have briefly ceased to breed. The species apparently bred on several of the Inner Hebrides but, again, most of the records were suppressed. A notable exception to this was the breeding group on Arran which was protected by the landowner.

The Red-throated Diver bred in its greatest numbers north of the Nevis range, especially in NW Scotland, although, even here, numbers decreased particularly in the

second half of the 19th century. Its stronghold in Scotland was considered to be Sutherland W of Durness, Eddrachillis and Assynt and, particularly, around Quinag mountain. Along the N coast of Sutherland it was common but gradually became less so towards the east so that only a few pairs were believed to breed in the east of that county and in Caithness. A few bred south to the Great Glen but through the south of the Moray region it was very rare; no records exist of breeding south of the Speyside forest marshes.

In the Outer Hebrides the species bred throughout the islands and was considered very common in some localities although numbers evidently fluctuated from year to year and it was sometimes considered scarce.

Persecution from collectors had reduced numbers breeding in Orkney. Red-throated Divers had been proven breeding during the 19th century only on Hoy. Only four pairs bred there by the end of the 1880s and a pair may have bred on one occasion at Stromness on the adjacent edge of Mainland.

Yell held the largest numbers of breeding pairs in Shetland. It was fairly common north of Lerwick on Mainland but did not breed in the south of that island. It bred occasionally on Unst but had not been recorded breeding on Foula or Fetlar.

A very small breeding group was discovered around a complex of small loughs in Donegal, Ireland in 1884. Unfortunately, the location was published and the nests were raided. In 1886 two pairs bred there but three clutches were taken. Thereafter almost all breeding attempts were foiled, and, between 1896 and 1900, it was presumed that the species had ceased to breed there. Since then, however, this population has increased.

In the 20th century the cessation of persecution and, latterly, active protection have allowed the British and Irish populations to increase. Apart from a few temporary outlying records, however, there has been almost no distributional change apart from a marginal expansion in E Highland and W Grampian since the *68–72 Atlas*. Shetland is, today, the Red-throated Diver's most important stronghold, in contrast to the 19th century accounts although habitat was probably as suitable then as now. It can only be surmised that, perhaps, persecution of the species in Shetland was particularly heavy during the 19th century and this kept numbers low, or that Red-throated Divers were previously under-recorded (L. Campbell in litt.).

Number of counties in which recorded:

Period	Probable breeding		Confirmed breeding		Combined		
	Br	Ir	Br	Ir	Br	Ir	Both
1875–1900	2	0	14	1	16	1	17
1968–1972	0	0	22	no data	22	0	22
			change		6		5
					38%		29%

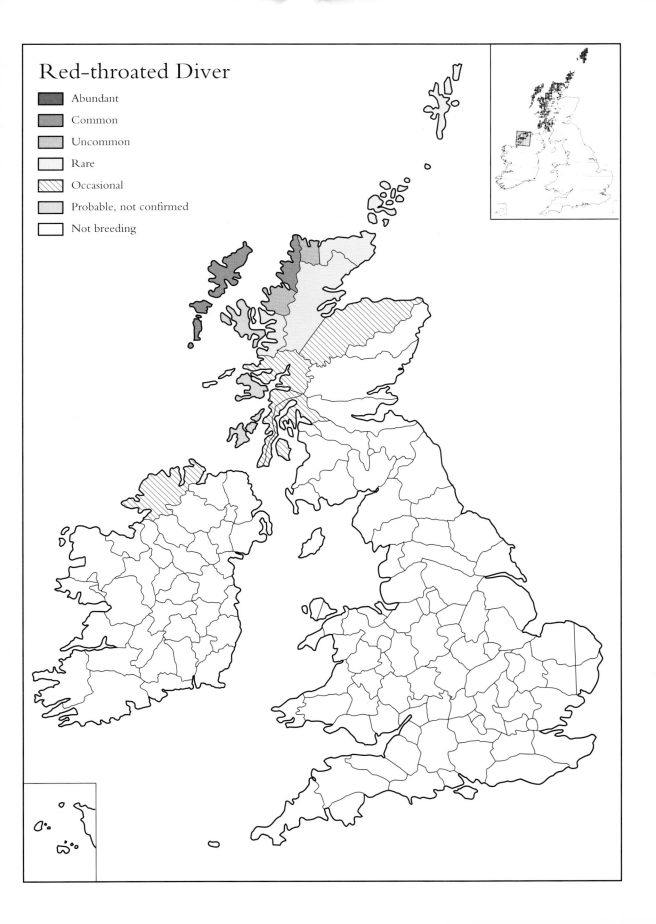

Red-throated Diver

- ■ Abundant
- ▨ Common
- ▨ Uncommon
- □ Rare
- ▨ Occasional
- ▨ Probable, not confirmed
- □ Not breeding

Black-throated Diver

Gavia arctica

At the end of the 19th century, the Black-throated Diver bred in its greatest numbers on the Scottish mainland in Inverness-shire, Ross-shire, Sutherland and Caithness. The species bred in smaller numbers in N Perthshire and probably bred in Argyll south as far as Knapdale and in parts of Kintyre. Although breeding had been claimed to have taken place in Shetland earlier in the century this was discounted (Evans and Buckley 1899) and breeding had been suspected in Orkney for many years but never proven. In the Outer Hebrides, however, Black-throated Divers bred in some numbers throughout the islands although numbers breeding fluctuated from year to year.

The Black-throated Diver's distribution in Argyll was not well known. It was suspected that the species bred in a few areas of Kintyre and further north, on the Moor of Rannoch and in Ardnamurchan, but there were very few records of nests or young being found.

In N Perthshire the species bred sporadically on the freshwater lochs of the interior and was apparently spreading southwards. This extension was severely limited through persecution; as an illustration, during the 1870s several regular pairs were known around Pitlochry but by the early 1890s only one pair remained.

Elsewhere south of the Great Glen Black-throated Divers bred in very small numbers and, in the Moray region, probably only a handful of lochs held breeding pairs. Further north, however, they were more common. The species had apparently substantially increased around Invergarry, Inverness-shire—another indication of a southward expansion of breeding. Black-throated Divers occurred in their greatest numbers throughout Ross-shire, and especially in Assynt, but also over much of Sutherland. In the extreme northwest of that county, however, it was decidedly rare and the Red-throated Diver was by far the most numerous of the two species.

There were few breeding records in the Inner Hebrides. Three or four pairs bred in Skye during the last quarter of the 19th century and another on the adjacent island of Soay in 1882. This pair bred again in 1883 but, unfortunately, the eggs were taken and eaten by a resident of the island.

It was said by the 19th century writers that the Scottish population of the Black-throated Diver was limited by persecution, especially at its most southerly breeding sites. Persecution was also periodically noted to have had an effect on breeding numbers up to the 1960s and, as the 20th century progressed, disturbance was increasingly blamed for affecting breeding success. This is still true of the population in N Perthshire, particularly of some easily accessible pairs and is a worry for the species' future in parts of Scotland. Notwithstanding this reservation, however, it colonised areas of SW Scotland during the 1950s (Arran around 1951 and S Ayrshire in 1956) (Parslow 1973) and subsequently expanded its range there with breeding proven in Dumfries and Galloway in 1974 (Batten *et al.* 1990). In the years between the *68–72* and *88–91 Atlases*, however, a decline was evidently underway with losses being apparent from the southern fringe. This decline has been attributed to recent reductions in breeding success, owing in part to losses through predation and flooding and, importantly, the failure of young to fledge successfully possibly through a reduction in water quality in the breeding lochs (Gibbons *et al.* 1993). These are certainly the main problems facing the Black-throated Diver today although it would seem that the species has been able to maintain good populations in its strongholds in NW Scotland and the Outer Hebrides throughout the last 100-150 years. The fluctuations in breeding range at the species, eastern and southern fringes are probably what would be expected and would certainly explain why persecution impacted most in the south (L. Campbell *in litt.*).

Number of counties in which recorded:

Period	Probable breeding		Confirmed breeding		Combined		
	Br	Ir	Br	Ir	Br	Ir	Both
1875–1900	2	0	11	0	13	0	13
1968–1972	7	0	19	0	26	0	26
			change		13	0	13
					100%		100%

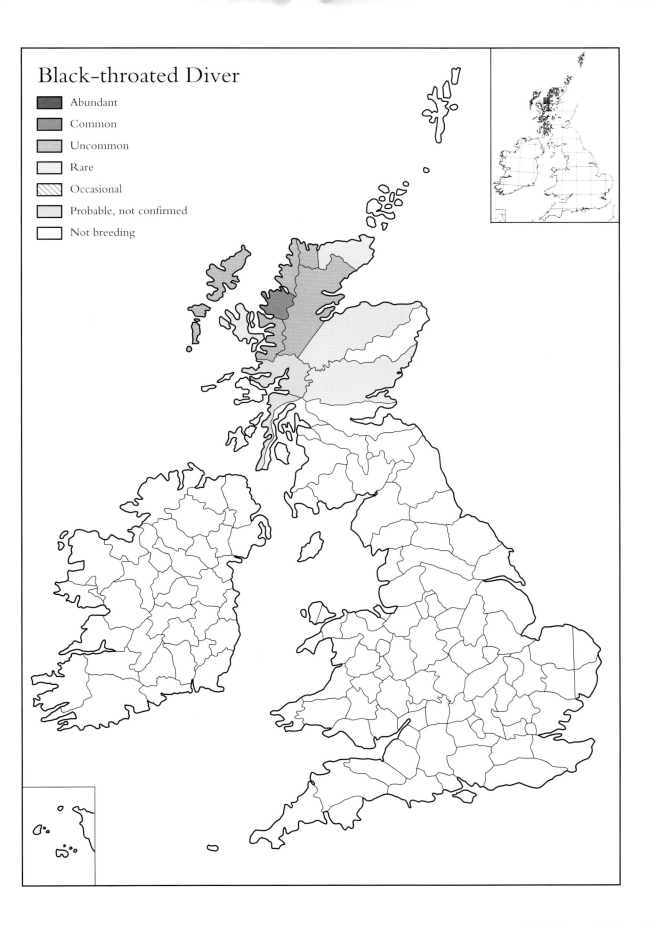

Black-throated Diver

- ■ Abundant
- ▨ Common
- ▨ Uncommon
- □ Rare
- ▨ Occasional
- ▨ Probable, not confirmed
- □ Not breeding

Little Grebe (Dabchick)

Tachybaptus ruficollis

The Little Grebe was widely distributed throughout Britain and Ireland during the 19th century although it bred in its greatest numbers in S England and S Wales. It was absent only from the Shetlands, some of the smaller marine islands and the Isles of Scilly. It apparently bred only occasionally on Skye, and probably bred on Loch Eishort on the island in 1883 (although two pairs regularly bred on nearby Raasay). Breeding was said to be occasional in Middlesex although was regular in some of the London parks.

In some areas of S England and Wales the Little Grebe was uncommon. In Cornwall, there were few suitable breeding sites (it bred mainly in the marshes of the Land's End district), in the Isle of Wight breeding apparently occurred only on the reclaimed land at Bembridge, and in Monmouthshire and Pembrokeshire breeding sites were said to be scarce. In the Midlands, NW England and SW Scotland there was some evidence that the Little Grebe increased in numbers around 1900 and the history of the Little Grebe in SW Scotland indicates that a northwards expansion may have taken place in Britain during the 19th century. The first note of Little Grebes breeding in Solway was of a nest on Dalswinton Loch in Dumfriesshire in 1866. From this point they evidently increased fairly rapidly

and were found throughout the region by the end of the century. The increase noted in the Forth region showed a similar pattern—the species was scarce or absent during the 1850s or 1860s and subsequently increased although in this case the increase took place well into the 20th century. It is not possible to discern from the records a 19th century increase in SE Scotland although it evidently occurred during the first few decades of the 20th century.

Evidence of an increase in N England is mixed. It was quite clear to Chislett (1953) that the Little Grebe's status in Yorkshire had not changed during his lifetime but in Durham it had clearly increased between the 1870s and the 1950s (Temperley 1951). In Lancashire too an increase had been noted through the same period. The suggestions of an increase in some of the Midlands counties (in Berkshire and Warwickshire for instance) may have been associated with the growth in abundance of gravel and quarry pits, canals and reservoirs. Parslow (1973) noted that the increases throughout Britain also coincided with a period of climatic amelioration, which may have had an effect through a reduction in hard winters. An apparent increase may also have been due to previous under-recording of this secretive species before field observation improved from the late 19th century (D. Moss in litt.).

In Ireland the Little Grebe bred in every county at the end of the 19th century, even on the larger marine islands such as Achill and Rathlin. It occurred on all the lakes and rivers of the country but was said to be particularly abundant along the Shannon and the lakes through which it passed.

In recent years losses have been apparent throughout the Little Grebe's British and Irish range. By 1968 it had become sparse in S Wales and between the *68–72* and *88–91 Atlases* breeding ceased in Cornwall, many parts of the Midlands and parts of Scotland. The most widespread decline has occurred throughout Ireland in all areas except Down and Antrim. The Little Grebe is particularly affected by hard winters and lower numbers were recorded following those of the 1940s and 1960s.

Number of counties in which recorded:

Period	Probable breeding		Confirmed breeding		Combined		
	Br	Ir	Br	Ir	Br	Ir	Both
1875–1900	1	0	106	34	107	34	141
1968–1972	1	0	103	34	104	34	138
			change		−3	0	−3
					−3%		−2%

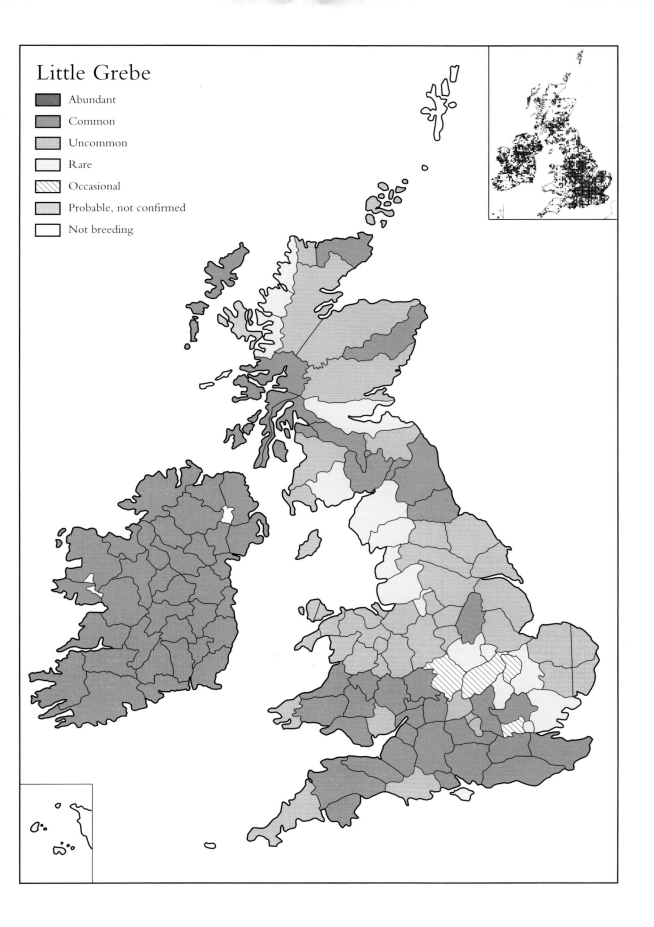

Little Grebe

- Abundant
- Common
- Uncommon
- Rare
- Occasional
- Probable, not confirmed
- Not breeding

Great Crested Grebe (The Grebe)

Podiceps cristatus

The Great Crested Grebe population in Britain had, by the 1870s, reached the stage where it had become very vulnerable. Around the middle of the century the species bred regularly only in Sussex, Hertfordshire, Suffolk, Norfolk, Worcestershire, Warwickshire, Shropshire, Lincolnshire, Cheshire and Yorkshire although in each only a few pairs bred. Nesting was occasionally recorded at that time from neighbouring counties but the groups that had bred in Huntingdonshire and Wales did not do so after 1860.

The fortunes of this species through the 19th century can be summed up by the succession of accounts from Norfolk, one of its strongholds at this time. Lubbock (1845) wrote of the large number of eggs that he had seen gathered on one broad in 1822—30–40 were often collected at a time as they were evidently a prized dish. The fensmen evidently also considered Great Crested Grebes a competitor for fish and many were killed to protect stocks. They were also shot for their feathers which were valued as a fashion accessory. A new market was found for Great Crested Grebe parts in the mid 19th century. In 1851 Robert Clarke and Sons, a furriers of London, exhibited the pelts of four birds (part of a consignment of 29 shot in Norfolk in full breeding plumage) at the Great Exhibition (Stevenson 1866–90). The skin of the breast and under-pelt was considered a substitute for animal furs and several were made up into ladies'

boas and muffs and the 'tippit' (head frill) feathers were used in millinery. This began a devastating trade that was responsible for accelerating the Grebe's decline. From 1857 onwards there was a steady traffic in the birds, particularly in Norfolk, where many Broads were easily accessible to unscrupulous gunners. The increased value of skins and eggs to collectors, the value of the feathers as a fashion accessory and the increasing accuracy and availability of shotguns combined to cause a severe reduction in Great Crested Grebe numbers. By the mid 1860s they bred in small numbers on only a handful of waters in Staffordshire, Suffolk, Lancashire, Yorkshire and, mainly, in Cheshire and Norfolk.

Harrisson and Hollom (1932) estimated the total population in Britain in 1860 to have been in the range 32–72 pairs. Following the passing of the Act for the Preservation of Sea Birds of 1869 (and subsequent improved legislation in 1872, 1876 and, especially, 1880) an almost immediate recovery was noted by Southwell (Gurney and Southwell 1886–87, Stevenson 1866–90). By 1890 the Great Crested Grebe had returned to breed on almost all of the broads from which it had been eradicated. Elsewhere in England an increase was noted from about the 1880s and several counties recorded first breeding records (Bedfordshire in the early 1890s and Northamptonshire in the 1880s, for instance). By the 1880s it had become established more widely than was apparent much earlier in the century and from the 1890s it colonised Scotland (in Dumfriesshire in 1891, the Forth region in the late 1880s and in Tay between 1894 and 1896). It was unclear, however, whether this rapid and widespread increase could be entirely accounted for by the gradual reduction in persecution.

In Ireland the Great Crested Grebe was generally distributed throughout the counties around the loughs of Connaught, the midlands and the northeast, although prior to the 1880s it apparently bred only in the northern counties (More 1890). The Great Crested Grebe was not harried to anything like the same extent in Ireland as it was in Britain and the apparent increase in Ireland may be evidence that some factor other than the cessation of persecution drove the late 19th century increase in both Ireland and Britain. Climatic amelioration was suggested by Parslow (1973) as a possible cause and there may have been an increase in available habitat due to the construction of larger reservoirs; however, the major cause of this widespread increase remains conjectural now, as it was in 1932 (Harrisson and Hollom 1932).

Number of counties in which recorded:

Period	Probable breeding		Confirmed breeding		Combined		
	Br	Ir	Br	Ir	Br	Ir	Both
1875–1900	2	0	37	19	39	19	58
1968-1972	2	0	79	25	81	25	106
			change		42	6	48
					108%	32%	83%

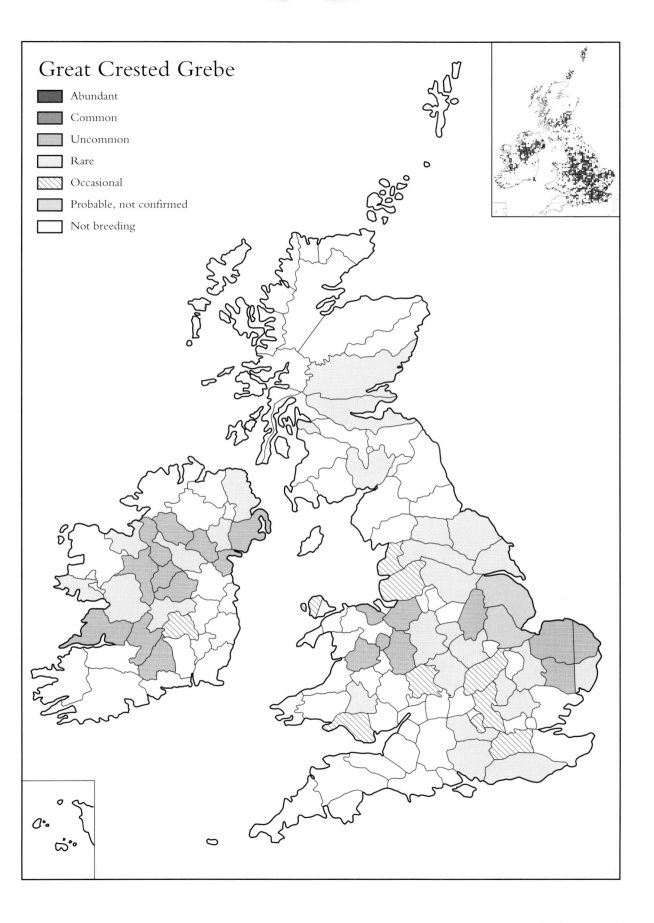

Great Crested Grebe

- ◼ Abundant
- ◼ Common
- ◻ Uncommon
- ◻ Rare
- ⧅ Occasional
- ◻ Probable, not confirmed
- ◻ Not breeding

Fulmar
(Fulmar Petrel)

Fulmarus glacialis

The extraordinary range expansion undergone by the Fulmar from its base in Iceland and The Faeroes to colonise Shetland, St Kilda, the Western Isles and the rest of Britain and Ireland has been well documented. The first colonists in Britain (except for those at the more ancient site on St Kilda) arrived during the last quarter of the 19th century. Writers in the 19th century believed that the colonisation of Britain and Ireland took place via St Kilda; modern research, however, considers this unlikely (Fisher 1952).

Until 1816, and possibly until 1839, St Kilda was the only breeding site of the Fulmar in the North Atlantic south of Iceland and, until 1878, was the only British site until the colonisation of Foula. The first published note of Fulmars in St Kilda was in 1697 (Martin 1698) and the first estimate of the population size on the islands, in the second quarter of the 19th century, based on the number of birds taken by fowlers, suggested about 20,000 breeding pairs plus about 10,000 non-breeders. The many accounts that were published of visits to these islands by 19th century naturalists suggest that the population of Fulmars remained stable throughout the rest of that century. The only oppos-

ing account, that of Harvie-Brown in 1912, was dismissed by Fisher (1952).

Fulmars possibly colonised 'the South Isles of Barra' in the Western Isles before 1831 but apparently were not breeding there after 1844. A prospecting pair were seen on Barra Head on Berneray in the Western Isles in 1898 and the first eggs in 1902. The outer Flannans were colonised in 1902 (possibly a little earlier).

Fulmars probably first bred in Shetland in the mid 1870s and were considered at the time to have been colonisers from The Faeroes. The first published breeding record was that by Garriock (1879) of a colony of about 12 pairs on Foula in 1878. This had increased to between 60 and 100 pairs in 1890. The first recorded breeding on Papa Stour (and the second new British site) was in 1891; these pairs were thought to originate from Foula. By 1895 four pairs were counted. A few Fulmars frequented the Ramna Stacks off Gruney in 1894 and 1895 and the colony here was considered established in 1897. A colony of six pairs was recorded in Esherness in 1896 and 57 pairs were recorded in four localities on Hermaness and Saxa Vord in 1897. Breeding was noted for the first time on the Noup of Noss in 1898. In June 1900 a pair or two flying around Fitful Head preceded the breeding of about 30 pairs in 1905.

On North Rona, Western Isles, Fulmars were seen in 1886 and 1887 and the first egg was taken in 1894. On the neighbouring island of Sula Sgeir many Fulmars were seen in 1887. North Rona was probably the source of Fulmars seen about the Sutherland cliff of Clò Mòr in 1897; they bred there possibly as early as 1900 but almost certainly by 1904.

Hoy in W Orkney was visited by Fulmars in 1896, 1898 and 1899 and breeding was first proven in 1900. In the same year nearby Dunnet Head on the Caithness coast had three Fulmars occupying two sites; breeding was strongly suspected in 1904 or 1905. The number of pairs breeding in Britain in 1899 was between 167 and 563 at nine sites and *ca* 20,000 pairs in St Kilda (Fisher 1952).

Rapid colonisation and population growth continued through the present century, involving a spread throughout the coasts of Britain and Ireland; 570,800 pairs were counted during the seabird survey of 1985–87: an average increase throughout the century of at least 8% per annum (excluding St Kilda), although the rate of increase has gradually slowed (to *ca*. 3.6% per annum during 1969–86) (Cramp *et al*. 1974, Lloyd *et al*. 1991). Nevertheless, St Kilda remains the largest colony at 63,000 pairs. The dramatic increase is largely unexplained but probably reflects a combination of factors that may include the provision of extra food by whalers and fishing trawlers, the appearance of a genotype within the Icelandic population that favoured expansion, or the warming of the eastern Atlantic (Fisher 1952, Lloyd *et al*. 1991).

Number of counties in which recorded:

Period	Probable breeding		Confirmed breeding		Combined		
	Br	Ir	Br	Ir	Br	Ir	Both
1875–1900	0	0	2	0	2	0	2
1968–1972	7	0	48	15	55	15	70
			change		53	15	68
					2,650%		3,400%

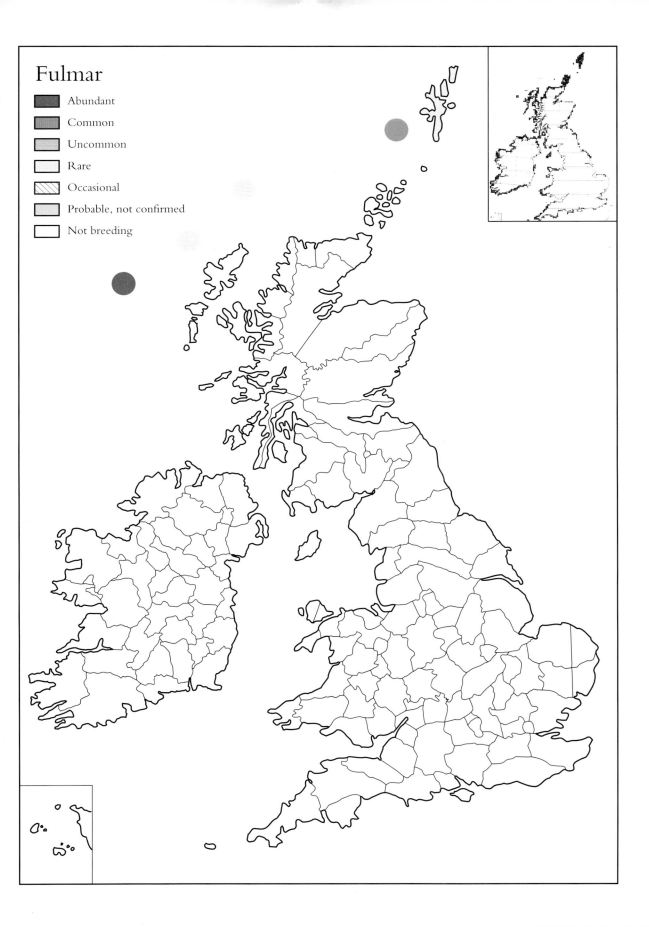

Fulmar

- ■ Abundant
- ▨ Common
- ▨ Uncommon
- ▢ Rare
- ▨ Occasional
- ▨ Probable, not confirmed
- □ Not breeding

Manx Shearwater

Puffinus puffinus

The Manx Shearwater breeding colonies were distributed at the end of the 19th century, as they are today, mainly on islands off the W and N coasts of Britain. The apparent increase in the number of colonies over the last 100 years is likely to have been an artefact of the increasing activity of birdwatchers and there is little evidence of any widespread change within those colonies that have been known since the 19th century although this is a notoriously difficult species to census accurately (Lloyd et al. 1991).

At least 300 pairs of Manx Shearwaters nested on Annet in the Isles of Scilly in the 1830s (Yarrell 1837–43) and still nested there and on other islands in the group in the 1870s (Rodd 1880). Manx Shearwaters were said to be 'very numerous' on Lundy Island, Devonshire (D'Urban and Mathew 1892). Of the Pembrokeshire islands, it was believed Manx Shearwaters bred on Caldy Island from accounts in the 1870s and 1880s. After 1887 Mathew was informed that they probably bred in the cliffs of Caldy, and also that four or five Shearwaters were seen leaving fissures in the cliffs of St Margarets in May 1893. Skomer Island was said, during the 19th century, to hold the largest British colony. Manx Shearwaters bred in some numbers on Skokholm Island and a few may have bred on Ramsey Island (Mathew 1894). A considerable colony existed at the NE end of Bardsey Island, Caernarvonshire in 1901 (Aplin 1902). Manx Shearwaters ceased breeding on the

Calf of Man perhaps during the 1790s, but definitely before 1827 (Ralfe 1906), either because of a rat infestation (Brooke 1990) or because of disturbance when people colonised the Calf (Yarrell 1837–43).

The record of an egg attributed to this species collected on Staffa in the Inner Hebrides before 1852 has been discounted but the assertion that Manx Shearwaters bred occasionally on one of the Treshnish Isles seemed more plausible to Harvie-Brown and Buckley (1892). A stack off Skye was colonised during the 1870s and 1880s; this may have been the Talisker Rocks where breeding took place in 1886 or 1887. In 1881 there were two colonies on Canna. The colonies on Rum may well have been increasing during the 19th century as they were evidently smaller than those on Eigg during the 1880s, a situation that has subsequently been reversed. Of the islands forming the St Kilda group, Soay probably held the largest colony. Here, however, fewer apparently bred than formerly following competition for nesting holes from Puffins. Smaller colonies had been known on all of the other islands but during the 1880s were considered to have been deserted (Wiglesworth 1903). Records from Hirta describe harvesting of young by the islanders since at least the 17th century. Elsewhere in the Hebrides a few pairs bred after the middle of the 19th century on Pabbay, Barra and, probably on a slope of scree and rubble on Berneray, although Shearwaters were decreasing on all of these islands. They formerly bred on Mingulay (Harvie-Brown and Buckley 1888).

The Manx Shearwater had evidently decreased in Orkney; in earlier years of the 19th century it bred in a number of localities, but by the 1880s the only place known still to be populated was Hoy where only a few bred.

In Shetland, Manx Shearwaters bred on Foula from at least 1774 and also on Fetlar (Evans and Buckley 1899). The colony on Unst was very small by the end of the 19th century and there was probably a colony on Yell (Brooke 1990).

The largest colonies in Ireland were those of the two Skelligs and Puffin Island, Kerry. Many Shearwaters bred on Rathlin Island, Antrim and some were known to breed on the Blaskets, Kerry, the Saltees, Wexford, some parts of the Wicklow and Dublin coast, Aranmore, Donegal and Old Lighthouse Island, Down. Breeding was believed to take place on some islands of W Cork, two islands at the foot of the Mayo cliffs and High Island and Inishmore, Galway.

Evidence of changes in Manx Shearwater numbers during the 20th century is scant. There are local published notes of colonies both increasing and decreasing but it seems likely that no widespread change has taken place at least since the first national counts of 1969–70 (Gibbons et al. 1993).

Number of counties in which recorded:

Period	Probable breeding		Confirmed breeding		Combined		
	Br	Ir	Br	Ir	Br	Ir	Both
1875–1900	0	3	8	7	8	10	18
1968–1972	3	0	10	5	13	5	18
			change		5	−5	0
					63%	−50%	

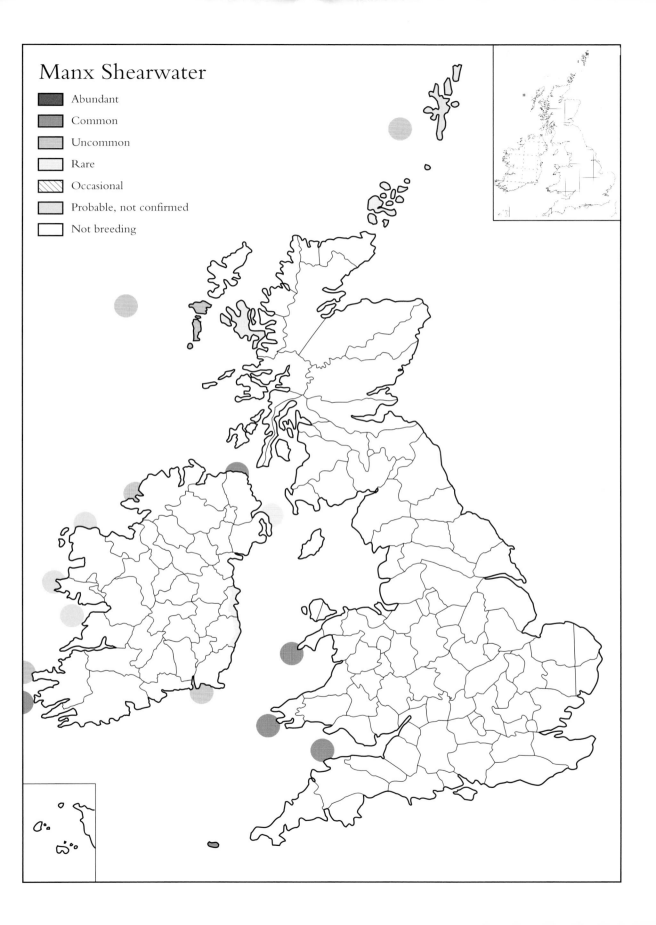

Manx Shearwater

- **Abundant**
- **Common**
- **Uncommon**
- **Rare**
- **Occasional**
- **Probable, not confirmed**
- **Not breeding**

Storm Petrel

Hydrobates pelagicus

It is likely that at no time during ornithological history has the complete status of the Storm Petrel been known. Certainly, modern biologists acknowledge the great difficulty in accurately censusing this species in its known colonies and suspect that there remain quite a few breeding groups waiting to be discovered (Gibbons *et al.* 1993). This was equally true of the 19th century; new colonies were discovered regularly and others were considered to have become extinct, especially during the closing decades of the century, and it is clear that the recorded status of the species at that time is likely to be incomplete and, to some extent, an artefact of observer effort. The Storm Petrel was regarded as rare during the early 19th century; however, as new colonies were discovered the species became regarded as reasonably numerous, although this was tempered by the loss of some breeding groups. These losses were said to have been caused, in the main, by competition from Puffins (although this is now considered unlikely, M. Tasker in litt.) and predation by cats and rats and have led some later researchers to suggest that the population may have decreased during the 19th century (Parslow 1973).

Known breeding sites outside Scotland and Ireland were confined to the Isles if Scilly (the main colony was on the islet of Gorregan, although breeding occasionally took place on Gull Rock) and Skomer, but breeding was suspected on other Pembrokeshire islands. In Scotland the Storm Petrel bred on many of the islets that surround Staffa and Iona (such as Soay), and on Staffa itself. It was known to breed on one of the Treshnish Islands and was suspected of doing so on others of the group. It bred on one of the Ascrib Islands at the mouth of Loch Snizort, the only site known at the time around Skye. Several sites were known off the Ross-shire and Sutherland coasts—the Storm Petrel bred on Longay and Foura Islands around the mouth of Loch Ewe, one of the Summer Isles, Roan Island in the Kyle of Tongue and was suspected of breeding in the Badcall Islands. In the Outer Hebrides it bred around Harris—on Shillay it had been recorded from 1830 and it bred on an island opposite West Loch Tarbert, but it had ceased to breed on Mingulay soon after the middle of the 19th century. One colony was known in St Kilda, a large group on Soay, although breeding was suspected on other islands, especially Boreray. It probably bred on one of the Flannan Islands and was confirmed doing so on North Rona in large numbers. In Orkney the most well known colony was that on Hunda but by the end of the century it had declined substantially. Small numbers bred throughout the group, especially on the smaller holms. The largest colonies in Shetland were those on the islands off Scalloway, especially Onxa and Papa, and on some of the small skerries off the west of Unst. Other sites recorded were Foula, at least four islands in Yell Sound, Papa Stour, summit of Saxaford on Unst, Nacka Skerry off Whalsey, Lady's Holm in Quendale Bay, the mainland near Brindister and occasionally eggs were found on Fair Isle.

The largest Irish colonies were on the Skelligs, the Blaskets, Puffin Island and Scariff off the Kerry coast, and, on Inishtearaght, 'several thousands' were believed to breed. A Storm Petrel and an egg were taken on an island off the Cork coast, probably in the vicinity of Clear Island. Other recorded colonies were on Mutton and Deer Islands off Clare, High Island off Galway and on the Mayo coast at Blackrock, several other islands north of Achill, near Belmullet, Pig Island and Illanmaster. Good numbers bred on Rathlin O'Birne, Roaninish and Tory Island off Donegal and two small islands off the Antrim coast.

It is difficult to determine whether any changes have occurred in the Storm Petrel population during the 20th century because of the difficulties involved in censusing the species accurately. Recent losses, where real, are probably mostly caused by brown rats which arrived in N Scotland only in the middle of the 19th century and reached some islands only during the 20th century.

Number of counties in which recorded:

Period	Probable breeding		Confirmed breeding		Combined		
	Br	Ir	Br	Ir	Br	Ir	Both
1875–1900	0	1	9	6	9	7	16
1968–1972	0	1	12	5	12	6	18
			change		3	−1	2
					33%	−14%	13%

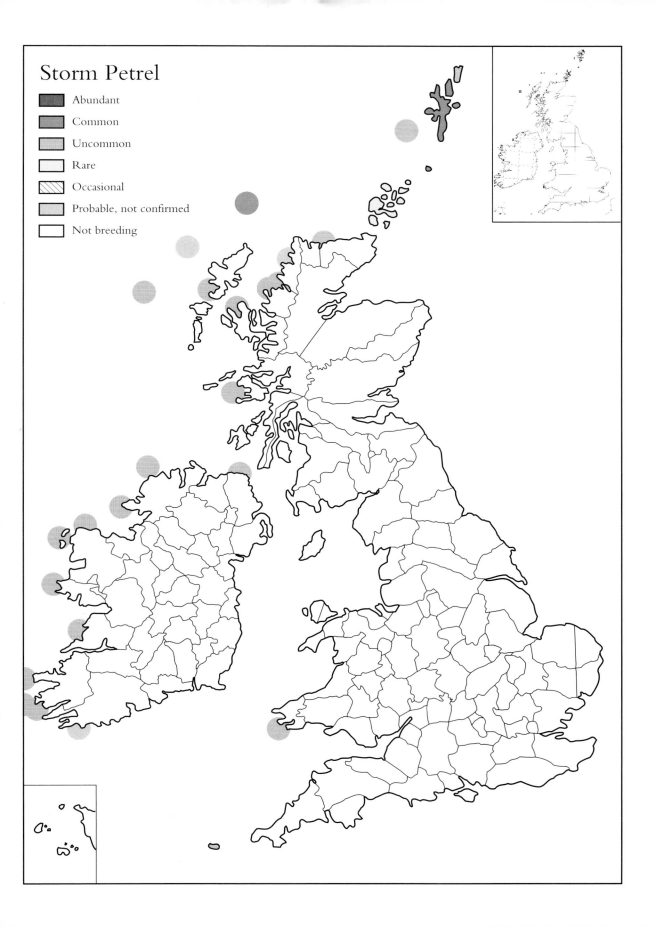

Storm Petrel

- **Abundant**
- **Common**
- **Uncommon**
- **Rare**
- **Occasional**
- **Probable, not confirmed**
- **Not breeding**

Leach's Petrel
(Fork-tailed Petrel)

Oceanodroma leucorhoa

The first specimen of Leach's Petrel taken in Britain was obtained by Bullock in St Kilda in 1818 and purchased by Dr. Leach 1819 in (Harvie-Brown and Buckley 1888). Only three other specimens were known at that time, all in French collections. Subsequently, many examples were identified throughout Britain and Ireland but it was not until 1840 that Mackenzie asserted that it bred on Boreray and N Hirta, although he had found no nest. In 1841 Sir W. E. Milner found the first egg. This was under loose rocks near the summit of Dun, an island next to the St Kildan island of Hirta, but it became clear to later naturalists that Leach's Petrel bred far more commonly on Boreray in the same group (Harvie-Brown and Buckley 1888). By the end of the century it had been recorded on all the main islands of the group—it was most abundant on Boreray, bred plentifully on Soay and slightly less so on Dun. A few pairs bred on Hirta and a small colony was discovered on Levenish in 1902. Leach's Petrels were evidently under great pressure at all of their St Kildan colonies as the islanders were paid large sums of money by collectors for specimens that they happily, and in quantity, supplied (Wiglesworth 1903). Elwes, in the 1860s, reported that a few pairs bred in holes and cracks in the dry peat walls at the top of the cliffs of Mingulay at the southern tip of the Outer Hebrides in the company of Storm Petrels (Harvie-Brown and Buckley 1888). At around the same time a large colony of Leach's Petrels was discovered in rough stony

ground near Braedinach at the NW end of Rum (Gray 1871). Breeding was never again claimed at either of these last two colonies, however. The Rum record must remain only a possibility but if Leach's Petrels were ever present there rats will probably have caused their extinction (M. Tasker in litt.). The colony on North Rona was first discovered in 1883; Leach's Petrels were said to be breeding abundantly in and around the thrift-covered ruins on the south side of the island, and were recorded there by Harvie-Brown in 1885 and 1887.

Examples of Irish breeding records were sparse. An early statement that Leach's Petrels bred on islets near Slyne Head, Galway was subsequently discounted by Thompson (1849–56) and others, but eggs have since been found from remote islets to the north and south of that site. The first confirmed report concerned an egg taken on Inishtearaght off Kerry in 1886. Sitting adults were found on the same island in 1887 and an adult and its egg were taken there in 1888. No more Leach's Petrels were found on the island during the 19th century but an egg was taken from a nest on nearby Inishnabro in 1889. In 1899 a heavily incubated egg was collected on Blackrock off the coast of Mayo and the last Irish breeding record until recent times was of three eggs taken on Walpole-Bond's behalf from Duvillaun Beg close to Blackrock in 1906. In 1946 and 1947 the Stags of Broadhaven off the Mayo coast were visited and birds seen and heard but these islands were not visited again by bird-watchers for another 35 years at which point it was estimated that about 200 pairs bred there, although only three nests were found (Waring and Davies 1983, Hutchinson 1989, M. Tasker in litt.).

In the early years of the 20th century a few more colonies were discovered. That in the Flannan Isles has proven to be an important colony and is one of the few that has clearly increased in numbers. The known northerly extent of British breeding was at North Rona during the 19th century. Nests were found on the adjacent isle of Sula Sgeir during the first decade of the 20th century and, later, new northerly limits of British breeding were reached when colonies were discovered on Foula and Ramna Stacks in Shetland.

When considering the Leach's Petrel population in Britain and Ireland it is important to remember that, owing to its extremely secretive nature whilst breeding and the isolated sites where breeding takes place, it is likely that the species is substantially under-recorded. This is likely to be the case even up to the present day and apparent colony establishment/extinctions may be artefacts of observer efforts (M. Tasker in litt.).

Number of counties in which recorded:

Period	Probable breeding		Confirmed breeding		Combined		
	Br	Ir	Br	Ir	Br	Ir	Both
1875–1900	2	0	2	2	4	2	6
1968–1972	0	0	4	0	4	0	4
			change		0	−2	−2
						−100%	−33%

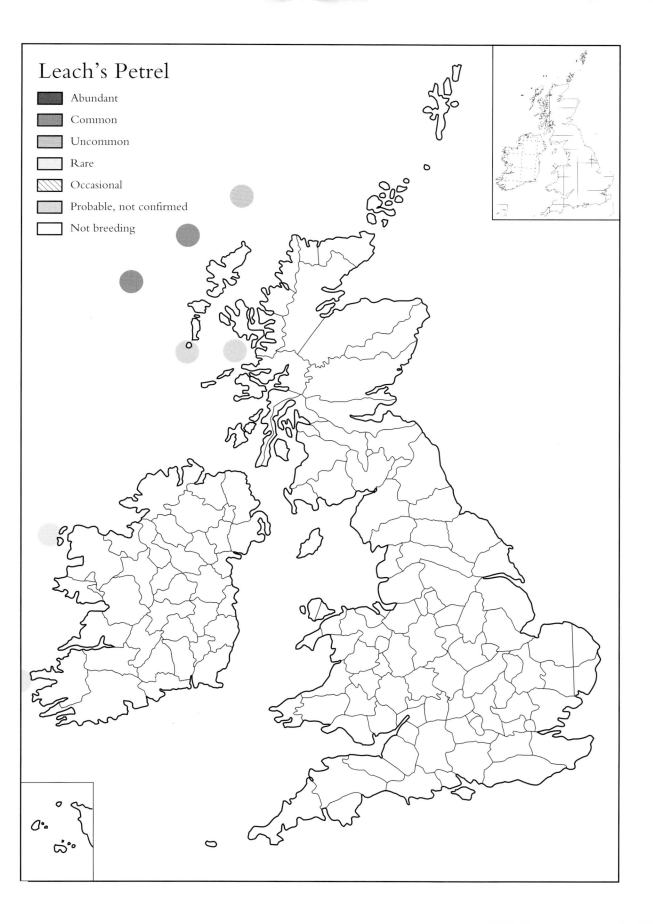

Leach's Petrel

- Abundant
- Common
- Uncommon
- Rare
- Occasional
- Probable, not confirmed
- Not breeding

Gannet (Solan Goose)

Morus bassanus

In 1900 there were nine gannetries in Britain and Ireland of the 15 known in the North Atlantic.

Lundy Island, Devonshire. The earliest mention of the Gannet on Lundy was in an inventory of the island from 1274. The first published counts were in 1887 of 16 nests on the adjacent Gannet Stone, and in 1893 of about 30 pairs on Lundy itself. Severe persecution, including egg collecting, however, reduced the numbers to three pairs on Lundy in 1900. No eggs were laid after 1903 and the island was abandoned sometime between 1906 and 1909.

Grassholm, Pembrokeshire. This colony was established sometime before 1820 but the first count was in 1883 of 20 nests. By 1886, 250 nests were recorded and numbers then remained fairly stable until the end of the century. The Gannets were heavily persecuted by fishermen and local people throughout the 19th century.

Ailsa Craig, Ayrshire. Gannets were first noted on Ailsa in 1526 and bred there throughout the following centuries. After about 1880 the demand for eggs and young for the pot diminished, but the few records of counts suggest that the population remained more or less stable at 5,000–7,000 pairs between the 1860s and 1940.

St. Kilda, Western Isles. An account of the islands by Martin in 1698 included a description of the gannetries here. Gannets were an important economic resource then and bred in very large numbers. Over time the annual harvest of Gannets fell from, perhaps, 22,600 in 1696 to around 3,200 in 1895 and only 300 in 1902 as the human population declined. The size of the three breeding sites made counts difficult and fraught with errors; however, in 1902 it was estimated that there were 3,500–4,000 nests on Stac Lee, 3,000 on Stac an Armin and about 8,000 on Boreray.

Sula Sgeir, Western Isles. The Gannets had been harvested by the Lewis islanders since at least the 16th century. This remote, uninhabited island was little visited by naturalists but, from the first published count of 7,000 pairs in 1883, numbers apparently remained stable into the 20th century.

Sule Stack or Stack Skerry, Outer Hebrides. This gannetry was first recorded in 1710, but its inaccessibility has caused it to be little visited. Accounts of the colony at the end of the 19th century suggest that the distribution of breeding birds (and perhaps its size) changed little up to counts of the colony in 1967 and 1969 and was probably in the order of 3,000–4,000 pairs.

Bass Rock. There have been numerous accounts of this colony since the 15th century. The breeding area on the rock then was larger than in 1900; the decline that took place was said to have been the result of heavy collection of eggs and chicks, especially following the widespread availability of accurate firearms. The Rock's proximity to Edinburgh put it within easy reach of collectors. In around 1900, estimates put the colony at between 7,000 and 10,000 adults.

Little Skellig, Kerry. The first mention of this colony was about 1748. In 1850 there were said to have been about a thousand Gannets, in 1880 60 and in 1882 300. From that point there was evidently a substantial increase: by 1906, the colony was estimated to hold 15–20,000 individuals. The increase may have been the result of immigration from the St Kilda colony following the end of the Gannet harvest there.

Bull Rock, Cork. In about 1858 11 Gannets' nests were counted here and in 1884 about 2,000 Gannets inhabited the rock but by 1891, this had fallen to 220: disturbance and depredations by workmen building the new lighthouse were blamed for the decrease. By 1902 the Gannets had recovered to their 1884 level when the lighthouse-keeper estimated the colony at nearly 2,000 individuals and the colony has flourished since.

At the end of the 19th century the breeding population of Gannets in Britain and Ireland was probably 40–50,000 pairs. It is clear that many colonies were subject to intense exploitation and persecution by humans. However, early in the 20th century this mass slaughter largely ceased following legal protection. Numbers of birds at existing colonies started to increase and new breeding sites were colonised. By 1984–88 the number of gannetries in Britain and Ireland had risen to a maximum of 22 with an estimated population of some 188,000 pairs (Lloyd *et al.* 1991).

Number of colonies and breeding pairs recorded:

Period	No. of colonies		No. of pairs	
	Br	Ir	Br	Ir
1900	7	2	*ca* 38,000	*ca* 11,000
1984–88	17	5	163,168	24,740
change	10	3	*ca* 125,000	*ca* 13,700
	143%	150%	*ca* 329%	*ca* 125%

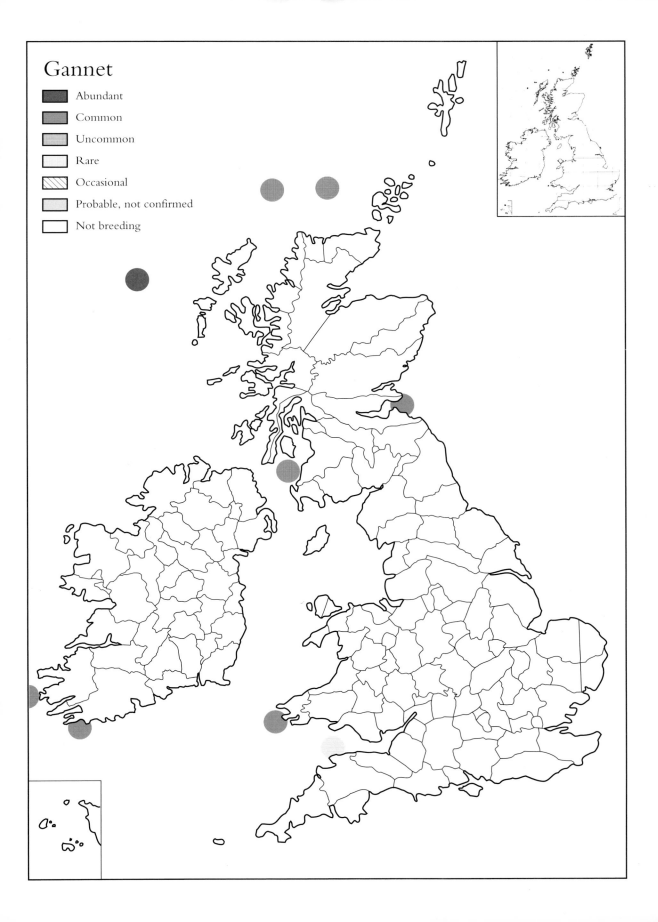

Gannet

- Abundant
- Common
- Uncommon
- Rare
- Occasional
- Probable, not confirmed
- Not breeding

Cormorant (Common or Great Cormorant)

Phalacrocorax carbo

The Cormorant was persecuted heavily during the 19th century, particularly on inland waters in the winter, in the main by those with fishing interests. During the breeding season the more accessible inland and/or tree colonies were harried most effectively by fishermen and many colonies were subject to the depredations of egg collectors.

The Cormorant's distribution during the 19th century is little different to that of today. It bred in its greatest numbers on the rocky shores of the west and northern coasts of Britain and Ireland but, in England especially, records of inland breeding were then infrequent.

In Suffolk there was a famous colony in the heronry around Fritton decoy near Herringfleet but Cormorants apparently did not breed there every year; the 50–60 nests of 1825 were the largest number recorded but also the last. The heronry had a history of periodic persecution that eventually caused its extinction and this was probably the cause of the Cormorant's withdrawal from the site. The old record of nests near Reedham in Norfolk may have referred to the same colony. In Dorset there was a tradition of a Cormorant's nest in a tree on the banks of the Stour near Blandford about 25km from the coast—the only inland record in the county. In Devonshire some colonies

had been deserted following the attentions of egg collectors. In Pembrokeshire a colony still existed in trees at Slebech at the mouth of the Eastern Cleddau River. The famous Bird Rock colony over 6km from the sea near Towyn, Merioneth has a long history and in Snowdonia in Caernarvonshire there was a colony on Llyn Gwynant but another on Llyn Peris was abandoned a few years before 1900. There was some disagreement whether Cormorants bred on the cliffs at St Bee's Head, Cumberland. Mitchell (1885) believed that they did but Macpherson (1892) indicated that the Cormorants found there used the cliffs only as a roost. This was the only site known between Anglesey and SW Scotland (a colony on the sea cliffs near Ballantrae in Ayrshire) although an inland colony on Loch Moan in that county existed until the 1890s (this colony was persecuted heavily—in 1867 a fishing party destroyed many eggs, probably over 1,000) and a colony 11km inland at Castle Loch, Wigtownshire had existed up to the 1860s. The status of the Cormorant in Kirkcudbrightshire and Dumfriesshire was unclear but it probably bred occasionally. Around the coasts of Scotland and its islands it bred sporadically but usually in far smaller numbers than the Shag.

Inland nesting was far more regular in Ireland than in Britain at the end of the 19th century. The freshwater loughs of Connaught and Roscommon supported a number of small colonies. On the east coast, between the Saltees and Antrim there were only two colonies—on Wicklow Head and on Lambay Island in Dublin; on much of the west coast Cormorants were scarce whereas Shags were common but on the north coast Cormorants also bred commonly.

Some local declines the 19th century caused by persecution slowed somewhat as persecution ceased during the early years of the 20th century but a decrease has continued slowly until the 1980s. For example isolated colonies (such as those in the Isles of Scilly, Shetland and Lambay Island) have decreased substantially, although numbers in NE England have increased. In 1865, 40–50 pairs nested in the Farne Islands, 'large numbers' bred in 1896 and by the early 1950s over 400 pairs were recorded. On the N Yorkshire coast several colonies abandoned during the 19th century through persecution were recolonised before 1950. Between the *68–72* and *88–91 Atlases*, numbers of Cormorant colonies decreased, particularly in NW Scotland, the Western Isles and Cornwall but data from the large seabird surveys of 1969–70 and 1985–87 suggest that overall numbers increased between those two dates. In recent years the population in Britain has increased at an overall rate of about 3% per annum (Sellers 1991). An interesting development has been the establishment and rapid growth of inland colonies in E England, perhaps by birds from the established tree nesting groups of Holland and Denmark (Sellers 1991).

Number of counties in which recorded:

Period	Probable breeding		Confirmed breeding		Combined		
	Br	Ir	Br	Ir	Br	Ir	Both
1875–1900	2	0	42	15	44	15	59
1968–1972	2	2	41	14	43	16	59
	change				−1	1	0
					−2%	7%	

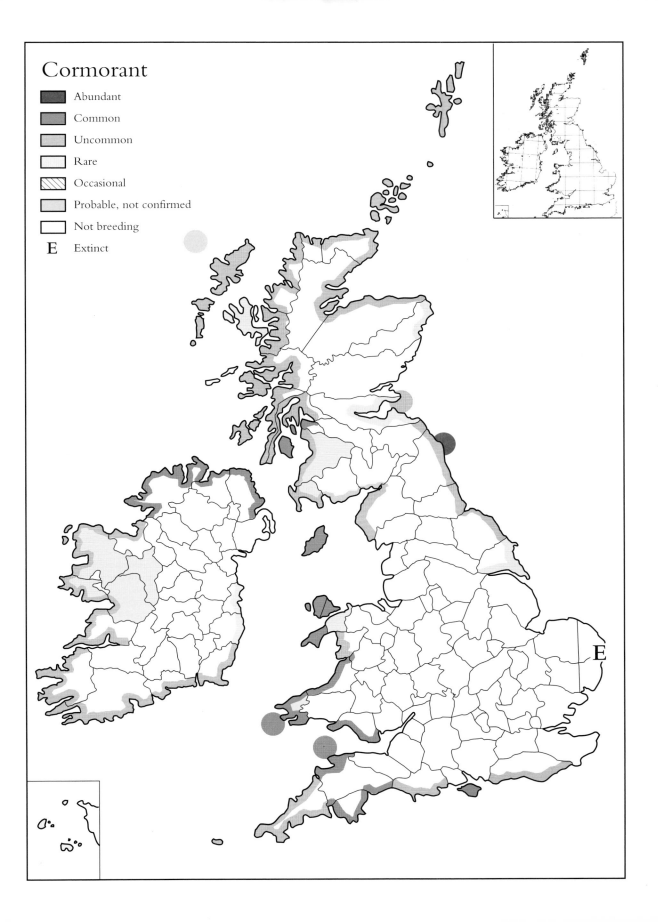

Cormorant

- Abundant
- Common
- Uncommon
- Rare
- Occasional
- Probable, not confirmed
- Not breeding
- **E** Extinct

Shag (Green or Crested Cormorant)

Phalacrocorax aristotelis

In England in the 19th century the Shag was largely confined to the SW counties. In Cornwall and Devonshire it was considered more common than the Cormorant particularly around Plymouth, and it bred in its largest numbers on the cliffs between Bolt Head and Hope. The Shag bred in many places along the Dorset cliffs but was most numerous on the cliffs below the Purbeck Hills. However, it is not clear whether it still bred on the Isle of Wight at the end of the 19th century. It certainly did so in the early years of the century at Freshwater and 'undoubtedly' still did so at the Culvers. Further north, an isolated colony existed on Flamborough Head, Yorkshire that was evidently of some size during the 18th century. It was already much smaller by the 1770s and was extinct prior to 1844; pairs that visited the cliffs subsequently were shot. The decline of the Farne Islands colony paralleled that at Flamborough, only a few pairs remaining by the 1920s, although it probably never quite died out here. A single pair was noted on the Pinnacles in 1873 and again in 1892 while by 1897 a handful of pairs probably bred.

Elsewhere on the Borders coast the Shag bred in several sites around St Abb's Head, Berwickshire, evidently in greater numbers than on the Farnes, up to the 1880s. It subsequently declined here, however, and, by 1911, was confined to a single site at Brander Cove where fewer than ten pairs remained. Shags bred in small numbers on the west side of the Isle of May and in greater numbers on the Bass Rock.

In Wales the species bred in a few widely separated colonies. In Glamorganshire it bred along the Gower coast but was more common in Pembrokeshire, perhaps more so also than the Cormorant, breeding all along the coast and on several of the off-shore islands. In N Wales it was confined to several places on Lleyn, especially St Tudwal's Island and Cilan Head and a few sites around the Anglesey coast.

The Shag was believed to have decreased in the Isle of Man, certainly from around the beginning of the 19th century and probably continuing throughout although it still bred in some numbers at the end of the 1800s.

In Scotland the Shag's stronghold was on the west and north coasts and islands. The species was recorded breeding from Burrow Head and the Mull of Galloway in Kirkcudbrightshire northwards and the colonies gradually increased in size with increasing latitude. In many places it bred in very large numbers (it was far more common here than the Cormorant) and was considered to be increasing, particularly on the mainland coast. In the east it bred in fewer numbers south of Duncansby Head, Caithness and not at all south of the Ord.

In Ireland it was most numerous on the west coast, in Galway, Mayo and Donegal especially, but it also bred commonly along the cliffs of both the north and south of the country. On the eastern coast it occurred much less frequently—between the Saltees, off Wexford, and Antrim only a few bred at two sites (Wicklow Head and the Dublin islands).

The 'Skart' afforded great sport in the 19th century, many being shot in all seasons seemingly for no other reason than target practice although a few were eaten; indeed, a pair was acclaimed as equal to 'a good plump hare'. This widespread persecution declined markedly during the 20th century and this is thought to be the most likely reason for the recent increase in numbers of Shags (Potts 1969). Between the turn of the century and the *68–72 Atlas* numbers have increased considerably in most areas for which information is available, the only exceptions being S Devon, the Clyde area and the northern Inner Hebrides. Increases were especially marked along the E coast of Scotland and England with numbers at existing colonies rising and new breeding colonies being established.

Number of counties in which recorded:

Period	Probable breeding		Confirmed breeding		Combined		
	Br	Ir	Br	Ir	Br	Ir	Both
1875–1900	0	0	31	13	31	13	44
1968–1972	1	0	40	20	41	20	61
			change		10	7	17
					32%	54%	39%

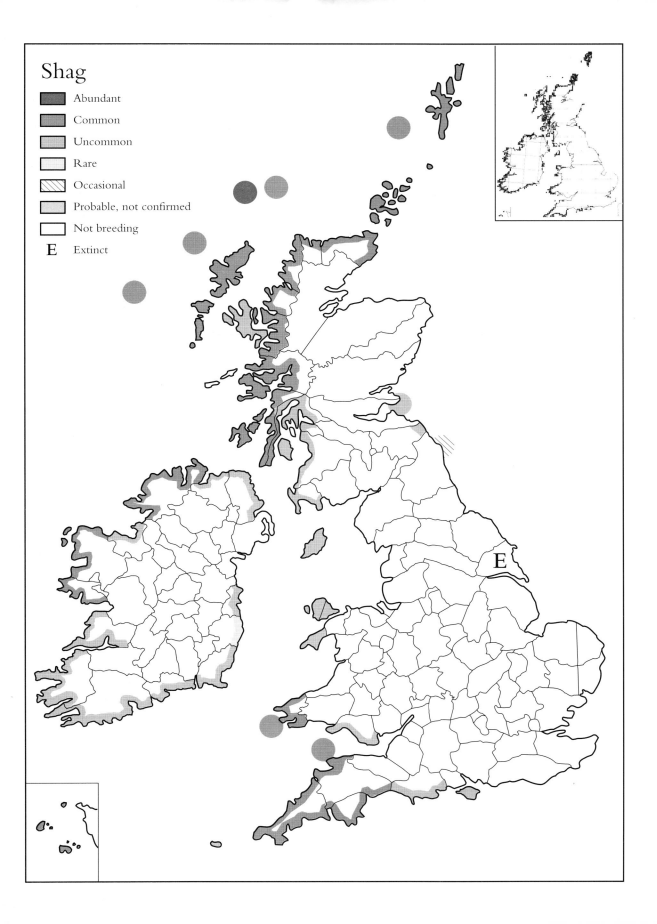

Shag

- ▨ Abundant
- ▨ Common
- ▨ Uncommon
- ▨ Rare
- ▨ Occasional
- ▨ Probable, not confirmed
- ▨ Not breeding
- **E** Extinct

Bittern

Botaurus stellaris

The Bittern bred over most of England, Wales and Ireland and in Scotland as far north as the Great Glen during the 18th century. The relentless drainage of marshes, bogs and lakes during that period banished it from much of the region prior to 1800. In the early years of the 19th century it bred regularly in only a few localities, most notably in the fens and broads of East Anglia; elsewhere it bred only sporadically. Regular breeding continued into the 1840s in some areas but the remnant Norfolk population ceased to breed by 1868. Occasional breeding probably continued to take place and the final 19th century record was that of a young female in down found near Ludham in 1886 (Stevenson 1866–90). Many birds continued to be recorded in the winter months and then, as now, a very few remained into the spring. Occasional breeding attempts were recorded or suspected throughout the remainder of the 19th century but the 1868 Norfolk record marked the effective extinction of the Bittern as a British breeding bird.

It can be speculated that habitat destruction was not the only cause of extinction. Certainly Bitterns were shot for the table and for fly dressing in the 18th and 19th centuries and there is no doubt that, once the rarity of the species was firmly established, collectors of skins and eggs hastened the decline, but the pattern of extinctions, generally prior to 1800 in the north and west and later further south, suggests that some other factor may have been involved. The Bittern is susceptible to severe winter weather and large declines in numbers have been noted in the 20th century during prolonged cold weather (Parslow 1973), which suggests that the cold climatic period up to the 1840s may have combined with habitat losses to cause the Bittern's extinction.

The reduction in persecution following the passing of the Wild Birds Protection Acts in the 1880s and 1890s and the ameliorating climate will have encouraged the recolonisation attempts in the first few years of the 20th century but by this time there was even less suitable breeding habitat than had existed in the 1860s. The first nesting record this century was at Sutton Broad, Norfolk in 1911 and by 1921 there were about ten nests on the broads (Ticehurst 1932). The first Suffolk breeding record followed in 1929. The population built up slowly to a peak in the 1950s mainly centred on the Norfolk Broads. Since then a serious decline has taken place that has continued to the present day. The drop in numbers from the late 1950s may have been caused initially by pesticides but, later, degradation of the Norfolk Broads may have caused further declines. Additionally, climatic factors may also be involved.

Where known the dates of last 19th century breeding follow. **Wiltshire**—was regarded as rare in 1820 and ceased breeding soon after. **Hampshire**—bred in Avington Park sometime between 1886 and 1889 for the last time although it had not been recorded regularly after the 1840s. **Suffolk**—last bred regularly in the 1820s although it may have bred in 1875 near Oulton. **Norfolk**—it had evidently ceased to breed regularly before 1850 but from 1866 birds were heard booming on Hoveton broad and the last definite record of breeding was in 1868 when two eggs were taken from a nest at Upton near Acle. A young bird in down was found in 1886. **Cambridgeshire**—bred near the Cam in 1821. **Warwickshire**—possibly bred in 1865. **Lincolnshire**—it was formerly common in the fens district, the Isle of Axeholm, the heathland marshes around Manton and Twigmoor and elsewhere. In the Isle of Axeholm it was still common around 1835 but had ceased to breed prior to 1860. **Cheshire**—ceased breeding in the reed beds surrounding the meres of the central plain in the early part of the century. **Northumberland**—probably bred at Newham until about 1820. **Tweed**—bred in Billie Mire, Berwickshire until its drainage in 1830. **Ireland**—generally it bred early in the century in Munster, Connaught and Ulster. **Tipperary**—a female with unfledged young was shot off a nest near Killenaule a few years before 1842. **Galway**— pairs seen irregularly on Crit Bog up to 1845. **Roscommon**—bred at Mantua probably up to the 1840s. **Londonderry**—booming was heard near Dungiven around 1820.

Number of counties in which recorded:

Period	Probable breeding		Confirmed breeding		Combined		
	Br	Ir	Br	Ir	Br	Ir	Both
1875–1900	0	0	1	0	1	0	1
1968–1972	1	0	5	0	6	0	6
			change		5	0	5
					500%		500%

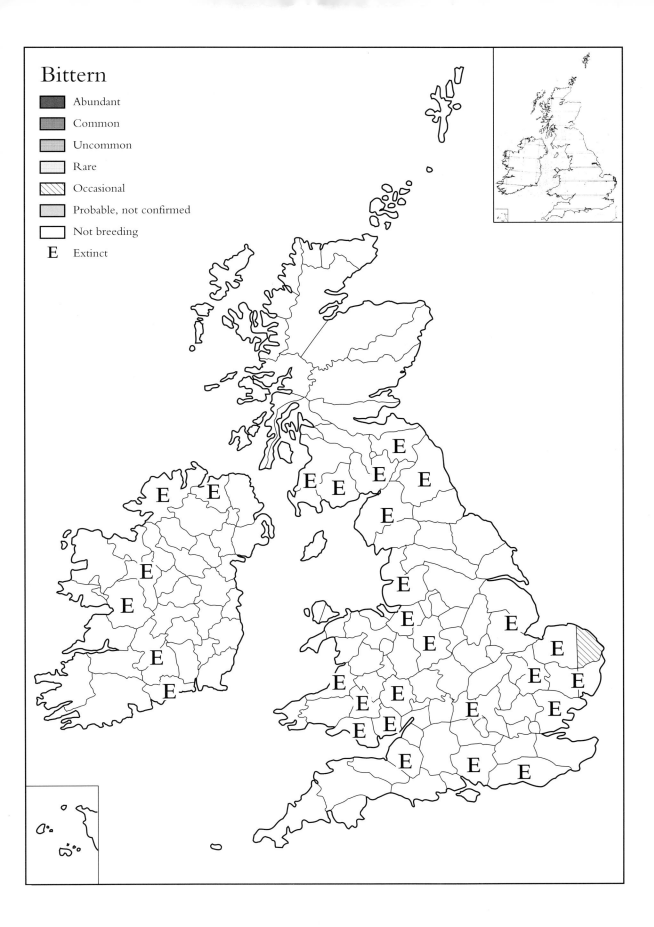

Bittern

- ■ Abundant
- ▨ Common
- ▦ Uncommon
- ▢ Rare
- ▨ Occasional
- ▨ Probable, not confirmed
- ▢ Not breeding
- **E** Extinct

Grey Heron

Ardea cinerea

By the beginning of the 19th century, the Grey Heron, for many years, had attracted a lot of attention for a number of reasons. At the height of the popularity of falconry the flight of a pair of Peregrines at a Grey Heron was considered one of the finest spectacles and many of the heronries that existed in England during the 19th century had been preserved to ensure the best hawking sport. Herons were also considered a delicacy for the table; many, particularly unfledged young, were taken and served at feasts. In addition, the spectacle of a busy heronry attracted many sightseers, often to the detriment of the success of the breeding attempts (Smith 1887).

Harting's (1872, 1873) attempts to document and describe all of the known heronries in Britain reveal that many of the largest about which he could obtain information were ancient and located on the English estates. It was clear, however, that from the early 1800s, hawking having fallen into decline, the consequent preservation of the heronries lapsed, nesting trees were cut down and the birds were harried for skins, eggs and young. Egg collecting, for example, caused the extinction of the last heronry in Rutland, at Burley, in about 1830. It was believed that the increase in persecution and lapsed protection led to both the dispersal of the very large colonies and, before the mid 1800s, the establishment of many new, smaller

colonies and isolated nests (Morris 1851-57).

Almost without exception the writers of late 19th century county and regional avifaunas detailed each of the heronries known to exist at the time that they wrote and in most counties of England and Wales the numbers of nests were recorded. The data thus available record that between 230 and 240 heronries existed in England and Wales around 1890 with between 5,000 and 5,600 nests. Less precise were the records of very small colonies (generally under five pairs) but it seems likely that there were 400–600 nests outside the larger colonies. In total, then around 6,000 nests were occupied in these two countries around 1890, although, particularly through the 1870s and 1880s, persecution had evidently reduced numbers substantially. For example, in Wiltshire by 1887 a number of heronries had been abandoned and only half as many pairs bred compared with the 1870s. Indiscriminate shooting had apparently caused most of the losses in that county.

The limited information on Scottish heronries suggests that the Grey Heron was expanding its range towards the north and west around the turn of the 19th century (Marquiss 1989) and was simultaneously dispersing into smaller colonies (although representing a large proportion of the heronry counts prior to 1914 in N and W Scotland, colonies of over 50 nests have not been noted since). From 1875 to 1900, the species was noted throughout the western mainland and Western Isles but most of the occurrences would have been of birds from some of the large colonies. Most notable of these were at Dunvegan Loch, Skye, on Ardnamurchan, Argyll and at an inland loch near Ben More, Sutherland (Marquiss 1989). Other breeding records were often of isolated pairs or very small groups frequently on coasts of the mainland and islands and they were often hidden (on ivy-clad cliffs for instance) but few of the known heronries were counted. The preservation of heronries for hawking in Scotland in the early 19th century was far less widespread than in England.

Apart from the effects of severe winters, the population as a whole has probably remained stable since 1928, the year that the first of the modern national heronry censuses was carried out. During this period, and including the effects of the severe winter of 1962/63, numbers have fluctuated between a little over 3,000 and around 9,500 nests yearly over the whole of Britain and Ireland, and between 2,000 and 6,500 nests in England and Wales although the population may be steadily increasing since its 1962/63 crash (*88–91 Atlas*). The estimation of around 6,000 nests existing in England and Wales around 1890 falls within this range and supports Nicholson's (1929) assertion that the Heron population was stable for many years prior to the first modern heron census. It remains a possibility, however, that the Heron population was larger than the modern normal range prior to about the 1870s.

Number of counties in which recorded:

Period	Probable breeding		Confirmed breeding		Combined		
	Br	Ir	Br	Ir	Br	Ir	Both
1875–1900	0	0	106	34	106	34	140
1968-1972	0	0	107	34	107	34	141
			change		1	0	1
					1%		1%

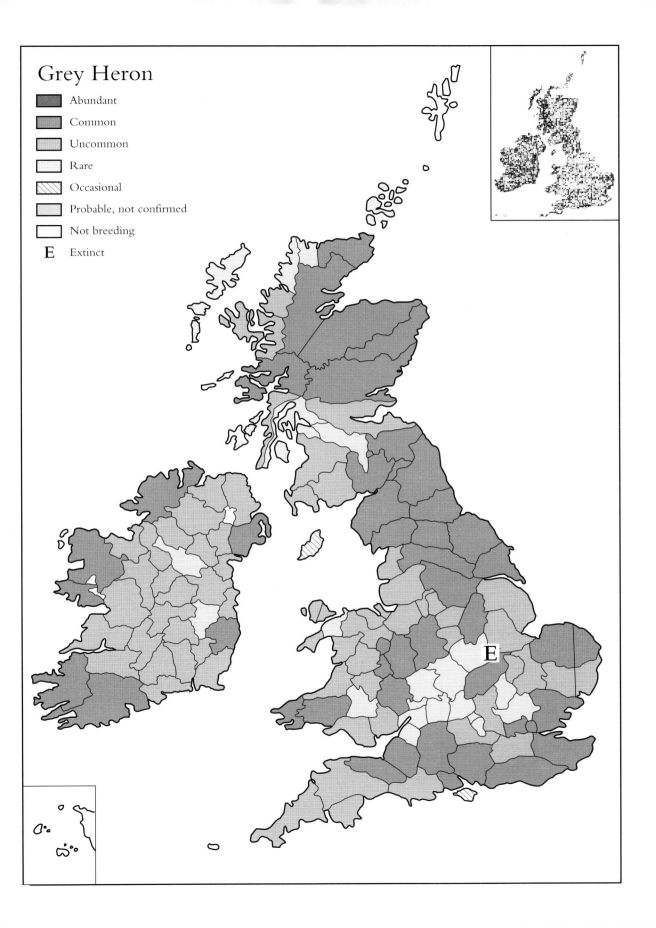

Grey Heron

- Abundant
- Common
- Uncommon
- Rare
- Occasional
- Probable, not confirmed
- Not breeding
- **E** Extinct

E

Mute Swan
(Tame Swan)

Cygnus olor

The determination of the distribution and population of the Mute Swan in the 19th century is imprecise. It was considered by almost all contemporary writers and naturalists as a domesticated bird and, in many cases, ignored. Many Swans were kept on ornamental waters at the time but were known only very rarely to breed in a wild or semi-wild state. In the few cases where swans were recorded breeding on unmaintained waters the assumption was made that, either, they were escapes from ornamental collections, and, hence, ignored or an attempt was made to attribute them to the 'Polish' variety. Such a large, conspicuous and familiar bird as the Mute Swan would have been unlikely to escape notice if it was breeding outwith wildfowl collections and, so, it can be assumed that, in general, it did not do so at that time.

Ticehurst (1957) has dealt in detail with its history. It is likely that, from very early times, the Mute Swan was an indigenous British species and bred in a perfectly wild state in and around East Anglia. Archaeological remains collected from peat deposits there, although dated only as 'centuries' old (Ticehurst 1957), are most likely to be of this species. It is probable that breeding continued there at least to the

10th and possibly through to the 13th century. Persecution took a great toll on the wild Mute Swans as they were killed for food but they were saved from extinction by the action taken by some people in England to breed them in a semi-domesticated state from at least 966. This was done for several reasons. Swans were kept as a status symbol, to provide distinctive gifts, for profit and food. As the wild populations were persecuted to extinction, the semi-domesticated swans thrived. In addition to this, human intervention also caused the spread of swans to areas they probably had not bred in for many years, if at all, aided by the supplementary feeding they received in the winter months. As time went on, the memories of the wild populations must have been gradually forgotten until the Mute Swan was known only from its semi-domesticated state and, hence, the popular belief grew that it was introduced to Britain by either the Romans or Richard I on his return from the Crusades. Intriguingly, however, the practice of Swan-keeping declined until it had almost ceased by the mid 18th century and very few flocks were in the hands of private owners into the 19th century (Ticehurst 1957). Apart from the Thames flocks, Swan ownership lasted in only one or two places, most notably in the fens (Birkhead and Perrins 1986). It seems likely that this may have caused the Mute Swan to decline in numbers, as many were probably killed by poachers. It is difficult therefore to understand the 19th century naturalist's reluctance to accept the Mute Swan as a wild bird, as few were apparently still artificially maintained then. Perhaps it is the case, then, that, although Mute Swans were not fed and positively protected, they were indirectly protected from poachers by the presence of gamekeepers on private estates and that the bulk of the Swans that survived the 19th century would have done so mainly on private waters.

Towards the end of the 19th century and in the early years of the 20th century the practice of keeping large, private wildfowl collections decreased further. Poaching also probably declined so that the Mute Swan population was able to expand out of private waters and it began to be regarded as a species that bred wild in Britain. Through the first half of the 20th century it spread and increased in Scotland and Ireland but, latterly, this has halted and small fluctuations now occur following harsh winters and other, man-made, causes. Since the widely reported lead poisoning issue, which led to the ban of lead fishing weights in 1987, the Mute Swan has increased significantly in those areas most affected and overall an increase has occurred, particularly in Ireland (Gibbons *et al.* 1993).

Number of counties in which recorded:

Period	Probable breeding		Confirmed breeding		Combined		
	Br	Ir	Br	Ir	Br	Ir	Both
1875–1900	37	0	65	24	102	24	126
1968-1972	0	0	105	34	105	34	139
			change		3	10	13
					3%	42%	10%

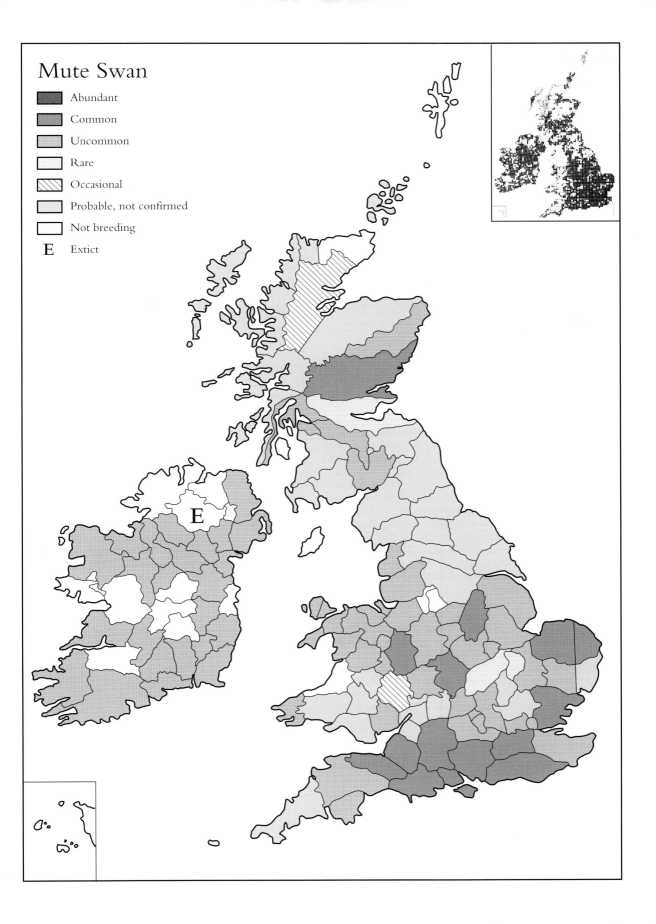

Mute Swan

- Abundant
- Common
- Uncommon
- Rare
- Occasional
- Probable, not confirmed
- Not breeding
- **E** Extict

E

Greylag Goose

Anser anser

At the end of the 18th century the Greylag Goose had a much wider distribution than during the following century. It was well known as an inhabitant of the East Anglian fens, where it was known as the fen goose, and had existed there for many years; bones attributed to this species have been found in the fenland peat (Ticehurst 1957). It seems likely that the drainage and cultivation of the fens were responsible for the Greylag's extinction in England. The bulk of these changes to the fens took place during the last quarter of the 18th century and it is probable that this species was lost then. There was little mention of the Greylag Goose in Norfolk and the date when it became extinct in that county can only be guessed at. Certainly it had been extinct for many years before Hunt (1829) wrote of it. The last accepted 18th century breeding record in Cambridgeshire took place in 1773 (Lack 1934). In Lincolnshire, it was often stated that the species died out between 1770 and 1800 but records of Greylag Geese 'obtained' seem to have continued for a few years later than in the other fenland counties. Although unfortunately not giving any specific dates or localities, Daniel (1807–13) seemed to consider that the Greylag Goose bred in the East Anglian fens at the time that he wrote. Its extinction in the carrs of E Yorkshire is similarly imprecise. It seems that the Greylag Goose became extinct there much earlier than in East Anglia but it

was breeding in the county during the early part of the 18th century.

The identification prior to 1775 of the 'Wild' and 'Great Harrow' geese that bred in counties Dublin and Down, Ireland must have been of this species although there is no physical evidence in support of the records or identification. Greylag Geese were breeding regularly in both counties in the 1770s and may have continued to breed for some years later. A domesticated flock, introduced about 1700, bred for many years semi-ferally in Fermanagh.

The Greylag Goose may still have bred on Skye into the last quarter of the 19th century; it bred on the nearby Ascrib Islands until 1867 and in 1890 there were two nests on Skinidin Island. It also bred on Priest Island and probably bred on one of the Summer Isles. A long history of hunting in the Outer Hebrides reduced the Greylag's numbers during the 19th century but it was still breeding throughout the islands in the 1880s. At the turn of the century it was increasing in numbers at its old haunts on the Scottish mainland and was spreading to new areas there following recent protection by landowners. The southernmost mainland breeding site was Loch Maree in West Ross and a number bred in the lochs of Coigeach there, although in this latter area some pairs had abandoned lochs that were regularly visited by anglers in increasing numbers and were said to have increased at others where afforestation close to the shore afforded improved security (Harvie-Brown and Macpherson 1904); however, it would be expected that afforestation would also aid the increase and success of predators (A. Prater in litt.). In E Sutherland the Greylag bred on the chain of lochs around the head of the Helmsdale river, but further south around Lairg and the head of Loch Brora persecution had probably caused its extinction in the 1890s. Further north and west, in Sutherland and in Caithness, it had bred in greater numbers prior to the 1880s—indiscriminate shooting had reduced numbers generally and caused its extinction on several lochs.

Notwithstanding the hope that protection would halt the fall in numbers, the indigenous population continued to decline, especially in mainland Scotland, through the early 1900s but was stabilised in around the 1950s or 1960s and has increased since then. The Greylag Goose has been domesticated for many centuries in Britain; many eggs were taken, particularly in East Anglia, to hatch into goslings for the pot. The accompanying map, however, does not record the distribution of feral Greylags as these were largely ignored by the 19th century writers. The feral population (resulting from escaped domesticated stock) has continued to thrive and is now distributed over much of Britain (especially the north and east) and Ireland.

Number of counties in which recorded:

Period	Probable breeding		Confirmed breeding		Combined		
	Br	Ir	Br	Ir	Br	Ir	Both
1875–1900	0	0	8	0	8	0	8
1968–1972	2	0	39	2	41	2	43
			change		33	2	35
					413%		438%

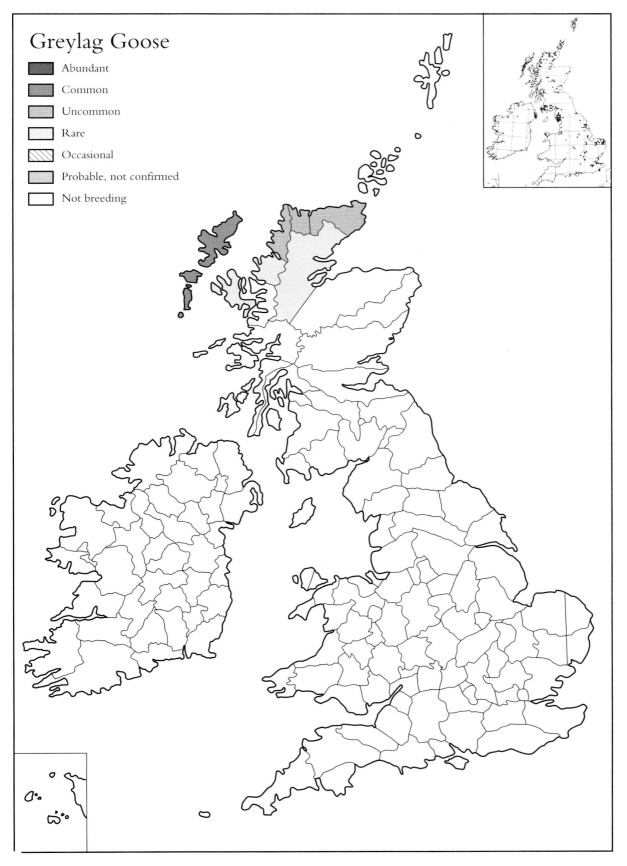

Greylag Goose

- Abundant
- Common
- Uncommon
- Rare
- Occasional
- Probable, not confirmed
- Not breeding

Canada Goose

Branta canadensis

The Canada Goose had been kept in a domesticated condition, particularly in England, since at least the 17th century. Willoughby noted it amongst the King's Wildfowl in St James's Park in 1678 and Linnaeus based his description of this species on a specimen from that collection. Latham (1785) noted that it was to be found on the ornamental waters of many 'gentlemen's seats'. This was evidently still the case throughout the 19th century but records of pairs breeding outwith these collections were very rare (examples were a pair that bred on an island on the Hurstbourne in Hampshire until 1890 and a feral pair that nested on the island in Edgbaston Park, Birmingham in 1885) and the county avifaunas gave few details of a species that was considered then to breed very rarely outside captivity. Some movement of the species occurred in the winter, and the county and regional accounts contain many examples of individuals shot and flocks seen at this time in many parts of Britain. During the last quarter of the 19th century these records became more frequent and Canada Geese were occasionally seen in an apparently free state during other times of the year. This led some naturalists (one of the earliest and most notable was Aplin 1889) to suggest that the Canada Goose should be considered on the same footing as the Pheasant, a species that was widely considered to breed in Britain in self-sustaining populations. The map that accompanies this account is, therefore, necessarily very incomplete.

Witherby *et al.* (1938–41) appear to have been the first to consider comprehensively the Canada Goose a feral species and it is very difficult to estimate its distribution and status (whether in preserved or wild living populations) prior to this acceptance. It was described at that time as widespread in England, although scarce or rare in the counties of the southwest and north and in Wales, and well established in the Tay and Forth regions of Scotland although scarcer in Moray. If the frequency of the records of birds seen and

shot outwith the wildfowl collections in each county/regional account during the 19th century is an indication of the number of birds kept there, then the description of the species' status in the late 1930s also describes that of the late 19th century. At that time most records of free flying Canada Geese came from the S, SE and Midland counties of England.

In Ireland very few wildfowl collections had examples of this species and records of Canada Geese seen were rare but almost invariably on the east coast and during the first six months of the year. This led to the assertion that they were escapes from English wildfowl collections rather than trans-Atlantic vagrants.

The status of the Canada Goose changed very little until the 1939–45 war, mainly because of its sedentary nature and the lack of natural predators in Britain. It declined substantially on estates in Scotland when winter feeding had to be abandoned during the war and, in England particularly, complaints by farmers of the damage caused to cereal crops led to attempts to control the population. Most direct methods (such as shooting and the destruction of eggs) had little effect so, in the 1950s and 1960s, many were rounded up in their flightless, post-breeding flocks, and transported to new areas. This has led to the establishment of many new sub-populations and overall numbers increased rapidly. Recent estimates of this increase (Owen *et al.* 1986) have been placed at 8% per annum and the potential maximum British population may be substantially larger than at present if the population is allowed to continue growing at this rate. Research is continuing into effective control methods.

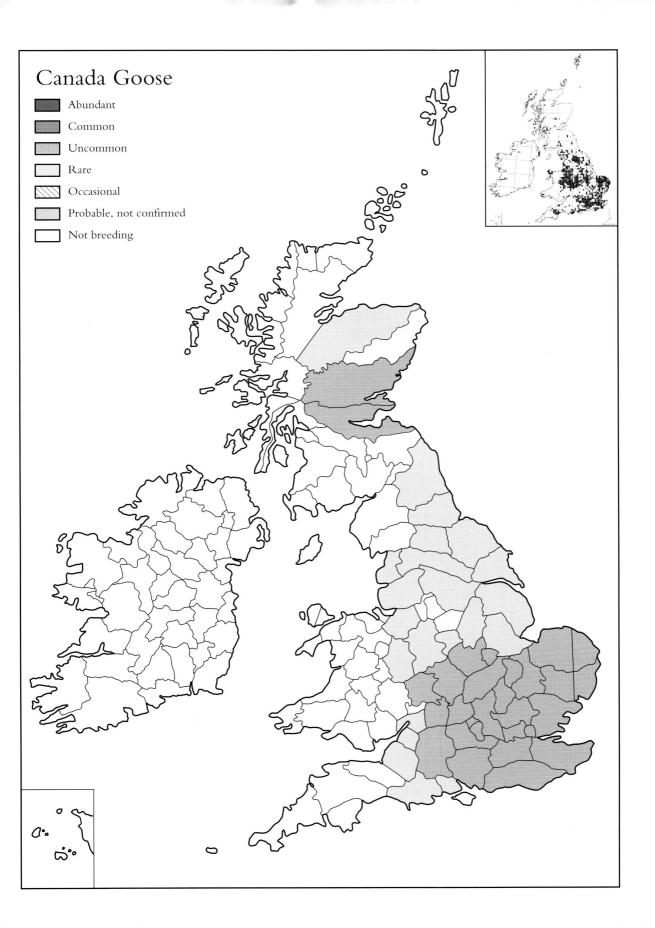

Canada Goose

- Abundant
- Common
- Uncommon
- Rare
- Occasional
- Probable, not confirmed
- Not breeding

Shelduck
(Sheld Drake,
Common Shelduck)

Tadorna tadorna

The Shelduck declined substantially in some counties of E and S England (for instance in Norfolk, Suffolk, Essex, Kent, Hampshire and Dorset) up to about the 1870s or 1880s. Indeed, it seems very likely that it became extinct in some of these counties (particularly in Kent) or had declined to the point where it was breeding only very occasionally (in Essex, Hampshire and Dorset) during the same period. On the other hand, in W Scotland, it was both increasing in numbers and expanding in range. Elsewhere no change in numbers had been detected and the population appears to have been stable.

The decrease in E England was almost certainly the result of persecution. In Norfolk, during the 17th century, the Shelduck evidently bred in great numbers, often far inland. It bred near Brandon around 32km from the coast, for instance, the attraction for the Shelduck being the warren. Rabbit warrens, when rabbits were farmed in great numbers in Britain, were regularly used as nesting sites by Shelducks where they were within reach of the coast. Shelducks were blamed for disturbing the rabbits and, particularly in

Norfolk, the warreners made considerable efforts to eradicate the ducks. This was apparently the reason for the Norfolk decline and probably caused the decline in Suffolk. The evidence suggests that the Shelduck declined to extinction between about the middle of the 19th century and the 1870s in other southern counties, probably because of persecution by the operators of rabbit warrens. As the practice of farming rabbits declined so the Shelduck was able to recover somewhat (although the rabbit's decline also caused the disappearance of many nest sites) and increased numbers were recorded from many counties by the end of the century.

In Ayrshire and S Argyll Shelducks were evidently increasing towards the end of the century and the increase in Argyll led to the colonisation of Loch Lomond. An increase had also been noted in the Outer Hebrides. Before the middle of the century the Shelduck was described as 'not uncommon' and inhabited only the islands of the Sound of Harris and North Uist. Just a little later it was described as breeding commonly on those islands and then Gray (1871) was able to record it as 'very common . . . over the whole Outer Hebrides'.

As the century turned it became evident that the increase was becoming more widespread. In SE England the increase in numbers that had begun during the 1880s led to an increase in breeding range. Sussex was colonised in 1904 and throughout the southeast counties the species spread to new areas. After the 1939–45 war the increase accelerated, particularly in the southwest. A particular feature has been the return to inland breeding sites. Most of these sites are within a relatively short distance of the sea but there have been colonisations of counties with no sea coast. Although an unconfirmed report attested to a nesting attempt near the Idle in Nottinghamshire during the 1860s the county had its first confirmed breeding record in 1921 in the Trent valley since when the Shelduck has bred regularly here and increased. In around 1936 it bred in the Nene Washes in Cambridgeshire and has colonised other sites in the county since then.

The dynamics of the Irish population during the 19th century is not clear. Ussher and Warren (1900) stated that, owing to its shyness and habit of breeding in burrows, its status was not well understood earlier in the century. It is probable, then, that any apparent increase in numbers may have been the result of a better understanding of the species' breeding range and not a real increase in numbers.

The 20th century has probably seen an increase in Shelduck numbers and, possibly, the saturation of its coastal and estuary habitats. This seems to have resulted in a widespread increase in inland breeding in Britain, a trend that became pronounced between the *68–72* and *88–91 Atlases* and follows the species' habits in other parts of its world range (Gibbons *et al.* 1993).

Number of counties in which recorded:

Period	Probable breeding		Confirmed breeding		Combined		
	Br	Ir	Br	Ir	Br	Ir	Both
1875–1900	0	0	56	14	56	14	70
1968–1972	0	0	71	22	71	22	93
			change		15	8	23
					27%	57%	33%

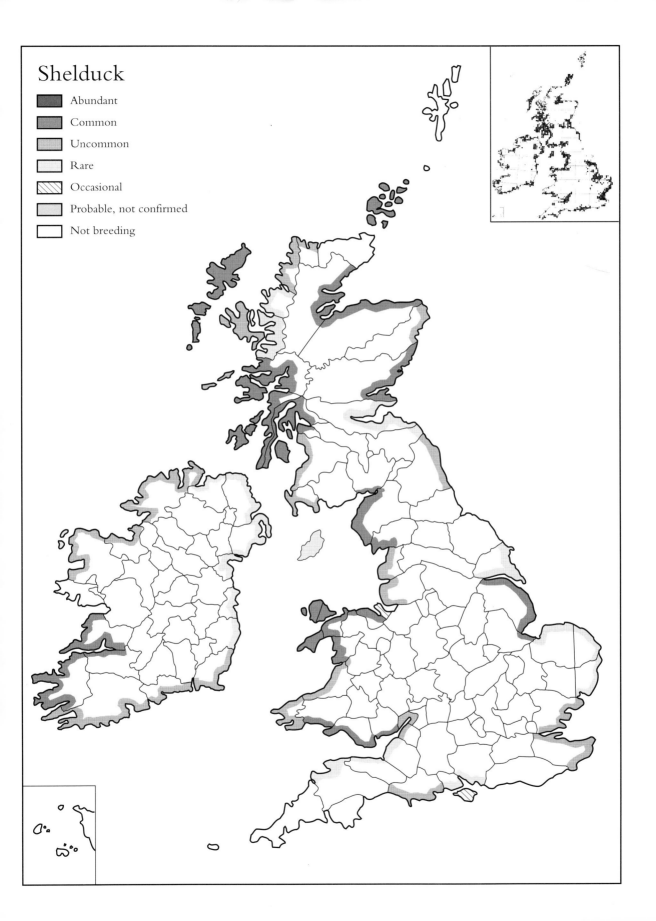

Shelduck

- **Abundant**
- **Common**
- **Uncommon**
- **Rare**
- **Occasional**
- **Probable, not confirmed**
- **Not breeding**

Wigeon (Widgeon)

Anas penelope

P. J. Selby and Sir William Jardine were the first to record breeding Wigeon in Britain. The nest was found in June 1834 on one of the islands of Loch Loyal in Sutherland; the eggs and nest down were taken and the duck was shot. Selby (1835) noted that pairs of Wigeon occurred on many of the smaller lochs around Lairg, and Jardine commented that more pairs were found on the Lochs Shin, Naver, Loyal and Hope. Breeding had probably taken place on the lochs around Lairg for some years. Later in the 19th century, as the area was more extensively surveyed by Harvie-Brown and others, the extent of breeding in E Sutherland became clear. The Wigeon at this time was recorded as breeding abundantly in some areas, particularly around Lochs Brora and Naver but breeding had not been confirmed in the west of the county. In Orkney the first dated breeding record was in 1891 on Hoy but Wigeon had apparently been breeding there for some years as Gray (1871) noted that the species had bred. In Shetland, although Evans and Buckley (1899) could not find a nest themselves, they accepted Saxby's (1874) record of nests from Yell, Hermaness in Unst and Hascosea. Interestingly, Saxby commented that he only heard of breeding in cold, 'backward' summers, confirmation perhaps of the influence the cold period in the middle of the 19th century had on the species' colonisation and expansion. In the Moray area an apparent increase in the numbers of wintering birds during the first half of the 19th century indicates that the subsequent expansion of breeding by the Wigeon may have been fuelled by these winter birds. Around 1850 the Wigeon was described during the winter as rare and 'occasionally seen'. Not until the 1880s was it described as abundant in winter and breeding was first noted in the 1890s from N Moray although an isolated group had been breeding on Loch Shin from 1835. At the end of the 19th century the Wigeon was still rare south of the Great Glen. It first bred in the Tay Basin on Rannoch Moor in 1866 and by 1874 was nesting commonly there. In 1897 a record of breeding that took place at Glensaugh Loch demonstrated the eastward expansion of the species' range from Rannoch. Although breeding took place commonly in the Forth area through the early years of the 20th century the only 19th century record here, on Loch Leven in 1888, was disputed. If this record is contrasted, however, with the record of suspected breeding in 1890, finally proven in 1893, near Ettrick in Tweed, S of Loch Leven in the direction of apparent colonisation, then the early Loch Leven record seems likely.

The foregoing provides a record of the early breeding and expansion of the Wigeon in Scotland from clear wild stock. The origins of the following English and Welsh records are less clearly unaided by introductions. In Yorkshire, the note of regular breeding around 1888 near Whitby lacks confirmation, but the provenance of the record on Skipwith Common near Selby in 1897 is far more substantial. A pair that bred in NE Lincolnshire in 1898 may have been introduced, but the origin of the pair that bred near Bala, Merioneth in the same year is less clear. Records from pinioned stock are not included here. The record of common breeding on the Severn Canal in Gloucestershire up to 1862 may have originated from turned down stock. The Irish counties marked on the map record the conviction that Ussher and Warren (1900) held regarding probable breeding in the light of numerous summer records throughout the 1880s and 1890s.

The pattern of the spread of the species in the 19th and early 20th centuries down the centre of the country continued until about the 1930s until the N Pennines were colonised. Further natural colonisation of this sub-arctic species then appeared to halt—more recent southerly breeding records were probably the result of escapes.

Number of counties in which recorded:

Period	Probable breeding		Confirmed breeding		Combined		
	Br	Ir	Br	Ir	Br	Ir	Both
1875–1900	3	5	10	0	13	5	18
1968–1972	4	0	30	0	34	0	34
			change		21	–5	16
					162%	–100%	89%

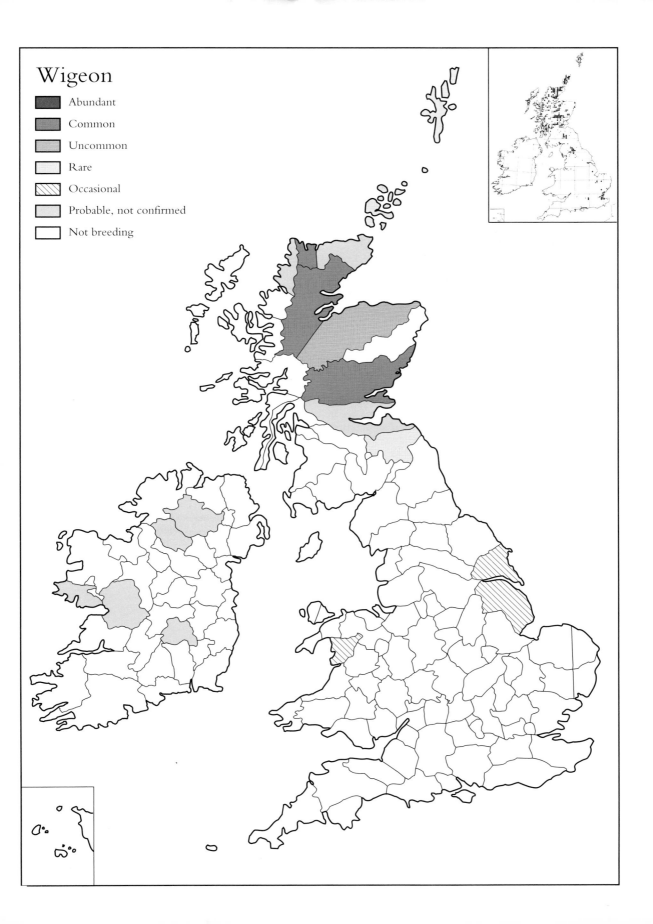

Wigeon

- Abundant
- Common
- Uncommon
- Rare
- Occasional
- Probable, not confirmed
- Not breeding

Gadwall

Anas strepera

For most of the 19th century the Gadwall was considered one of the rarest English winter ducks and examples were keenly sought after by the collectors. It had been recorded on a few occasions from other parts of Britain but Tiree in the Inner Hebrides was the only place that accommodated overwintering Gadwalls in any numbers and they had only really become numerous there after 1870. In about 1849, however, a pair were taken in Dersingham Decoy, a few miles north of King's Lynn in Norfolk and presented to the Reverend John Fountaine who removed a small portion from the pinions of both birds and released them on the lake at Narford (now Narborough), Norfolk, where they bred in the following year. Their progeny have bred there ever since. By 1875 up to 70 Gadwall were present on the lake but local shooters had prevented the group expanding any further. Around 1880, pairs evidently began breeding on nearby waters. In 1881 one of Lord Walsingham's keepers found nine nests on the estate at Stanford, in 1882 the Gadwall bred, probably for the first time, on a mere on Wretham Heath and in 1884 it bred at Tottington. Up to 1890, further breeding attempts were recorded in this area of SW Norfolk and breeding may have occasionally taken place on the Broads then. During the late 1890s Gadwalls colonised the waters around Thetford. In 1897 they were found breeding for the first time on the Croxton Estate near Thetford, Norfolk and during the same year over the border into Suffolk at Euston, Elvedon and other local

lakes. Interestingly, it was considered that the rapid increase in numbers was supported by visiting wintering birds pairing with the resident, and introduced, population (Stevenson 1866–90). In this area of SW Norfolk and NW Suffolk the Gadwall consolidated its numbers for the next 30 years or so but no further expansion of range occurred although a pair or two were suspected of breeding in NE Suffolk very occasionally from about 1914.

In 1908 two pairs of Gadwall were observed on Loch Leven, Kinross-shire and were considered to have been breeding. Breeding was proven the following year when two nests were found on the side of the loch and has continued ever since, the group proving to be a source of breeding pairs on adjacent waters from the 1920s. Away from Loch Leven, breeding has remained sporadic in Scotland; although recorded from the border to Sutherland, other regular breeding colonies do not exist.

In 1933 the Gadwall bred for the first time in Ireland—a nest and ten eggs were found in Armagh and since that time breeding has been recorded from other northern counties.

From the 1930s Gadwalls have bred on many lakes and pools throughout Britain and Ireland and their numbers are evidently still increasing. The extent to which the colonisation of Britain depended solely on the 1850 introduction and to what extent the expansion has been supported by truly wild birds is unknown. Since the initial introduction in Norfolk many others have taken place up to about 1970; however, evidence whether this was the case on Loch Leven is ambiguous (Millais 1902, Walpole-Bond 1938) and the increase in Britain is possibly part of the same effect that has allowed increases in Scandinavia and Iceland during the 20th century. Climatic changes have been connected with these other increases (Parslow 1973) whilst in Britain the gravel pits and other new bodies of water provided over the last few decades have provided ideal wintering and breeding habitat (Gibbons *et al.* 1993). It is intriguing that the successful expansion that has occurred late this century (although the Gadwall is still an uncommon breeder even now) did not occur right from the early days of initial colonisation (notwithstanding the heavy hunting pressure) (A. Fox in litt.).

Number of counties in which recorded:

Period	Probable breeding		Confirmed breeding		Combined		
	Br	Ir	Br	Ir	Br	Ir	Both
1875–1900	0	0	2	0	2	0	2
1968–1972	3	1	24	2	27	3	30
			change		25	3	28
					1,250%		1,400%

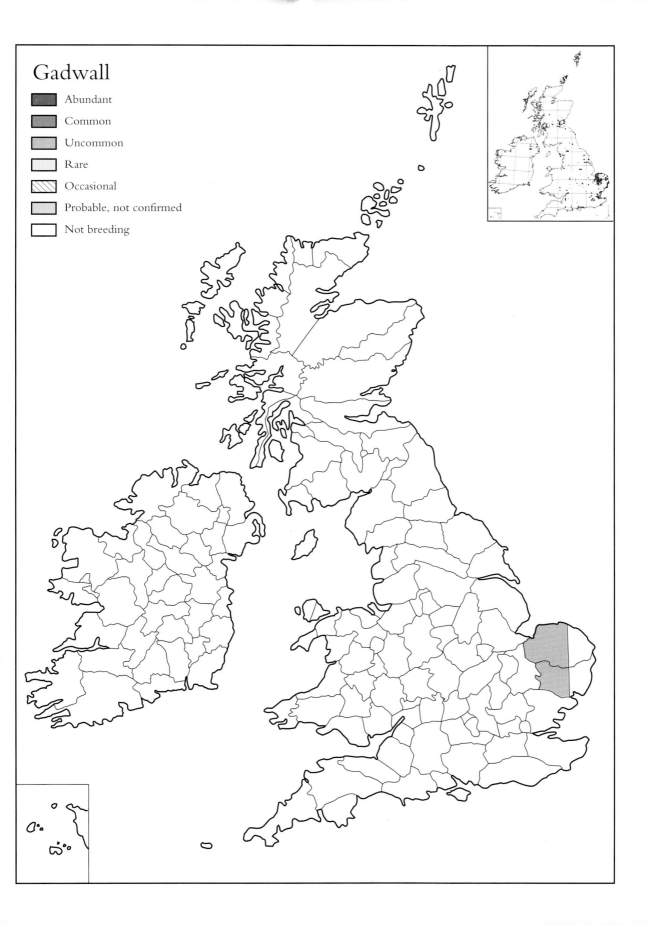

Gadwall

- **Abundant**
- **Common**
- **Uncommon**
- **Rare**
- **Occasional**
- **Probable, not confirmed**
- **Not breeding**

Teal (Common Teal)

Anas crecca

The Teal had been recorded breeding in most counties of Britain and Ireland during the late 19th century. Scotland was its main regular haunt although it bred regularly, but in small numbers, elsewhere, especially in Norfolk. It had been recorded breeding rarely in most other English counties and Wales. In Ireland it bred in every county, except Dublin, in limited numbers. Its breeding status was poorly understood during the early years of the 19th century and Yarrell (1837-43) was only able to record it from widely spaced localities. The difficulty in finding Teals' nests and the habit of broods to stay concealed amongst emergent vegetation made it very difficult to prove breeding and may have led to it being under-recorded. This fact, combined with the counties that, by the end of the century, had recorded the Teal as extinct, suggests that the Teal may have been more widespread in England during the 18th and early 19th centuries than later. It seems probable that the drainage and enclosure activities through the 18th and 19th centuries caused a widespread decline in Teal numbers although this had been specifically mentioned in only a few counties, for instance in Norfolk, Cheshire and Lancashire. An indication that destruction of habitat suitable for breeding Teals caused their withdrawal from lowland areas and began the long-term retreat to upland areas is demon-strated, for instance, by Forrest's (1907) records of breeding between Conway and Rhos in N Wales—something quite inconceivable now (A. Fox in litt.).

In contrast to the probable long term decline following habitat destruction there was evidence of an increase of breeding range into SW England towards the end of the century. Breeding had not been recorded in Devonshire until about the mid 1800s. After that it became evident that Teal bred in very small numbers at Slapton Ley, perhaps birds that had been injured during shooting days there. By the 1890s numbers had increased. Smith (1869) was not aware of any breeding records in Somerset but D'Urban and Mathew (1892) suspected that Teal may have bred on the peat moors, a belief confirmed later by Blathwayt (1906).

Regular and substantial breeding groups of Teal existed in East Anglia (where it was evidently declining as the broads and fens were drained) and the border counties of Herefordshire and Shropshire where it was believed to be increasing.

The Teal's main breeding range was centred around the Scottish uplands and moors. From the southwest hills to the Highlands it bred commonly and generally more abundantly than the Mallard although some areas at the fringes of the species' range had recorded a decline following changes in the agriculture of the lowlands (for instance in Cumberland and parts of SE Scotland).

Notwithstanding some local changes in Teal numbers recorded during the late 19th century it seems likely that the population had reached a stable level by the end of the century. This assessment would also apply to most of the 20th century up to the *68–72 Atlas* survey. Overall distrib-ution had not changed although decreases had been noted in a few regions. Parts of E and central Scotland had been almost abandoned between about 1930 and the 1960s and, during the same period, numbers of Teal decreased in parts of Galloway. Breeding is more sporadic in parts of SW England now than before the 1939–45 war and a slow decline has become evident in parts of SE England. These latter declines were probably the result of further habitat losses (Parslow 1973, Sharrock 1976).

The *88–91 Atlas*, however, described a substantial decrease in breeding range since the *68–72 Atlas*. The pat-tern throughout Britain and Ireland has shown a dramatic contraction of range and fragmentation of breeding popula-tions. Habitat loss, caused by drainage and agricultural changes in lowland Britain and afforestation in the uplands, is almost certainly the main cause of the decline.

Number of counties in which recorded:

Period	Probable breeding		Confirmed breeding		Combined		
	Br	Ir	Br	Ir	Br	Ir	Both
1875–1900	2	0	95	33	97	33	130
1968–1972	8	1	92	33	100	34	134
			change		3	1	4
					3%	3%	3%

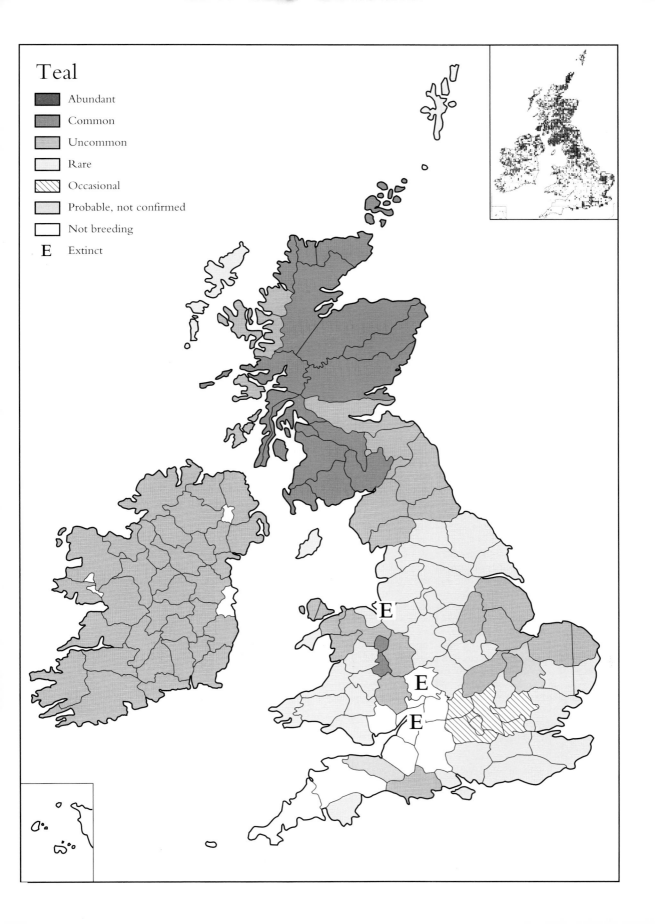

Teal

- Abundant
- Common
- Uncommon
- Rare
- Occasional
- Probable, not confirmed
- Not breeding
- **E** Extinct

Mallard
(Wild Duck)

Anas platyrhynchos

It is evident that the Mallard was much more numerous in Britain and Ireland prior to the large-scale agricultural changes that had taken place from the 18th century. These improvements had rendered thousands of hectares of marsh and standing water to land capable of growing arable crops. Even during the first half of the 19th century it appeared to be a comparatively scarce breeding species, although distributed throughout 'nearly' all counties, and was particularly thinly distributed in S England (Morris 1855, More 1865).

This species has had considerable economic importance over a number of centuries. The Mallard was domesticated, and later modified, very early on in human history and led to the proliferation of the 'farmyard' duck variants that exist today. The taking of wild ducks, particularly during the winter, led to the development of one of the most sophisticated means of killing birds ever devised. Duck decoys were already common during the reign of King John (1199–1216), particularly through S and E England. They remained an important means of catching wildfowl (Mallards were most frequently taken; Wigeon and Teal were the other main species) until the development and extensive use of accurate firearms. As the 19th century progressed the majority of duck decoys fell into disuse. An account of the decoys of Essex (this county and Lin-

colnshire probably had more than any other) was given by Christy (1890). He was able to locate the sites of or references to 31 decoys in the county but just three were still in use and, of these, the annual harvests had fallen to a level that had made them largely unprofitable. The Grange Decoy in Tillingham Marsh took 1,500–2,000 wildfowl annually by 1891 but over 10,000 had been taken in some previous years. The neighbouring Marsh House decoy was evidently falling into decline. Between 1859 and 1865 the average yearly catch was about 3,500 but this had fallen to 2,500 during the early 1880s, and, before 1890, numbers had fallen further still to about 2,000 ducks caught annually. Old Hall (no. 1) decoy was tenanted by J. H. Salter who preferred to shoot the adjacent marshes. The decoy was still used occasionally up to 1891 but the numbers of wildfowl taken were small, not recorded and, apparently, not a shadow of the 'fabulous' numbers caught in former times.

The distribution of the Mallard during the last quarter of the 19th century was more sporadic in S England than elsewhere. In counties with little water it occurred in far fewer numbers than elsewhere but was increasing in some counties around the turn of the century as the Wild Birds Protection Acts, prohibiting the shooting of birds during the breeding season, took effect. In Berkshire, for example, an increase was noted following the ban on shooting on the Thames.

Little further widespread change in Mallard numbers has occurred through the 20th century. Locally, further losses of wetland through drainage and, in some cases, through construction and development, have resulted in decreases in the numbers of Mallards. On the other hand, new flooded sand and gravel pits and reservoirs dug during the 20th century have provided breeding sites, particularly in England. The status of this species is confused by the release of captive reared birds—nearly 84,000 during the survey period of the *68–72 Atlas* and probably significantly more since (Harradine 1985).

Number of counties in which recorded:

Period	Probable breeding		Confirmed breeding		Combined		
	Br	Ir	Br	Ir	Br	Ir	Both
1875–1900	0	0	108	34	108	34	142
1968–1972	0	0	108	34	108	34	142
			change		0	0	0

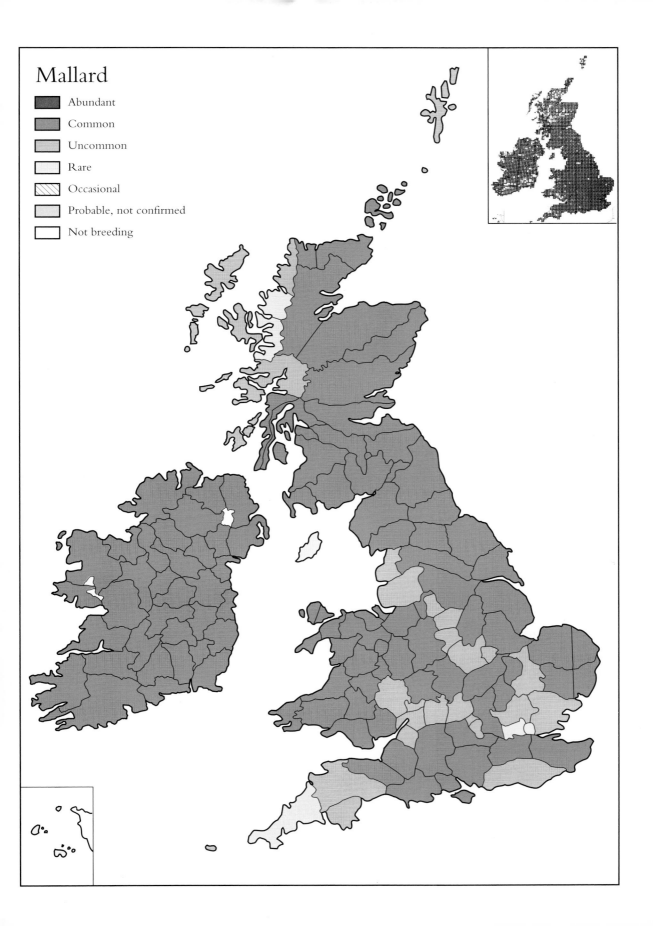

Mallard

- Abundant
- Common
- Uncommon
- Rare
- Occasional
- Probable, not confirmed
- Not breeding

Pintail

Anas acuta

ticularly sensitive to water levels. The Loch Leven group, for instance, bred until 1946 but then ceased until 1962 since when a very few have bred annually. The first English breeding record occurred in Kent in 1910 although a female Mallard paired to a male Pintail bred near Knutsford, Cheshire in 1890. Colonisation of other parts of Scotland, England (especially since 1951 in some southern counties) and the N of Ireland (between 1917 and 1938) has taken place. At the present time potentially the most important breeding area is the Ouse Washes and nearby Nene Washes in Cambridgeshire (Parslow 1973, and Gibbons *et al.* 1993).

The only place where the Pintail bred regularly in the 19th century was on Loch Leven in Fife. Breeding was first recorded there in 1898 when several pairs were noted and nests and eggs found. The numbers breeding at that time indicate that it probably bred for some years before the first nests were found. This breeding group subsequently increased in numbers and spread to surrounding lochs. Elsewhere, breeding had been proven or suspected in a number of areas in Britain and Ireland but all of these records were of sporadic breeding. A record on Dhu Loch, Glendale in Skye in 1889 resulted in the nest being robbed and the adults leaving the area. Earlier records of nests being found and attributed to this species following identification of the nest down (from a loch in Sutherland in 1882 and on Haskeir off Canna, one of the Inner Hebrides, in 1878 and 1881) appear to be either discounted or overlooked by later writers. A series of eggs in the British Museum collection were labelled as taken in Inverness-shire in 1869 and an egg in an Irish collection was said to have been of this species and taken near Abbeyleix in Laois.

Records of breeding Pintail increased during the 20th century, but its scattered distribution and withdrawal from apparently suitable and regular breeding sites suggest that it is not comfortably established in Britain. Breeding is essentially opportunistic and its nesting habits cause it to be par-

Number of counties in which recorded:

Period	Probable breeding		Confirmed breeding		Combined		
	Br	Ir	Br	Ir	Br	Ir	Both
1875–1900	0	0	3	0	3	0	3
1968–1972	4	0	16	3	20	3	23
			change		17	3	20
					567%		667%

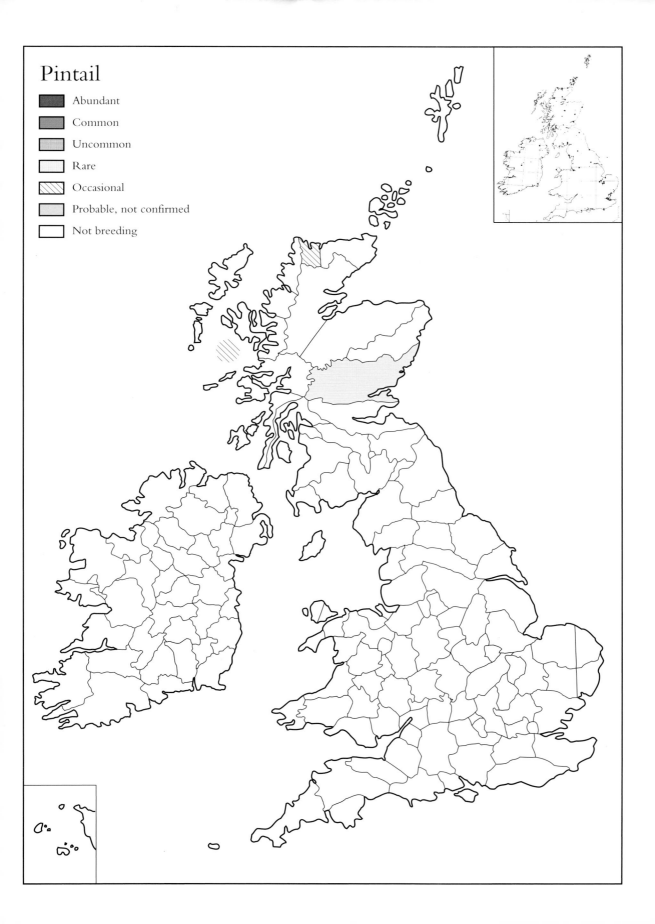

Pintail

- Abundant
- Common
- Uncommon
- Rare
- Occasional
- Probable, not confirmed
- Not breeding

Garganey
(Garganey Teal)

Anas querquedula

The Garganey bred only in E England during the 19th century. Its history there is not clear. Authors of the accounts of the birds of Norfolk based their belief that it bred in that county on circumstantial evidence such as the discovery of partially formed eggs in shot females, the observation of pairs in breeding plumage in summer and the occurrence of 'flappers' (young birds not yet capable of flight) in late summer. This was the case until the first nest was discovered and described in the Broads in 1862. From the 1870s records of nests became more frequent, increasingly so through the remaining decades of the 19th century. At first the Garganey was apparently confined to the Broads district in Norfolk but the apparent increase in the number of reported nests later led some authors to consider that the species was increasing after about 1870 (Gurney and Southwell 1886–87). Other evidence of the possible increase of the Garganey came from Essex where only two records of passage birds were known to Christy (1890) but the number increased following his account and Glegg (1929) was able to note 19 taken in the county during the 1890s. The only breeding record of the Garganey in the 19th century in Essex was of a brood of six raised on the Crouch marshes in 1896. The first record of breeding in Suffolk was in 1873 near Leiston on the coast when a brood of eight or nine was seen. Three further nests were found in the county

during the remainder of the 1870s and other evidence suggested that breeding may have taken place on other occasions. Thereafter, however, proven accounts of breeding ceased until the 20th century suggesting that breeding died out or was very sporadic, although a pair observed in May 1898 in W Suffolk may have had a nest (Ticehurst 1932). In Kent, it was believed that Garganey had probably bred for many years in small numbers but proof of breeding was scarce. It was suspected of doing so in the N Kent marshes, but no nest had been found up to the end of the 19th century; the only positive record of breeding in Kent during the period were the two nests found in Romney Marsh in 1900. The series of breeding records from 1880 on the north side of Teesmouth in Durham gave hope of permanent colonisation of that county, but breeding ceased in 1887, probably due to overshooting. Birds from this group were regularly seen in the adjoining part of Yorkshire and it is probable that the pair that bred in that county in 1882 (and, indeed, may have bred regularly at the site) were from this source (Nelson *et al.* 1907). Prestwick Carr in Northumberland may have held breeding pairs prior to its drainage in about 1855. Only one other accepted record of breeding exists from the 19th century, that of a female and young seen in a marshy meadow near Fareham in Hampshire in 1897. Breeding was believed to have taken place in Cambridgeshire and Huntingdonshire but had evidently ceased prior to the 1890s although no evidence exists to confirm this (Dixon 1893).

The increase in numbers was confirmed during the early 20th century along with a corresponding increase in the number of counties that recorded regular breeding. The increase was attributed to the cessation of spring shooting (Ticehurst 1909) but occurred in England coincidentally with an increase in Scandinavia, especially during the 1930s and 1940s (Parslow 1973). The main increase occurred in SE England, but early in the 20th century the recolonisation of Yorkshire and the first breeding attempts in Somerset led to the establishment of breeding groups there. The increase continued through the 1939–45 war and briefly accelerated in the last few years of the 1940s but ceased about 1952 (Parslow 1973). At the present day the Garganey breeds locally throughout England, sporadically in Scotland and Wales and occasionally in Ireland. Losses of breeding habitat in some areas have contributed to local declines most notably, and importantly, following the drainage of parts of the fens of E England (Gibbons *et al.* 1993).

Number of counties in which recorded:

Period	Probable breeding		Confirmed breeding		Combined		
	Br	Ir	Br	Ir	Br	Ir	Both
1875–1900	0	0	6	0	6	0	6
1968–1972	10	0	29	0	39	0	39
			change		33	0	33
					550%		550%

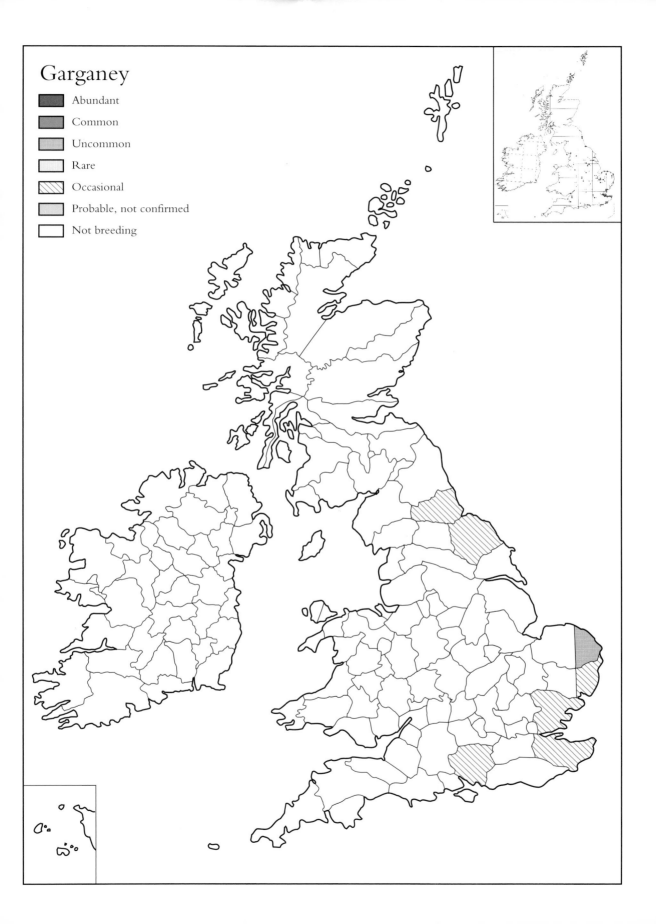

Garganey

- ■ Abundant
- ▨ Common
- ▨ Uncommon
- ☐ Rare
- ▨ Occasional
- ▨ Probable, not confirmed
- ☐ Not breeding

Shoveler (Shoveller)

Anas clypeata

Proven instances of the Shoveler breeding in Britain were rare in the early years of the 19th century. Breeding was known to have taken place regularly (Yarrell 1837–43) in the Norfolk marshes (particularly around Yarmouth) and was still regular, but decreasing, in Romney Marsh, Essex. In other E English counties south from Lincolnshire and in Ireland breeding was suspected at that time but not proven. By the 1850s Norfolk was the only English county where breeding was known to take place, but only a few pairs were said to do so regularly. Macgillivray (1840–42) was not aware of any record of the species in any season in Scotland, attesting to its rarity then, but Selby (1833) believed that the Shoveler bred in Scotland and Berry (1939) commented that the species bred in the Tweed area 100 years before his report was published, perhaps repeating Selby's assertion. In 1843 a nest was found on the shore of the Forth estuary and by 1848 the Shoveler was breeding in the Clyde region. Breeding was suspected but had still not been proven in Ireland (Morris 1851–57, Morris 1855).

Suitable breeding habitat, although it was said to be still rapidly decreasing during the middle of the 19th century through drainage activities, was widespread in Britain and Ireland but the naturalists of the time believed that uncontrolled wildfowling was responsible for the limitation on the numbers of Shoveler breeding, and it was suspected that

this may have been responsible for a diminution in both breeding and wintering numbers from the late 18th century. Numbers continued to fluctuate, and breeding occasionally took place in many counties, until the Act for the Preservation of Wildfowl of 1876 and stricter control of wildfowling licences afforded some protection (Evans 1911). During the last quarter of the 19th century breeding continued to take place irregularly in suitable habitats throughout Britain and Ireland and, noticeably, the old, regular, populations centred in Norfolk and in SE Scotland started to expand. Breeding began to take place regularly in counties bordering these population centres from the 1880s and, aided by the Wild Birds Protection Acts of the 1880s and 1890s in which the Shoveler was specifically protected, by the end of the century, the species was firmly established there. The expansion accelerated into the 20th century.

By the 1930s Shovelers were breeding regularly in all but eight English counties. In Wales the species bred only along the south coastal counties and in Anglesey, and on the Scottish mainland it bred regularly in most counties up to Loch Ness and sporadically elsewhere. It bred regularly on Tiree and irregularly on Islay and parts of the Outer Hebrides and a breeding group had become established in Orkney. Similarly, an increase in numbers had occurred in Ireland but, starting from a more established base in the 19th century, the subsequent increase was not as extensive as elsewhere. Although new sites were colonised locally up to the 1950s, and, overall, numbers may have increased, particularly in England, habitat losses in other areas balanced out much of the increase. The increase in Britain and Ireland was part of the widespread increase noted in W Europe and was probably permitted by an amelioration of summer climate (Voous 1960, Parslow 1973). After the 1950s numbers in protected sites continued to grow and these populations thrived. Elsewhere, however, there are indications of a withdrawal from more marginal sites and those that have become unsuitable through drainage and agricultural changes. Overall, in Britain and Ireland, the population may be reflecting the declining numbers now evident in much of their NW European range (Gibbons *et al.* 1993).

Number of counties in which recorded:

Period	Probable breeding		Confirmed breeding		Combined		
	Br	Ir	Br	Ir	Br	Ir	Both
1875–1900	6	1	33	17	39	18	57
1968–1972	2	2	78	10	80	12	92
			change		41	−6	35
					105%	−33%	61%

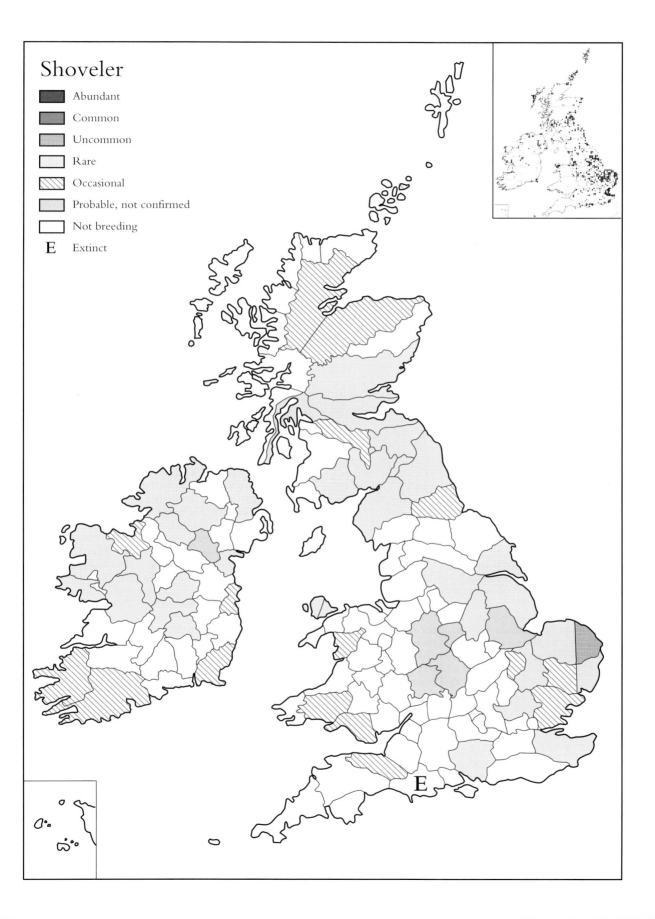

Shoveler

- Abundant
- Common
- Uncommon
- Rare
- Occasional
- Probable, not confirmed
- Not breeding
- E Extinct

Pochard

Aythya ferina

The earliest published reference to the Pochard breeding in Britain appears to be the note in the Catalogue of Norfolk Birds (Sheppard and Whitear 1826) that it bred at Scoulton Mere and had done so since, at least, 1818. In August 1827 three Pochards shot on Hickling Broad turned out to have been birds of the year and may have bred there. 'Flappers' were noted regularly from Scoulton after 1827 but, by the 1840s, Pochards no longer bred there (Lubbock 1845). Adults were periodically seen in May, June and July on a number of Norfolk waters throughout the next few decades but no firmer indication of breeding was recorded until 1875 when both eggs and young were found on Stanford and Tomston Meres in the southwest of the county. By the 1880s Pochards were breeding here in some numbers but there was no evidence that they bred anywhere else in the county.

Norfolk was the only county in which Yarrell (1837–43) knew breeding had taken place. Then, in June 1844 a female was shot from a nest on Scarborough Mere in Yorkshire. Pochards bred here for some years subsequently but died out during the second half of the century. In 1854 it became apparent that they bred on Hornsea Mere 'in considerable numbers'; in 1881 up to 50 pairs were present there and protection of the colony allowed it to thrive

throughout the rest of the century. During the 1860s breeding began to take place in the Wakefield area from which it evidently spread to other waters in the area.

More (1865) was able to add Hertfordshire to the list of counties in which the Pochard was known to breed. It colonised Tring Reservoir in about 1850 and rapidly increased—50–80 nests were found there each year around 1887. The marshes of the Blackwater estuary in Essex became a regular breeding site from 1886 when a pair successfully bred. By 1888 16 or 17 pairs bred in the area and did so throughout the rest of the century. During the last couple of decades of the 19th century the Pochard was recorded breeding in a number of other English counties although some (for instance in Kent) were the descendants of pinioned stock.

The first definite indication of breeding in Scotland took place in 1871 when a pair bred on Loch Awe in Argyll (although it was suspected of breeding on Loch Loy, Moray in 1848 by St John (1863), a site at which it has subsequently bred). The main colonisation of the southeast of the country, however, took place northwards to Perthshire from the late 1870s or 1880s. The spread continued northwards and reached Moray and Nairn in the 1880s and 1890s and, perhaps, Sutherland in 1887 and possibly even earlier (Baxter and Rintoul (1922), however, dispute this). The spread into the southwest began later. In 1893 the Pochard was found breeding on moorland lochs in Wigtownshire. It had occasionally, by the 1890s, been discovered breeding on some of the Western Isles (for instance on Loch Bhassapol, Tiree from 1891 until at least 1913) and Orkney. The colonisation of W Scotland may have resulted from birds that were released or escaped from Lord Dunmore's wildfowl collection. It seems probable that the breeding record on Harris in 1892 was from this source and his Lordship was known to set birds free at this time (Baxter and Rintoul 1922, A. Fox in litt.).

The increase continued into the 20th century. Numbers increased steadily up to the 1930s and resulted in Pochards breeding locally throughout England, E Wales, Anglesey and S Scotland. At this point numbers stabilised in Scotland (and the breeding range may even have begun to retract). Shortly after the 1939–45 war the Pochard increased markedly in Kent. The main breeding site here is in the marshes in the north of the county. Elsewhere in the southeast increases at about this time have been attributed to the spread of birds introduced into the London parks. Although colonised in 1907 (breeding was first proven in Roscommon), Ireland has never held breeding colonies of any size; breeding today takes place regularly only in Roscommon, Cork and on Lough Neagh.

Number of counties in which recorded:

Period	Probable breeding		Confirmed breeding		Combined		
	Br	Ir	Br	Ir	Br	Ir	Both
1875–1900	1	0	19	0	20	0	20
1968–1972	2	6	71	6	73	12	85
			change		53	12	65
					265%		325%

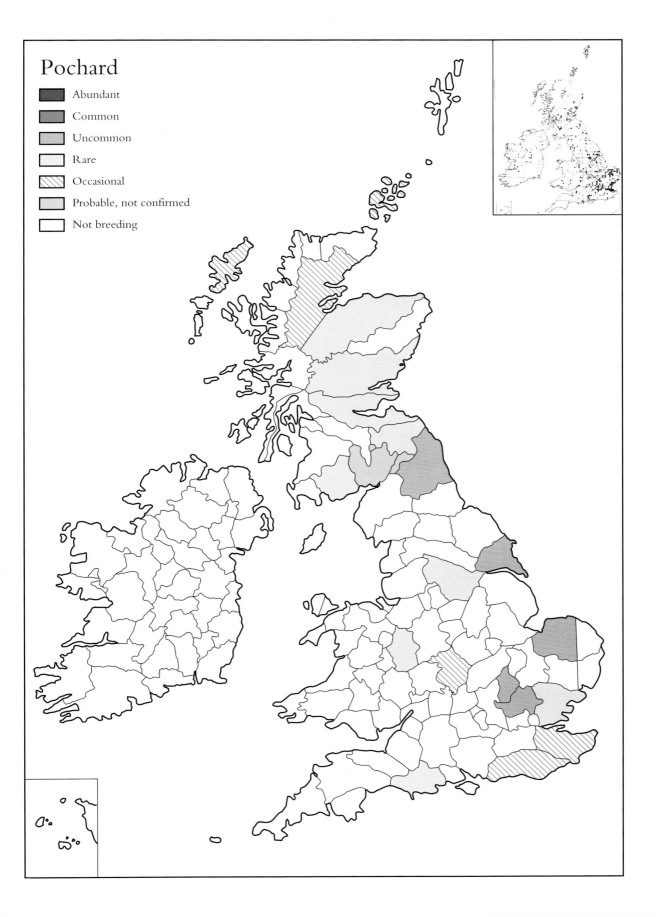

Pochard

- Abundant
- Common
- Uncommon
- Rare
- Occasional
- Probable, not confirmed
- Not breeding

Tufted Duck

Aythya fuligula

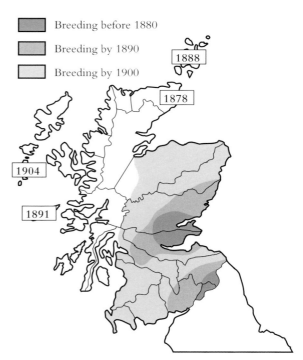

Breeding before 1880
Breeding by 1890
Breeding by 1900

1888
1878
1904
1891

The extension of the breeding range of the Tufted Duck in Scotland during the 19th century.
(adapted from Harvie-Brown 1906).

The Tufted Duck was known only as a regular but uncommon winter visitor to Britain during most of the first half of the 19th century. The first dated breeding records came from Malham, Yorkshire and Osberton, Nottinghamshire in 1849 but both counties claimed evidence of earlier breeding. In Yorkshire it was said to have remained throughout the summer at Hornsea Mere in the East Riding for a few years prior to 1849. Whitaker (1907) inferred that pairs were nesting on Rainworth waters in Nottinghamshire in the 1830s and that before that they did so on the decoy lake at Park Hall. In 1872 Whitaker found nearly 20 pairs breeding on various waters in the county and believed that many more did so on waters that he had not visited. Other early records came from Derbyshire and Sussex, where the Tufted Duck bred occasionally from about 1853. Other counties recorded breeding from the 1870s but a rapid increase became apparent in England from the 1880s when groups became established in S England and the Midlands. It was suggested (in, for instance, Cheshire and Norfolk) that the Wild Birds Protection Acts, especially that of 1880, by enforcing a closed season for shooting, allowed the rapid increase in numbers and range that became apparent from the mid 1880s.

Although there were no very early records, the spread of the Tufted Duck in Scotland paralleled that of England. This increase may have been fuelled by the colonisation of Northumberland in 1858, where breeding took place regularly from the 1870s, and from colonisations around the Firth of Tay (see map).

Breeding was first proven in Ireland during the late 1870s at Lower Lough Erne. From that time the Tufted Duck was recorded from many other waters from the Shannon to those of the northeast by, at least, *ca* 1880. This led Ussher and Warren (1900) to postulate that the colonisation of Ireland must have taken place many years before 1877.

Most English counties were colonised by 1912 and most English waters by the 1930s. The increase continued in Scotland and occasional breeding had taken place in parts of Wales and SW England by the 1930s. Berry (1939) wrote that, in Scotland, only Shetland, the NW Highlands and parts of Argyll remained to be colonised. The increase has continued to the present day, the proliferation of new flooded gravel pits and reservoirs since the 1939–45 war being a significant factor in both the spread in range and increase in abundance of the species. In addition, the introduction, spread and increase of the zebra mussel (*Dreissera polymorpha*), first recorded in Britain in 1824, has also been implicated in the Tufted Duck's prosperity, being a major food item (D. Hill in litt). The apparent lack of Tufted Duck in a line from Cape Clear to Dundalk Bay during the 19th century is mirrored by the *68-72 Atlas*, supporting the view that the number of lakes more than one ha in size is a limiting factor in the distribution of the species in Ireland (D. Hill in litt).

Number of counties in which recorded:

Period	Probable breeding		Confirmed breeding		Combined		
	Br	Ir	Br	Ir	Br	Ir	Both
1875–1900	1	4	27	13	28	17	45
1968-1972	0	0	69	4	69	4	73
	change				41	-13	28
					146%	-76%	62%

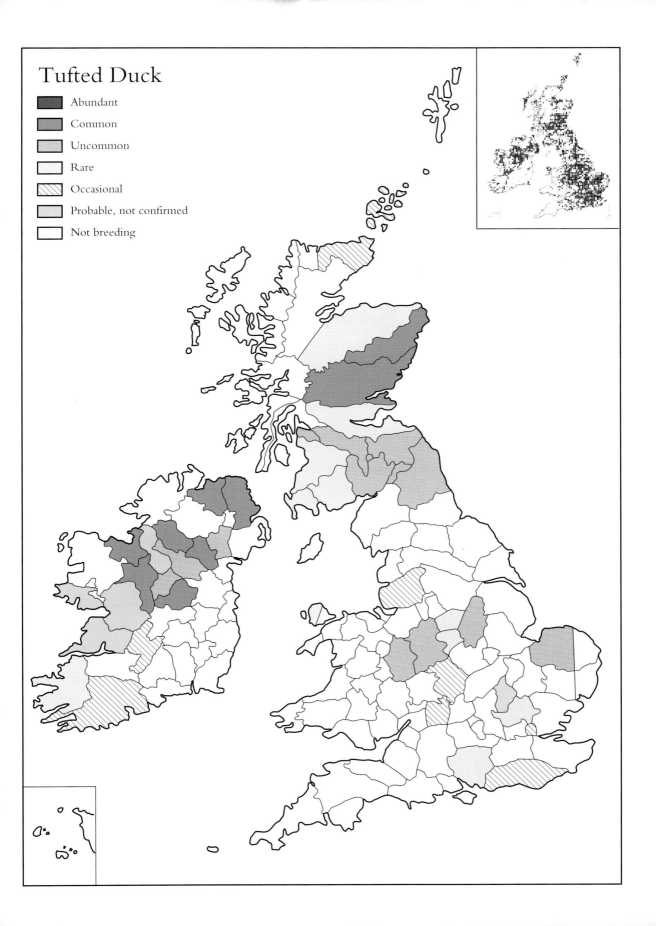

Tufted Duck

- **Abundant**
- **Common**
- **Uncommon**
- Rare
- Occasional
- Probable, not confirmed
- Not breeding

Scaup (Scaup Duck)

Aythya marila

Selby (1835) recorded that a single female Scaup shot by Jardine in Sutherland in 1834 was accompanied by a young bird that escaped. This was between Lochs Eriboll and Hope on the north coast. In June 1868 an adult male was shot on a loch in W Sutherland which 'from the bird's unwillingness to leave, even when repeatedly shot at' led the shooter to consider that a female and nest were hidden nearby (Harvie-Brown and Buckley 1887). The species was reported to have bred in Orkney prior to 1890 (Buckley and Harvie-Brown 1891) and a clutch of seven Scaup eggs was reputedly taken at Tentsmuir in 1880 (reported in Berry 1939 but not fully referenced) but there is considerable doubt about both records (A. Fox in litt.). The first published authenticated record of a nest was by Noble (1899) in which he recounted that he had found a nest with eggs in rushes on an island in an unidentified Sutherland loch in the year of publication. This was not the earliest record, however. Some years later, after many rumours circulating amongst Scottish naturalists and much discussion in the natural history journals, it became clear that two pairs bred in South Uist in the Outer Hebrides in 1897. Scaup bred at the same site again in 1898 and 1899 and were recorded there on a number of occasions subsequently. These are all of the 19th century breeding records of the Scaup.

The 20th century nesting records are summarised in the accompanying table.

It seems likely that the Scaup may breed further south than its normal N Holarctic range during periods of a cooler climate. It seems significant that there was only one breeding record between the 1914–18 and 1939–45 wars, a warm climatic period in Britain (Sharrock 1976). In general, however, this species favours shallow, eutrophic, brackish waters which are rare habitat away from Orkney, the Western Isles and the Mullet Peninsula in Ireland. Since none of these areas is showing great change, it seems likely that breeding on the edge of its range in this way will always be sporadic at the few suitable sites (A. Fox in litt.).

Year	Location	Notes
1900-13	South Uist	Up to three pairs bred or were suspected of doing so in six years.
1939	Caithness	A brood was recorded.
1944	Lincolnshire	A female and young brood were seen at Tetney.
1946	West Ross	One pair bred on a coastal island.
1954-66	Orkney	Up to three pairs bred or were suspected of doing so in eight years at two sites.
1969	Orkney and North Uist	One pair bred at each site
1970	Perthshire	Three nests were suspected.
1971	Angus	One pair bred.
1973-79	Orkney	A single pair bred in three years on Mainland.
1988-91	Caithness, West Ross and Anglesey	One pair bred at each site.
1989	Lincolnshire	One pair bred.
1990	'Scotland North'	One pair bred.

Sources: Baxter and Rintoul 1953, Sharrock 1976, Batten *et al.* 1990, Gibbons *et al.* 1993.

Number of counties in which recorded:

Period	Probable breeding		Confirmed breeding		Combined		
	Br	Ir	Br	Ir	Br	Ir	Both
1875–1900	0	0	1	0	1	0	1
1968-1972	0	0	4	0	4	0	4
			change		3	0	3
					300%		300%

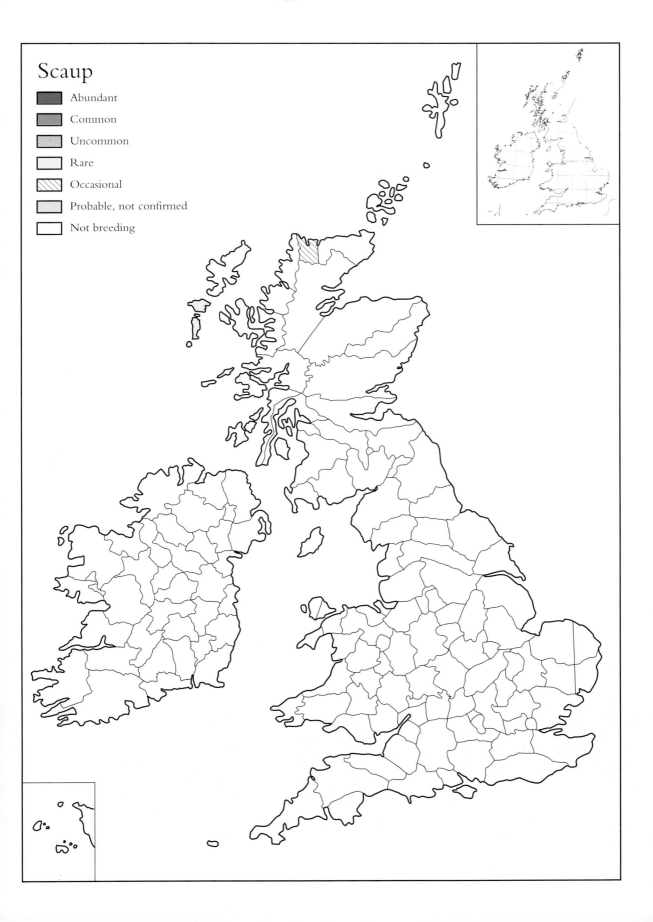

Scaup

- **Abundant**
- **Common**
- **Uncommon**
- **Rare**
- **Occasional**
- **Probable, not confirmed**
- **Not breeding**

Eider

Somateria mollissima

Eiders had been recorded breeding on Scottish islands for many centuries, but were not recorded from the Scottish mainland until 1807. Since then this species has increased greatly in numbers and range, apparently most rapidly from about the 1850s onwards.

The Eider was evidently overlooked in Shetland in the early 1800s. It was Saxby's (1874) opinion that it bred more numerously in the early part of the century but had decreased until about 1861 when numbers stabilised, especially in the northern isles. The decline was the result of shooting, both for food and for sport. Fewer adults were apparently shot in the late 1800s, and numbers may, indeed, have increased somewhat from the 1880s (Baxter and Rintoul 1953).

In Orkney the Eider was known to breed in only a few places on some of the northern islands during the first half of the 19th century and numbers were evidently kept down by the islanders, who ate both birds and eggs. Following protection on some islands numbers increased substantially, for example from a few to about 200 pairs on Eynhallow, an islet off Rousay, by 1887.

Prior to 1850, in the Outer Hebrides the Eider bred only around the Sound of Harris and on North Rona but then increased substantially. It bred for the first time on North Uist in about 1860 and from there populated many other islands in the group by 1888. Along with Haskeir, Colonsay seems to have been the centre of the Eider's range expansion. Local tradition had it that the Eider was introduced to Colonsay from Norway about the end of the 9th century. Whatever the truth of this the Eider bred numerously on this island in the 19th century and, from the 1870s, spread to most of the other islands in the group. It was not, however, recorded breeding on the Argyll coast before the end of the century.

Up to the 1880s Eiders were scarce in Sutherland, only a few nest sites on islets off the north coast being known, but in the 1890s many apparently invaded the west coast. Eiders did not breed on the Caithness mainland; however, eggs were taken on the Pentland Skerries in about 1885. Skye appears to have been colonised via the Ascrib Islands. The first nests were found on the Ascribs in 1884 but were robbed. At around this time the first summer birds were noted on the N coast of Skye, and the West Ross mainland seems to have been colonised during the late 1890s. By the end of the century, however, breeding was still uncommon in this region. On the eastern mainland coast the Eider bred more commonly. In Dee it bred mainly around the mouth of the Ythan, and here it was abundant. Further south it had evidently bred for a number of years. Nests were easy to find in 1850 in Fife and Eiders here increased in numbers, but not in breeding range, through the 19th century. The Eider had bred sporadically on the Berwickshire coast for many years and, since the first record in 1807, it bred commonly on the East Lothian coast. It bred in fluctuating numbers on the islands of May (first mentioned in 1638), Bass (heavily persecuted but a few pairs bred each year), Fidra, Eyebroughty, Inchkeith, Inchcolm and the Lamb.

The only English breeding site was on the islands off the Northumbrian coast. From at least 1840 the Eider nested irregularly on Coquet Island but persecution caused its extinction probably during the 1870s. It had bred in small numbers on Holy Island and occasionally at Ross Links on the adjoining coast but its main haunt was the Farne Islands. Here too persecution had curtailed numbers until protection was organised by the Northumbrian County Society. In 1895 150 broods were hatched on the islands.

The increase noted during the latter half of the 19th century continued through the 20th. The Eider continued to increase on the W coast of Scotland and spread southwards to breed in some numbers on the SW Scottish coast and, in 1949, to colonise Walney. The early breeding records off the Northumberland coast led to regular breeding by the 1930s and the first nest in Ireland was found (on an island off the W Donegal coast) in 1912.

Number of counties in which recorded:

Period	Probable breeding		Confirmed breeding		Combined		
	Br	Ir	Br	Ir	Br	Ir	Both
1875–1900	0	0	13	0	13	0	13
1968–1972	1	0	24	5	25	5	30
			change		12	5	17
					92%		131%

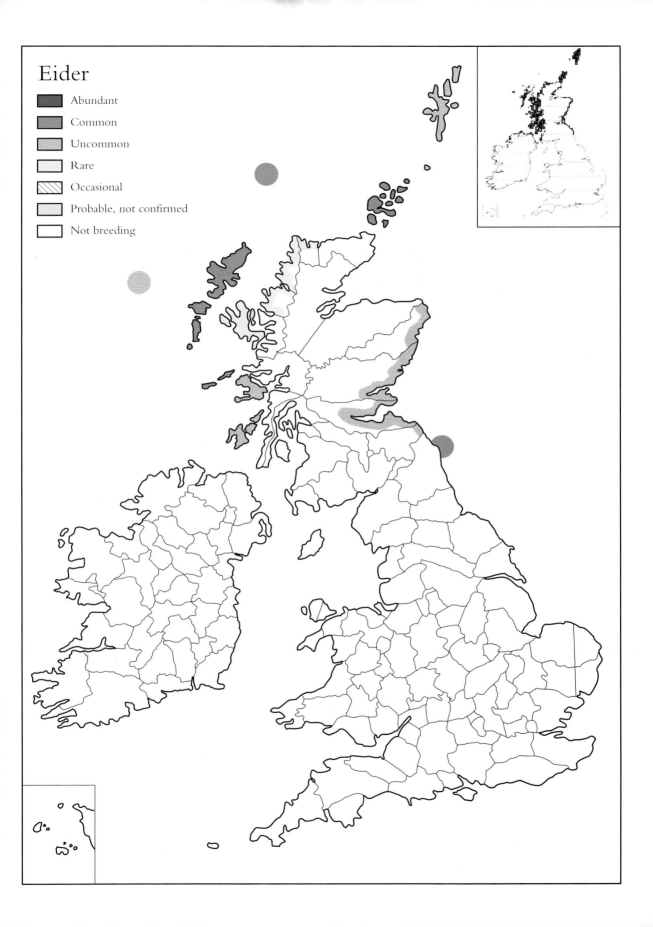

Eider

- **Abundant**
- **Common**
- **Uncommon**
- **Rare**
- **Occasional**
- **Probable, not confirmed**
- **Not breeding**

Common Scoter (Black Scoter)

Melanitta nigra

The Common Scoter was unknown as a breeding species in Britain before the middle of the 19th century (Yarrell 1837–43, Morris 1851–57, Morris 1855). On the authority of Dunbar, More (1865) was able to confirm breeding on the moors of Caithness, especially around Thurso where it bred on one or two lochs there. Evidently, however, Dunbar's first record was from the side of a loch in NE Sutherland in 1855 but it is unclear whether his records demonstrate recent colonisation of Scotland. The Common Scoter had long been known as a winter visitor to the coast of NE Scotland; the number of accounts of the ingenious means employed in their capture indicates that local people were familiar with them. Visits to these remote areas by sportsmen, collectors and naturalists were uncommon before the second half of the 19th century and so a small population may have bred there, undiscovered for many years. The subsequent slow spread into other parts of Scotland, however, suggests that it is possible that Sutherland and Caithness were colonised sometime during the first half of the 19th century.

The status of the Common Scoter in Caithness had changed little by the closing years of the 19th century, only a handful of regular sites being known. Records of breeding in Sutherland were few and did not occur further west than Tongue. The Common Scoter evidently bred in very few numbers along the NE coast but there are hardly any dated records. Nevertheless it seems probable that it bred in Cromarty and Inverness-shire. In 1897 nesting was recorded on Tiree, where, although the nest was not found, the adults and five young were seen. A record of breeding on the Earnly Marshes near Chichester, Sussex in 1891 (Dixon 1895), if accurate, probably referred to escaped birds.

Up to the 1930s breeding was recorded sporadically from other parts of Scotland. Breeding was first proven in Shetland in 1911, Ross-shire in 1913 and Perthshire in 1921 (one can speculate that the Tiree record indicates that sporadic breeding may have occurred in W Scotland during the closing years of the 19th century). After the 1930s breeding became more regular, especially in Shetland and the W Highlands.

The most important development during the 20th century was the colonisation of, and subsequent increase at, Lower Lough Erne in Fermanagh in 1905. This site became the most important in Britain and Ireland although, from about 1970, numbers of Common Scoters there declined substantially. A number of other sites became established in Ireland, particularly in Mayo, from 1948, and overall numbers there have remained broadly stable.

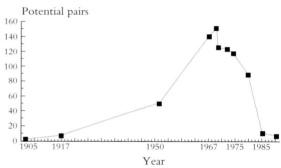

The number of potential pairs of Common Scoter on Lough Erne, 1905–1900. Numbers prior to 1967 are an approximation.

Sources: 1905–50 (Hutchinson 1989); 1967–91 (88–91 Atlas)

Number of counties in which recorded:

Period	Probable breeding		Confirmed breeding		Combined		
	Br	Ir	Br	Ir	Br	Ir	Both
1875–1900	1	0	2	0	3	0	3
1968–1972	0	0	9	2	9	2	11
			change		6	2	9
					200%		300%

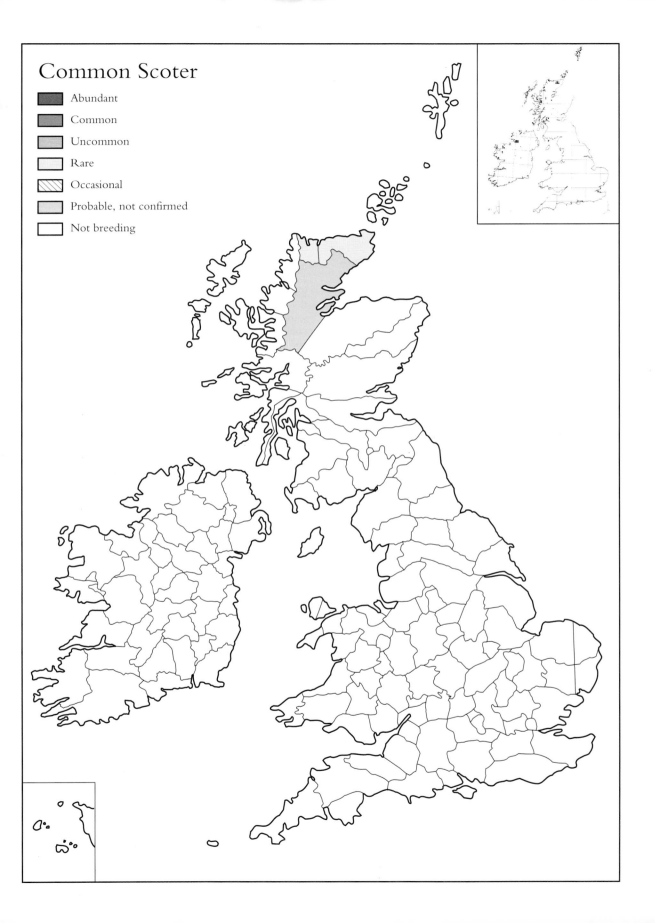

Common Scoter

- Abundant
- Common
- Uncommon
- Rare
- Occasional
- Probable, not confirmed
- Not breeding

Red-breasted Merganser

Mergus serrator

The Red-breasted Merganser bred throughout the Scottish mainland north of the Clyde and Forth valleys and most of the off-shore islands during 1875–1900. This line formed the effective southern boundary of the species' breeding range in Britain although occasional breeding was recorded a little further south. In Ireland it was a species of the upland and moorland areas and so was absent from many of the intensively farmed eastern and southern counties. The comparatively well populated Irish midlands supported breeding populations on the larger loughs there.

During the first three or four decades of the 19th century the Red-breasted Merganser bred only in W Scotland and apparently no further south than Loch Awe in Argyll (Yarrell 1837–43). By the mid 1860s its southern breeding limit had extended at least as far as Loch Lomond, Argyll (More 1865) and it was described as breeding commonly there by the end of the century. Evidence seems to suggest that a fairly rapid southerly expansion was underway at this time as, although only sporadic, nesting was recorded near the Ayrshire coast from 1867 on (Paton and Pike 1929). The species was first recorded breeding in the Forth region,

on Loch Coulter, in 1867 (Rintoul and Baxter 1935) and it quickly spread to other lochs. Neither Yarrell nor Morris (1851–57) had recorded breeding on the eastern side of Scotland and early reviews of the historical status of the Red-breasted Merganser in Scotland suggest that it did not breed there until the 1860s or 1870s. Harvie-Brown surmised that an extension of range began, in an easterly and southerly direction, from about the middle of the 19th century. He added that the expansion in the east was inhibited by persecution from gamekeepers and ghillies who were unfamiliar with the species but conscious of the apparent competition for salmon. At the end of the 19th century the Red-breasted Merganser still bred most commonly in the west and north of mainland Scotland, especially in N Argyll and the Northern Isles.

Up to around 1930 records confirmed the continuing southward spread. By this time the Red-breasted Merganser was breeding commonly in Dumfriesshire and fairly so in Kirkcudbrightshire although it had not colonised the gap between its southern breeding limit in 1900 and the Solway counties. After the 1930s the expansion slowed somewhat, but the Red-breasted Merganser continued to consolidate its initial expansion in, especially, the Moray and Solway regions. In Ireland, by the 1930s, the species' breeding distribution had changed a little—Cork was colonised in around 1920, Wexford in 1929 and breeding had been confirmed in Longford, Antrim and Armagh.

The Red-breasted Merganser was first recorded breeding in England in 1950 in Cumberland. After this the species spread rapidly to Westmorland, N Lancashire and NW Yorkshire. In 1953 it colonised N Wales when a pair bred in Anglesey. It spread to the Welsh mainland in 1957 when it nested in Merioneth, and breeding first took place in Caernarvonshire in 1958. By the time of the *68–72 Atlas* pairs were apparently breeding in the Peak district of Derbyshire, proved doing so in 1973, and an outlying pair bred in Glamorgan. The species was scarce in S and E Ireland and was extinct in a few counties in which breeding had been recorded in around 1900. In the period between the *68–72* and *88–91 Atlases*, further changes apparently took place. Thinning of the central and SW Scottish populations was complemented by increases in the breeding range of the Derbyshire and Welsh populations. The suspected long-term decline in Ireland was borne out by a number of losses throughout the interior of the country, suggesting that a retreat to the north and northwest coasts is taking place. The effect of the large-scale persecution that takes place in both Ireland and Scotland is unknown but cannot be ignored as a contributory factor to the declines in both countries.

Number of counties in which recorded:

Period	Probable breeding		Confirmed breeding		Combined		
	Br	Ir	Br	Ir	Br	Ir	Both
1875–1900	0	5	20	16	20	21	41
1968–1972	2	0	38	20	40	20	60
			change		20	-1	19
					100%	-5%	46%

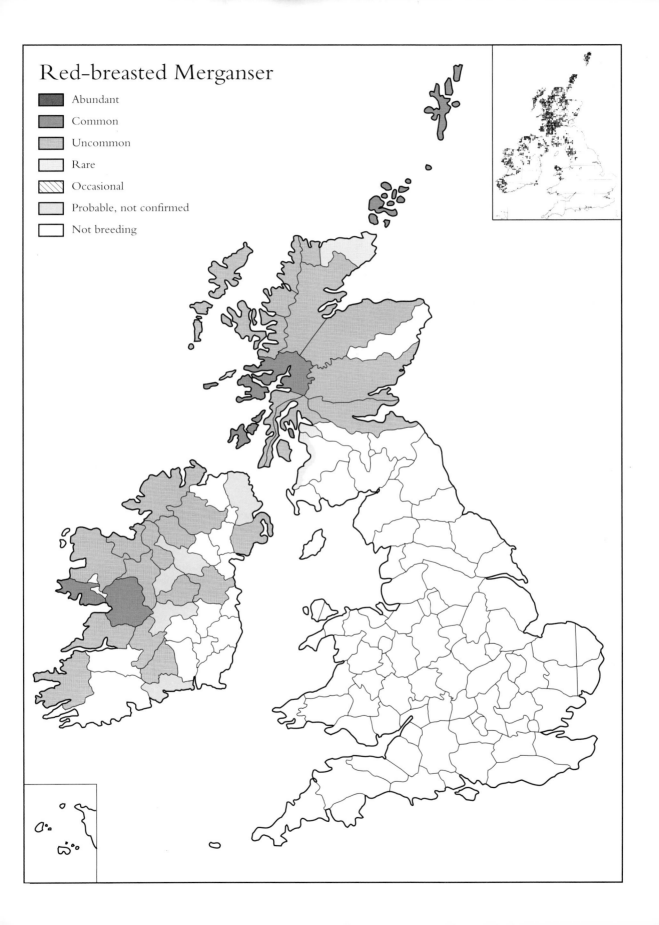

Red-breasted Merganser

- **Abundant**
- **Common**
- **Uncommon**
- **Rare**
- **Occasional**
- **Probable, not confirmed**
- **Not breeding**

Goosander

Mergus merganser

For most of the 19th century the Goosander was recorded only as an occasional winter visitor to many English counties and a regular visitor in Scotland, particularly to the Western Isles, Orkney, Sutherland, Caithness and East Lothian. (Morris 1851-57). Low (1813) asserted that the Goosander once bred in Orkney (i.e. sometime during the 18th century) but it did not do so during the 19th century (Morris 1851-57). There were no further claims of breeding Goosanders in Scotland until those of Gray (1871). He recounted Dewar's assertion that a duck was shot, and the eggs taken, from a nest near Loch Maddy on North Uist, Western Isles in 1858. Gray also stated that a site on the northwest side of the island held breeding Goosanders and that he had received eggs, said to have been of this species, from South Uist in 1862. Harvie-Brown and Buckley (1888) discounted these records, particularly in view of the early dates, although Harvie-Brown (1906) did assert that the species had bred in Perthshire from 1864. Throughout the rest of that decade breeding was suspected at a number of sites but it was not until 1871 that the first widely accepted breeding record occurred. This was of a clutch of ten eggs and nest down taken from a hollow tree at Loch Ericht in Perthshire (Harvie-Brown 1906); later in the same year, a female Goosander and seven ducklings were seen on Loch Awe, Argyll (Harvie-Brown and Buckley 1892).

Thereafter, the Goosander became increasingly regularly recorded in summer in W Scotland and breeding became

more frequent. During the last three decades of the 19th century Goosanders colonised parts of Argyll, Sutherland, Ross-shire, parts of the Moray Basin and Tay.

The Goosander rapidly increased in Argyll so that Harvie-Brown and Buckley (1892) were able to record that breeding was not uncommon throughout the region. Breeding was confined at this point, however, to the mainland. The earliest record of a nest of the Goosander in the NW Highlands was at Loch Fionn, West Ross in 1876 although Harvie-Brown and Macpherson (1904) considered that it may have first bred in the area about 1870. It then spread rapidly east into N Moray and, simultaneously, north, nesting on Loch Assynt in 1878, and thence into W Sutherland. Goosanders soon colonised Inverness-shire (in 1892) and Nairnshire (in 1895) and probably spread via Findhorn, Moray, eastwards and northwards along the coast to Sutherland. Perthshire was also rapidly colonised. A female with a brood was seen on Loch Rannoch in 1872 and then an influx into the area in 1875/76 was followed by more breeding records. A pair nested on the Teith, in Perthshire in 1877 and another in the early 1880s, and breeding was subsequently recorded there throughout the century. In 1879, a pair of Goosanders bred in a hollow tree on Loch Achray and another on an island on the Tay, and by 1890 they were considered to have multiplied rapidly in the Tay region, especially in the west.

In the early 20th century the Goosander consolidated its Scottish range and slowly spread southwards, occasionally breeding as far south as Dumfriesshire (first colonised on the Annan in 1926). This situation continued until the 1940s when the Goosander spead into England. Although summering Goosanders had been noted since the 1920s, breeding was first proven in Northumberland in 1941 and in Cumberland in 1950. Up to around 1965 its numbers gradually increased in these counties but in NW Scotland and Berwickshire the population was severely reduced by fishermen protecting fish stocks. This persecution may have been responsible for checking the species' southward spread (Meek and Little 1977).

From the mid 1960s further, southward, expansion was evident. Breeding was confirmed for the first time in Durham (1965), NW Yorkshire (1970) and N Lancashire (1973). First breeding records occurred during the *68-72 Atlas* survey for Ireland and Wales (Cardiganshire). Major colonisations of parts of N England, parts of the lower Pennines, Devon and Cornwall have taken place but the major increase in numbers has occurred in Wales, with much of the uplands being colonised, and from this area east into Shropshire (1987) and Herefordshire (1988). There appear to have been some losses throughout Scotland, and the major limitation on numbers appears still to be persecution by fishermen (Gibbons *et al.* 1993).

Number of counties in which recorded:

Period	Probable breeding		Confirmed breeding		Combined		
	Br	Ir	Br	Ir	Br	Ir	Both
1875–1900	0	0	9	0	9	0	9
1968–1972	0	0	26	1	26	1	27
			change		17	1	18
					189%		200%

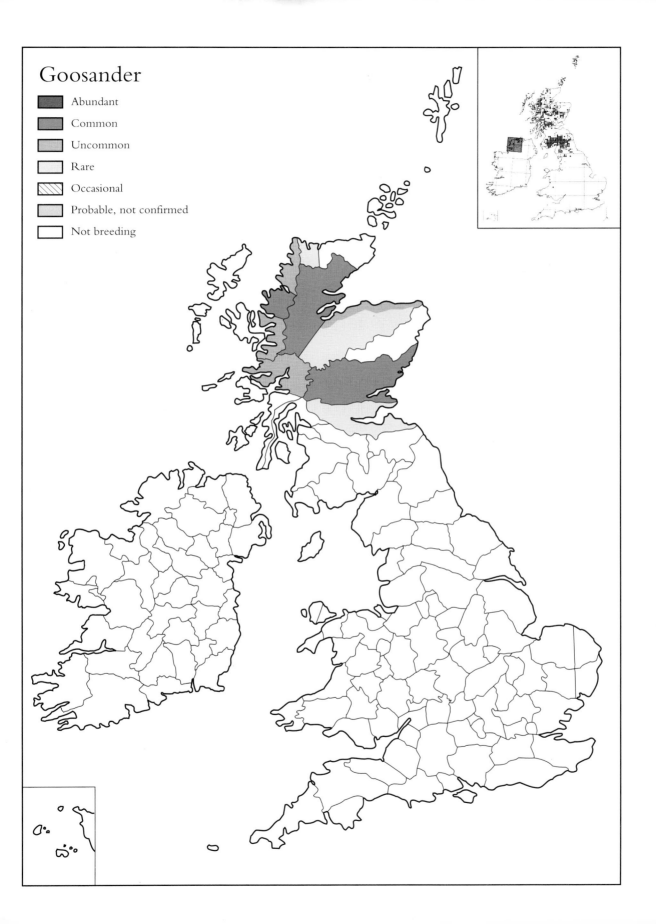

Goosander

- **Abundant**
- **Common**
- **Uncommon**
- **Rare**
- **Occasional**
- **Probable, not confirmed**
- **Not breeding**

Honey Buzzard

Pernis apivorus

At no time in written ornithological history has the Honey Buzzard been anything but a rare summer visitor in Britain. In the 1800s, as now, the species attracted a lot of interest on the rare occasions when it was found breeding. Sporadic breeding evidently occurred widely, but the New Forest was the main regular breeding area. Even here, though, an apparent decline was taking place.

In the first record outside the New Forest, a female was shot off her nest in Wellgrove Wood near Henley-on-Thames, Oxfordshire in early July 1838; two eggs were taken from the nest and the male was shot soon after. In Nottinghamshire, of 14 Honey Buzzards recorded trapped or shot between 1842 and 1905, eight were taken in late spring or summer and so may have been breeding. A pair were shot whilst nest building in Waverley Wood, Warwickshire in June 1841, and a nest was taken and an adult bird shot near Coventry in 1867. Evidence of a nesting attempt in Staffordshire from an estate near the Shropshire border is not conclusive: a bird shot on the nest there in 1841 was first considered to have been a Goshawk but was not preserved and the eggs were subsequently ascribed to a Honey Buzzard. The female of a pair trapped at Clungunford, Shropshire in June 1865 on dissection was believed to have recently laid eggs. An earlier undated record also exists for Shropshire. Breeding was most regularly recorded from the New Forest. Gilbert White (1789) wrote about one of the nests, 'A pair of honey buzzards … built them a large shallow nest, composed of twigs and lined with dead beechen leaves, upon a tall slender beech near the middle of Selborne Hanger [Hampshire], in the summer of 1780'. The single egg was taken and, later, the female was shot. Since then, Hampshire has been famous for its breeding Honey Buzzards but published records show that the species was collected almost to extinction in the county by the end of the 19th century. At least 16 nests were recorded taken in the New Forest during the 1860s, the principal period of collecting, following publication of nesting sites

by Wise (1862). In the 1870s only three nests were recorded and between 1880 and the end of the century there was only one definite breeding attempt. Between 1880 and 1915 the Hon. G. Lascelles, the Deputy Surveyor in the New Forest, aided by a team of watchers, took great pains to protect the nests of the Honey Buzzard. Local folklore suggests that the team withheld much information about the species in the New Forest, that the published records of breeding were only the tip of the iceberg and that the species was more numerous than the literature suggests (C. R. Tubbs in litt.). The first Herefordshire breeding record is of a female shot and three eggs taken from a nest in Newent Wood a few years prior to 1869. The male was recorded shot a few days earlier. An adult male and two young reported shot in Whitfield Woods were sent to a taxidermist in Hereford in 1880. Honey Buzzards were recorded as having bred in 1877 in the same woods, and, in 1895, at Bishop's Wood, Ross, eggs were taken and the nesting adults killed. First year birds, probably from Wyre Forest, were taken to a Gloucestershire stuffer in 1878, 1879 and 1880. A number of early records suggest that the Honey Buzzard bred in Durham. Two birds of the year were shot near Sunderland in 1831. Hancock (1874) considered it one of the commonest of the large birds of prey in Durham; this was probably a result of the decline of other raptors, not of any increase in Honey Buzzard numbers. Hancock did not record any nests but did say that a number of first year birds were taken, sometimes two or three together. The only well-authenticated breeding record was of a nest found with two young in a beech tree in 1897 at Gibside in the Derwent Valley. An adult and a barely fledged bird were subsequently sent to the bird stuffers. The same nest was repaired but no eggs were laid in 1898; breeding was suspected in nearby Shotley Bridge in 1899. Evidence that breeding had taken place here in 1896 and up to 1899 was given by Temperley (1951). The young of a nest were shot near Hexham, Northumberland in 1841. A record of a male shot and three eggs taken from a nest near Abergeldie, Aberdeenshire was undated but two eggs and the male and female were taken from a nest near Ballogie in 1867. Honey Buzzards were seen around a wood in East Ross for five or six summers prior to a nest being found and two eggs taken in June 1871.

The 20th century status of the Honey Buzzard has not changed from that of the 19th, with up to a handful of pairs breeding in the Hampshire New Forest and less regular breeding taking place elsewhere (especially in S England and Scotland). The total population is possibly about 30 pairs (Batten *et al.* 1990).

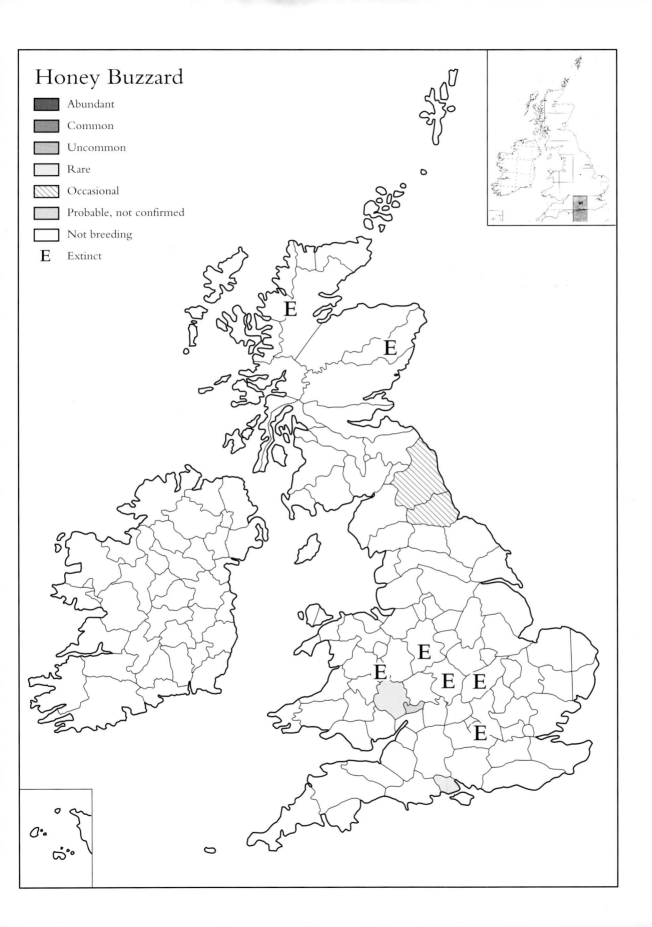

Honey Buzzard

- ███ Abundant
- ███ Common
- ███ Uncommon
- ░░░ Rare
- ▨ Occasional
- ▦ Probable, not confirmed
- ☐ Not breeding
- **E** Extinct

Red Kite
(Gled, Glead)

Milvus milvus

At the beginning of the 19th century the Red Kite bred throughout Britain, and only in areas of SE England had it clearly become extinct prior to this time. The decline was likely to have begun in the 17th and 18th centuries. The Red Kite was valued as a useful scavenger in towns and cities, and was therefore protected—as sanitation improved so this protection lapsed (Rintoul and Baxter 1935). The speed of the decline in the late 18th and 19th centuries was striking and suggestions were made at the time to account for it, in the belief that persecution alone could not have been responsible. Locally, in the early 19th century, storms removed many large nesting trees (Harvie-Brown 1906) and a series of severe winters caused high winter mortality (Lilford 1895). However, persecution certainly had the largest effect throughout the century; the Red Kite was an easy bird to shoot, trap or poison and some were killed by tackle makers to make fishing flies, the tail feathers being particularly in demand for this purpose (Rintoul and Baxter 1935). The last English breeding attempts probably took place in Shropshire. A dated record exists from near Bishop's Castle, Shropshire in 1863 when a female was shot from its nest, but Kites probably bred into the mid 1870s near Ludlow (Beckwith 1887–93).

In Scotland the Red Kite was generally distributed throughout up to about the middle of the 19th century but declined rapidly thereafter. By the 1860s the species was found regularly only in Inverness-shire, Perthshire and Aberdeenshire (Gray 1871) but regular breeding ceased during the 1870s although occasional breeding pairs were recorded into the 1880s. The 'last of the old race' was said to have been killed at Glen Garry, Inverness-shire in 1882 but a clutch of eggs taken in Caithness in 1884 was presented to the British Museum and Red Kites may have

bred on Skye as late as 1886 (Baxter and Rintoul 1953).

From 1890 breeding was confined to Wales. It had ceased in the Cardiganshire Teifi valley before 1900. The Tywi Valley in Cardiganshire and Carmarthenshire held the main population of up to 12 pairs, and other pairs bred in the upper Wye, the upper Usk and its tributaries in NW Brecon and in neighbouring parts of Radnor. By 1900, just 20 territories held breeding pairs and until the 1930s the population continued to dwindle. From less than two successful known broods per year in the early 1930s the Red Kite then began a recovery. It was tortuously slow at first but the 1939–45 war allowed a respite in persecution and recovery has continued to the present day—in 1993 103 pairs bred in its Welsh stronghold (Davis 1993). A reintroduction programme into England and Scotland led to successful breeding attempts in 1992. The early age of first breeding and the high productivity of these pairs has raised the hope that Red Kites will quickly recolonise some of their old haunts.

Where known the dates of last 19th century breeding follow. **Devonshire**—still common near Buckfastleigh *ca* 1825 and said to be breeding in Dean Wood in 1855. **Dorset**—still common in 1800. **Hampshire**—last nest taken 1864 near Stockbridge. **Kent**—bred rarely in 1844. **Wiltshire**—bred up to *ca* 1860. **Gloucestershire**—last bred on the Cotswolds *ca* 1860 and in the Forest of Dean *ca* 1870. **Oxfordshire**—became extinct in the 1830s. **Worcestershire**—disappeared from the Malverns between 1850 and 1870. **Warwickshire**—nested near Allesley up to 1825. **Essex**—eggs taken near Maldon in 1854. **Suffolk**—bred *ca* 1835 near Bures. **Cambridgeshire**—bred in the 1820s and probably up to the 1840s. **Bedfordshire** —common in 1813. **Northamptonshire**—nests taken during the 1840s in the Lady and Great Wadenhoe Woods. **Huntingdonshire**—common to 1845. **Leicestershire**—bred in Belvoir Woods in 1850. **Rutland**—common in Holywell and Pickworth Woods in the 1830s. **Lincolnshire**—last eggs taken in Bullington Wood, Wragby in 1870. **Lancashire**—last bred about 1800. **Cumberland**—last nest record near Keswick in 1809. **Northumberland**—possibly bred Eglingham in the 1830s. **Monmouthshire**—last bred near Nantderi *ca* 1869. **Glamorgan**—a female and eggs were collected from a nest near Cardiff in 1853. **Pembrokeshire**—nested on the Cardiganshire border through the first half of the 19th century. **Merioneth**—bred at the top of the Dysynni and Dyfi Valleys to, at least, 1855. **Montgomeryshire**—common near Newtown in the 1830s, probably until the 1850s. **Tweed**—bred to *ca* 1800. **Clyde**—Bred Glen App (Ayrshire), last bred Arran 1829, one or two nests in Dunbartonshire 1856, three nests in Argyll 1858. Became extinct in Clyde in 1850s. **Argyll**—last nest found 1858, possibly bred to 1860. **Sutherland**—last bred *ca* 1850. **Channel Islands**—was still breeding on Jersey *ca* 1815.

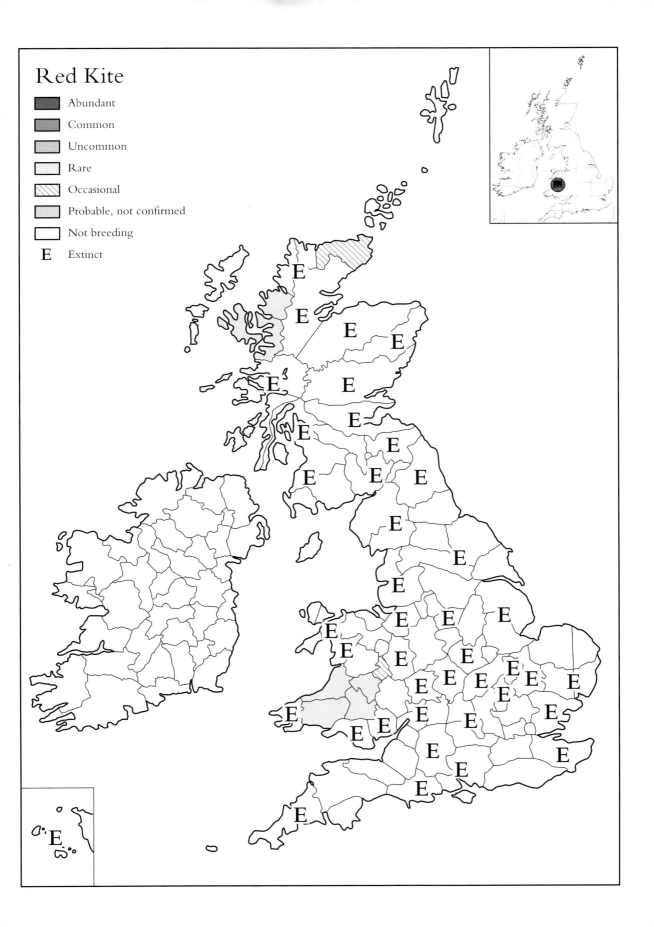

Red Kite

- ◼ Abundant
- ◼ Common
- ◻ Uncommon
- ◻ Rare
- ▨ Occasional
- ◻ Probable, not confirmed
- ◻ Not breeding
- **E** Extinct

White-tailed Eagle (Erne)

Haliaeetus albicilla

The decline of the White-tailed Eagle in Britain and Ireland seems to have been a direct consequence of human activity. The development of farming from Anglo-Saxon times probably began the long-term decline of the species that culminated in its extinction at the beginning of the 20th century (Love 1983). It probably once bred widely throughout lowland Britain and Ireland but suitable habitat was lost as widespread forest clearances and marsh drainage took place, and the early farmers also took measures to protect livestock from predators such as eagles. By the 18th century only a handful of White-tailed Eagle pairs remained in England and none survived in Wales. The population in Ireland became extinct in the 1890s, and that in Scotland in the early 20th century.

Although they are referred to in old Welsh literature (Love 1983), recorded in Holocene cave deposits (Harrison 1980) and as visitors to the country (Lovegrove *et al.* 1994), there are no written records of White-tailed Eagles having bred in Wales. It is curious that this species became extinct at such an early date in apparently suitable habitat but the very local Golden Eagle population also seems to have died out very early (Forrest 1907) perhaps indicating a common factor.

It seems likely that the last English Ernes died out in the Lake District in the 1790s. Yarrell (1871–85) stated that a pair or two nested in the Lakes until 1794, and this may also have been Macpherson's (1892) latest breeding record, which, after re-interpretation, probably took place in 1791 in Eskdale, Cumberland. A record of a pair seen in Ullswater (a former breeding site) in 1835 is often quoted as the last nesting record of the species in England; however, there is no evidence that this pair attempted to breed (Love 1983). Other late English records included an eaglet taken from a nest on the Culver Cliffs, Isle of Wight in 1780 [this

was discounted as a Buzzard by Cohen (1963) but it does not seem an unlikely record (Love in litt.)] and a nest, possibly of this species, destroyed by a snowstorm on the Isle of Man in 1818, according to Yarrell (1871–85), but Ralfe (1906) concluded that it was destroyed during the 1780s.

Scotland held the only British breeding White-tailed Eagles during the 19th century. The species bred occasionally in some counties of the south but mainly on the northern and western coasts and islands (Love 1983). The bulk of the lowland pairs (including those in the Solway region) had been exterminated by 1800 and the few remaining pairs died out around the middle of the century. Other isolated sites, for instance in St Kilda, Fair Isle and Orkney, were abandoned before 1850. The decline of the core population accelerated in Scotland from the 1840s coinciding with an increase in the human population, and their livestock, on the coast (the main breeding areas of the White-tailed Eagle). It seems clear that persecution by humans was responsible for the decline (Love 1983).

After 1875 the species still bred in the Hebrides, parts of Ross, Sutherland, Orkney and Shetland. In Ross it nested up to 1889 in Ben Damph Forest but breeding on the Scottish mainland ceased with the last nest in Sutherland in 1901 (although at least five eyries were tenanted in 1887 as far inland as Ben Hee). The species had been recorded breeding on many of the islands of W Scotland. For instance, the last breeding record on Rum concerned a clutch taken in 1907; one of the adults was shot that year but a pair were shot at the same locality in 1909. The White-tailed Eagles on these islands were gradually exterminated, the last being on Skye. After 1860 there were seven occupied eyries on the cliffs of NW Skye and others elsewhere on the island; the eyrie at Glenbrittle in the Cuillins was used up to 1884 when the female was shot on the nest, and, by 1893, the only eyrie in regular use on Skye was around Dunvegan Head, although another pair bred irregularly. Breeding persisted around Dunvegan Head until 1916—the last breeding record in Britain. In Shetland five pairs were recorded breeding up to 1899 but in 1910 the last pair bred for the last time (on Yell) as the male was shot that year. The female of this pair (shot in 1918) was the last of the White-tailed Eagles in Britain.

In Ireland the White-tailed Eagle had bred on the marine cliffs of Munster, Connaught and Ulster in the 1800s—eyries elsewhere had already been abandoned. The last recorded nest in Kerry was taken in 1889 and the species bred for the last time at Horn Head, Donegal *ca* 1891. Breeding persisted for some time later in Mayo but ceased prior to 1911 (Ussher and Warren 1900), probably in 1898 (Jourdain 1912).

Attempts to reintroduce White-tailed Eagles into Britain in 1959 and 1968 were unsuccessful, but the latest attempt, on Rum, which began in 1975 and ended in 1985, has led to up to three pairs breeding or attempting to do so each year since 1984 (Gibbons *et al.* 1993).

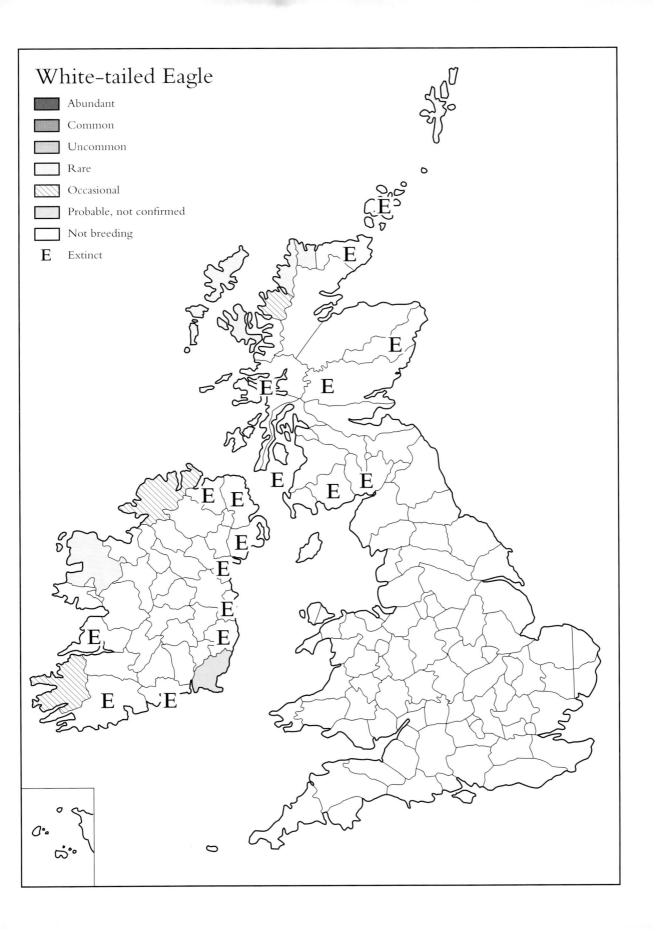

White-tailed Eagle

- ■ Abundant
- ■ Common
- ▨ Uncommon
- □ Rare
- ▨ Occasional
- ▨ Probable, not confirmed
- □ Not breeding
- **E** Extinct

Marsh Harrier
(Moor Buzzard)

Circus aeruginosus

Great difficulty was experienced by the naturalists of the 19th century in separating the different species of Harrier in the field, thus care must be taken with the older records; by the last quarter of the 19th century, enough was known about the identification and habits of the species for records to be considered with less reserve.

Before the 19th century the Marsh Harrier probably bred in many English and Welsh counties, but habitat loss due to drainage must have severely reduced its numbers and distribution. As the 19th century opened, breeding still occurred in a few English and Welsh counties and over much of Ireland but because of further drainage activities and persecution from gamekeepers and collectors, by the 1870s, the Marsh Harrier in Britain bred only in Northumberland and Norfolk. In Northumberland, at the beginning of the 19th century, it had bred regularly on the bogs of Newham and Kimmer Loughs, Alnwick Moor and Coldmartin Moss. The last breeding record in the county was of eggs taken about 1880. The Marsh Harrier had also been very common in the Norfolk Broads and fenland in the early 1800s. Drainage and persecution served to eradicate it from the Fens by around 1850 and substantially reduce its numbers in the Broads until, by the mid 1880s, just a pair

or two could be found breeding there. The last known pair in Britain were trapped in 1899 in Norfolk before eggs were laid.

The Marsh Harrier was described as one of the most abundant of Ireland's birds of prey in 1853 but persecution caused numbers to decline rapidly so that, by the end of the century, only a few bred on the midland bogs, parts of Galway and on one estate in Leix. There were a number of breeding pairs noted in the late 1890s but in 1917 none was known to breed.

Recolonisation of Britain was recorded in 1911 when a clutch was taken near Horsey, Norfolk. Breeding was again recorded in 1915 and 1921, and from 1927 has been recorded every year. Until 1944 up to five nests were known per annum, slowly increasing to 15 by 1958 and between 1940 and 1960 breeding took place in five English and two Welsh counties, although regularly only in Norfolk and Suffolk (J. Day in litt). A decrease in numbers from 1959 was probably caused by reduced breeding success following the introduction of organochlorine pesticides but an increase that followed from 1971 (just one pair bred that year in Britain, at Minsmere) was probably brought about by recruitment from abroad and sustained by a drop in mortality (Day 1984). There has been an increasing number of summering birds recorded in Ireland, particularly from 1966, but breeding has not yet been proven to have taken place (Hutchinson 1989).

Details of 19th century breeding prior to 1875 follow. **Essex**—last bred *ca* 1825 at Tolleshunt D'Arcy. **Oxfordshire**—may have bred on Otmoor *ca* 1814. **Cambridgeshire**—probably last bred *ca* 1860 in Wicken Fen. **Lincolnshire**—last bred 1836 in the Isle of Axholme. **Cheshire**—probably bred to *ca* 1820 in the Mersey valley. **Lancashire**—last bred *ca* 1860 around Martin Mere, Pilling and mosses on the northern border. **Yorkshire**—last bred *ca* 1830. Common earlier near Doncaster, in Cleveland and on Wemmergill Moor. **Lakeland**—was said to breed all over the area during the first half of the 19th century. **Brecon**—last bred prior to 1882, but the record was not considered acceptable by Ingram and Morrey Salmon (1957). **Cardiganshire**—a former numerous resident of Borth and Tregaron Bogs prior to 1870. **Pembrokeshire**—a common resident some time prior to 1880. **Anglesey**—'...used to breed in the bogs in west ...'. **Caernarvonshire**—found near Llandudno prior to 1863. **Cork**—bred near Ballycotton to *ca* 1870. **Waterford**—formerly bred *ca* 1820. **Tipperary**—formerly bred in the marshes on the Kilkenny border. **Mayo**—bred on Lough Mask to 1859. **Fermanagh**—gamekeepers poisoned the last breeding pair at Lough Erne in 1840. **Donegal**—last bred, probably in the south, *ca* 1870. **Ulster**—'not very uncommon on the moors' in 1874. Thompson (1849–56) noted breeding in some other counties.

Number of counties in which recorded:

Period	Probable breeding		Confirmed breeding		Combined		
	Br	Ir	Br	Ir	Br	Ir	Both
1875–1900	0	0	2	5	2	5	7
1968–1972	0	0	3	0	3	0	3
			change		1	−5	−4
					50%	−100%	−57%

108

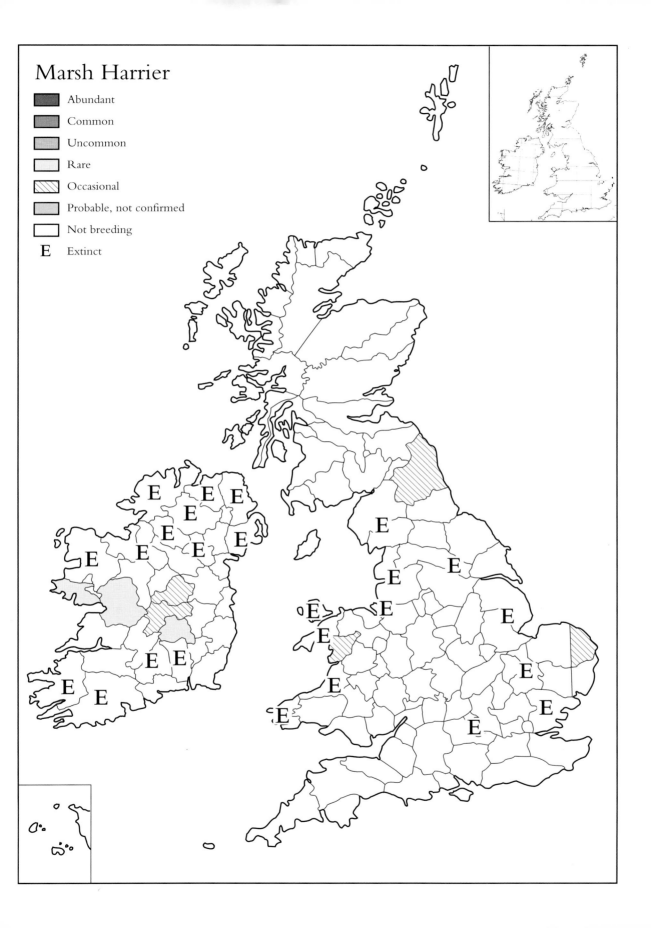

Marsh Harrier

- ◼ Abundant
- ◼ Common
- ◼ Uncommon
- ◻ Rare
- ▨ Occasional
- ▨ Probable, not confirmed
- ◻ Not breeding
- **E** Extinct

Hen Harrier

Circus cyaneus

The map overstates the status of the Hen Harrier in 1900, reflecting more accurately the picture in 1875. The rapid retraction in range from most areas during the final 25 years of the century, and especially after 1890, meant that, by 1900, breeding was taking place with any certainty only in Kintyre, Arran, North and South Uist, Orkney, Kerry, Cork and the mountains of Connaught. Away from these areas there were only sporadic breeding records by the end of the 19th century.

Regular breeding sites before the 1830s in England were Exmoor in Devonshire, the New Forest in Hampshire and, perhaps, in Northumberland and Durham. In Wales at this time, the Hen Harrier bred commonly in parts of the south and on some of the northern moors, but here, as in England, by the middle of the century breeding was only occasional. The great decrease that had taken place in the Borders by 1850 was followed later by a decrease in N Scotland. The early losses were likely to have been caused mainly by the destruction of breeding habitat through enclosure and drainage. Persecution, before the growth of interest in shooting and consequent preservation activities, was probably light, and there are few records of Hen Harriers being shot prior to the 1830s—usually only the few that raided poultry coops. From this time, however, persecution increased with the increase in game preservation, and numbers of Hen Harriers began to decrease. Declines (and extinctions) were first noted on their lowland breeding sites as a consequence of the combination of habitat loss and persecution and, by the 1850s, breeding was recorded only on grouse moors. Intensive gamekeeping on these moors was responsible for the final decline from around 1850. The ground-nesting habit of the Hen Harrier and the breeding adults' reluctance to leave the vicinity of the nest made it an easy target for gamekeepers on the moors. A (probably exaggerated) record of 351 killed in Ayrshire in the four years from 1850 attests to their abundance at that time; within 15 years they were regarded as almost extinct there (Gray and Anderson 1869).

Up to the 1914–18 war breeding may have taken place regularly on Arran and, up to the 1940s, in SW Ireland. The only places where continuous breeding has taken place to the present day have been the Outer Hebrides and Orkney. A recovery elsewhere began when breeding returned to the Scottish mainland in 1939 and thence to Tayside, Moray and Sutherland by 1946. Regular breeding in S Scotland and N Wales, and the start of an expansion in Ireland, took place over the next 20 years and the subsequent recolonisation of England continued this recovery. Since the 1970s the population has been more or less stable although local losses have been caused by habitat loss and continuing persecution. Populations continue to increase in parts of Scotland.

Where known the dates of last 19th century breeding follow. **Wiltshire**—probably bred near Lavington. **Kent**—last bred 1845. **Essex**—some summer records but no nests had been found. **Oxfordshire**—not uncommon in mid Oxfordshire in the 1840s. **Suffolk**—last bred in 1875. **Norfolk**—bred occasionally; the last recorded nest was near Horsey in 1861. **Gloucestershire**—last bred 1860 in the Cotswolds. **Worcestershire**—last bred around 1800. **Lincolnshire**—last bred 1872 on Raventhorpe Common near Scunthorpe. **Derbyshire**—eggs taken in 1870 from Drakelow. **Cheshire**—probably bred on the east hills. **Yorkshire**—bred on the Danby Moors in 1850. **Montgomeryshire**—bred regularly on moorland above Llangunnog in the 1860s. **Tweed**—bred around Lauder until *ca* 1842. **Tay Basin**—ceased breeding by 1832. **Wicklow**—bred on Wicklow Mountains in 1871. **Fermanagh**—bred in the mountains near Lack in the 1850s. **Londonderry**—bred on the Tyrone border in the first half of the century.

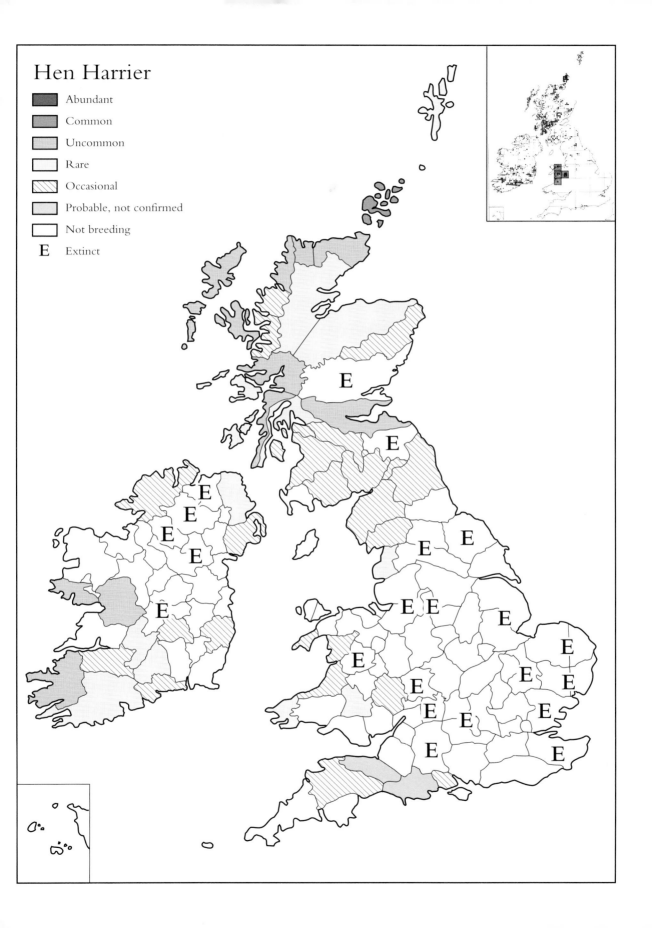

Hen Harrier

- **Abundant**
- **Common**
- Uncommon
- Rare
- Occasional
- Probable, not confirmed
- Not breeding
- **E** Extinct

Montagu's Harrier (Ash-coloured Harrier)

Circus pygargus

The Montagu's Harrier was first discriminated from the Hen Harrier in 1802 by George Montagu from a specimen collected in Wiltshire. The two species are very difficult to distinguish in the field, and were particularly so before the days of good optics, so that early records must be treated with some suspicion.

In the last quarter of the 19th century there were four discrete areas in England where breeding was more or less regular. In Cornwall the species bred every year around the Lizard despite being persecuted heavily by local gamekeepers. A gin trap baited with an adder was said to have been a particularly efficient method of capture. Numerous records throughout Devonshire indicated that breeding probably took place but was not proven. Just over the border, on the Somerset side of Exmoor, a nest was taken in the 1860s. Breeding was regular in Hampshire in three areas. Most of the pairs bred in the New Forest, with smaller numbers on the coast in the southeast and northeast of the county. Nesting was also occasionally recorded in

Dorset and there were two undated records from Wiltshire. In Kent Montagu's Harriers had bred regularly on the North Downs, in 1865 for the last time, and in the open areas of the Blean Woods a nest taken there in 1887 was probably the last. A nest was taken on the Worth Marshes in 1897 that was the last recorded in the 19th century and the last in the county until the 1940s. It is probable that Montagu's Harriers bred on the Romney Marshes up to the late 1860s. Traditionally, the population breeding in the fens of East Anglia had been the largest. Certainly this was so until the middle of the century but drainage and land reclamation caused the extinction of this Harrier in many areas soon after. Breeding was sporadic by the turn of the century in Suffolk, mainly in the east of the county around Euston and Cavenham in Breckland. Breeding was more regular in Norfolk, a nest or two being reported every year but few birds escaped being killed and even fewer managed to raise a brood. Breeding ceased on Feltwell Fen in the southwest of the county after it was drained. Nesting was first recorded in Wicken Fen in Cambridgeshire in 1851. There were no further records until 1890 when breeding began again and was regular until the turn of the century before ceasing again. In 1904 breeding resumed and continued irregularly until the late 1940s.

Outside these main areas old records exist of breeding near Leweston, Pembrokeshire in 1854 and Wolsingham Park, Durham in 1835, and about this time Montagu's Harriers were believed to be breeding regularly in Northumberland. The records suggest that, although the species was never common, local decreases had taken place in the 19th century following persecution and drainage of traditional breeding areas, particularly in the fenlands of the English eastern counties.

The British population remained at fewer than 20 pairs from 1900 to 1945. A post war increase reached 30 pairs by 1953 with breeding recorded in nine counties in England, two in Wales and, for the first time, one in Scotland (J. Day in litt). Numbers increased in the northeast, the species returned to N Wales (it had bred there earlier in the 20th century) and was recorded for the first time in Ireland. Wherever increases were recorded the commonest nesting habitat was young conifer plantations at this time, although reed beds remained the main nesting habitat in East Anglia. From the late 1950s a decline began that, apart from a brief respite between 1963 and 1968, continued to the mid 1970s. In 1974 there were no breeding records. Subsequently, Montagu's Harriers have bred in fluctuating, but very low, numbers.

Number of counties in which recorded:

Period	Probable breeding		Confirmed breeding		Combined		
	Br	Ir	Br	Ir	Br	Ir	Both
1875–1900	2	0	8	0	10	0	10
1968–1972	9	0	5	1	14	1	15
			change		4	1	5
					40%		50%

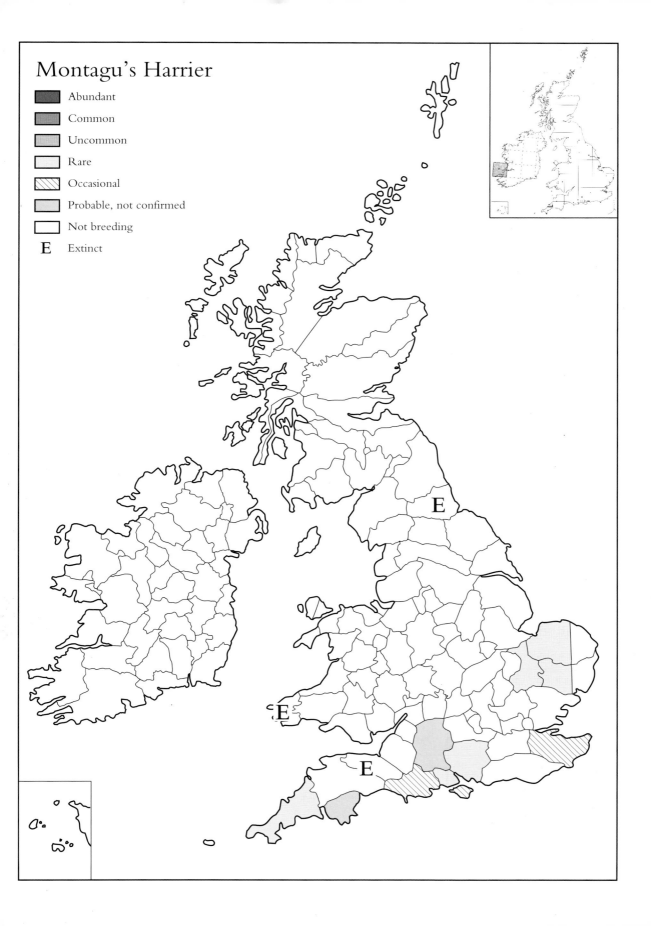

Montagu's Harrier

- **Abundant**
- **Common**
- **Uncommon**
- **Rare**
- **Occasional**
- **Probable, not confirmed**
- **Not breeding**
- **E** Extinct

Goshawk

Accipiter gentilis

The history of the Goshawk breeding in Britain up to its extinction during the 19th century is very difficult to unravel. It is apparent that, in Scotland especially, old records were confused with the Peregrine and, as such, many interesting records are untrustworthy. Nevertheless, it seems clear that the Goshawk was already very scarce at the beginning of the 19th century. The main period of extensive deforestation in Britain occurred in the lowlands and some parts of the uplands prior to the 16th century (Dimbleby 1984) and, so, it is probable that the main decline took place then (Petty 1989).

Of the old records of breeding Goshawks in Scotland Baxter and Rintoul (1953) compiled a number that they thought were authentic. The first was by Pennant (1771), who, during his tour of Scotland, was informed that they bred in the forests of Invercauld, Aberdeenshire. Colonel Thornton (1804), on a sporting tour of N England and the Highlands in 1786, was given a gift of a wild bred female Goshawk still in down by the Laird of Rothiemurchus. It had been taken from a nest in the forest formed by Glen More and Rothiemurchus in Inverness-shire. Thornton believed that this female was the first British bred bird trained to hunt and was very disappointed when he lost it

only a month later. This is an indication of its extreme rarity even at this time. Another 18th century record comes from the Reverend John Lapslie (in Sinclair 1791–99) who said that the Goshawk bred near Campsie, Stirlingshire.

During the first half of the 19th century the Goshawk was said to breed regularly in the Forest of Darnaway, Moray (St John 1848) but only a few years later was regarded as rare both there and at Glen More (St John 1863). A national enquiry in the early 1860s led to the assertion that the Goshawk bred in the woods of Castle Grant and Dulnan (Dulnain) on Speyside (More 1865) and in 1871 two eggs were said to have been taken at Balmacara, West Ross. Millais said that he received two Goshawks shot in the woods of Rohallion, Perthshire in 1883 (Harvie-Brown 1906). The gamekeeper stated that they had bred for several years there and the gamekeeper of neighbouring Kinnaird killed Goshawks during the same period. Following further enquiries Millais surmised that they had recently bred over the whole forest from Rohallion to Trochray and up the main valley of the Tay as far as Logierait (Ballinluig) (Harvie-Brown 1906). The Goshawks killed at Rohallion were the last recorded breeding in Scotland.

Just two English breeding records during the last quarter of the 19th century were accepted by Witherby *et al.* (1938–41). A female was recorded shot from a nest in a larch plantation in Normandy Park, Lincolnshire in 1864 (Cordeaux 1899). In Yorkshire, a record of three eggs taken from a nest near York in 1863 was not accepted but a record of a female shot on her nest and four eggs taken in May 1893 by the gamekeeper at Westerdale, Cleveland was deemed accurate (Nelson *et al.* 1907). The origin of this female was not known, however. The apparent lack of a mate (a male was never seen) indicated to some that the female was an escaped falconer's bird whereas her wildness (several attempts were made to shoot her) proved to others that it was a natural breeding attempt. Apart from these known breeding attempts, the many records of birds on passage, far more frequent in the 19th century than later, may well have led to sporadic breeding in the eastern counties of Britain.

The recolonisation of Britain by Goshawks was facilitated by both accidental and deliberate releases of falconers' birds. They may have been present in Sussex in the 1920s and since that time they have increased slowly, but relentlessly, throughout Britain. Breeding became regular from the mid 1960s and the population proliferated in the 1970s, a period during which large numbers of birds were imported and many released (Marquiss 1981). The present population of about 200 pairs may be larger than at any time since the 18th century.

Number of counties in which recorded:

Period	Probable breeding		Confirmed breeding		Combined		
	Br	Ir	Br	Ir	Br	Ir	Both
1875–1900	0	0	5	0	5	0	5
1968–1972	6	0	7	0	13	0	13
			change		8	0	8
					160%		160%

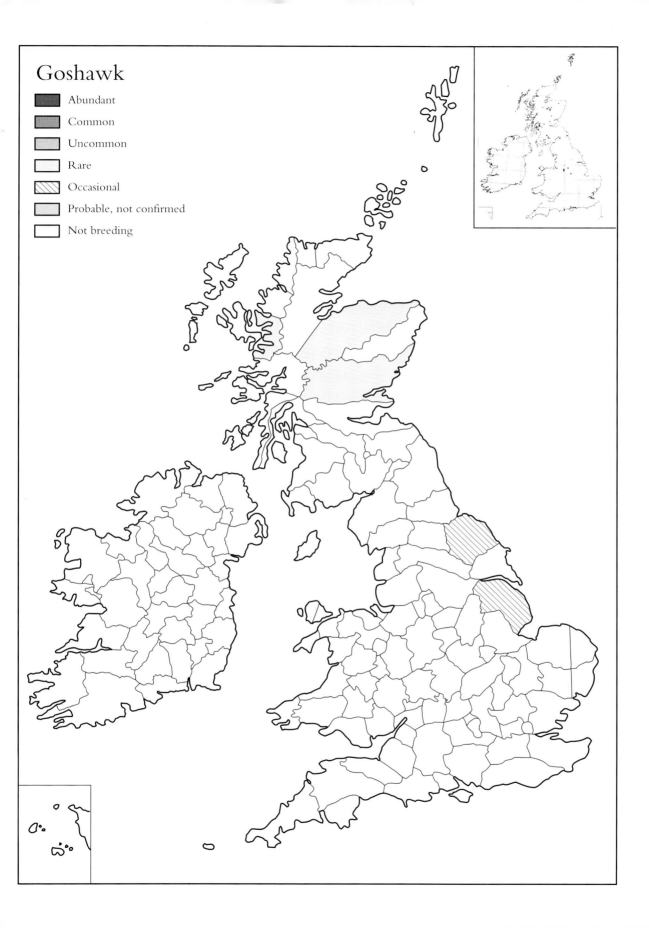

Goshawk

- **Abundant**
- **Common**
- **Uncommon**
- **Rare**
- **Occasional**
- **Probable, not confirmed**
- **Not breeding**

Sparrowhawk

Accipiter nisus

The map is testament to the resilience of the Sparrowhawk against the best efforts of the Victorian landowners and their gamekeepers to eradicate it in the 19th century (Newton 1986). This resilience results from a high reproductive rate, an early age of first breeding and strong density dependent factors that control Sparrowhawk numbers. The population normally includes a high proportion of non-breeding, non-territorial birds able to occupy vacated territories rapidly. In the past many Sparrowhawks were shot or trapped on game-rearing estates but as long as unkeepered woods remained in the neighbourhood of preserved areas, continual replacement of shot birds was possible (Newton 1986). This aspect of the Sparrowhawk's biology was probably recognised in the 19th century (Lilford 1895). Notwithstanding this persecution, only south and east of a line drawn from the Severn estuary to the Wash was it reported as having decreased. This was especially true of East Anglia where the number of gamekeepers was higher than elsewhere (Newton 1986); even so it was believed still to outnumber the Kestrel (Borrer 1891). Evidence of the futility of heavy persecution comes with the numbers reported shot. On an estate at Bettws-y-coed, Caernarvonshire 738 were killed in the 28 years ending in 1902 (Forrest 1907), an average of over 26 per year, far more than the area could support at any one time; and throughout

Cheshire, despite heavy persecution, Sparrowhawks had not declined even in heavily preserved woods (Coward and Oldham 1900). Game preservation may, in fact, have had a positive effect. At a time when tree cover in Britain was reaching a minimum, woodland and other cover was conserved in game rearing areas, providing ideal habitat, not only for game, but also for Sparrowhawks and their songbird prey. The gamekeepers were far more successful in eliminating the Sparrowhawk's own predators, especially the pine marten and Goshawk, which may have served partially to balance the efforts to eliminate the Sparrowhawk. The relatively new practice of planting conifer woods provided new nesting habitat and, especially in Scotland, this led to local increases, particularly as these new woods were not keepered (Harvie-Brown and Buckley 1895). This was also true of Ireland but, in general, the country of the west, coast and mountains was very sparsely wooded and provided few nesting sites. In fact, many recorded nests were in tall overgrown hedgerows (I. Newton in litt.).

That persecution had reduced numbers in some areas, particularly in E England, was confirmed during the first half of the 20th century, when increases were noted during and following the 1914–18 and 1939–45 wars. Game preservation and, consequently, game keeping declined sharply during the wars and the intervening period, and it never recovered to the levels of the 19th century. The increase in Sparrowhawk numbers was particularly marked during the 1939–45 war and, by this time, it could be quantified by ringing data (Newton 1986). The population then crashed within 15 years of the war ending and by the end of the 1950s it was apparent that this decline was very widespread. A national enquiry into the status of the species in 1960 reported that numbers had fallen in almost every county in England and Wales. A second survey in 1963 included Scotland and Ireland and confirmed the extent and severity of the decline. The results showed that Sparrowhawks were virtually extinct in ten eastern and southern English counties and had been reduced to a handful of pairs in several others (Parslow 1973). This decline was linked to the introduction of new organochlorine pesticides, such as DDT, aldrin and dieldrin, and was most marked in areas with most tilled land where use of these pesticides was extensive (Newton and Haas 1984). The Sparrowhawk population responded very quickly to restrictions placed on the use of these pesticides in the early 1960s and the *68–72* and *88–91 Atlases* marked the recovery.

Number of counties in which recorded:

Period	Probable breeding		Confirmed breeding		Combined		
	Br	Ir	Br	Ir	Br	Ir	Both
1875–1900	0	0	105	34	105	34	139
1968–1972	3	0	101	34	104	34	138
			change		−1	0	−1
					−1%		−1%

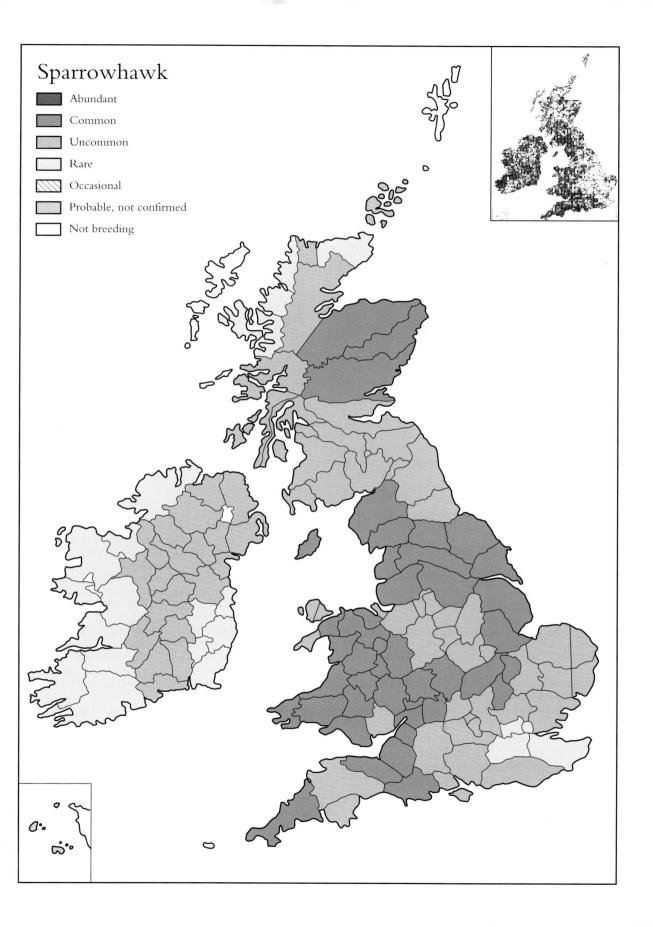

Sparrowhawk

- Abundant
- Common
- Uncommon
- Rare
- Occasional
- Probable, not confirmed
- Not breeding

Buzzard
(Common Buzzard)

Buteo buteo

At the beginning of the 19th century the Buzzard bred in almost all of the British counties and some of the northernmost counties of Ireland. Even at this time it is evident that this was a reduced distribution from that of even earlier times. By 1890, though, the distribution of the Buzzard had shrunk towards the west and north in Britain and the species had probably become extinct in Ireland. Even in those counties where it was still breeding it was, in the main, a rare bird. In S Wales a very few pairs of Buzzards hung on as they did in NW England and S Scotland. Only in the SW of England, parts of the NW of Scotland and the Tay Region was it breeding in anything like its former numbers. In 1875–1900 the Buzzard population was probably as low as it had ever reached in Britain and Ireland since ornithological records began. This drastic decline, which perhaps started as early as the 15th century with an Act of James II of Scotland which listed the Buzzard as vermin, continued as the era of game shooting began and persecution was waged on the Buzzard by, particularly, gamekeepers, but also farmers and sportsmen (C. Tubbs in litt). The Buzzard was the largest of the common birds of prey and so tended to be blamed for any damage done to game or stock. Its habits also made it easy prey: its slow, lazy flight made it an easy target when shot at, and its habit of perching, often quite low down, made trapping with tools like the pole-trap a relatively effective means of control. Once local populations had been reduced by gamekeepers, collectors of specimens and eggs made a significant contribution to the decline of the Buzzard during the second half of the 19th century (C. Tubbs in litt).

The population of Buzzards declined further during the first years of the 20th century but during the 1914–18 war a recovery began that accelerated markedly until around 1954. Both the 1914–18 and 1939–45 wars took people from the land and relieved much of the persecution. By 1954 the population of Buzzards, especially in the W England and Wales, had returned to a level not reached since around the first half of the 19th century; Moore (1957) suggested that the total population was around 12,000 pairs at this time. The myxomatosis plague of rabbits in that year, however, led to a reduction in Buzzard population density (C. Tubbs in litt). Buzzard densities, particularly in SW England, Wales and its English border country, became comparable to many on continental Europe, where rabbits were never a major prey animal, and breeding activity was reduced for several years after (C. Tubbs in litt.). The gradual recolonisation of parts of the English Midlands and Northern Ireland that had been taking place in the early 1950s was checked. In some areas, in the years following the reduction in rabbit numbers, further declines in the Buzzard population were attributed to pesticides as the Buzzard turned to sheep carrion. Since around 1960, numbers have started to recover (*68–72 Atlas*).

The *88–91 Atlas* demonstrates encouraging evidence of an expansion of range along the eastern edge of the Welsh and SW English population and an increasing population in S Scotland and, especially, in N Ireland.

Where known the dates of last 19th century breeding follow. **Kent**—last bred 1820. **Surrey**—last bred *ca* 1840. **Essex**—last bred 1835. **Hertfordshire**—last bred 1865. **Oxfordshire**—last bred during 1840s. **Suffolk**—last bred W Suffolk in 1875. **Norfolk**—last bred *ca* 1840. **Northamptonshire**—last bred 1840. **Huntingdonshire**—last bred *ca* 1840. **Gloucestershire**—last bred northwest in 1891 and the Severn vale in 1889. **Worcestershire**—last bred 1855. **Lincolnshire**—last bred 1888. **Leicestershire**—last bred *ca* 1835. **Rutland**—last bred 1827. **Nottinghamshire**—last bred 1825. **Yorkshire**—last bred SW in 1880 and mid Yorkshire in 1863. **Northumberland**—last bred 1850. **Tweed**—last bred *ca* 1840. **Londonderry**—last bred *ca* 1885. **Donegal**—last bred 1883.

Number of counties in which recorded:

Period	Probable breeding		Confirmed breeding		Combined		
	Br	Ir	Br	Ir	Br	Ir	Both
1875–1900	0	0	49	2	49	2	51
1968–1972	2	0	68	3	70	3	73
			change		21	1	22
					43%	50%	43%

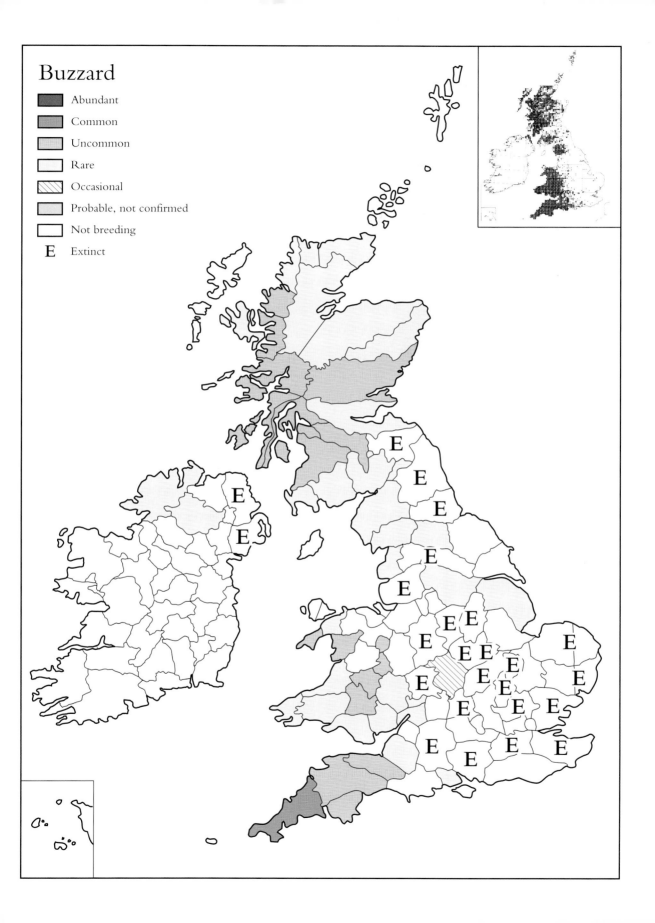

Buzzard

- **Abundant**
- **Common**
- **Uncommon**
- **Rare**
- **Occasional**
- **Probable, not confirmed**
- **Not breeding**
- **E** Extinct

Golden Eagle

Aquila chrysaetos

Breeding records of the Golden Eagle from the 18th and early 19th centuries are very difficult to separate from those of the White-tailed Eagle. That they both underwent severe persecution at the hands of gamekeepers and shepherds is beyond doubt, the Golden Eagle forsaking areas at the periphery of its main breeding range by the early 1800s. Breeding had been suggested in Derbyshire in 1668 and N Yorkshire before 1790 (Chislett 1953, Fryer 1987) but had probably ceased in England in the 1780s. A nest found in Martindale in the Lake District was the last recorded. The evidence for former breeding in Snowdonia does not include accounts of nests being found, although it was believed that breeding perhaps took place to the middle of the 18th century (Lovegrove *et al*. 1994).

In Ireland, after 1875, the Golden Eagle still bred in five counties. In Kerry it had bred on all three peninsulas but became extinct before 1900. It last bred on the Dingle in the 1880s; and on the Macgillycuddy Reeks the eggs and young were taken from the last nests in 1883. South of the Kenmare River the last breeding adults were trapped on their nest in 1894. In Galway breeding continued into the 1880s in the Maam Mountains and some Golden Eagles were still breeding in Mayo until 1898; some reports suggest that they bred until 1910 or 1911. Golden Eagles frequently attempted to reestablish themselves in the moun-

tains on the Sligo/Leitrim border and they did so briefly during the 1870s in Fermanagh. Most of the eyries of Donegal were vacated before 1890 but a pair appeared in 1898 and breeding was recorded there until 1910. Breeding had ceased during the 19th century in other counties of Ulster and the northwest and the mountains on the Tipperary/Waterford border. The last of the Irish Golden Eagles were reported to have been one shot in Donegal in 1915 (Barrington 1915) and an old female, known to have been in the area for 10 years, trapped and destroyed near Ardara, Donegal in 1926 (Kennedy *et al*. 1954).

The numbers of Golden Eagles in Scotland decreased significantly during the 19th century (Love 1983). The guns, traps and poisoned baits of the gamekeepers and shepherds started the decline, while the English collectors of skins, eggs and young continued it. Breeding had taken place in S Scotland up to the middle of the 19th century and in the west of the Forth region a little later. The history of the decline, and subsequent recovery, of the Golden Eagle in the main breeding areas of Scotland was well documented. The Golden Eagle population reached its low point during the 1870s when only 80 eyries were known to be used regularly and another 20 irregularly (Baxter and Rintoul 1953). The decline had been the result of heavy persecution, mainly by shepherds, which had taken place as sheep farming grew during the first half of the 19th century. In some areas the toll was huge. In Sutherland in nine years around 1830 466 adults and nestlings were killed, and a shepherd on Skye in 1832 killed 25 adults. The 1870s saw a decline in sheep farming and the conversion of much of the land to deer forest. With this change in land use persecution lessened somewhat and the Golden Eagle began to recover so that by the end of the century numbers had increased substantially.

This recovery continued in the 20th century, particularly following the two great wars when persecution was reduced further with the call-up of gamekeepers to active service. Breeding pairs returned to S Scotland in 1948, the Antrim coast during the 1950s and England in 1969. Locally, setbacks have been apparent following the myxomatosis outbreaks since the 1950s and accumulation of sheep dip residues from carrion. A survey in 1982–83 found 511 home ranges occupied, 424 by pairs (Dennis *et al*. 1984).

Where known the dates of last 19th century breeding follow. **Kirkcudbrightshire**—bred on the Galloway Hills up to *ca* 1860. **Ayrshire**—two pairs bred at Loch Mackaterick in 1837. **Forth**—bred on Ben Lomond into the 1860s. **Waterford**—bred up to *ca* 1855. **Tipperary**—bred in the Knockmealdown Mountains in 1858. **Londonderry and Tyrone**—eggs taken from the Sperrin range in the 1860s. **Antrim**—bred to 1850 in Glenariff. **Down**—bred up to *ca* 1834 in the Mourne Mountains.

Number of counties in which recorded:

Period	Probable breeding		Confirmed breeding		Combined		
	Br	Ir	Br	Ir	Br	Ir	Both
1875–1900	0	2	17	4	17	6	23
1968–1972	0	0	22	0	22	0	22
			change		5	−6	−1
					29%	−100%	−4%

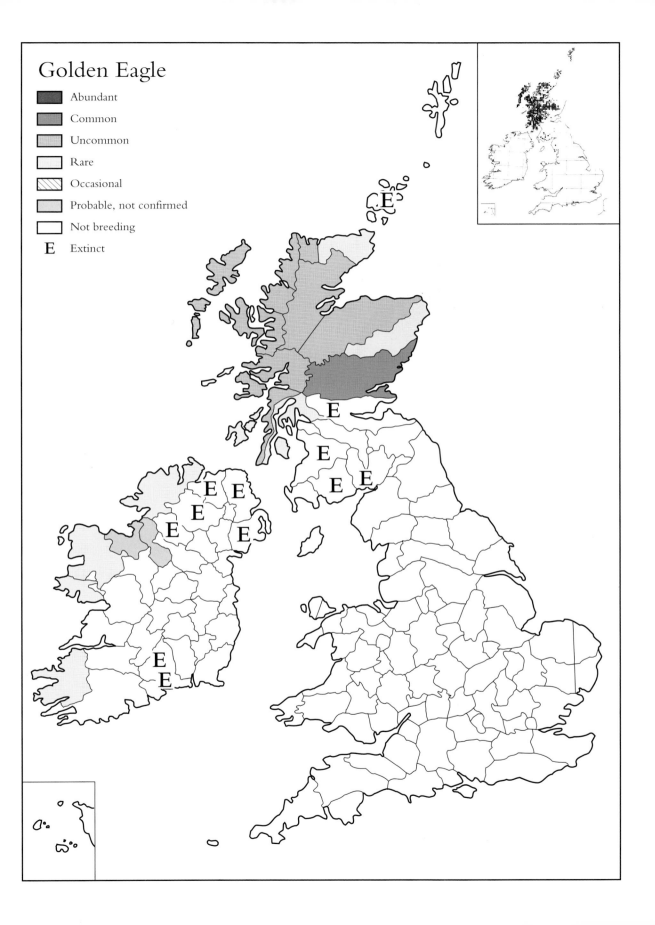

Golden Eagle

- Abundant
- Common
- Uncommon
- Rare
- Occasional
- Probable, not confirmed
- Not breeding
- **E** Extinct

Osprey

Pandion haliaetus

The Osprey became extinct in Britain in 1916 for a period before its recolonisation in 1954. The history of its final years in Scotland was well documented, although the accounts omitted the names of some of the nesting locations.

The evidence for former breeding in England is very slim. A nest in Whinfield Park (Whinfell) in Westmorland was considered by Willughby and others to be that of a White-tailed Eagle, but some authors thought it was an Osprey's nest. Ospreys were also recorded apparently breeding on the Westmorland bank of Ullswater at the end of the 18th century (Macpherson 1892).

Records of breeding in Dumfriesshire were either dismissed or considered very unlikely (Gladstone 1910) but records in the other Solway counties were accepted. In Wigtownshire nesting on an unnamed loch took place until about 1860 (Service 1902) and in Kirkcudbrightshire Ospreys bred into the 1870s. The nesting site on Loch Doon, Ayrshire, was not accepted by some but others asserted that Ospreys bred there up to the 1860s. The dates of extinction of the other sites in the Clyde region were not given, but it is unlikely that breeding on Loch Enoch and on Inchgalbraith in Loch Lomond took place after 1870. In the Forth region breeding ceased at the only recorded site, the Lake of Menteith in S Perthshire, in the 1830s or 1840s. Apart from up to two pairs breeding on Loch Awe up to the 1830s little else is recorded concerning breeding Ospreys in Argyll. Three sites were very well documented up to the 1840s and 1850s in NW Sutherland. During this period, or soon after, relentless egg-taking caused their desertion.

During the 1860s and 1870s sporadic nests were recorded from a number of lochs in Inverness-shire and elsewhere in the Highlands. Few of these were documented fully for fear of disturbance. The latest of these sporadic nesting attempts, on Loch Ordie near Dunkeld, failed in 1886 when the female was shot. The tree was cut down and the nest and remaining egg were presented to the Perth Museum in 1887. Two regular sites remained occupied until around the turn of the century. The nest on Loch Arkaig near Fort William had a long history but little is documented about it except that Ospreys ceased to breed there in 1908. The history of the famous Loch-an-Eilein site is well documented and stands as testament to the extinction of one of the last pairs of the 'old race'. The following is a summary of the history of the final years of this nest and adjacent sporadic breeding at what was probably an alternative but less well known nest site in that territory.

Loch-an-Eilein: 1880, reared two young; 1881, birds present but did not breed; 1882–86, no record; 1887, eggs taken; 1888, reared three young. Loch Gamhna: 1889, eggs taken. Loch-an-Eilein: 1890, eggs taken. Loch Gamhna: 1891, eggs taken. Loch-an-Eilein: 1892, one probably shot; 1893, no record; 1894, two young reared; 1895, young probably reared; 1896, two young reared; 1897, probably two young reared; 1898, pair present, breeding failed; 1899, three adults present, breeding failed; 1900–02, birds present but they did not breed.

Only one further nesting attempt was made in Britain after 1908, at Loch Loyne in 1916, until the 1950s. An increase in the number of spring and summer records of Ospreys led to successful breeding in Strathspey in 1954. From 1955 to 1958 breeding was thwarted by egg collectors and disturbance but since then, following protection, the recolonisation of Scotland has continued.

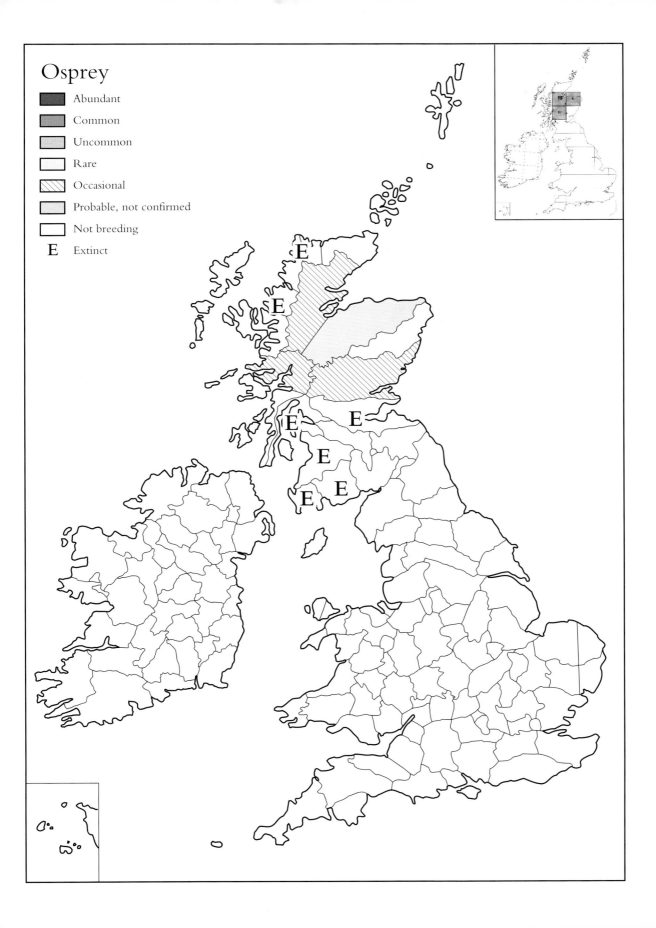

Osprey

- ■ Abundant
- ▨ Common
- ▨ Uncommon
- □ Rare
- ▨ Occasional
- ▨ Probable, not confirmed
- □ Not breeding
- **E** Extinct

Kestrel

Falco tinnunculus

The Kestrel was ubiquitous in Britain and Ireland during the 19th century although its hold in Shetland was tenuous. It bred on all, or nearly all, the islands of Shetland at the end of the 19th century although not commonly. In the early years of the century it may not have bred there at all (Dunn 1837) and it ceased breeding there again in 1905. Over the rest of Britain the Kestrel had declined up to the 1880s and 1890s perhaps because of the loss of inland nest sites but certainly because of persecution from gamekeepers. This decline was noted in many counties of S and E England, the Midlands, N England and parts of Scotland.

Potential nest sites in woodland were presumably scarce up to the second half of the 19th century (Yarrell 1837–43, Harting 1866, Haines 1907) as there were few records of Kestrels nesting in hollow trees at that time. The extent of woodland was at its lowest in the 19th century, and dead or dying trees, which would have provided suitable nest sites, were quickly removed for construction and ship building or for use as fuel. In addition, Kestrel numbers decreased in some open areas where the successful eradication of corvids, especially Carrion Crow and Magpie, had reduced the number of old nests available for Kestrels to breed in (Borrer 1891).

Kestrels, along with other predators, were killed as vermin on all game-rearing estates. This persecution was blamed as having caused serious declines in Essex, Middlesex, Caithness and the Moray region but can be assumed to have had a much wider effect. An indication that the destruction of Kestrels was nearly complete in some areas is suggested by the devastating effect of late 19th century vole plagues on grassland in the Borders (M. Shrubb in litt). With few predators to control their numbers the voles soon multiplied. The observations of increases in Kestrel numbers in the vole plague years of 1875–77 and 1890–93 and the very large clutches that resulted (12 eggs in one case but these may have been laid by two females (Village 1990) reinforced the understanding of the role that the Kestrel played in keeping down vole numbers. The Kestrel's diet of rodents began to be appreciated and as the century turned this understanding had percolated through to many gamekeepers and persecution began to ease (Bucknill 1900, Ticehurst 1909).

In Ireland it was said that no other bird bred more widely apart from, perhaps, the Wren but the absence of voles in the country meant that Kestrels never bred as densely as in Britain except for, perhaps, on the coast.

In general, Kestrels were noted as being relatively more numerous on cliff coasts than inland. This was noted all along the S coast from Cornwall to Sussex, in Pembrokeshire, parts of N Wales, E and W Scotland and in Ireland. It seems likely that these concentrations arose because they were left in peace there and they found a comparative abundance of nest sites (M. Shrubb in litt).

The early years of the 20th century saw a general increase in Kestrel numbers as persecution decreased, although further, local, losses were attributed to gamekeepers. An interesting development has been the increase in urban breeding, especially from the 1930s (Oakes 1953). In the years following the 1939–45 war increases were noted in many southern counties and locally in other areas (Parslow 1973, Smith 1974). Numbers declined markedly, however, in S and E England between 1959 and 1963. The decline was especially marked in farmland areas and was likely to have been caused by the application of toxic chemicals to seed dressings (Village 1990). Numbers declined elsewhere less conspicuously and, apparently, recovered more quickly (*88–91 Atlas*). In recent years losses in W Scotland, Pembrokeshire and Ireland have become apparent that have been largely unreported in the past, especially that in Ireland, and no obvious, single factor has been suggested to explain them.

Number of counties in which recorded:

Period	Probable breeding		Confirmed breeding		Combined		
	Br	Ir	Br	Ir	Br	Ir	Both
1875–1900	0	0	108	34	108	34	142
1968–1972	0	0	107	34	107	34	141
			change		–1	0	–1
					–1%		–1%

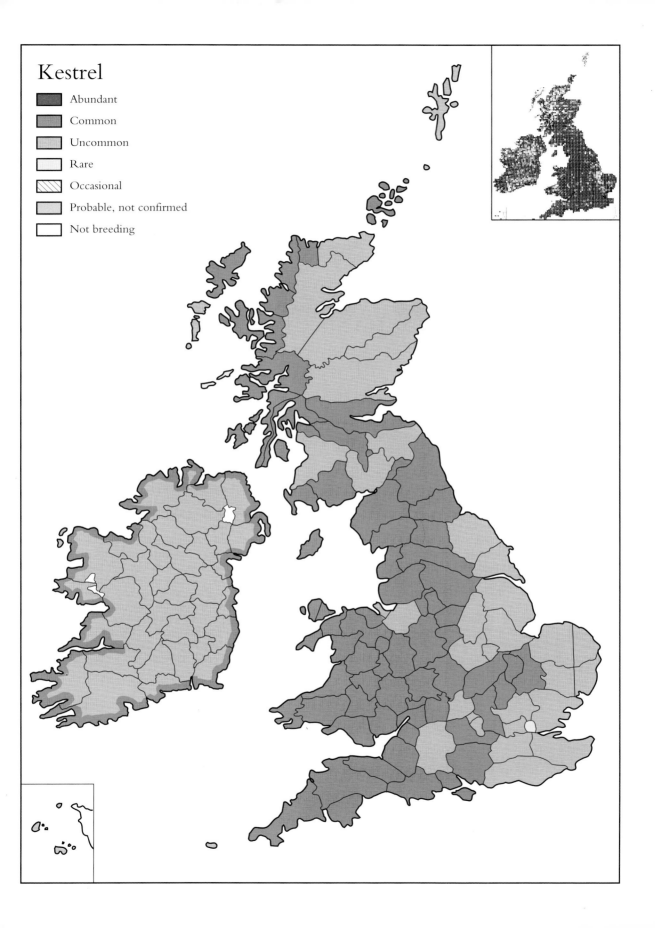

Kestrel

- Abundant
- Common
- Uncommon
- Rare
- Occasional
- Probable, not confirmed
- Not breeding

Merlin

Falco columbarius

In the 19th century the Merlin bred over much of Wales, the Pennine range, the moors of NE Yorkshire, the Cheviots and throughout Scotland and Ireland in suitable localities. It also occurred in areas lying outside this main breeding range. It was believed that a pair or two bred on Exmoor, Somerset (Blathwayt 1906), and in Sherwood Forest, Nottinghamshire (Sterland 1869, Whitaker 1907). A record of breeding in Hampshire, however (nests were reportedly taken in 1859, 1861 and 1862), was later dismissed (Cohen 1963). Nesting was said to have occurred in N Lincolnshire in 1860, 1862 and 1875 (Smith and Cornwallis 1955) and in Essex Merlins bred in the marshes of Paglesham and the Rochford Hundred during the first half of the century; identification was confirmed when young taken from the nest at the latter location were raised to fledging (Christy 1890).

Many writers wrote of declining numbers, particularly in N England and Scotland. The Merlin's habits made it easy prey on its breeding grounds—pole traps were particularly successful and destruction of its nests was relatively simple. In addition, many were killed on lower ground outwith the breeding range, particularly by collectors. In Scotland, however, it was suspected that it bred in relatively large numbers in remote areas little visited by either naturalists or sportsmen. In Wales it bred mainly on upland moors but lowland nesting took place in Lleyn, Caernarvonshire and Anglesey. The Welsh population appears to have been stable. All of the mountainous counties of Ireland were host to breeding Merlins, particularly in the west, as were Dublin and Wicklow. The Merlin also bred on the great red bogs of the central plain, but nowhere in Ireland was it common; indeed over much of its Irish range it was outnumbered by the Peregrine (Ussher and Warren 1900). Although shot on occasion, it was not persecuted to the same extent in Ireland as it was in Britain and the population appears to have been stable.

Most other species that had been persecuted as a result of game preservation were able to recover their numbers in the early years of the 20th century when persecution became less intensive. The Merlin, however, continued to decline over much of its traditional range. Its ground nesting habit in Britain and Ireland, a special feature compared with populations elsewhere, is possible only where the management of moorlands significantly reduces ground based predators (Parr 1991). The reduction in moorland preservation in the early 1900s will therefore have had a detrimental effect. An exception to this picture of decline was the apparent colonisation of SW England. Suspected for many years, breeding was finally proven on Exmoor, Devonshire in 1907 and then on Dartmoor in 1920. The population in Devonshire increased slowly and breeding was proven in Cornwall in 1954. The decline elsewhere accelerated during the 1950s and apparently paralleled that of other raptors, but, unlike them, the Merlin failed to recover when restrictions on the use of the most persistent organochlorine pesticides were introduced in the 1960s. By 1990 it had withdrawn from a number of areas where it had formerly bred. Losses in Ireland have been huge and in Wales it had disappeared from much of the southern and border counties. In contrast, however, the Merlin populations in Northumberland and upland Wales are increasing, suggesting that they may be recovering here. A factor in this recovery may be the increasing use of the margins of new conifer plantations for nesting, and adjacent open areas for feeding, a recent habit in British and Irish populations but much more familiar in most parts of its world range. It should be added that until recently most effort was expended searching for Merlin nests on the ground. It is now realised that a large proportion nest in old nests in trees in some areas of Britain (Parr 1991) and records from the 19th century confirm that the habit was fairly widespread then (e.g. Forrest 1907).

Number of counties in which recorded:

Period	Probable breeding		Confirmed breeding		Combined		
	Br	Ir	Br	Ir	Br	Ir	Both
1875–1900	3	0	98	26	101	26	127
1968–1972	4	2	49	22	53	24	77
			change		−48	−2	−50
					−48%	−8%	−39%

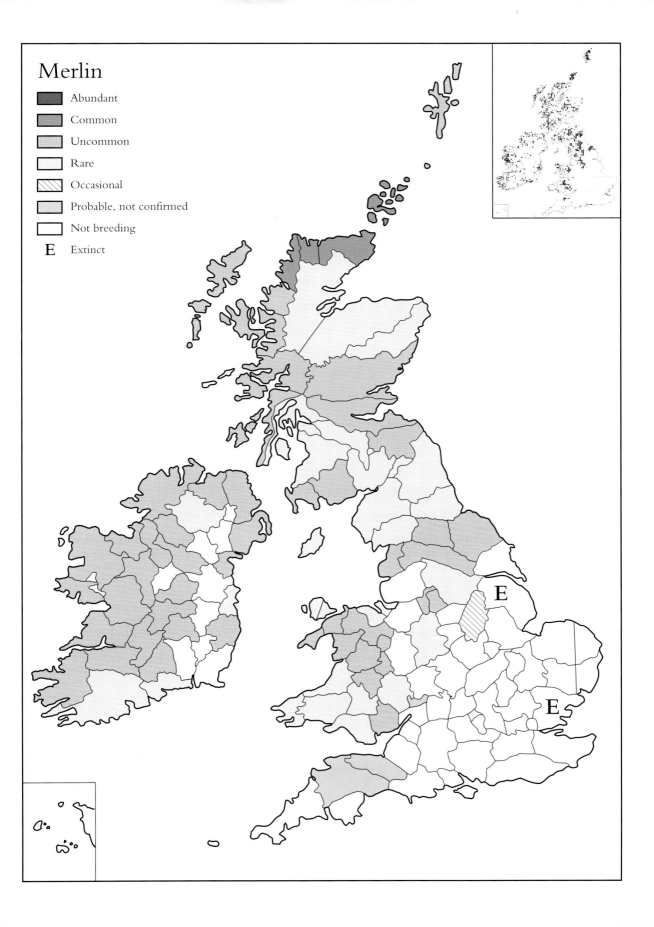

Merlin

Abundant
Common
Uncommon
Rare
Occasional
Probable, not confirmed
Not breeding
E   Extinct

Hobby (Hobby Hawk)

Falco subbuteo

The main breeding range of the Hobby towards the end of the 19th century was south of a line drawn from the Severn estuary to the Wash. It bred regularly a little north of this, especially in Lincolnshire, but elsewhere breeding was more sporadic. Breeding records from the first half of the century were scarce and, although the bird was noticed frequently on passage and in suitable habitat during the nesting season, nests were rarely found (Yarrell 1837–43). As naturalists and gamekeepers became more familiar with the species, however, records increased, and by the 1890s the Hobby's distribution had become better understood. It seems likely that the persecution of Crows and Magpies in, especially, E England, limited the Hobby's distribution at this time through lack of nests for it to take over (Walpole–Bond 1914). In the east of its range particularly, the Hobby was recorded as having decreased in numbers, although both Fuller *et al.* (1985) and Parr (1994) have suggested that there may have been under-recording when Hobbies in some habitats and areas were missed.

In Devonshire, it bred regularly in the woods on the southern edge of Dartmoor but, although suspected, had not been proven to breed in Cornwall. Nests were occasionally found in the woods of Dorset but far more regularly in the wooded districts of Hampshire. Breeding in Somerset was rarely proven and, in Wiltshire, breeding had not been recorded in the north

of the county although numerous records existed from the south. There were no breeding records for Surrey and Sussex, although Nethersole-Thompson (1931) felt that they had been overlooked in the past in Sussex. In Kent no more than three or four pairs bred annually (in the east and centre of the county) and the Hobby had evidently decreased substantially there following persecution by gamekeepers; although known not to prey on game, Hobbies were often mistaken for Sparrowhawks and shot as such. While they remained scattered throughout the wooded parts of most southern counties, they had formerly bred more commonly in Essex, Suffolk, Norfolk and Bedfordshire. They bred regularly in the woods of Rutland from the 1880s onwards, but had not been recorded since the 1840s in Leicestershire, and Walpole-Bond's (1914) statement that Northamptonshire was 'the probable head-quarters of the species' suggests that they may have been under-recorded there during the 19th century.

On the fringes of the main range, breeding had been recorded only twice along the coast of W Glamorgan although the Hobby was breeding regularly in the woods of the centre of Herefordshire. A nest had been recorded in parkland on the Shropshire/Staffordshire border around 1870 and Hobbies had been recorded there regularly during subsequent summers. In Cheshire and NW Derbyshire breeding was recorded on a few occasions in the 1890s. Further north, breeding had taken place in the 1860s and 1870s in S and E Yorkshire. In S Perthshire, an adult and three young were discovered nailed to a gamekeeper's gibbet in 1887 and nesting may have taken place there three or four years earlier.

Some changes have occurred during the 20th century in the species' status. The Sussex/Surrey gap was closed in the first few years of the century and breeding subsequently stabilised there. Records decreased from Kent and other eastern counties by the 1950s, however, so that the main population was then considered to be centred around Hampshire on the lowland heaths and downlands there (Sharrock 1976). Sporadic breeding apparently occurred at a decreasing frequency outside the normal range but details are scant (Parslow 1973). This view of the British breeding population in the 20th century has since been contested, however. Retrospective analysis of historical records and studies carried out in the early 1980s in central England suggested that the Hobby bred far more widely than had previously been thought and that a substantial portion of the population was breeding in farm and woodland areas outwith the heaths and downland previously regarded as traditional (Fuller *et al.* 1985). These atypical habitats had been overlooked for more than half a century, but, interestingly, recall the descriptions of breeding sites of the 19th century. However, even if it is clear that the distribution of the Hobby might not be far different today to what it was 100 years ago, there is evidence that numbers outside the 'core' range of central S England have increased, particularly in the E Midlands, in the last 10 years (Gibbons *et al.* 1993, Parr 1994).

Number of counties in which recorded:

Period	Probable breeding		Confirmed breeding		Combined		
	Br	Ir	Br	Ir	Br	Ir	Both
1875–1900	1	0	36	0	37	0	37
1968–1972	4	0	23	0	27	0	27
			change		−10	0	−10
					−27%		−27%

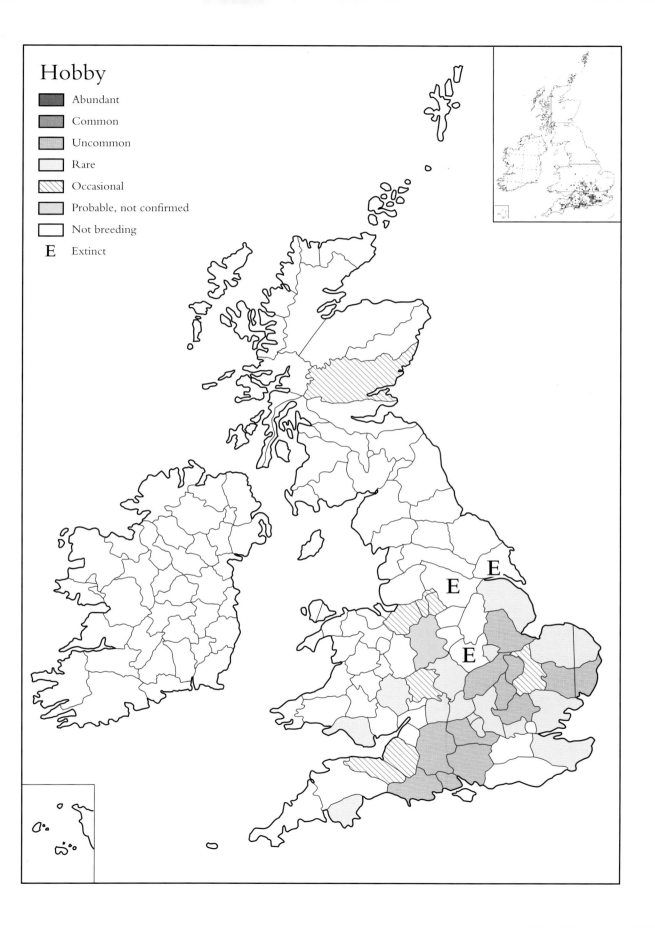

Hobby

- ■ Abundant
- ▨ Common
- ▨ Uncommon
- ▢ Rare
- ◪ Occasional
- ▨ Probable, not confirmed
- ▢ Not breeding
- **E** Extinct

Peregrine Falcon

Falco peregrinus

The Peregrine had declined somewhat in numbers, and slightly in distribution, by the end of the 19th century. It had apparently been able to survive the depredations of falconers for many hundreds of years. The falcons were taken from traditional eyries and it is apparent from the early records that these numbered only a few of those that must have been in existence. The taking of young often meant the scaling of dangerous cliffs and so those on the more inaccessible precipices were generally safe. The decline started as game preservation became more widespread and firearms more accurate, this combination becoming significantly effective during the early 19th century. The shooting and trapping of breeding adults near to their nests was a fairly simple affair and many birds were killed at traditional nesting places annually over a long period (Ratcliffe in litt). Wandering adults and birds of the year were also shot throughout Britain and Ireland in the winter.

In S England breeding was confined to the counties of the southwest, the Isle of Wight, Sussex and Kent. On the sea cliffs of Cornwall, Devonshire and Dorset the Peregrine was still holding its own but had declined in Somerset. There were a very few inland eyries in Wiltshire in the late 19th century: these included Salisbury Cathedral and possibly one other church spire (Smith 1887). The eyries on the Isle of Wight cliffs had been known for many years but had declined to two pairs by the end of the century; yet in Sussex and Kent there was evidently little decline. Breeding had been recorded in Norfolk and Suffolk around the beginning of the 19th century, on church steeples in both counties, and also on Hunstanton cliff in Norfolk. In N England, most pairs were inland. Breeding had become sporadic by 1900 in the Peak District, and was sparse in the Pennines and Cheviots further north. Most of the population, of probably at least 30 pairs, was in the Lake District, and there is no real evidence of an appreciable decline here. Some of the more accessible nesting places in the less rugged moorland districts had become deserted, though

(Ratcliffe in litt). The Isle of Man population was stable at 10–11 pairs.

In Wales the situation was evidently incompletely known. Many pairs bred on the coastal cliffs, as well as inland; known strongholds were in Pembrokeshire, Merioneth and Caernarvonshire. There is little evidence concerning earlier numbers in Wales although as keepering may not have been so widespread here little, if any, decline apparently took place.

In Scotland, although shot heavily on the grouse moors, especially in the east, Peregrines were left alone to a large extent elsewhere, and in the most elevated and remote regions of the Highlands and Islands were holding their own both on rugged coasts and inland. In lowland, and more heavily peopled, regions they had decreased through persecution but only by a relatively small degree. The number of eyries in Scotland during the 19th century is difficult to ascertain as the writers were careful not to disclose sites for fear of persecution (mainly from the resident gamekeepers but also by visiting English falconers and collectors) and much of the remoter regions were incompletely surveyed.

The reduction in game preservation and numbers of gamekeepers on the land as a result of the 1914–18 war allowed the Peregrine to recover some lost ground and increase its breeding success (Ratcliffe 1980). By the beginning of the 1939–45 war numbers were at a high and stable level but an emergency Order of 1940 made it lawful for authorised persons to destroy Peregrines and their eggs to protect military carrier pigeons; around 600 birds were killed and many young and eggs destroyed until the Order expired in 1946 (Ferguson-Lees 1951). Large as this destruction was (the British population was reduced by an estimated 13%—Ratcliffe in litt) numbers started to recover quickly after the war. A far more serious decline began around 1956 when the first effects of organochlorine pesticide contamination were noted. By 1963 Peregrine numbers were less than half their normal level, the decline being most severe in England and Wales, and this new low was maintained until about 1967 (Ratcliffe 1980). From this point a slow, but strong, recovery has taken place to a level that is probably higher than at any other time this century (*88–91 Atlas*).

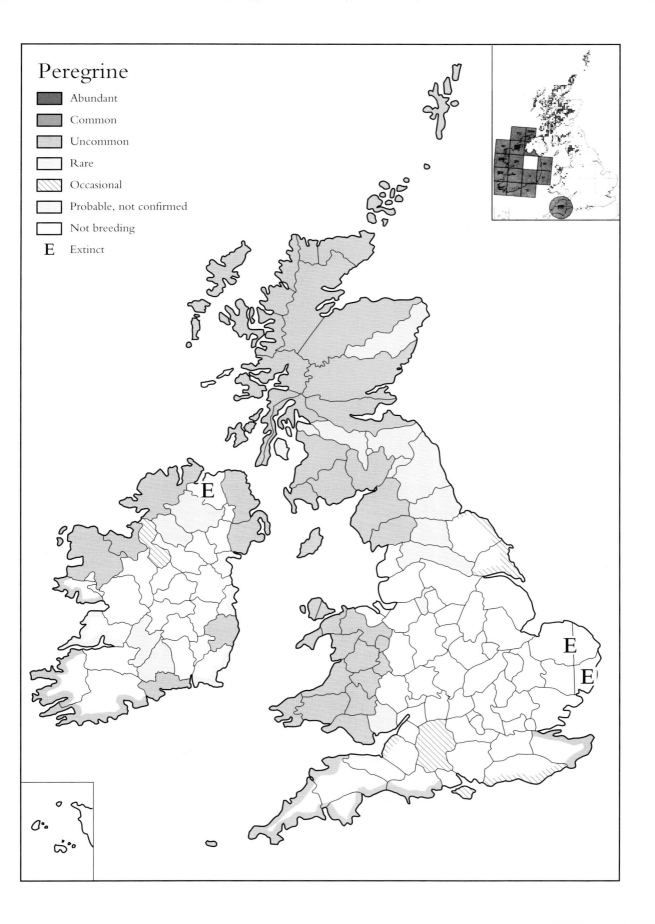

Peregrine

- ■ Abundant
- ■ Common
- ■ Uncommon
- □ Rare
- ▨ Occasional
- □ Probable, not confirmed
- □ Not breeding
- **E** Extinct

Red Grouse

Lagopus lagopus scoticus

The closing years of the 19th century and the period up to the 1914–18 war saw the heyday of grouse shooting and the management of moorland for the preservation of Red Grouse had developed to a highly sophisticated level. The Red Grouse was economically the most important species on the moors and attracted most attention; the Black Grouse was the only other important species there but was predominantly a species of the moorland edge. Before concerted management of the moors for Red Grouse, that is before the end of the 18th century, their numbers were probably much lower.

Red Grouse occurred throughout Ireland and on most heather moorland in Britain but not on lowland heath (and, hence, it was a species of the north and west). The species had, however, been recorded elsewhere. The early record of a natural and persistent group in the Hampshire New Forest is probably erroneous and may have been confused with the Black Grouse (Morris 1855) although a number of introductions in the area had been attempted (P. J. Hudson in litt). Other records from S and E England were the result of introductions. In Wales, productive moors were recorded in most counties. The best were in Merioneth, Denbighshire and Montgomeryshire although they were never as productive in total numbers as those in N England

and Scotland (although some densities may have been higher, Hudson in litt). The most renowned Welsh moor was the 3,000ha Ruabon Estate in Denbighshire where an average of over 4,000 Red Grouse were shot annually between 1900 and the 1914–18 war. In S Wales the Red Grouse occurred in fewer numbers than on the Snowdonia moors. It had evidently declined in Carmarthenshire, Glamorgan (where industrialisation in the uplands had destroyed its habitat) and Pembrokeshire (the last record was of a brace shot on the Preseli Mountains in 1885). A few were found in the uplands over the border into Monmouthshire, Herefordshire and Shropshire (in the latter county a small population still exists on the Long Mynd and the Stiperstones—Deans *et al.* 1992). From the N Staffordshire moors and through the Pennines into N England the Red Grouse bred, and was preserved, in all suitable habitat. In the Borders, where grouse shooting had a long history, it was considered that numbers had decreased from the early 19th century. Here, and elsewhere in Scotland, by the end of the century it is apparent that alternative uses for the land were reducing the extent and quality of suitable grouse habitat. Many heather moors were destroyed by sheep grazing, were ploughed up or were converted to deer forest. In Ireland the population was probably more stable, but was at a lower density than on Scottish moors, as the practice of large-scale management was not common.

As the decline in the management of sporting estates began in some areas during the 1914–18 war and more generally from the 1939–45 war so the degradation of grouse habitat accelerated. The consequent increase of bracken, as well as extensive planting of conifers in the uplands, caused the loss of much heather moorland. Despite this, however, evidence from shooting bag records shows that numbers of Red Grouse increased between the wars. It has been suggested that a series of warm, dry summers during this period encouraged good heather growth, crucial for the survival of broods in the following year, but this view is not accepted by some (P.J. Hudson in litt). Further degradation of habitat occurred after the 1939–45 war as a consequence of the almost complete cessation of moor management that occurred then. During the war, in 1945, many areas of Scotland that formerly held the largest numbers of Red Grouse were almost entirely deserted (Baxter and Rintoul 1953), and once the grouse go the moors are sold for alternative forms of land use (for instance forestry). Although subject to large local cyclic fluctuations, the Red Grouse population has continued to decline to the present day in most areas due to predation and habitat loss although, in areas where predator control is still rigorous, numbers of Red Grouse appear stable.

Number of counties in which recorded:

Period	Probable breeding		Confirmed breeding		Combined		
	Br	Ir	Br	Ir	Br	Ir	Both
1875–1900	0	0	57	34	57	34	91
1968–1972	0	0	62	34	62	34	96
			change		5	0	5
					9%		5%

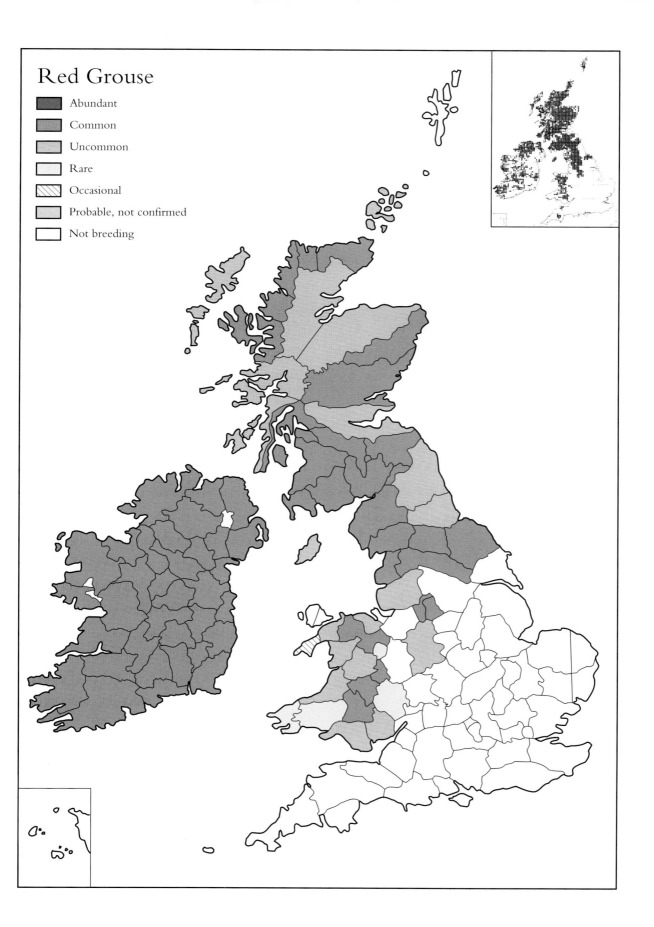

Red Grouse

- Abundant
- Common
- Uncommon
- Rare
- Occasional
- Probable, not confirmed
- Not breeding

Ptarmigan

Lagopus mutus

The Ptarmigan was much more widespread and probably bred in larger numbers in Britain prior to the 19th century than it did subsequently. Evidence of this former distribution is meagre, but it almost certainly bred in N England and may have done so on Cadair Idris in N Wales and in Ireland.

The evidence for a former Irish population rests solely on suggestions that the Gaelic name for the Ptarmigan is the similarly sounding Tarmachan, an ancient name that may have come from Ireland (Yarrell 1837–43), and that what appeared to be ancient bones found in a cave in Waterford may have been of this species (Ussher and Warren 1900). Other than that, 10–15 birds were turned down in Donegal late in the 19th century but soon disappeared (Ussher and Warren 1900). The evidence for breeding in Wales is even more scant. Early 19th century writers recorded that Ptarmigan had formerly bred there but this assertion appears to be based on no more than a tradition, the original source being lost (Forrest 1907). Evidence for its former breeding in Cumberland came from 18th century writers who may have seen them there. Both Pennant (1771) and Heysham (1794) wrote of the Ptarmigan inhabiting the hills around Keswick and a specimen taken on Skiddaw near that town in 1841 was exhibited in a local

museum for some years. It must have been very rare by that time, however, because local men who knew the hills well in the 1820s could not recollect ever seeing one (Macpherson 1892).

Game records from the end of the 17th century attested to the occurrence of the species in Kirkcudbrightshire and Dumfriesshire and it held out in the hills above Sanquhar in the 18th century and, possibly, into the 19th. The often quoted record of a number taken on these hills during the winter of 1822 or 1823 in very bad snow may have concerned individuals from more northern hills. A number introduced on to these same hills in 1847 may have lasted for a couple of seasons but not longer (Gladstone 1910). The original source for the assertion of former breeding on Arran is not clear (Dixon 1895, Paterson 1901). Other hills in S Scotland evidently used to hold breeding pairs (Baxter and Rintoul 1928, Rintoul and Baxter 1935) but the most southerly breeding site at the end of the 19th century was on Ben Lomond in S Perthshire and, here too, Ptarmigan were much rarer than formerly. The main breeding range was on the Grampian Mountains and Highlands, from Mount Battock in the east almost to the west coast and then north. Ptarmigan bred on many of the western islands including the Outer Hebrides and had bred on Orkney up to 1831 when the last birds were shot on Hoy. Throughout the western and northern fringes of its range it bred in fewer numbers at the end of the century than earlier. In the Outer Hebrides breeding was confined to Lewis and Harris but had occurred on South Uist in the past. Numbers on Islay, Jura and Rum were far smaller than they had been. From Assynt northwards severe decreases had been noted over the second half of the 19th century which were believed to have been a result of in-breeding occurring in the now isolated groups (Harvie-Brown and Buckley 1895) or because the conversion of many of the grouse moors to deer walks was altering the vegetation of the hills (Harvie-Brown and Macpherson 1904). Modern research suggests that habitat loss and overgrazing are responsible for most of the declines of the Ptarmigan (P. J. Hudson in litt).

Research carried out in the 20th century has suggested that population fluctuations over a ten year cycle, particularly in the Cairngorms, are a feature of Ptarmigan biology, possibly through changes in behaviour or food, and that temporary extinctions of isolated populations are a feature of these fluctuations (Sharrock 1976). An alternative view, however, is that Ptarmigan are only shot when Red Grouse numbers are high and, hence, bag records show fluctuating numbers of Ptarmigan (P. J. Hudson in litt). Apart from the loss of breeding birds from Lewis in 1938 and some breeding groups in the S Cairngorms no widespread change has occurred in the Ptarmigan population during the 20th century (Parslow 1973, Gibbons et al. 1993).

Number of counties in which recorded:

Period	Probable breeding		Confirmed breeding		Combined		
	Br	Ir	Br	Ir	Br	Ir	Both
1875–1900	0	0	14	0	14	0	14
1968-1972	0	0	15	0	15	0	15
			change		1	0	1
					7%		7%

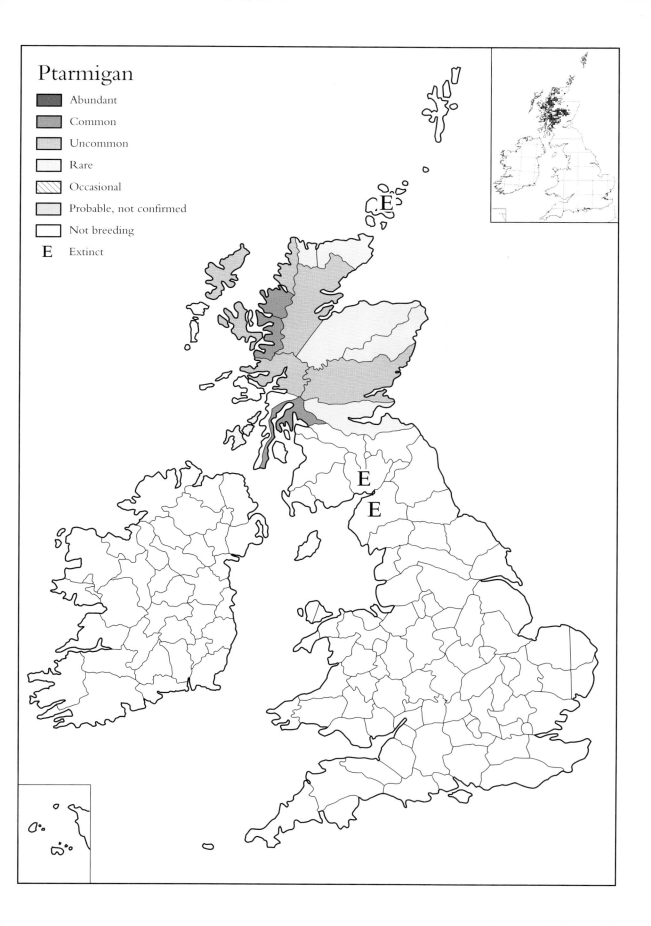

Ptarmigan

- Abundant
- Common
- Uncommon
- Rare
- Occasional
- Probable, not confirmed
- Not breeding
- E Extinct

Black Grouse

Tetrao tetrix

The history and status of the Black Grouse in Britain in the 19th century was well recorded but, in some English counties, even by the 1840s, it became difficult to distinguish between natural and introduced, or even reintroduced, populations. It had been suggested by a number of writers (Yarrell 1837–43) that by the early years of the 19th century the Black Grouse had been shot to extinction in many English counties (but this may not have been the case in the light of later evidence of a worldwide decline at that time (Hudson 1989)). Black Grouse were recorded regularly in the 16th and 17th centuries and some early accounts mentioned birds obtained in Kent, Surrey and Sussex. They were recorded less regularly in the 18th century and the last was shot in Kent in 1851 (Ticehurst 1909). The early birds seem to have been a natural population but the 19th century Black Grouse possibly spread from introductions (Ticehurst 1909). Black Grouse had been extinct on the Hurtwood, a tract of heath between Guildford and Dorking in Surrey, since the late 1760s. In 1815 some grouse were turned out there and, the heath apparently still being suitable for the species, they flourished. They spread to other heaths in the northwest of the county and, by the 1840s, had reached Berkshire.

Many attempts had been made to introduce the Black Grouse to Norfolk. None was successful, however, proba-

bly until the 1860s. Neither Yarrell (1837–43) nor Morris (1855) included it in their lists of counties in which Black Grouse had been recorded but, by 1866, it had evidently become established (Stevenson 1866–90). The successful introduction was made on the Sandringham estate near King's Lynn and from there it gradually spread on to neighbouring estates. By the 1880s, however, it was declining rapidly. Other places into which Black Grouse had been introduced, or reintroduced, more or less successfully, were Sussex, Kent, Buckinghamshire, Suffolk, the Orkney Isles, N Wales and Ireland.

In SW England the Black Grouse was probably indigenous. Into the last quarter of the 19th century it bred from the Hampshire New Forest into Dorset. Exmoor, on both sides of the Devonshire and Somerset border, had a healthy population and then, from Dartmoor it bred in declining numbers into Cornwall. The Black Grouse had been noted as a Welsh resident since at least 1693. The 19th century saw a general decline, especially in the northern and southern counties, despite the efforts made to preserve game generally at that time. The populations in Brecon and Montgomeryshire, and some of the adjacent English counties, were more stable, however.

From the counties of the N Midlands (from the Staffordshire moors, the Derbyshire hills and the forests of Nottinghamshire) Black Grouse increased in numbers northwards. Harvie-Brown and Macpherson (1904) summed up the Black Grouse's status in Scotland at the end of the 19th century thus: 'Though nowhere in the west of Ross-shire or Scotland north of Argyll so numerous as it is in the south of Scotland or even in the central districts, Blackgame are still birds of the birch woods in the north and are in considerable numbers'.

In England and Wales the Black Grouse continued to decline rapidly and was extinct in most southern counties by 1905 and in many of the rest by the 1930s. These declines have followed the loss of suitable breeding habitat resulting from agricultural changes but, in some areas, particularly in Wales and Scotland, maturing conifer plantations have provided new habitat and, from the 1940s and 1950s, Black Grouse began to increase in those areas. The positive effect of the new forests is likely to be short-lived, however, since once the canopy is formed Black Grouse move out (P. J. Hudson in litt).

Where known the dates of last 19th century breeding follow. **Wiltshire**—bred sparingly in the south but ceased to do so about 1820. Stragglers from the New Forest were shot in the extreme southeast up to about 1860. **Sussex**—last bred around 1840. **Kent**—may have bred into the first decade of the 19th century. **Isle of Man**—introduced, persisted for a while, but was extinct again between 1800 and 1850.—**Denbighshire**—an introduced stock probably ceased breeding during the 1870s although stragglers from Montgomeryshire were shot into the 1880s.

Number of counties in which recorded:

Period	Probable breeding		Confirmed breeding		Combined		
	Br	Ir	Br	Ir	Br	Ir	Both
1875–1900	1	0	58	0	59	0	59
1968–1972	3	0	37	0	40	0	40
			change		−19	0	−19
					−32%		−32%

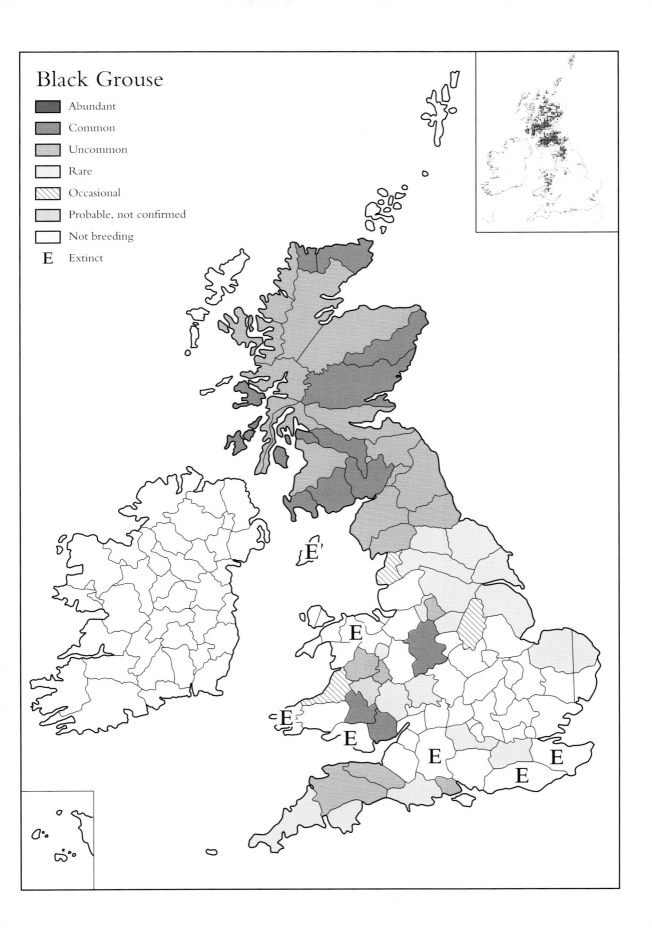

Black Grouse

- **Abundant**
- **Common**
- **Uncommon**
- **Rare**
- **Occasional**
- **Probable, not confirmed**
- **Not breeding**
- **E** Extinct

Capercaillie

Tetrao urogallus

The history of the Capercaillie in Britain and Ireland was studied in great detail by many naturalists of the 19th and 20th centuries, the most notable of which were Harvie-Brown (1878, 1879) and Pennie (1951). They recorded firstly, the extinction of the native British race in Scotland, Wales and Ireland in the 18th century and in England, probably, much earlier and then the introduction of Swedish birds into Scotland in the early 19th century.

There is little evidence of this species in England. Yarrell (1871–85) noted that what appeared to be ancient Capercaillie bones were found in caves in Teesdale and quoted a reference concerning a rent of 'one wode-henne [Capercaillie] yearly' payable to the Bishop of Durham for land in the 14th century. It must have become extinct in England much earlier than the mid 17th century suggestion of Witherby *et al.* (1938–41). Pennant (1778) provided the only reference to the Capercaillie in Wales. He referred briefly to the beasts of the chase and included the 'Ceiliog coed, or Cock of the Forest'. His brief description of the bird and its habits suggests that he was referring to the Capercaillie.

Capercaillie were common in the Irish woods in the 17th century according to Willoughby and O'Flaherty (Ussher and Warren 1900) but during the following century the species gradually became extinct. Smith (1750) observed that it was 'now rarely [found] in Ireland since our woods have been destroyed' and Pennant (1776) stated that in around 1760 a few were still found near Thomastown, Tipperary. Although 'Wild Turkeys' were spoken of into the 19th century there was no evidence that it survived into the late 18th century.

A Scottish Act of Parliament of 1621 that prohibited the buying or selling of Capercaillie suggests that it was becoming scarce even at that time. The last of the native race were confined to the Inverness-shire woods and were generally accepted to have been exterminated there during the 1770s, although two were shot in Ballochbuie Forest, Aberdeenshire in 1785. The disappearance of the Capercaillie has almost invariably been attributed to the destruction of the natural pine forests. There was, however, enough suitable forest left for subsequent reintroductions so the effect of persecution on this species must not be underestimated (P. J. Hudson in litt).

Lloyd, a 19th century sportsman, seems to have been the first to conceive the idea of restoring the Capercaillie to Britain. After a few failed attempts they were successfully introduced to Taymouth Castle, Perthshire in 1837 and 1838. By the 1860s they had spread far beyond the Breadalbane Estate following the woods in the Tay valley and by 1879 almost every suitable piece of woodland in Perthshire had been colonised and the species had spread into neighbouring counties particularly to the northeast through Angus into Kincardineshire. This, and the subsequent, expansion was assisted by numerous other introductions. The counties that had been colonised by 1900 are Perthshire (1837), the Isle of Arran (1843), Angus (1856), Stirlingshire (1863), Fife and Kinross (1864), Dunbartonshire (1867), Argyll (1875), Kincardineshire (1878), Aberdeenshire (1878), Moray (1886), Ross-shire (1890), Banffshire (1890s), probably Nairn (1890s) and Inverness-shire (1892) (Bannerman 1953–63).

The Capercaillie's maximum distribution was reached about the period of the 1914–18 war when many trees were felled and this effectively temporarily halted the expansion. The maturation of the Forestry Commission plantings from 1919 allowed it to resume an increase in numbers but between the *68–72* and *88–91 Atlas* a severe decline has taken place. This may be the result of human activities, a period of wet summer weather or increased numbers of predators. It is also likely that overgrazing has had an impact on the invertebrate prey of the Capercaillie (P. J. Hudson in litt).

Number of counties in which recorded:

Period	Probable breeding		Confirmed breeding		Combined		
	Br	Ir	Br	Ir	Br	Ir	Both
1875–1900	0	0	6	0	6	0	6
1968–1972	1	0	7	0	8	0	8
			change		2	0	2
					33%		33%

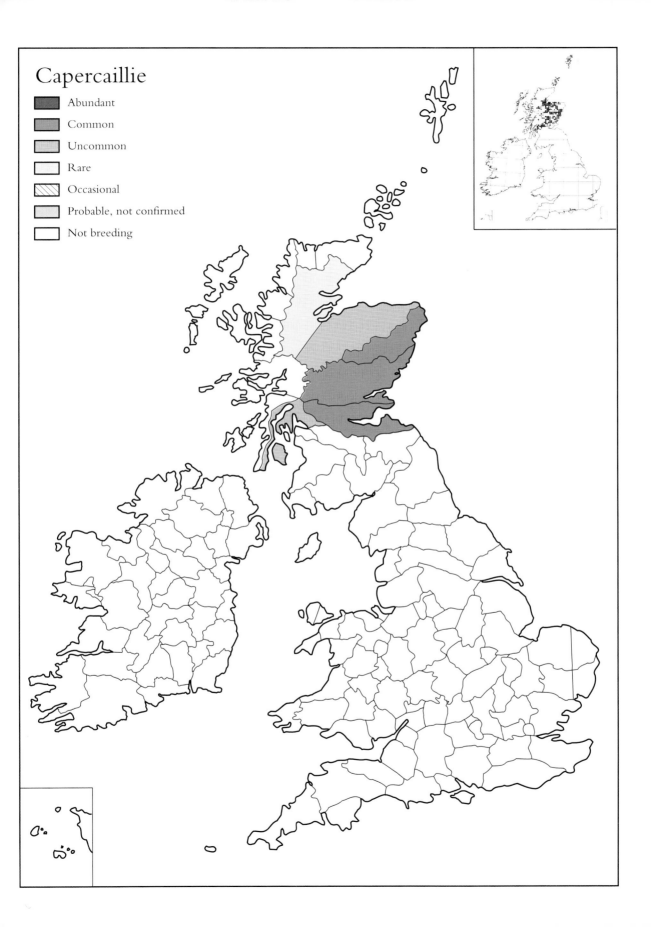

Capercaillie

- Abundant
- Common
- Uncommon
- Rare
- Occasional
- Probable, not confirmed
- Not breeding

Red-legged Partridge (French Partridge)

Alectoris rufa

The first attempt to introduce the Red-legged Partridge to Britain was orchestrated by Charles II. A number of birds were turned down near to Windsor, Berkshire in 1673 but they did not persist for more than a couple of seasons. Further introductions were attempted by English noblemen throughout the country but with no success. The Red-legged Partridge probably became established in Britain following its introduction near Orford, Suffolk in 1770 by the Marquis of Hertford. This introduction was supported by another at the same time at Rendlesham, Suffolk by Lord Rendlesham. Many other attempts in SE England to introduce it from live imported stock had failed. The 1770 introduction was a large-scale attempt, however, and derived from birds locally reared under chickens, from eggs imported from France—hence its common name of the time. Introductions have been attempted throughout Britain as far north as Orkney and in some areas of Ireland up to the present day but the core population is largely derived from the Suffolk introductions. It is a curious fact that the French Partridge has been introduced on very

many occasions but, since at least the early 1800s, it has been regarded as an unsatisfactory sporting bird owing to its propensity to escape on foot instead of the wing, its poor flying ability, its poor flavour and its suspected displacement of the much more satisfactory Partridge.

By the last quarter of the 19th century the Red-legged Partridge had spread throughout the counties of SE England and was breeding commonly there. In the central and E Midlands and the south coast counties as far as Dorset it bred less frequently but, apparently, sustainably. In Wales it had been recorded from most counties but bred regularly only in Brecon and Merioneth—in both cases from introductions. It had spread north, probably via Lincolnshire, into parts of Yorkshire. Other counties recorded occasional breeding following introduction attempts but did not hold populations that were able to sustain themselves. The patchiness of the Red-legged Partridge's distribution, particularly at its fringes, gives an impression of a species undergoing a dynamic extension of range. The spread continued into the 20th century.

Up to 1930 the Red-legged Partridge continued to spread further west to Somerset and Shropshire and north into North Yorkshire. A small contraction of its western edge occurred after 1930 and local population changes occurred up to around 1960 when numbers increased substantially in its core East Anglian stronghold.

The *68–72 Atlas* presents what is probably the maximum extent of the species' sustainable range in Britain. This is the product of the growth and stabilisation of the population during the 19th and 20th centuries and represents the area of Britain that can offer the continental-type climate and land-use characteristics that are typical of its natural range in France, Spain and other parts of Europe. Apparent increases of range up to the *88–91 Atlas* were the result of further introductions. An interesting and complex future is likely for the Red-legged Partridge as attempts to increase sustainability of introductions through hybridisation with, and releases of, Chukars work their way out of the system.

Number of counties in which recorded:

Period	Probable breeding		Confirmed breeding		Combined		
	Br	Ir	Br	Ir	Br	Ir	Both
1875–1900	0	0	44	0	44	0	44
1968–1972	0	0	67	0	67	0	67
			change		23	0	23
					52%		52%

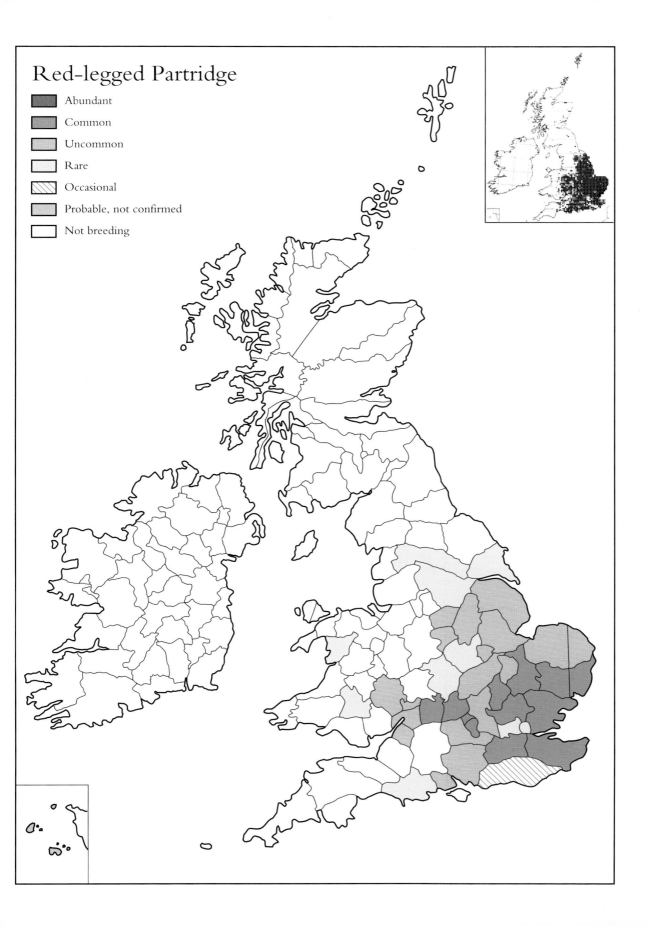

Red-legged Partridge

- Abundant
- Common
- Uncommon
- Rare
- Occasional
- Probable, not confirmed
- Not breeding

Grey Partridge
(Common Partridge)

Perdix perdix

Accounts from the early years of the 19th century indicate that the Partridge was increasing, particularly so in England and S Scotland. Agricultural changes taking place then apparently suited this species, the greatest numbers being found in the most intensively farmed areas (Yarrell 1837–43, Morris 1855). Increased drainage of marshes and wetlands throughout its range and the ploughing of mosses in N England at least from the 17th century provided new breeding sites that, formerly, were not suitable (Macpherson 1892), and the cultivation of the Scottish uplands brought the Partridge to the edges of the moorlands where it effectively replaced the Red Grouse (Yarrell 1837–43, Harvie-Brown 1906). Its numbers at the time were at their highest where protection from predation and poaching was at its greatest and most coordinated (Morris 1855, Dixon 1895).

In Ireland, however, Thompson (1849–56) made special note of local decreases and proposed a number of causes. The one most cited at the time (and the reason for local decreases in some English counties) was arsenic seed dressings (Young 1804, Hawker 1844 in Potts 1986). Dr H. W. Fuller (in The Lancet in 1848) investigated the cause of death of a great number of Partridges in Hampshire and concluded that they had been poisoned by seed corn that had been steeped in an arsenic solution prior to planting to kill wireworm. This was a relatively new technique and was being used increasingly throughout Britain and Ireland (Morris 1855). Nevertheless, the largest Partridge bags in Ireland were recorded in the 1870s (G. R. Potts in litt); numbers were stated to have decreased in the country towards the end of the 19th century but reasons other than arsenic were proposed for the decline. A combination of the decline of wheat growing in the 1870s, the use of breech loading shotguns and poaching were all blamed, but overall, it was considered that the wetter climate in Ireland did not suit the species as well as that in England (Ussher and Warren 1900).

On the northern and western fringes of their range in Britain the populations were probably not viable without introductions and sustained preservation. Introductions into the Isle of Man from the 17th century onwards suffered mixed fortunes but, with improved preservation techniques, they thrived from the 1830s onwards (Ralfe 1906). The wet climate of W Scotland and its islands did not allow the survival of wholly independent populations and, on the Outer Hebrides, a number of introduction attempts had been made since about 1790 on Lewis, all of which failed rapidly (Harvie-Brown and Buckley 1888, Harvie-Brown 1906). Bids to introduce the species to Orkney were only slightly more effective; remnants of the initial introductions persisted for a few years but never long term (Buckley and Harvie-Brown 1891). The situation in Wales was not so clear. No evidence of a long–term decline was noted during the 19th century by the contemporary writers; indeed, when conditions were good the Partridge was often regarded as occurring commonly. Harsh winters and wet summers, however, severely knocked back numbers (Mathew 1894, Forrest 1907, 1919). Studies of game book records have suggested that numbers have been decreasing in Wales from the end of the 19th century (Parslow 1973, Tapper 1992).

Much research has been carried out in an attempt to understand the dramatic decline that has occurred during the 20th century. In Ireland the decline was temporarily suspended by protective legislation in 1932. In Britain as a whole the decline was apparent from the 1939–45 war and accelerated from the 1960s (Potts 1986). A number of factors are likely to have contributed to this failure: a series of cooler, wetter summers has been blamed, as have various aspects of changing agricultural practices. The effect these have on chick survival rates has been suggested as the main factor for the decline (Gibbons *et al.* 1993). Since chick survival rates were already lower in the wetter west, the decline there has had a greater impact than in the (drier) east (Potts and Aebischer in press).

Number of counties in which recorded:

Period	Probable breeding		Confirmed breeding		Combined		
	Br	Ir	Br	Ir	Br	Ir	Both
1875–1900	0	0	104	34	104	34	138
1968–1972	0	0	93	32	93	32	125
			change		−11	−2	−13
					−11%	−6%	−9%

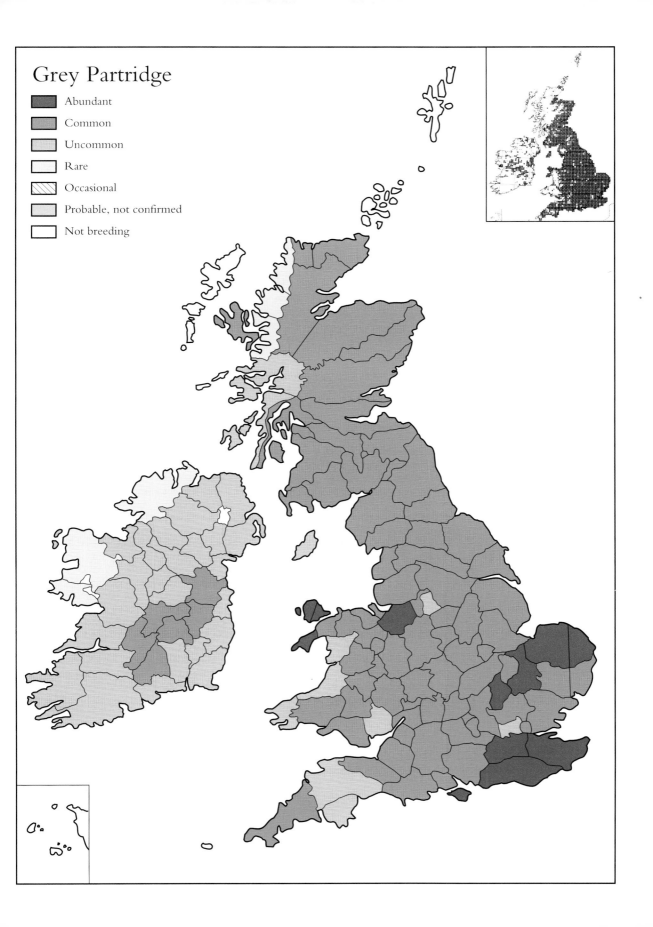

Grey Partridge

- Abundant
- Common
- Uncommon
- Rare
- Occasional
- Probable, not confirmed
- Not breeding

Quail

Coturnix coturnix

Quail nests were occasionally found in nearly all counties and regions of Britain during the last quarter of the 19th century. Although finding nests is not easy, it seems likely that Quail bred annually, but in very small numbers, over much of the country. It had evidently decreased substantially during the 19th century, probably since at least 1800. The population reached a low level in about 1865 from which it did not recover, although the low numbers were relieved by 'Quail years', those most noted being 1870 and 1893; 1885, 1887 and 1892 have also been cited, but apparently with little cause (Moreau 1951). The decline was noted in most counties of England and some in Wales and Scotland. There were many explanations for the decline but they fell into two main groups—agricultural change and human depredation.

Breeding habitat losses of many kinds were most frequently blamed for the decline. Enclosure and improvement of rough grassland (Saunders and Clarke 1927) evidently destroyed many suitable breeding areas. The new agricultural habitats were not completely unsuitable for the Quail during the breeding season but continuing changes in farming techniques rendered even these habitats less suitable as the century progressed. The rough grasslands were replaced, in some cases, by the cultivation of clover and other animal forage crops but these declined towards the end of the century (e.g. Stevenson 1866–90, Lilford 1895, Ticehurst 1909). The destruction of tall, old hedges with tangled bottoms removed some breeding sites (Ticehurst 1909) whilst the mechanisation of mowing was said to have been responsible for the loss of many nests. One farmer in Lancashire said that he had killed many whilst mowing grass and 'took the heads off three birds in one day' (Aplin 1889, Mitchell 1885). Other suitable breeding habitat was lost to urbanisation (Steele-Elliott 1897–1901). Moreau (1951), however, doubted that changes in agricultural methods, and in particular the introduction of the mowing machine, were responsible for the decline. In some areas the decline took place without any such changes. Both Moreau (1951) and Nicholson (1951) thought that human depredation was the most important factor in the decline of Quail populations.

The Quail was shot wherever it was encountered in Britain, particularly in the autumn prior to its departure, but also during the breeding season. Eggs were collected for the table whenever they were found but the bulk of the destruction of this species evidently took place on the continent. 'Incredible' numbers were taken (they were either shot or, more often, netted) in the Mediterranean countries for the table and many were imported into Britain for that market (Borrer 1891, Lilford 1895, Whitaker 1907). Early in the 19th century over 100,000 were recorded taken in one day on the W coast of Naples; towards the end of the century a single vessel took 40,000 into the port of Marseilles and, even as late as 1913, 1,858,000 Quail were exported from Egypt alone (Moreau 1927).

The agricultural history of Ireland was probably responsible for a different pattern of decline following an earlier increase. The increase in the planting of wheat (less intensively grown than in England) and the consequent weedy stubble fields apparently suited the Quail. It remained common until about 1850 but after the famine much tilled land reverted to pasture or moor and, after about 1880, it was regarded as effectively extinct in the country. Occasional nests and broods were noted before the 1893 'Quail year' that brought a number of breeding records.

Numbers of breeding Quail in Britain and Ireland remained at a, generally, very low level until about 1942. It may be coincidental that regulation of spring hunting along the Mediterranean coasts began in 1937, and that numbers have gradually increased to the present day since that time, despite marked annual fluctuations. Interestingly, both *68–72* and *88–91 Atlas* surveys included Quail years (1970 and 1989) that were the largest recorded at the time during the 20th century.

Number of counties in which recorded:

Period	Probable breeding		Confirmed breeding		Combined		
	Br	Ir	Br	Ir	Br	Ir	Both
1875–1900	0	0	100	18	100	18	118
1968–1972	21	4	28	3	49	7	56
			change		−51	−11	−62
					−51%	−61%	−53%

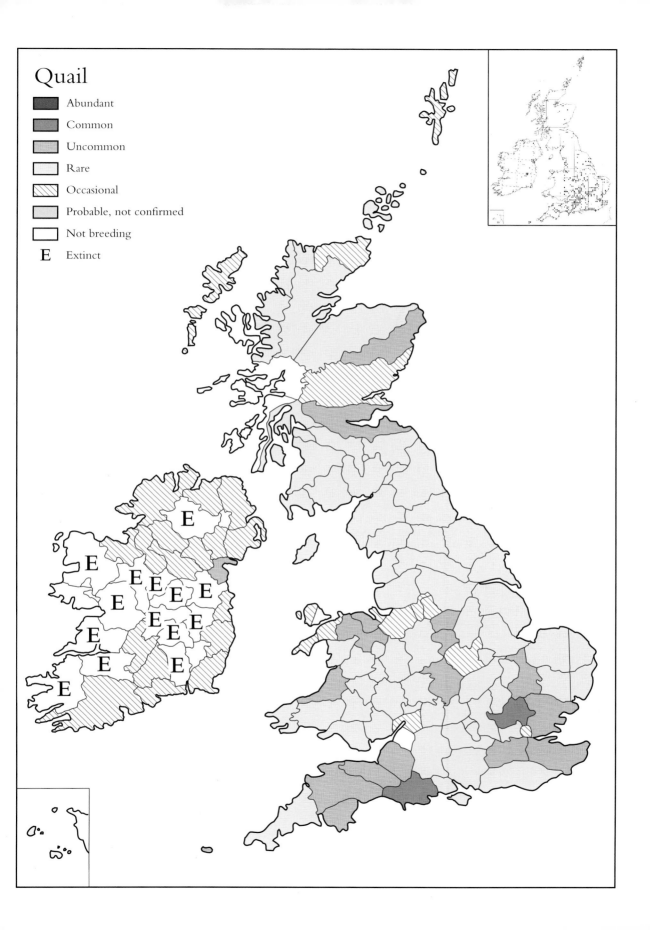

Quail

- ◼ Abundant
- ◼ Common
- ◼ Uncommon
- ◻ Rare
- ▨ Occasional
- ▦ Probable, not confirmed
- ◻ Not breeding
- **E** Extinct

Pheasant

Phasianus colchicus

The Pheasant was absent only from the Northern Isles, some of the Inner Hebrides and the Isle of Man at the end of the 19th century. In many areas, however, numbers were maintained only by regular reinforcements of turned down birds. This was especially true of most areas of Scotland and Ireland.

Many traditions exist of the origin of the Pheasant in Britain. Yarrell (1837–43) quoted Daniels who believed that Jason and the Argonauts first brought the Pheasant to Europe from the banks of the Phasis (Rion) in Colchis (Georgia) *ca* 3250 years ago. It was commonly considered by some that the Romans brought it to Britain (Dixon 1895, Ticehurst 1909) or that it was introduced later, *ca* 1299 (Morris 1855, Cramp *et al*. 1977–94) or during the 14th century (Yapp 1983). Whatever the species' origin it had been recorded from Wales and Scotland by the 16th century (Marchant *et al*. 1990) and was considered numerous in Ireland by this time (Ussher and Warren 1900). It is almost certain, then, that feral Pheasant populations existed in the 1500s across much of the country (Robertson and Woodburn 1993).

It is, of course, hard to separate out human influence, but experience with other better documented introductions in the United States suggests that Pheasants would have rapidly established self-sustaining populations. Management, in particular predator control and rearing, would increase local densities but Pheasants can exist at lower densities without it (P. A. Robertson in litt). With the development of the modern shotgun and the influence of the Prince of Wales (later Edward VII) in the 1860s, driven Pheasant shooting became both possible and fashionable. This form of shooting requires high densities of game and led to large increases in rearing, predator control and habitat management to increase the existing feral populations (Robertson in litt). East Anglia and Sussex were undoubtedly the best areas for Pheasants at the turn of the 19th century, as seen by the trend to purchase large estates in those areas, purely for the shooting at that time (P. A. Robertson in litt). The introductions, from around the middle of the 19th century, were of birds other than the nominate *colchicus* group, mainly those of the *torquatus* group, the so-called Chinese Ring-necked Pheasant, and by the end of the century it became very difficult to find a pure specimen of the old race (Tapper 1992), particularly as the ring-neck is a dominant genetic character.

Intensive pheasant management, beginning in the mid 1800s, has continued through to the present. Numbers of Pheasants during the present century are certainly much higher than would occur without management but the Pheasant is established as a truly feral species across much of the country. All historical hunting accounts and bag records suggest that the Pheasant's distribution has not changed since the mid 1800s, apart from some spread in the Scottish glens (P. A. Robertson in litt). It is difficult to determine the status of naturally sustained populations in Britain and Ireland because of the continuing artificial maintenance of local populations but it is apparent that wild populations have declined, particularly as a consequence of agricultural intensification since the 1939–45 war (Tapper 1992). It is also apparent that maximum densities have been reached artificially in some areas, partial testimony to the reason for the increasing overall numbers during the 20th century, but shooting returns in areas where the population is not assisted by introductions have fallen since 1982 (Gibbons *et al*. 1993).

Number of counties in which recorded:

Period	Probable breeding		Confirmed breeding		Combined		
	Br	Ir	Br	Ir	Br	Ir	Both
1875–1900	0	0	104	34	104	34	138
1968–1972	0	0	101	34	101	34	135
			change		−3	0	−3
					−3%		−2%

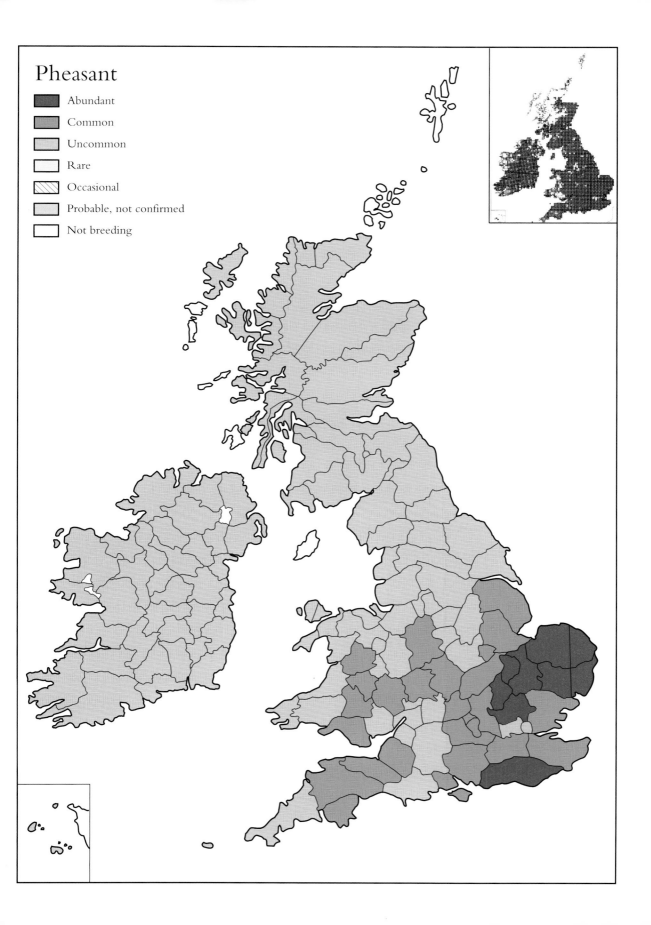

Pheasant

- ■ Abundant
- ■ Common
- ■ Uncommon
- □ Rare
- ▨ Occasional
- ▦ Probable, not confirmed
- □ Not breeding

Golden Pheasant

Chrysolophus pictus

that is estimated to number between 1,000 and 2,000 birds at the present day (*88–91 Atlas*).

The Golden Pheasant was first imported into Britain during the 18th century but attempts at introducing it into the wild were not made until the 1880s. The poor survival of introduced Pheasants in W Scotland and its islands led a number of estates to experiment with other species, including this one, with no greater success than the release of Golden X Lady Amherst's hybrids in 1895 near Newton Stewart on the Dumfriesshire/Kirkcudbrightshire border. By 1905 these had reverted to the pure Golden Pheasant type and are probably the origin of the present population in that area.

Introductions of Golden Pheasants in Norfolk and Suffolk at the end of the 19th century (prior to 1880) followed the search for gamebirds to supplement Pheasant shooting. Turkeys, Virginia or Bobwhite Quail and Red Grouse were also attempted at that time (Ruffer 1977), but only the Golden Pheasant remains. Introduced to Elveden, near Thetford by Maharaja Victor Duleep Singh, it was unpopular as a shooting bird as it prefers to run or fly very low when chased. Nevertheless, the species thrived throughout the 20th century, especially in the new conifer forests planted in the Brecks.

This group was the origin of the present population in that area and constitute the majority of a British population

Number of counties in which recorded:

Period	Probable breeding		Confirmed breeding		Combined		
	Br	Ir	Br	Ir	Br	Ir	Both
1875–1900	0	0	4	0	4	0	4
1968–1972	0	1	8	0	8	1	9
			change		4	1	5
					100%		125%

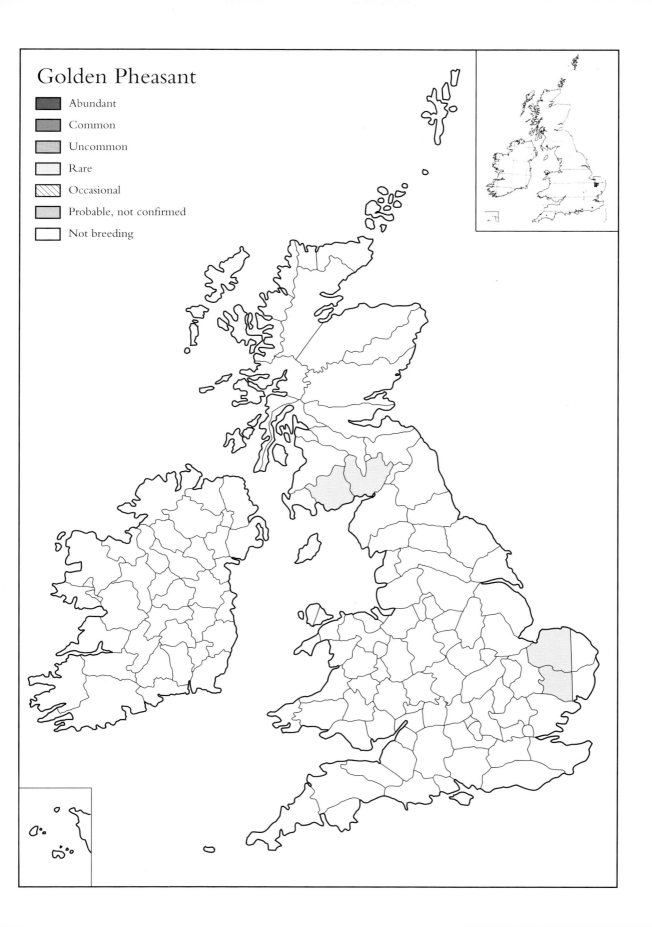

Golden Pheasant

- ■ Abundant
- ▨ Common
- ▨ Uncommon
- □ Rare
- ▨ Occasional
- ▨ Probable, not confirmed
- □ Not breeding

Lady Amherst's Pheasant

Chrysolophus amherstiae

The Lady Amherst's Pheasant was first imported into England from the mountain ridges of China, Tibet and Burma in July 1828 by Lady Sarah Amherst. Captive breeding proved difficult and was not successful until 1871. During the 19th century two main introductions into the wild were attempted. The first was by Robert Gordon of Bute who bred many exotic species of pheasant, amongst other birds and mammals, which he released at Mount Stuart. Of the pheasants that he released only the Golden Pheasant survived; the Lady Amherst's Pheasants disappeared through hybridisation with the former. (Some of Gordon's other introductions were not always so unsuccessful. He released several kangaroos in 1912; one survived for some years and often appeared in front of beaters heading pheasant drives.)

Lady Amherst's Pheasants were introduced into Woburn Park in Bedfordshire in 1890. From this initial introduction they have gradually spread beyond the estate boundary and along the Greensand Ridge, aided by other introductions during the 20th century in the county, and have bred there up to the present day. Trodd and Kramer (1991) estimated the Bedfordshire population at around 100–200 individuals. The isolation of suitable breeding habitat and the skulking nature of the species means that unaided expansion is unlikely, whilst its ability to interbreed with the Golden Pheasant can cause the disappearance of breeding groups as has happened in other areas through the 20th century.

Number of counties in which recorded:

Period	Probable breeding		Confirmed breeding		Combined		
	Br	Ir	Br	Ir	Br	Ir	Both
1875–1900	0	0	1	0	1	0	1
1968–1972	2	0	4	0	6	0	6
			change		5	0	5
					500%		500%

150

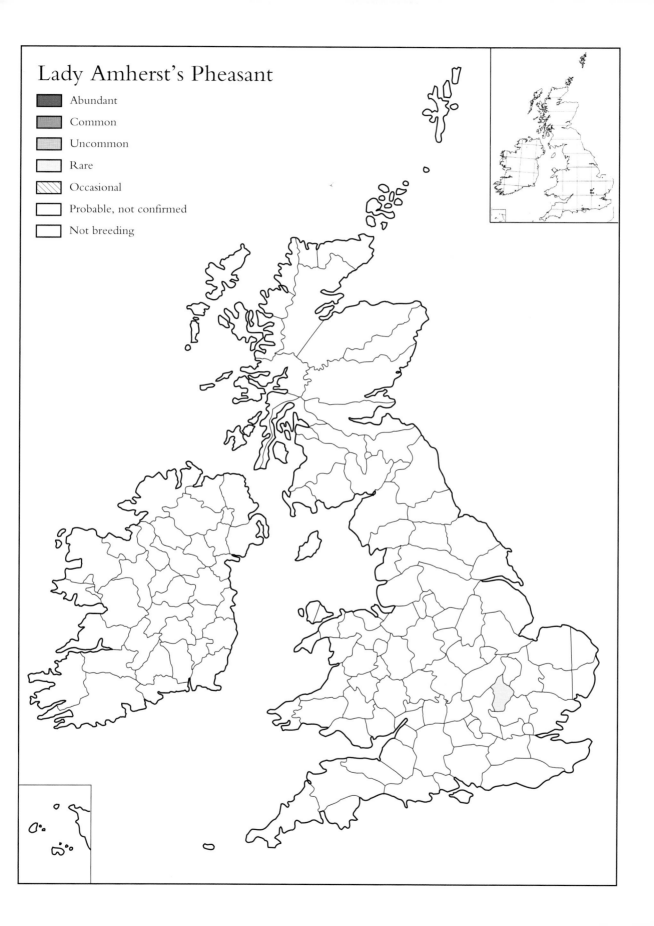

Lady Amherst's Pheasant

■	Abundant
▨	Common
▥	Uncommon
□	Rare
▨	Occasional
□	Probable, not confirmed
□	Not breeding

Water Rail
(Water-Rail)

Rallus aquaticus

At the end of the 19th century the Water Rail was widely distributed and, in many areas, considered a common bird. Proof of breeding was then, as now, difficult to obtain owing to the secretive nature of the bird and its nesting habits. The 19th century naturalists, however, went to great lengths to prove breeding, whilst the Rail's eggs were highly rated by collectors for both display and eating. The result is that for all but some areas of the Pennines, Bedfordshire and Hertfordshire (where breeding was suspected, but not proved), the NW coast of Scotland, Orkney (where breeding was only suspected and the meadow and loch probably used on Mainland was drained) and Shetland the Water Rail was claimed as a breeding bird. Indeed, in some parts of S Wales, the S Midlands, some areas of the south coast and land around the Tay and Dee it was believed to breed commonly.

Even at this time, though, the Water Rail was under pressure around the country. Drainage was blamed for reductions in both breeding and wintering numbers in many counties in England and some in Wales. In some areas, particularly Norfolk and Suffolk, because of their proximity to the insatiable markets of London, egg gatherers emptied so many Water Rail nests and shot so many birds for the table that some writers considered these activities serious enough to have caused local declines in populations. In one season over 200 eggs were supplied from the

Yarmouth area to one dealer alone. However, in general, the Water Rail was considered particularly common throughout East Anglia. Local extinctions took place as the 19th century progressed and land drainage and clearance of certain waterways accelerated but there is little evidence that there had been any widespread change in Water Rail numbers throughout the 19th century. Indeed, up to the late 1930s, the general distribution of the Water Rail in Britain gave the impression that little had changed during the first quarter of the 20th century (Witherby *et al.* 1938–41). The species was described as breeding in most marshy districts, especially Norfolk and Ireland, but more rarely in the far north of Britain. By inference, it was apparently now breeding in Orkney.

As the 20th century progressed gaps appeared in the distribution so that by the 1960s Water Rails were considered not to breed over much of the Midlands and NE England, parts of N Wales, Cornwall, Devonshire, most of the Borders, central Scotland and West Scotland. The Water Rail's stronghold remained parts of East Anglia and Ireland. The *68-72 Atlas* survey confirmed some of this picture. By this time, however, re-colonisation of Cornwall, the English Midlands and parts of NE England appears to have taken place. The canals that had fallen into disuse have provided suitable habitat—certainly, the English Midlands has a dense network of these artificial waterways. Relatively recent increases have been linked quite widely, in places such as the Midlands and SE England, with the increase in extraction of sand, gravel and chalk and coal subsidence/flashes which have all provided suitable nesting habitats (D. Glue *in litt*). Equally, a higher proportion of the population now breeds on nature reserves where sympathetic management and the creation of wetlands have helped greatly.

The *88–91 Atlas* recorded a broadly comparable distribution to that of the *68–72 Atlas* but with an apparent thinning over much of the range. A number of causes are postulated for this apparent decline, not least of which is the difficulty in recording breeding. Further loss of habitat was ascribed to loss of the dense water margin vegetation that the Water Rail requires, through, for instance, the canalisation of waterways. Further drainage of wet areas has taken place and construction on coastal marsh has occurred. The Water Rail's vulnerability to severely cold winters was mentioned by Dobinson and Richards (1964), suggesting that the winters of 1963 and the early 1980s may have reduced numbers. If the influx of the Water Rail into western coastal districts during periods of exceptional cold in areas of the British mainland, noted in Wales and, especially, in Ireland by the 19th century writers, gives an indication of this vulnerability, then some of the fluctuations noted may be explained thus.

Number of counties in which recorded:

Period	Probable breeding		Confirmed breeding		Combined		
	Br	Ir	Br	Ir	Br	Ir	Both
1875–1900	2	0	97	34	99	34	133
1968–1972	12	3	31	31	43	34	77
			change		−56	0	−56
					−57%		−42%

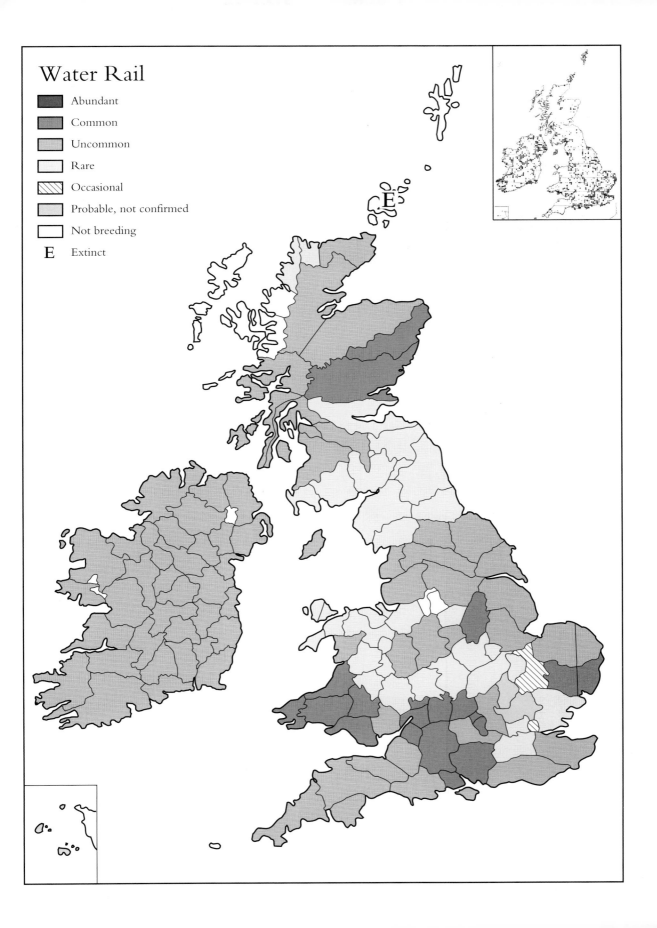

Water Rail

- **Abundant**
- **Common**
- **Uncommon**
- **Rare**
- **Occasional**
- **Probable, not confirmed**
- **Not breeding**
- **E** Extinct

Spotted Crake

Porzana porzana

In the 19th century ornithologists were uncertain whether the Spotted Crake in Britain was a summer breeding migrant, arriving early in the spring and leaving in late autumn, sometimes a late spring arrival, sometimes a partial migrant or a migrant most commonly met with in autumn and winter. Following a review of the early and current literature, migration reports and correspondence with several other ornithologists, Aplin (1890, 1891) concluded that it was an early spring migrant arriving from the second week of March onwards, and that it probably bred in every county of England and Wales that afforded the marshy ground or lake or river banks with suitable cover that the species required. It was much more uncommon in Scotland where it had only been recorded breeding on the east side but had been recorded in the west in autumn. On the Scottish mainland it had been recorded as far north as Ross-shire but stragglers had reached the Orkneys and Shetland. Aplin also concluded that it habitually remained up to the end of October and often into the beginning of November, but in some counties, particularly in W and S England (e.g. Cumberland, Lancashire, Hampshire, Cornwall) the species frequently, if not habitually, remained throughout the winter whilst occasional occurrences had been noted elsewhere.

Confirmed instances of breeding, however, were rare and many of the records that do exist rest solely on observations or the collection of recently fledged young. Where there were regular records of birds shot in the summer or recently fledged young in a county it seems probable that irregular breeding at least took place. Nevertheless, owing to the extremely secretive nature of this species, it is likely to have been far more widespread than was recorded. On the other hand the practice by sportsmen of beating through marshes and reed beds with dogs, an activity that is likely to flush the smaller crakes and rails, would serve to produce sight records at least, and of course, the shooting of specimens of small crakes solved the difficult identification problems associated with these species.

A note of caution should be attached to both Aplin's conclusions regarding the Spotted Crake's distribution in Britain and the map accompanying this account. There appear to be far more records of nests found prior to about 1860 than subsequently, whereas records of probable breeding based on the criteria mentioned become more numerous later. It appears significant that, as ornithological interest widened and knowledge improved through the 19th century, fewer nests were found. This appears to confirm the assertion of Alexander and Lack (1944) that this species began a fairly rapid decline during the first half of the 19th century, something that Aplin was not able to identify. This decline will have followed the widespread land drainage and reclamation activities during the 18th and early 19th centuries. Consequently, the Spotted Crake was probably breeding very locally at the end of the 19th century. It is also likely that the Spotted Crake's loud calls would have attracted the attention of local sportsmen who would have shot them to find out what was making the noise. Thus the combination of drainage and persecution might have made a sustainable scattered population unsustainable (C. Mead in litt).

The Spotted Crake had the merest toe-hold in Ireland by the middle of the 19th century—the only nest recorded was taken in Roscommon in 1851. Its apparent absence from Ireland during the second half of the 19th century is surprising as much suitable breeding habitat existed then.

By 1900 only a handful of Spotted Crakes bred in Britain. Throughout the 20th century the species probably bred annually in eastern counties (Parslow 1973) and now breeds regularly only in Cambridgeshire and Inverness-shire (Gibbons *et al.* 1993).

Number of counties in which recorded:

Period	Probable breeding		Confirmed breeding		Combined		
	Br	Ir	Br	Ir	Br	Ir	Both
1875–1900	14	0	30	0	44	0	44
1968–1972	11	0	2	0	13	0	13
			change		−31	0	−31
					−70%		−70%

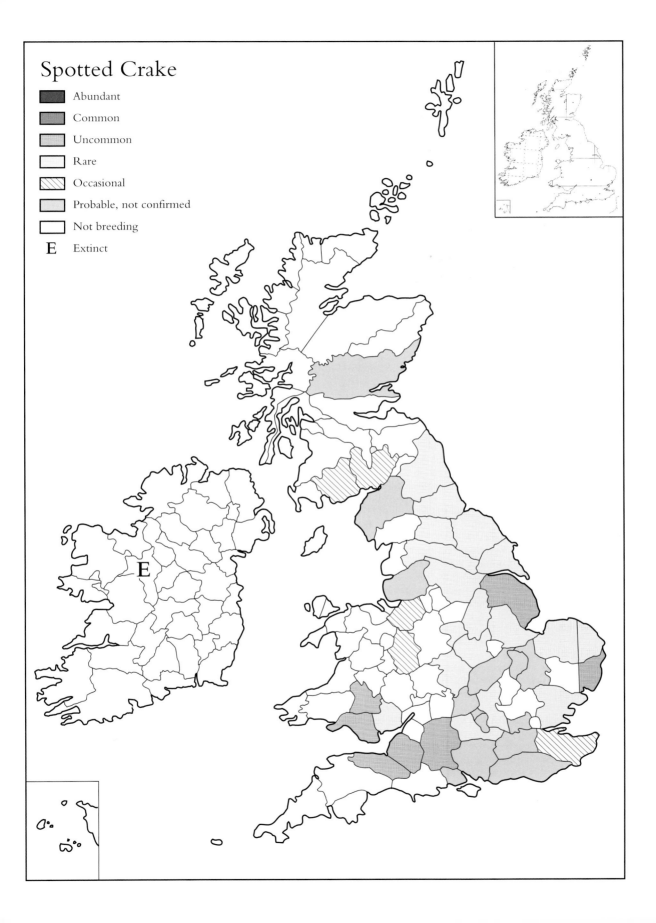

Spotted Crake

- **Abundant**
- **Common**
- **Uncommon**
- **Rare**
- **Occasional**
- **Probable, not confirmed**
- **Not breeding**
- **E** Extinct

Baillon's Crake

Porzana pusilla

recorded since, and with decreasing regularity, breeding has not been proven, or indeed suspected, to this day.

At least three and perhaps five nests of Baillon's Crake were found during the 19th century, in 1858, 1866 and 1889, the only instances of confirmed breeding in Britain. The details of these records are as follows.

Two nests were found in 1858. Six eggs were taken from a nest on the 6th June that Evans (1904) believed had been found in Cambridgeshire. Wolley (1864–1907) received two of these eggs, the first in November 1858 and the second in 1893 but the dealer who supplied both eggs jealously guarded the information of the nest's discovery and would give few details. Wolley, in his records, recorded the place of discovery as 'East Norfolk?'; however, Sealy (1859), the dealer who received the eggs, stated that they came from Cambridgeshire. He also noted that this rail was seen unusually commonly that year and a number of specimens had been shot in the same locality.

A nest of seven eggs was taken, along with the brooding female, by a fensman in August 1858 from the Isle of Ely in Cambridgeshire.

Two nests were taken in 1866. The four eggs from the first of these nests came to light in Yarmouth Market on 9th June having been taken by a reed cutter on Heigham Sounds near Hickling. On being interrogated later, the finder recalled seeing two birds near the nest that were described as Baillon's Crake. A second nest, containing five eggs, was found on the 7th July very close to the site of the first and was presumed to be a replacement clutch for that nest. No further confirmation can be attributed to this account and it was pointed out that identification from eggs alone is doubtful as they are so similar to those of the Little Crake (Patterson 1905), which although it has never been proven to breed in Britain, was a bird often shot in the reedbeds. Another nest was recorded taken in June 1886 from the same locality, but few details exist of its discovery. A nest recorded by Witherby *et al.* (1938–41) that was found on Sutton Broad in Norfolk in May 1889 was considered acceptable.

Although Baillon's Crakes have been occasionally

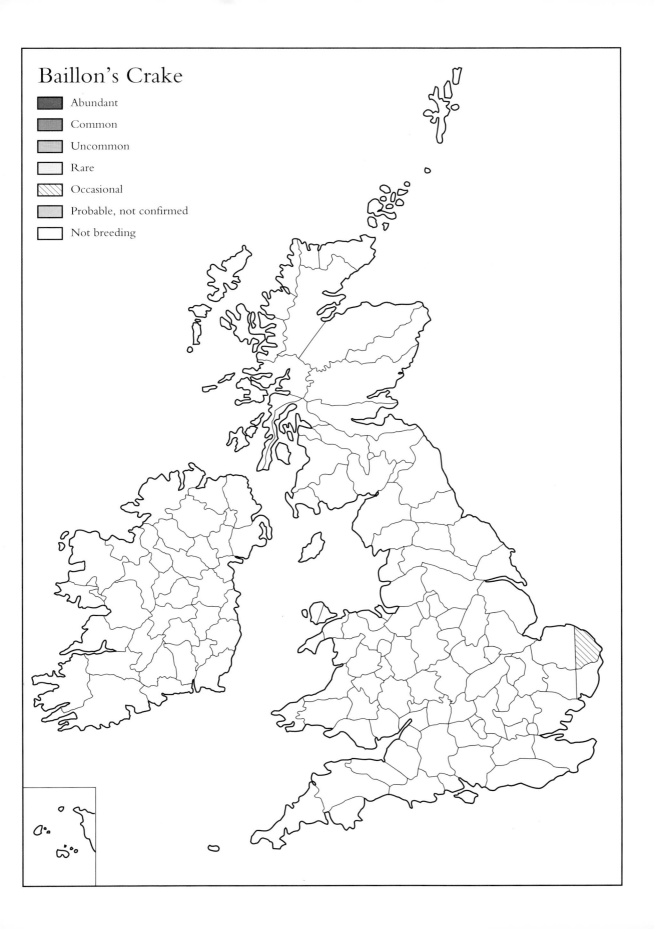

Baillon's Crake

- ☐ Abundant
- ☐ Common
- ☐ Uncommon
- ☐ Rare
- ☐ Occasional
- ☐ Probable, not confirmed
- ☐ Not breeding

Corncrake (Land Rail)

Crex crex

The decline of the Corncrake in Britain and Ireland has been more dramatic than that of any other bird species since the late 19th century. During the last quarter of that century the Corncrake bred in every county of Britain and Ireland including all but the most exposed islands; indeed, the species bred as widely as almost any other species of bird. Only in Devonshire, Kent, Essex and Nottinghamshire was it considered rare in Britain, and, although breeding was sporadic in Norfolk, Corncrakes bred commonly there when they returned in the spring in good numbers.

Corncrakes were found in tall grass and herbs, particularly in hay-meadows, up to the margins of unenclosed moorland and, less often, in arable crops (Norris 1947b). In much of the Highlands of Scotland the species had probably already declined substantially by the late 19th century because of the conversion of hay and arable crops in the broad Highland valleys (straths) to sheepwalk as a result of the Highland Clearances of the preceding 100 years (R. Green in litt). However, in the lowlands the Corncrake was a common species and its abundance probably changed little during the first 80 years of the 19th century.

Towards the end of the 19th century some writers started to note that numbers were decreasing. Although it was recognised that numbers varied from year to year these writers linked a slight decline to the increase in the mechanisation of mowing. Whilst harvesting crops and cutting, hay farmers, in earlier times, recognised the culinary value of the Corncrake (two Land Rails were said to be a present fit for a Queen) and took great care not to disturb the nest—with the advent of machines this care was not taken and many nests and chicks were destroyed as a result.

The contraction towards the west that took place from about 1880 is evident from the map compiled by Norris (1945, 1947b) following an enquiry into the status of the Corncrake in 1938. By detailed investigation Norris was able to show that rapid declines in Corncrake numbers occurred at different times in different parts of Britain and Ireland. The earliest declines occurred in the last 20 years of the 19th century in S and E England, but populations in NW Ireland, Orkney, Shetland and the Hebridean islands were still showing no signs of serious decline in 1938. In each region, declines followed the widespread introduction of mechanical mowers. Other influences also contributed later in the 20th century. The introduction of tractors to replace horses, and other mechanical innovations, allowed hay-making to be completed in a shorter time, so that the proportion of hay-meadows mowed during the most vulnerable part of the Corncrake's breeding season increased (Green 1995a). In some areas hay-meadows were also replaced by sheep pastures, which were unsuitable for Corncrakes.

By 1968–72 the Corncrake had disappeared from most of the mainland of Britain, but remained widespread in Ireland, though in reduced numbers. The slower range contraction in Ireland is probably a consequence of the later spread of tractors which did not come into widespread use in W Ireland until the late 1960s and 1970s. However, a dramatic decline in Corncrake numbers took place in Ireland in the 1980s (Sheppard and Green 1994). Population declines have continued throughout the range up to the 1990s, except in the Scottish Islands of Lewis, Coll and Tiree, where the persistence of suitable hay-meadow habitats and late mowing dates allow successful breeding (Green and Stowe 1993, Green and Williams 1994).

Number of counties in which recorded:

Period	Probable breeding		Confirmed breeding		Combined		
	Br	Ir	Br	Ir	Br	Ir	Both
1875–1900	0	0	108	34	108	34	142
1968–1972	33	0	58	34	91	34	125
			change		−17	0	−17
					−16%		−12%

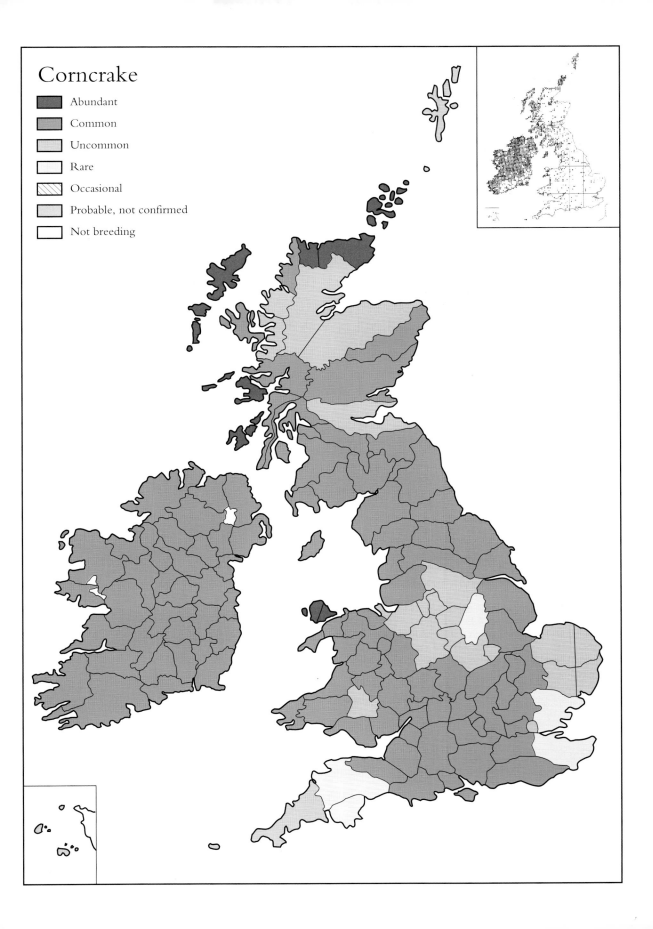

Corncrake

- Abundant
- Common
- Uncommon
- Rare
- Occasional
- Probable, not confirmed
- Not breeding

Moorhen (Waterhen)

Gallinula chloropus

Moorhens bred commonly throughout most of Britain and Ireland in the 19th century. In only a few northern and western areas of Britain, where unproductive acidic upland waters did not provide suitable conditions for breeding, were they more thinly distributed. This was especially true of W Scotland and the islands; indeed, in Shetland Moorhens were recorded breeding on only five occasions in the 19th century, the first record being a nest and eight eggs found in 1890 near Spiggie.

The Moorhen's ability to breed in almost any type of wetland area, from rivers, lakes and reservoirs to the banks of ditches and small streams, meant that the population was very stable throughout the 19th century, although in some areas of Scotland a considerable decrease was noticed after the severe winter of 1878–79 (Harvie-Brown 1906) from which it, apparently, swiftly recovered. The drainage of wet areas so often mentioned by the 19th century naturalists seems not to have affected overall numbers of the Moorhen and it very quickly adapted to the new canals, reservoirs, gravel and marl pits dug in increasing numbers at that time.

Up to about the 1940s a general increase was noted in Scotland (Rintoul and Baxter 1935, Baxter and Rintoul 1953). This may well have occurred elsewhere and may

have been facilitated by a period of agreeable climatic conditions at the time. The series of harsh winters since the 1940s seems to have caused a decrease in Scotland but few quantitive data exist for any of these fluctuations. The CBC index, which halved between 1962 and 1963, showed that very high mortality occurred during the prolonged 1962/63 winter. The long breeding season of the Moorhen, with several broods per season and many repeat layings following failed attempts (Wood 1974, Gibbons 1987), allowed numbers to increase again very quickly. Since 1963 no widespread changes have occurred and the population is probably stable overall (Marchant *et al.* 1990).

During the 20th century the breeding range of the Moorhen has contracted throughout N Scotland, especially in the west, compared to that recorded in the 19th century. In NE Scotland this may have been a result of increased land drainage (Buckland *et al.* 1990), whereas decreases elsewhere are unexplained. By 1991 the Moorhen had withdrawn from most of the Scottish islands, and only in Orkney, North and South Uist and Islay was it still breeding in any numbers (Gibbons *et al.* 1993). These recent losses may be related to the appearance of feral mink in the wild in the 1950s. Certainly there is strong circumstantial evidence that the Moorhen population of Lewis and Harris has been decimated by feral mink since 1969 (Gibbons *et al.* 1993). Declines in the western counties of Ireland have been linked to drainage—a consequence of the increased mechanisation of farming since the 1960s (Hutchinson 1989).

Number of counties in which recorded:

Period	Probable breeding		Confirmed breeding		Combined		
	Br	Ir	Br	Ir	Br	Ir	Both
1875–1900	0	0	108	34	108	34	142
1968–1972	3	0	105	34	108	34	142
			change		0	0	0

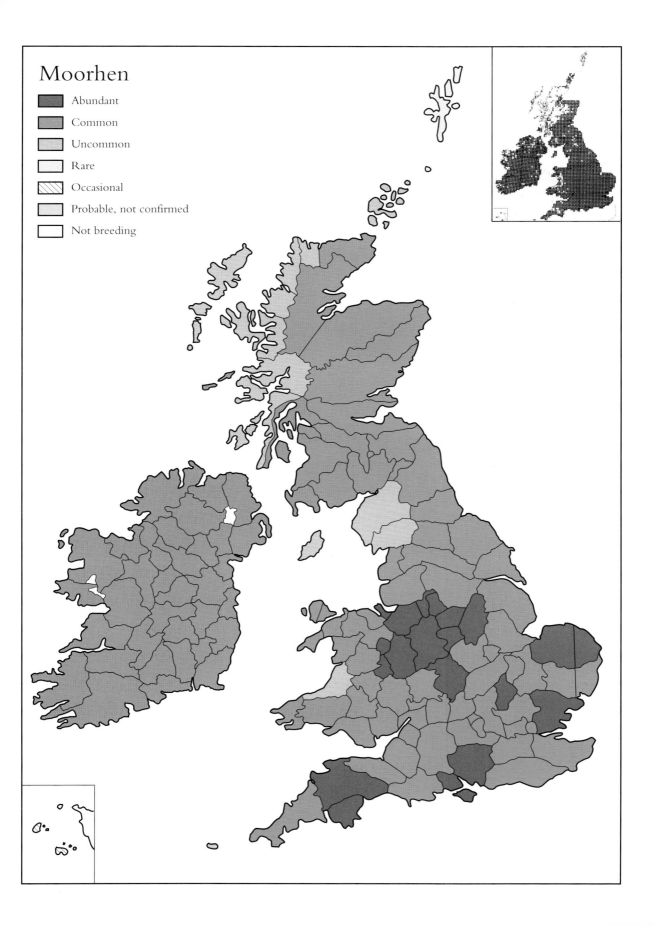

Moorhen

- Abundant
- Common
- Uncommon
- Rare
- Occasional
- Probable, not confirmed
- Not breeding

Coot

Fulica atra

The Coot bred throughout Britain and Ireland in the 19th century. Nearly all counties had recorded regular breeding; only some of the smaller off-shore islands did not hold pairs and Coots were very scarce in W Scotland. They were necessarily recorded as local, distribution being dependent on the availability of shallow pools, lakes, slow moving streams and rivers with suitable vegetation for food and nesting.

Of interest today, given the lack of explanation for their decline, are the accounts of breeding in N and W Scotland where Coots are now mostly absent. Saxby (1874) was not aware of any breeding records from Shetland, although he was aware that the Coot was a rare winter straggler to Unst. However, Evans and Buckley (1899) recorded regular breeding in the marshes between Loch Spiggie and Brow in the south of Mainland and in 1890 it was ascertained that the Coot bred in fair numbers on Hillwell Loch. In Orkney it was considered a common species and it bred wherever there were suitable localities; it was similarly common in the Outer Hebrides, especially so on Lewis, Harris and North Uist, though rarer on Benbecula and southwards. On the N Scottish mainland it was regarded as common in Caithness but far less so in Sutherland; where it did occur there it was mainly seen in the east of the county.

Further south along the northwest coast there were no records for West Ross though Coots did breed from Arisaig southwards. Breeding was recorded on Skye in 1889 and probably took place sporadically throughout the last quarter of the 19th century. Further south the Coot was more common and bred on some of the Inner Hebrides, especially on Tiree. It bred throughout the E Highlands, from SE Sutherland southwards on the larger, more sheltered lochs; indeed it was plentiful on the lochs and lochans of the Abernethy forests.

In most regions of S Scotland, England and Wales the population was considered stable—no changes in numbers were recorded. The exceptions were the fenland counties where Stevenson (1866–90) suggested that the diminution of numbers that had taken place during the first half of the 19th century was in direct proportion to the area of fen that had been converted to agricultural land; however, other evidence suggests the species had increased in some areas of reclaimed land, for instance at Bembridge on the Isle of Wight.

The status of the population in N and W Scotland in the first half of the 20th century is difficult to judge. All evidence suggests that a slow decrease took place, particularly on the islands, and from the 1950s regular breeding ceased in Shetland and numbers decreased in Orkney. In England, the acceleration of road building and urbanisation and the attendant demand for building materials created a large number of flooded pits, particularly in the southeast and the Midlands. These new habitats were attractive to Coots and local increases in numbers were recorded from the 1920s. Apart from other, local, increases, in Monmouth and Cornwall for instance, there was little change in status up to the 1960s (Parslow 1973).

The *88-91 Atlas* provided the first quantitative evidence of the decline in range that has probably been developing in Scotland and, to a lesser extent, parts of N and SW England and Wales, during the 20th century. The losses in Scotland are apparent in the northeast and are probably a continuation of the earlier losses there. In Ireland the losses apparent from about the 1960s have been blamed on land drainage (Hutchinson 1989) though this is unlikely to be the sole cause.

Number of counties in which recorded:

Period	Probable breeding		Confirmed breeding		Combined		
	Br	Ir	Br	Ir	Br	Ir	Both
1875–1900	0	0	103	34	103	34	137
1968–1972	0	0	100	34	100	34	134
			change		−3	0	−3
					−3%		−2%

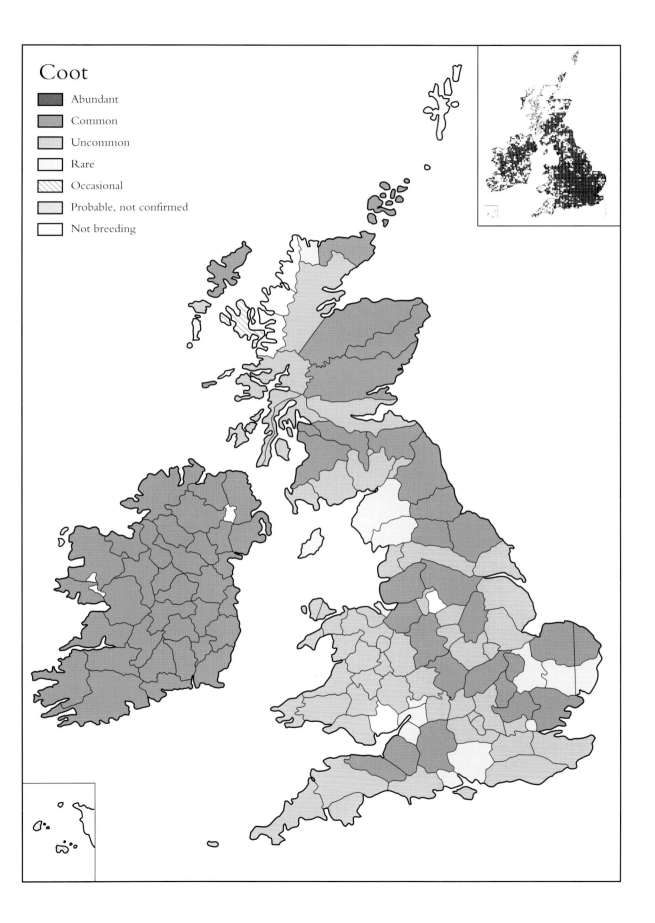

Coot

- Abundant
- Common
- Uncommon
- Rare
- Occasional
- Probable, not confirmed
- Not breeding

Oystercatcher

Haematopus ostralegus

In the 19th century the Oystercatcher was, almost exclusively, a species of the coast. Few parts of the British and Irish coastline were without breeding pairs although there was evidence that disturbance following the increasing use of beaches for leisure was causing declines in some counties of S and E England, and in some areas the Oystercatcher disappeared as a breeding species. Despite its relatively widespread distribution the Oystercatcher was never a common species in the east right up to the Scottish border; the species bred mainly on the wilder west coasts. Inland breeding was very uncommon and occurrences at any season were rarely recorded. Outside Scotland the Oystercatcher was not recorded at all away from the coast. In the counties of the Scottish Solway the bulk of the population bred in small numbers around the coast and off-shore islands but breeding also occurred occasionally up to 25km inland on gravel beds and the low meadows along the rivers Annan, Nith and Dee in the counties of Dumfriesshire and Kirkcudbrightshire.

The habit of breeding inland in this area appears to have been fairly recently acquired, a record of a bird shot inland in 1880 being considered a notable event. In 1890 the first nest was found on the Nith. Certainly, as the century turned, this habit was increasing and breeding was recorded on the rivers Annan, Nith and Dee with increasing frequency. Inland breeding in the eastern Scottish Highlands had been known to occur for many years but was not well documented until the mid 19th century and not recorded at all at the end of the 18th century. The spread of inland breeding probably first took place adjacent to the N Grampian coast in the 1840s. By the late 1860s Oystercatchers were breeding on the banks of Loch Ness and round to Aberdeenshire. As the century progressed breeding spread further up the rivers of the Cairngorms although the Oystercatcher bred far less frequently on the banks of lochs.

Breeding took place abundantly on the coast and islands of the W Ireland. In the east and southeast it bred rarely only on the off-shore islands. The only inland breeding records were of a few nests found on islands in Lough Erne in Fermanagh.

Coastal breeding declined further in S and E England as disturbance increased in the early years of the 20th century. In contrast, however, inland breeding in Scotland increased in frequency and extent, and spread, from around 1900, up the rivers of the English Solway and by the 1920s into the rivers of Northumberland. As the century progressed this spread in Scotland and N England continued, whilst, in S England, numbers were increasing in breeding sanctuaries established in Norfolk and elsewhere. In Ireland colonisation of the east coast began during the early 1920s and increased subsequently; however, the main breeding population still occurred on the west coast and islands. It is likely that disturbance elsewhere continued to reduce numbers and this was particularly apparent in mainland Wales.

The *88-91 Atlas* illustrated the continuing spread in inland areas. This was apparent in NE England, N Wales and Cheshire and around the Severn estuary. The habit of East Anglian pairs to nest some distance from the coast in coastal fields led to an expansion further inland. On the Cornwall and N Devon coasts breeding more or less ceased sometime between the two Atlases. Inland breeding in Ireland is still centred around Lough Erne. The occasional inland records elsewhere in Ireland do not reflect the extent of inland breeding elsewhere in the species' range.

Little has been written concerning what amounts to a fundamental change in breeding behaviour that has occurred, not only in Britain, but also over many parts of Europe, and has led to widespread inland breeding. A number of factors could have contributed to this change in behaviour, including changes in climate and agricultural practice, but these have not been adequately studied (J. Cayford in litt).

Number of counties in which recorded:

Period	Probable breeding		Confirmed breeding		Combined		
	Br	Ir	Br	Ir	Br	Ir	Both
1875–1900	0	1	55	11	55	12	67
1968-1972	2	0	80	17	82	17	99
			change		27	5	32
					49%	42%	48%

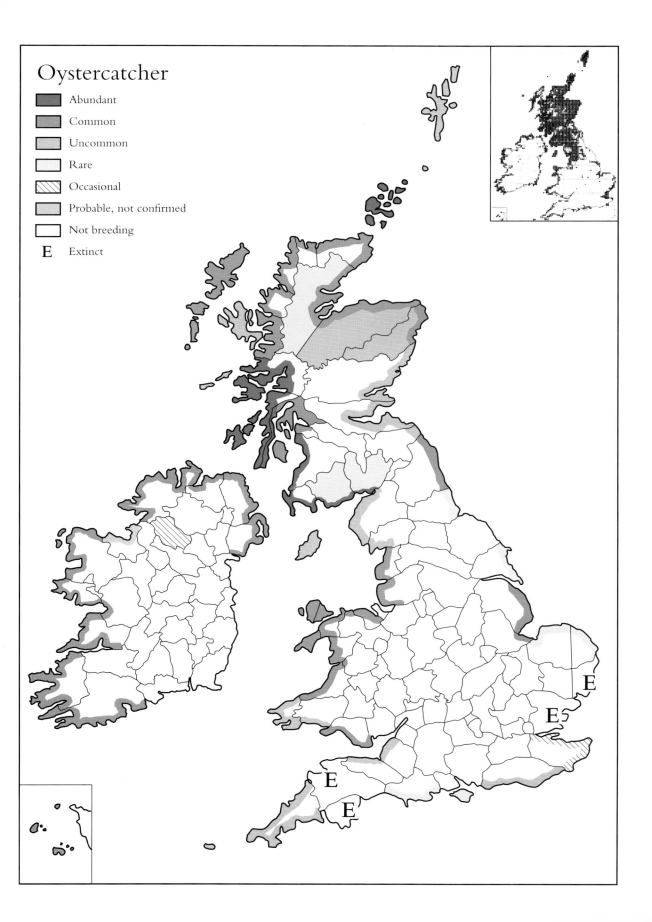

Oystercatcher

- **Abundant**
- **Common**
- **Uncommon**
- **Rare**
- **Occasional**
- **Probable, not confirmed**
- **Not breeding**
- **E** Extinct

Avocet

Recurvirostra avosetta

The Avocet formerly bred along the E coast of England from the Humber to Sussex, regular breeding probably taking place up to the end of the 18th century. Borrer (1891) noted that Avocet were recorded in Sussex in summer and winter and assumed that this indicated that it had bred there. It certainly bred on the Yorkshire side of the Humber, and, in the absence of any dated records, we can only surmise that it probably continued to nest there into the 1820s and, perhaps, the 1830s, based on the evidence of a breeding account from the Lincolnshire side of the estuary. This oft-quoted record was contained in a letter of 1861 to More whilst he was enquiring into the status of the breeding birds of Britain (More 1865). The informant stated that he found Avocet eggs floating on water during a spring tide 'about 24 years before' (say 1837). The site was a sand bank at the mouth of the Trent in Humberside. One of the parent birds was collected at the same time. The Avocet became extinct here following drainage of the breeding sites (especially reclamation of saltmarshes and improved control of water on coastal grazing marshes), egg collecting for food and the collecting of specimen eggs and birds (Nelson *et al.* 1907).

It became extinct in coastal Fenland in the very early years of the 19th century but the only site specifically mentioned as holding breeding pairs, in 'vast numbers' about 1806, was Fosdyke Wash, at the mouth of the Wash in Lincolnshire. In Norfolk, its stronghold, its last breeding places were evidently on the Broadland coast. In 1816 an adult with young was observed in the Winterton marshes and was the last, or almost so, to breed there. Enclosure and the conversion of land for arable crops, or disturbance by people and cattle, destroyed the breeding sites of the Avocet at Horsey where the number of breeding pairs was severely reduced by 1819. Some still apparently bred there in 1824 but ceased to do so by 1828—these were the last of a breeding group that numbered in the 'hundreds' (probably individuals) in the Broads even at the turn of the 18th century (Stevenson 1866–90).

The Avocet probably bred numerously on Romney Marsh up to the very early years of the 19th century. Its extinction in the N Kent marshes occurred at about the same time. It nested on this side of the county up the Thames as far as Gravesend. The last records of nesting in Kent were at Dungeness in 1842 when a nest of young was found and in the following year two birds, considered to have recently fledged, were shot at the same locality (Ticehurst 1909).

The former Kent records have long been considered the last breeding records in Britain before the 20th century recolonisation. There are, however, two further records from Suffolk that require consideration. In Suffolk regular breeding ceased when some Avocets were killed on their breeding grounds near Orford probably during the 1820s. Nothing further was reported of the breeding of the Avocet until a gunner reported that he had shot three or four on the merelands near Thorpeness in about 1882 and that a pair had bred on the 'farther' mere near the fir plantation there in the same year. Apparently the tenant of the millhouse had taken the eggs and eaten them! A female Avocet was shot at the same place on 18th May 1893 and contained well developed eggs (Ticehurst 1932).

It was not until 1938 that Avocets were once again reported breeding when two pairs unexpectedly nested and probably raised young on a brackish lagoon in Wexford, Ireland. Breeding was not repeated there however. During 1941–46, following the closure of the English east coast to the public, breeding took place in both Essex and Norfolk. In Suffolk in 1947 four pairs bred at Minsmere, Suffolk, and four or five pairs on Havergate Island. Although sporadic breeding had been recorded elsewhere on the east coast from Norfolk to Kent, up to the mid 1970s regular breeding took place only at the sites colonised in 1947. The number of pairs at Havergate rose to over 100 and at Minsmere to 35 during the *68–72 Atlas* period (Parslow 1973, Sharrock 1976). At the present time the Avocet has started to recolonise its former breeding range—at least from the Wash to Elmsley Marshes (and perhaps in Dorset) and between 355 and 521 pairs were confirmed breeding during the *88-91 Atlas* survey period (*88–91 Atlas*).

Number of counties in which recorded:

Period	Probable breeding		Confirmed breeding		Combined		
	Br	Ir	Br	Ir	Br	Ir	Both
1875–1900	1	0	0	0	1	0	1
1968–1972	2	0	1	0	3	0	3
			change		2	0	2
					200%		200%

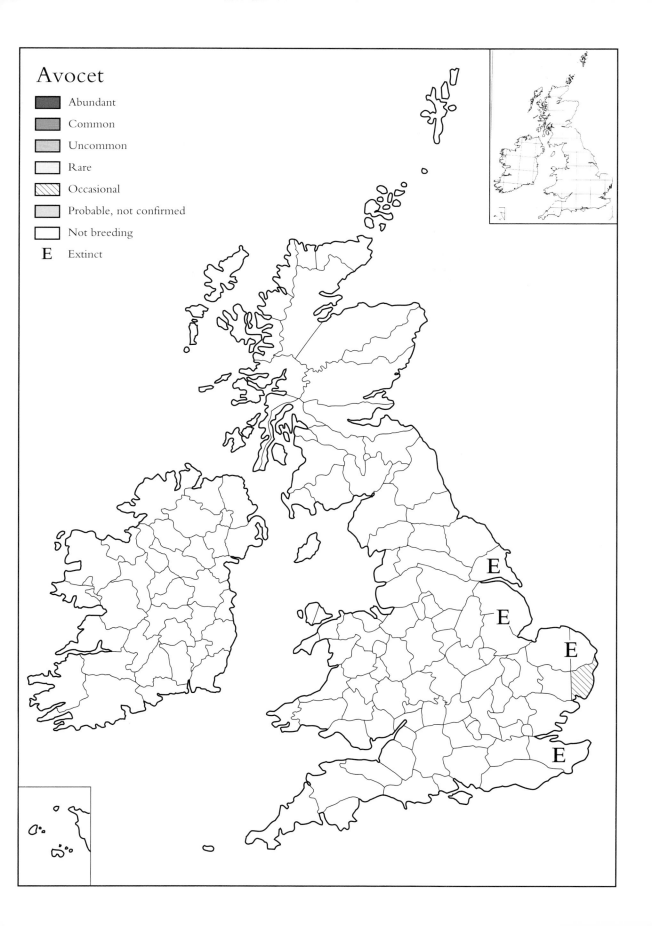

Avocet

- ■ Abundant
- ▨ Common
- ▨ Uncommon
- □ Rare
- ▨ Occasional
- ▨ Probable, not confirmed
- □ Not breeding
- **E** Extinct

Stone Curlew (Great Plover, Norfolk Plover)

Burhinus oedicnemus

It seems probable that the Stone Curlew was never more widely distributed than the accompanying map illustrates and that its decline began before 1850 at the edges of its range. Up to the 1840s the Stone Curlew was widely distributed over the Wiltshire downs but then declined substantially; by the late 1880s, the species was restricted to two sites, one on the North Downs and one on Salisbury Plain. The Stone Curlew still bred regularly in the chalk uplands of Dorset but many nests were destroyed when the young wheat was rolled in the spring. This was also mentioned as a substantial cause of nest losses in Hampshire but the species still bred plentifully in the centre of the county. In Sussex by 1891 the Stone Curlew had declined substantially but still bred from the South Downs to the coast. The species was probably distributed throughout the higher parts of Kent, especially on chalk, up to the mid 1800s but by the end of the century it was confined to Dungeness beach—four or five pairs were seen there during the 1890s but, under protection, 17 pairs successfully reared young in 1905. Its last nesting attempt in Surrey took place about 1900 at Caterham; it had previously bred commonly along the Hog's Back. The Stone Curlew was never common in Essex but it

bred annually at least up to 1902 on the border with Cambridgeshire. It bred throughout the chalk hills in N Hertfordshire from Royston to Hitchin, but had declined by 1899. The Stone Curlew became extinct in Buckinghamshire around the middle of the 19th century; however, it recolonised the county soon after and bred in stable numbers until a substantial decline began from about 1910. Stone Curlews had bred throughout Oxfordshire from the Cotswolds to the chalk hills in the south; by the 1880s, however, just one or two pairs bred, it was believed annually, on the western slope of the Chilterns and continued doing so into the 1900s. In Berkshire in 1901 the Stone Curlew still 'breed[s] in most localities suited to their habits' but most frequently in the part of the county adjacent to the Oxfordshire site. Stone Curlews bred throughout the heaths and Brecklands of Suffolk and in the 1880s, although having decreased, were most common in the Brecks. In Norfolk the Stone Curlew decreased up to the 1870s but then increased again, especially in the west, through the 1880s. In Cambridgeshire it had evidently declined substantially; it formerly bred plentifully in the east of the county but by 1904 it was recorded only occasionally. Up to the mid 19th century it bred commonly on the chalk hills in S Bedfordshire but it died out here around 1890. Records of breeding on the W Cotswolds in Gloucestershire ceased in the 1890s. Stone Curlews had bred in S Worcestershire in the 1830s but there were no subsequent records. The species became scarce on the heaths of NW Lincolnshire by about 1870 and ceased to nest there in the early 1900s. It ceased to breed in Leicestershire early in the 19th century but continued nesting in Rutland into the 1880s. It declined substantially around Sherwood Forest, Nottinghamshire and, in 1891, bred for the last time in the county on the fringe of Rufford Forest. It bred not uncommonly on the E Yorkshire moors and wolds up to the mid 1800s but decreased following changing land use so that by 1907 it bred 'in a few secluded districts'.

The population decline and range contraction were probably initially caused by conversion of semi-natural grasslands and heath to arable land and conifer plantations. Breeding populations persisted at low densities on spring-sown arable land in some areas, but changes in farming practice, in particular the decline of spring-sown crops and of mixed farming, have adversely affected Stone Curlews even in these areas, by reducing the availability of sparsely vegetated nest sites and short pastures rich in invertebrate prey (R. Green in litt). In the 1950s the suitability of the few remaining fragments of chalk downland and Breckland heath declined because the reduction in grazing pressure from rabbits following the myxomatosis epizootic allowed the vegetation to become too tall and dense (Green and Griffiths 1994). The population continued to decline until the 1980s, but has since stabilised, probably in response to conservation measures (Green 1995b).

Number of counties in which recorded:

Period	Probable breeding		Confirmed breeding		Combined		
	Br	Ir	Br	Ir	Br	Ir	Both
1875–1900	2	0	22	0	24	0	24
1968–1972	0	0	15	0	15	0	15
			change		−9	0	−9
					−38%		−38%

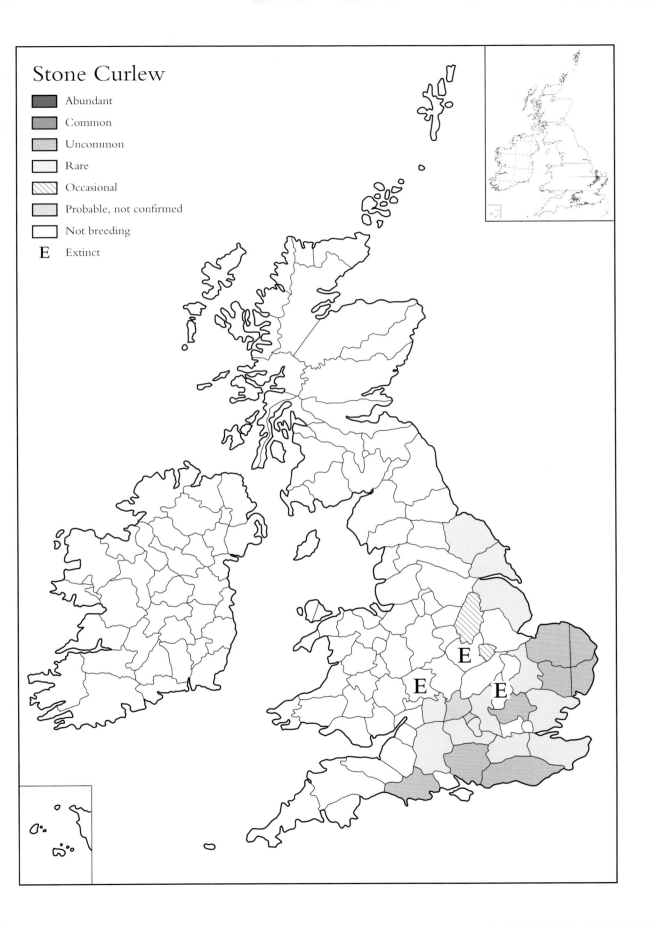

Stone Curlew

- Abundant
- Common
- Uncommon
- Rare
- Occasional
- Probable, not confirmed
- Not breeding
- **E** Extinct

Ringed Plover

Charadrius hiaticula

The Ringed Plover bred on the shores of almost every British and Irish county or region at the end of the 19th century; only the coastline of Monmouthshire, the west shore of the Severn Estuary, had not had breeding recorded. A number of areas in which breeding took place then are of interest to 20th century ornithologists. For example, the Ringed Plover was said to nest commonly at many places on the Pembrokeshire coast by Mathew (1894) and he gave an example of a nest in a rabbit warren near Stackpole. Lockley *et al.* (1949) noted that breeding took place at several sites, from Newport to Tenby, in the county. It seems likely that tourist developments have led to the present-day absence of the Ringed Plover from the Pembrokeshire coastline. A similar decline has occurred on other parts of the Dyfed coast (Lovegrove *et al.* 1994). It seems likely that a decline in SW England since the 19th century has also been due to human disturbance. Detail is scant of this species' status in Cornwall in the 19th century where it was said to be 'Generally distributed along the seashore, where it breeds upon the shingle' (Rodd 1880) and in Devonshire its status was described thus: 'The Ringed Plover breeds all round the coast where there is a pebbly beach'.

In several areas it was recorded breeding away from the sea coast. The nesting group on the brecks of W Suffolk and over the border into Norfolk had been known since before 1825. Up to at least 1856 the Ringed Plover bred very commonly on the rabbit warrens there (probably some hundreds of pairs) but by the end of the century the species had evidently declined substantially and bred there in only limited numbers, although it may have increased a little before the warrens were destroyed in the 1920s and 1930s (Ticehurst 1932). Breeding in more limited numbers took place on the heaths of the east of these counties.

In Worcestershire it was suspected of occasionally nesting alongside the Avon. A few birds were shot on Frensham Great Pond in Surrey through the last quarter of the 19th century before a nest and two eggs were found there in 1909, on Kingsbury Reservoir in Middlesex, a number of birds were collected but a nest not found until the early 20th century. It must be remembered, however, that these early suspected breeding records may refer to passage migrants. In the Cheviots, on both sides of the Scottish border, the Ringed Plover bred in some numbers on the shingle banks alongside the larger rivers almost to their sources and through many other parts of Scotland it bred sparsely in similar sites and alongside some freshwater lochs.

In addition to the coastline, the Ringed Plover bred on all of the larger loughs in Ireland from Ulster through Connaught to Leinster. In Laois nests had been recorded from the edges of the marshes there.

In the closing years of the 19th century some evidence of local declines were published. On the beaches of Lancashire disturbance had banished the species from some localities. In Cheshire and the banks of the Tees and Humber in Yorkshire persecution from egg and specimen collectors had diminished numbers substantially. Overall, however, numbers appeared to remain stable into the 20th century until, during the years between the wars, a widespread decline became apparent. This period saw a dramatic increase in human use of the coasts for, mainly, recreational purposes and the development of numerous bungalow and caravan sites and sea-defence works. The consequent disturbance and loss of habitat caused the abandonment of many former breeding sites and, as the 20th century has progressed, so this effect has worsened, particularly in SW England. Where the coastline was preserved, however, the Ringed Plover thrived such as in the Norfolk sanctuaries. From about the 1950s inland nesting has been more frequently recorded from some English counties. This tendency has paralleled the spread of inland nesting Oystercatchers, particularly along the rivers of the northern counties. In other parts of England inland breeding has been facilitated by new gravel pits, reservoirs and other wetland sites but river beds and industrial sites are also important.

Number of counties in which recorded:

Period	Probable breeding		Confirmed breeding		Combined		
	Br	Ir	Br	Ir	Br	Ir	Both
1875–1900	0	0	62	26	62	26	88
1968–1972	2	0	75	25	77	25	102
			change		15	−1	14
					24%	−4%	16%

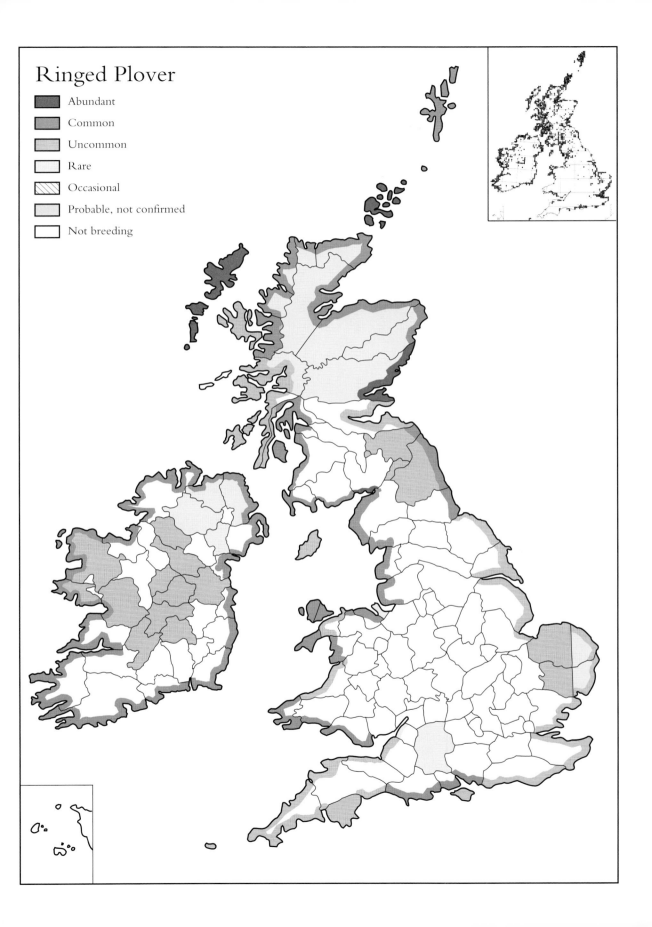

Ringed Plover

- Abundant
- Common
- Uncommon
- Rare
- Occasional
- Probable, not confirmed
- Not breeding

Kentish Plover

Charadrius alexandrinus

The Kentish Plover was first described and named as a British bird by Latham (1785) from four specimens collected at Sandwich, Kent in 1787 and 1791. During the early years of the 19th century the species was discovered breeding along parts of the Kent and Sussex coasts and was also seen regularly on the coast of Norfolk around Great Yarmouth. As time progressed, and the rarity of the Kentish Plover was recognised by the shoreland inhabitants, then collecting of eggs and skins began in earnest. Records of specimens in collections suddenly soared about the middle of the century in Norfolk and, at Hastings in Sussex, dogs were trained to find nests.

By the 1880s, in E Sussex, the Kentish Plover was apparently breeding in far fewer numbers than formerly but they were still fairly common, especially about Rye Harbour and Winchelsea. The species had been recorded further west along the coast and may have bred near Hastings earlier in the century. Its stronghold, however, was in Kent. In the first quarter of the 19th century the species nested around the bays of Sandwich and Pegwell and, further west, it bred as far as Deal. It is possible that, up to the 1840s, it nested around most of the Kent coast. In 1843 the locality of a large colony at Dungeness was first published (Yarrell 1837–43). Publication brought in collectors from London and N England and, an indication of how many must have bred there, 'hundreds' were said to have been shot in the next four years (Harrison 1953). Current estimates of breeding pairs in various places in Europe (Piersma 1986) lead to the conclusion that, if indeed so many were killed in Kent in the 1840s, then the breeding colony must have been huge by modern standards. There were no estimates of the size of the Dungeness breeding group but the 17km stretch of shingle between Rye Harbour and Dungeness evidently held the largest number of breeding pairs and, in 1842, the species 'Bred in tolerable plenty near Margate' (Wolley 1864–1907). Other recent research also suggests that the early 19th century breeding population on the SE England beaches may have been large. The Kentish Plover

has a high survival rate of about 75% (Page *et al.* 1983, K. Lessells, unpublished data, in litt). In addition, its breeding success is very low: Lessells (in litt) found that over 90% of nests were predated and Page *et al.* (1983) estimated that only 0.49 young were fledged per female per breeding season. These aspects of the Kentish Plover's biology suggest that it is particularly vulnerable to additional sources of mortality such as shooting (K. Lessells in litt) and that if hundreds of Kentish Plover were shot then the initial population must have been large. It is known, however, that Kentish Plovers may move considerable distances between breeding attempts (Székely and Lessells 1993, Stenzel *et al.* 1994) so that shot birds may have been replaced by birds moving in from elsewhere.

As the century progressed breeding ceased over much of Kent. Colonies existed from 1870 until the 1890s at Dungeness, still the main colony where up to 15 pairs bred, Shellness in Sandwich Bay, where up to three pairs bred in the late 1880s, and a location on the N Kent coast. The 1890s saw the extinction of the outlying colonies, including those in Sussex, but also the beginning of a revival at Dungeness. A set-back in 1902 occurred when, despite a good breeding season, 21 birds were shot, at least 12 of which were breeding. This led to only 12 pairs breeding in 1903 but success was high and persecution low so that 1904 saw an increase in breeding pairs. In 1905, the first year of full-time protection, more than 21 pairs reared young. This increased to 44 pairs in 1906 and 1907/08 saw between 30 and 40 pairs breed. Gradually, from this peak, numbers decreased steadily. Destruction of the nesting area through the building of a railway, roads and holiday bungalows took place during the 1920s until breeding ceased about 1931 (Harrison 1953). Only occasional nesting has taken place since in Britain. Pairs nested in Sussex from 1949 to 1956, Suffolk in 1952 and Lincolnshire in 1979. Last breeding took place in the Channel Islands in 1975 (Batten *et al.* 1990).

Disturbance now makes it difficult for the species to breed at some of its former natural haunts and ground and avian predators could have a significant effect on any attempts at recolonisation. In parts of NW Europe, however, the species has colonised fenced and, hence, undisturbed, sandy industrial areas and this remains a possibility on SE England (Batten *et al.* 1990).

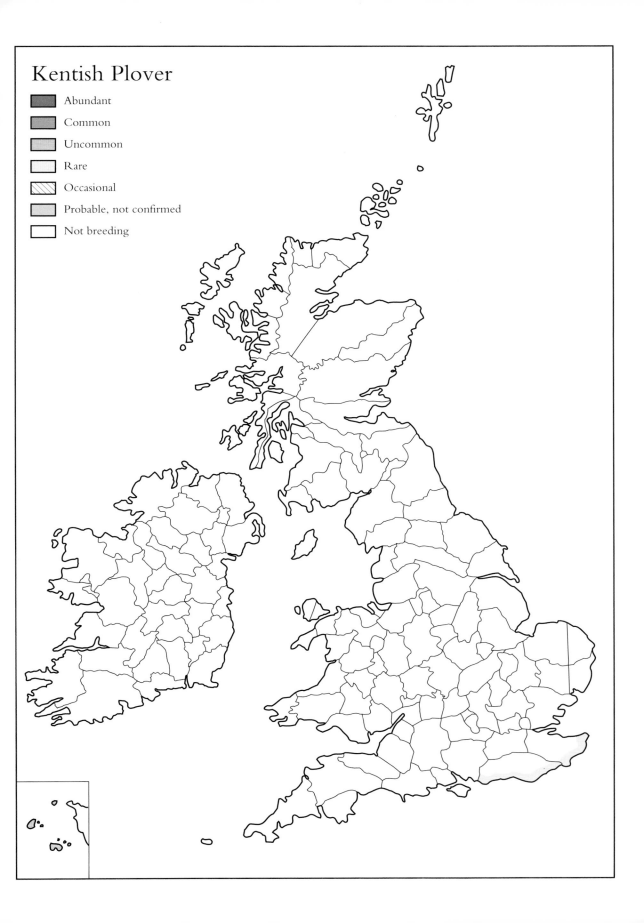

Kentish Plover

- Abundant
- Common
- Uncommon
- Rare
- Occasional
- Probable, not confirmed
- Not breeding

Dotterel

Charadrius morinellus

The Dotterel is a breeding bird of high mountains and as such must have been overlooked in many parts of its range in the 19th century. Its main breeding range in Britain at the end of the century was in the Scottish Highlands. Pairs did breed elsewhere, however, and, although difficult to quantify exactly, the species may have been quite widespread in N England.

The first positive record in England was of a clutch of eggs taken on Skiddaw in Cumberland in 1784, but it was not until 1835 that a description was published (Macpherson 1892) of the nest and eggs of an 'English' breeding Dotterel. That record encouraged many Dotterel hunters to make the trip to the Lakeland fells and, particularly in the second half of the 19th century, many nests were found there. Some evidence exists that it may also have bred on some of the Yorkshire moors at this time. The records show, however, that from about the 1860s numbers of 'English' breeding Dotterels began to fall. D. A. Ratcliffe in Nethersole–Thompson (1973) cautiously estimated the total annual breeding strength, up to about 1860, as 50–75 pairs. By the last few years of the century annual nesting was recorded in only single figures and some well-known Dotterel sites, such as on Crossfell in Cumberland, were no longer used. Total breeding numbers in England, then, was apparently fewer than 20 pairs annually, but possibly as low as ten pairs in some years.

In Scotland there were many more breeding Dotterel. In Dumfriesshire a nest found close to the western border and another found in the mountains above Loch Dungeon in Kirkcudbrightshire led to the assertion that breeding occurred sparsely along these hills, although by the end of the century breeding had probably ceased here. In N Scotland, the Dotterel was known to have bred in N Perthshire, Forfarshire, Aberdeenshire, E Inverness-shire and East Ross. North of the Spey valley Dotterel were said to be scarce, although breeding may have taken place more frequently up to about 1860. The species' western breeding limit was Ben Alder. On the moors south of the Cairngorms a decrease was apparently underway from the 1850s or 1860s, and by the end of the century breed-

ing had probably ceased in Aberdeenshire where formerly it had been regular. Once again, 1860 was mentioned as the point at which the decrease in that county became apparent. Persecution of the Dotterel, both on the breeding grounds and during passage, had taken place for many years. The flesh was considered a great delicacy and caused its destruction during migration; the feathers, moreover, were in demand for fishing fly dressing and were more valuable than the carcass in the 19th century. The Scottish population might have been sustainable in the face of this persecution had it not been compounded by the Victorians' demand for trophies of skins and eggs.

The breeding range of the Dotterel was evidently contracting around the end of the 19th century and into the 20th. Breeding seemed to cease in England about this time, but sporadic records occurred in other areas, for instance in West Ross and Roxburghshire. A warmer climate during the first half of the 20th century will not have suited the requirements of this, essentially, Arctic species, but a cooling trend in the last 30 years has been linked with improved fortunes of the Dotterel in parts of Europe, but notably not in Austria or Finland. Breeding in Cumberland and Westmorland resumed sometime during the first half of the present century and records were obtained in Sutherland and Kirkcudbrightshire in 1967, N Wales in 1969 and in the east lowlands of Scotland in 1970. The *68–72 Atlas* estimated that the total British population numbered between 60 and 80 pairs, and up to 100 pairs, at that time. The *88–91 Atlas* estimated the British population at more than 860 'pairs', with fewer than ten pairs in England and Wales. This higher estimate indicates much better observer coverage in the Scottish Highlands, but also seems to indicate an increase in the population (Galbraith *et al.* 1993). Numbers south of the Scottish Highlands seem to be below that of the 1800s, possibly because of recent deterioration of breeding habitat under sheep grazing pressure and acidic deposition (Thompson and Brown 1992).

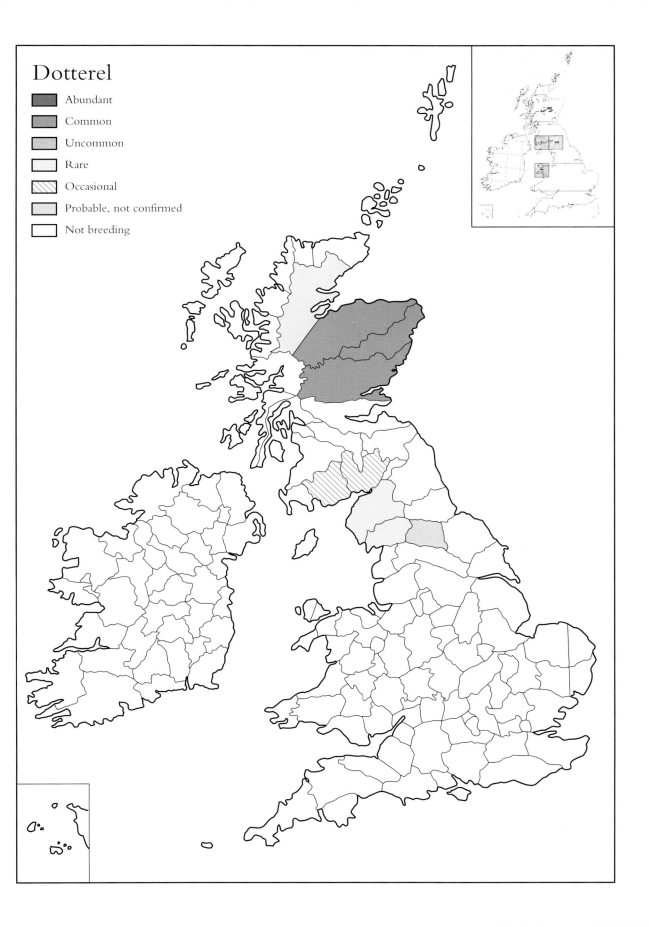

Dotterel

- Abundant
- Common
- Uncommon
- Rare
- Occasional
- Probable, not confirmed
- Not breeding

Golden Plover

Pluvialis apricaria

The Golden Plover is, par excellence, the wader of hill and moorland in spring and summer. As such its distribution at the end of the 19th century was coincident with those habitats in Britain and Ireland.

Its main breeding areas were in Scotland and W Ireland (with local populations elsewhere in Ireland), N England and Wales; an isolated group bred on Exmoor and, probably, the Mendip Hills in Somerset. It must be added, however, that the assertion that breeding took place in Somerset, and indeed in Devonshire on Dartmoor up to the 1830s, was based on hearsay and later writers treated the records with great caution. In Wales the most southerly regular breeding population was that of Brecon, mainly in the Eppynt Hills, although breeding occurred locally throughout S Wales possibly extending west into the Prescelly Mountains. The Golden Plover's main breeding area in Wales was on the moors of Denbighshire and Merioneth, centred around Corwen and Bala, although even here, nests were found only irregularly. Breeding took place far more regularly in England from the Peak District through to the N Pennines. The Golden Plover bred regularly on the N Lancashire moors and was common on the North York moors but was found breeding only sporadically on the moorlands of the Cumberland hills, although more regularly on the flows of the English Solway.

In Scotland it was widely distributed and common in places, particularly the Highlands and the Northern and Western Isles, but by the last decade of the century a decrease was evidently under way. In Assynt, for instance, it had been regarded as very common in places in the 1870s and 1880s but as the century turned few pairs could be located, and some areas, particularly in the west, had apparently been entirely forsaken. In Ireland it bred, in the main, on the mountain tops and so was distributed in the higher uplands of the country, although numbers also bred on the lower reaches and bogs at the base of the mountains of Connemara and Mayo.

The dynamics of the Golden Plover population changes during the 20th century are complex. Harvie-Brown (1906) had already noted the fluctuating nature of breeding groups in Scotland: areas were forsaken coincidentally with others being colonised. This pattern continued in, especially, England and S Wales with losses from the Welsh south coastal counties and English border counties being balanced by gains in SE Lancashire and on Dartmoor in Devonshire. Overall, however, numbers in England and in the N Wales stronghold probably remained stable overall during the first half of the 20th century. Little evidence exists to determine the extent of the decrease in Scotland, north of the Forth/Clyde valley, during this period. It is probable that it did continue, but slowly.

Following the 1939–45 war losses became more apparent, particularly in England, Wales and S Scotland whilst in Ireland the species' range was retreating rapidly towards the northwest. There seems to have been a downward trend in numbers in the British Isles, and elsewhere in Europe, and this may be partly attributable to a warmer climate early this century. More probably, however, agricultural intensification (both of moorland and the wintering grounds), afforestation and predation have accounted for losses. A brief respite occurred during the 1970s when the population may have increased slightly because much of the conversion of moorland to rough grassland favoured this species (D. Thompson in litt.). The *88–91 Atlas* revealed further thinning of the population that had occurred since the *68–72 Atlas* survey. This may be due to additional, more subtle, changes in the uplands related to predation and the disappearance of some preferred breeding habitat (Parr 1992). The patchy decline of good moorland management practices and increased grazing pressure have created either more expanse of rank heather growth or the intensification of rough grassland and moorland through re-seeding neither of which suits breeding Golden Plover (Batten *et al.* 1990; Thompson *et al.* 1994). It has been suggested that increased disturbance from walkers, and other recreational use of the hills, particularly since the 1939–45 war, will deter Golden Plovers from settling. Recent research in the Pennines, however, an area with both Golden Plovers breeding at high densities and large numbers of walkers, suggests that this is not always the case (D. Thompson in litt.).

Number of counties in which recorded:

Period	Probable breeding		Confirmed breeding		Combined		
	Br	Ir	Br	Ir	Br	Ir	Both
1875–1900	2	2	50	17	52	19	71
1968–1972	2	0	49	7	51	7	58
			change		−1	−12	−13
					−2%	−63%	−18%

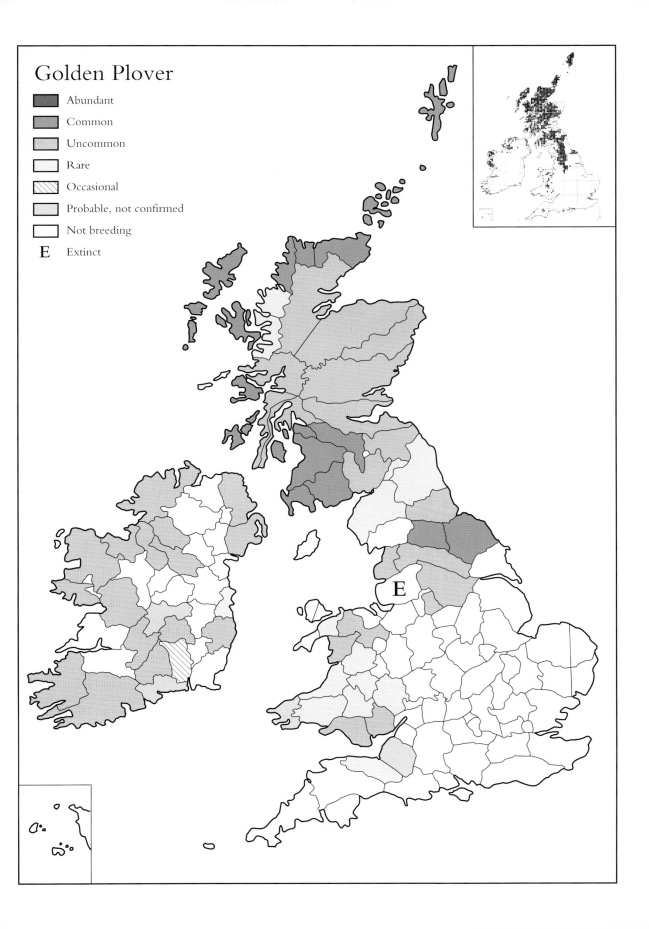

Golden Plover

Abundant

Common

Uncommon

Rare

Occasional

Probable, not confirmed

Not breeding

E   Extinct

Lapwing (Peewit, Green Plover)

Vanellus vanellus

The Lapwing was a common and familiar bird of the countryside throughout Britain and Ireland in the 19th century and was, apparently, absent only from the Isles of Scilly and the Channel Islands. It had, however, decreased within the memory of many of the writers of the 19th century avifaunas and was apparently still declining during the last quarter of the century. This was evident over much of England, from Surrey to the Lake District and to mid and E Scotland. In Ireland it had declined in some localities.

In Surrey, especially near to London, the decline in numbers was caused by the loss of breeding habitat brought about by drainage and by the depredations of the egg gatherers. The Lapwing had nested in Richmond Park 'in large numbers' in the 1830s, for instance, but by the 1890s it had probably ceased to do so. Stevenson (1866–90) also blamed the enormous change in Lapwing numbers in Norfolk since the first quarter of the 19th century on drainage and enclosures, coupled with the egg gathering that took place. The numbers of eggs taken were large. In the 1820s and 1830s a single egger could take nearly 2,000 a season, and about 2,500 were sent from Romney Marsh to Dover market one year. In Banffshire over 1,600 passed through the hands of one middleman before 15th April 1893. The high prices paid for this delicacy encouraged overzealous collecting—

the same price was paid for a single Lapwing's egg as would be paid for a score of Black-headed Gull's eggs. Although egg gathering had reduced numbers throughout Lakeland, it seems that in the uplands of Cumberland (and perhaps elsewhere in N England) the conversion of moorland and bog to pasture had created habitat more suited to the Lapwing and so, locally, it had increased since the first half of the 19th century. Evidence from the old Statistical Account of Scotland, however, suggests that numbers had declined in the uplands in the wake of the plough (Rintoul and Baxter 1935). Nevertheless, the egg collectors did not ignore Scotland. The development of this activity was slower than in S England because of the difficulty in transporting the harvest to the centres of the human population. This changed with the building of the Highland railway after the mid 1800s and the number of eggs taken quickly increased. The decline of the Lapwing in Scotland thus accelerated. This decline had been noted in the Forth, Dee and Moray regions but, from the middle of the century, the number of wintering birds increased substantially in the Highlands, perhaps resulting from the ameliorating winter climate.

It is likely that the depredations of the egg gatherers only exacerbated a long-term decline that had occurred in the wake of the conversion of wet and marginal land to agriculture (M. Shrubb in litt). Habitat losses more or less ceased with the agricultural depression in the 1870s, however, and the Lapwing population may have recovered if it was not kept in check by egg gathering.

In Ireland the Lapwing bred in every county and was locally numerous, especially in N Leinster, Connaught and Ulster, and it bred on many marine islands (for instance on the Saltees, Lambay, the Copelands and Rathlin). Its numbers had decreased in some localities, not due to the taking of eggs, as the market for these delicacies was very small in Ireland, but by netting of large numbers in their autumn flocks for food.

Further reclamation of waste land and egg collecting caused a continuing decline of the Lapwing until the Lapwing Protection Bill of 1926. As a result of this Bill a rapid, although temporary, recovery in population became evident but the long-term declining trend was resumed with the post-1945 agricultural revolution and has continued to the present day. Many activities of modern farming have been responsible for the decrease—further losses of pasture and marginal land, the intensification of grassland cultivation, increased stocking levels, increasing mechanisation and the change to autumn grown cereals have all caused the loss of Lapwing nesting and feeding habitat (Gibbons *et al.* 1993).

Of intriguing interest is the broad similarity between the abundance map in the *88-91 Atlas* and the map in the present account. The main differences are the collapse of the Welsh population and the comparatively greater abundance in East Anglia today.

Number of counties in which recorded:

Period	Probable breeding		Confirmed breeding		Combined		
	Br	Ir	Br	Ir	Br	Ir	Both
1875–1900	0	0	108	34	108	34	142
1968-1972	0	0	108	34	108	34	142
			change		0	0	0

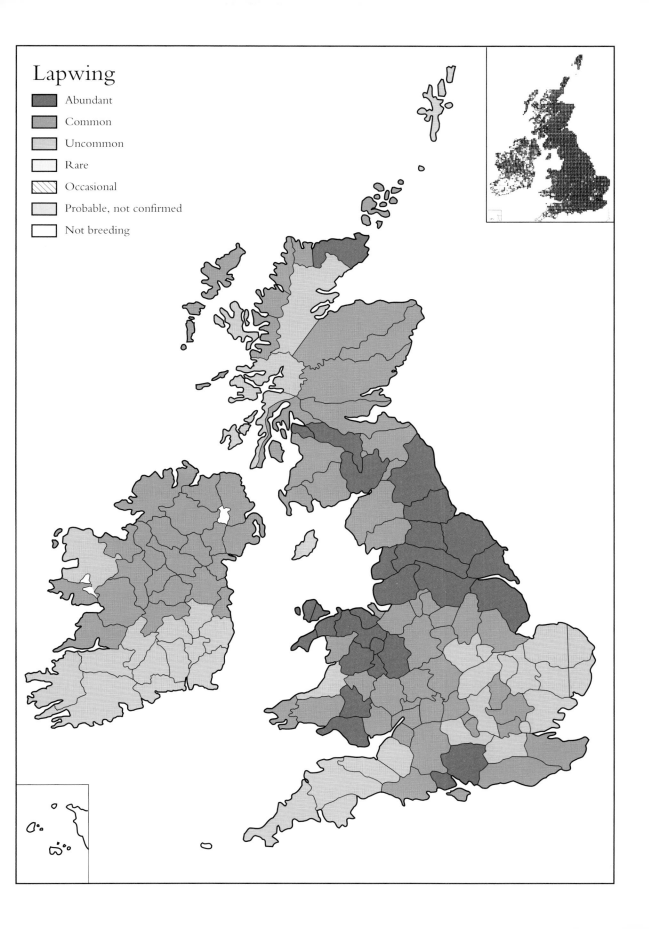

Lapwing

- **Abundant**
- **Common**
- **Uncommon**
- **Rare**
- **Occasional**
- **Probable, not confirmed**
- **Not breeding**

Dunlin

Calidris alpina

During the last quarter of the 19th century breeding Dunlins were distributed widely, mainly on moorland, from Shetland and many of the Western Isles south through mainland Scotland to the S Pennines. Local populations existed in Wales, Cornwall, Devonshire and Lincolnshire. In Ireland the species was distributed mainly in the west and north and, although the upland (mainly northern) populations were probably stable, it was decreasing rapidly on its lowland breeding sites through destruction of its coastal marsh and heathland habitats.

The latest 19th century breeding records on Bodmin Moor, Cornwall and Dartmoor, Devonshire were in the 1860s. Notwithstanding the paucity of actual nests found, all writers on the birds of Cornwall and Devonshire, well into the 20th century, considered the Dunlin a breeding species in those counties, although no further nests were found until the 1920s and 1930s. One or two pairs of Dunlin were said to breed on Scotton Common, Lincolnshire in the northwest of the county until the early years of the 1900s. The Dunlin was reported breeding on the hills near Abergavenny, Monmouthshire some years prior to 1939 and probably during the 19th century (Lovegrove *et al.* 1994) and was considered to have probably nested on the western slopes of the Prescelly Mountains in Pembrokeshire (Mathew 1894). In Cardiganshire it nested on the Teifi Bog and around the upland lakes and it also bred in small

numbers on several moors around the Snowdonia range. The Dunlin nested on the marshes of the Dee estuary on both the Flintshire and Cheshire sides. Eleven eggs were recorded taken from the marshes near Puddington and Shotwick in Cheshire in 1871 but no further records exist. Shortly after this time the marshes were converted to agricultural land and the site became unsuitable for Dunlin. Similarly, the lowland mosses and marshes of S Lancashire had been deserted probably at about the same time and for the same reasons.

From the Pennines of N Derbyshire the Dunlin bred sparingly through N England and into Scotland. Here it was widespread throughout the country: Gray (1871) wrote that in W Scotland the Dunlin bred 'on almost every moorland and marshy tract where the Snipe or Golden Plover is met with'. He had several times taken eggs on the Renfrewshire hills within full view of the city of Glasgow. Dunlin bred on many of the larger Western Isles; for instance in 1898 and 1899 it was said that hundreds bred on Tiree, and in the Outer Hebrides it was considered that Dunlin bred abundantly throughout the islands. Its nests were found in many parts of Tentsmuir, Fife, around the turn of the century (Baxter and Rintoul 1953).

In Ireland the Dunlin evidently bred in small numbers in many parts of Leinster, Connaught and Ulster, although nests had been found only in the counties of Wicklow, Mayo, Westmeath, Londonderry and Donegal. In other counties birds seen in breeding plumage in May or June led Ussher and Warren (1900) to consider that breeding took place there.

Through the 20th century the lowland populations of the Dunlin continued to decline (for instance at Marton Mere in Lancashire, the Solway salt marshes in Cumberland and on Tentsmuir, Fife) but, overall, in its upland habitats it has probably managed to maintain numbers. Locally, losses of upland habitat have resulted from afforestation, and numbers have declined in parts of Wales and in Kirkcudbrightshire, for instance, as a result (Parslow 1973); in Sutherland and Caithness a reduction of 17% in the Dunlin population has been attributed directly to afforestation (Stroud *et al.* 1987). Sharrock confirmed the difficulty in assessing Dunlin numbers accurately owing to the difficulty in proving breeding (*68–72 Atlas*) and, so, few of the trends are quantified. The *88-91 Atlas*, however, reported an increase of about a fifth in the number of 10-km squares in which breeding was proven or suspected since the *68–72 Atlas* survey, although densities in many squares may well have decreased (J. Reid in litt.).

Number of counties in which recorded:

Period	Probable breeding		Confirmed breeding		Combined		
	Br	Ir	Br	Ir	Br	Ir	Both
1875–1900	6	8	38	5	44	13	57
1968–1972	8	1	39	10	47	11	58
change					3	–2	1
					7%	–15%	2%

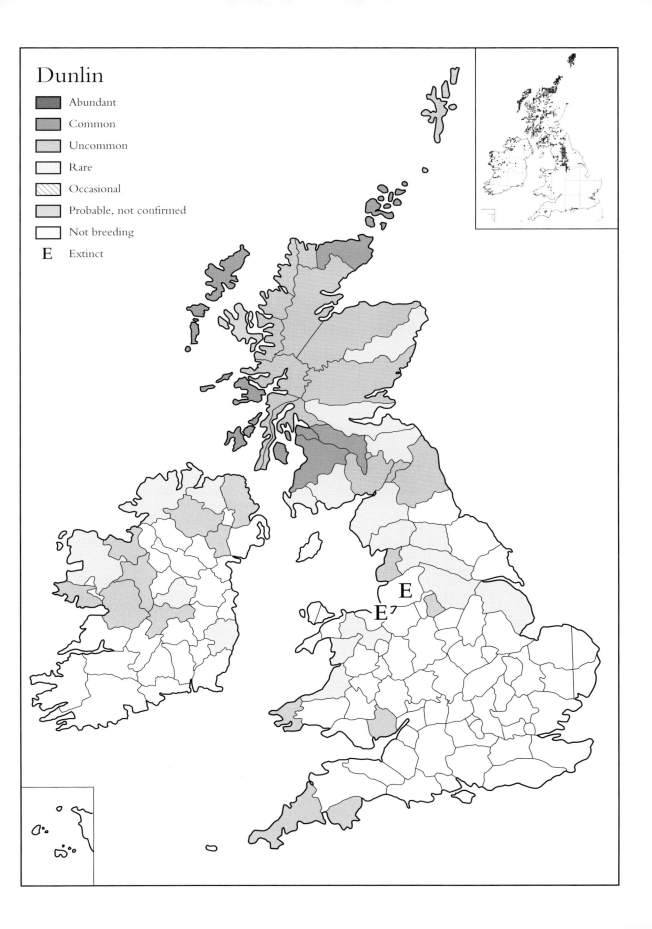

Dunlin

- ◼ Abundant
- ◼ Common
- ◻ Uncommon
- ◻ Rare
- ▨ Occasional
- ◻ Probable, not confirmed
- ◻ Not breeding
- **E** Extinct

Ruff

Philomachus pugnax

The Ruff was a widespread, though uncommon, breeding species along the east coast counties of England up to the end of the 18th century. It occurred on inland marshes, wet heathland and saltmarshes. Breeding took place in Northumberland, Durham, Norfolk, Suffolk, Yorkshire, Lincolnshire, Northamptonshire, Huntingdonshire and, possibly, Essex. It was a regular, and sometimes common, passage migrant at this time and many were taken in nets and by horsehair nooses for the table. The birds were then caged for two or three weeks whilst being fattened and when sold fetched a very high price. Only Royalty and noblemen could afford this highly esteemed bird. Fewer were taken in the breeding season, but, at this time, the eggs were also taken for food. The noblemen whose grounds it frequented afforded the Ruff some protection because of its economic value, but this was not upheld legally. Although persecuted widely, however, the decline of the Ruff really began when its breeding sites were drained or ploughed for agriculture.

By 1800 the Ruff had ceased to breed in Northamptonshire. Breeding in Yorkshire and the fenland of Huntingdonshire was only occasional by this time. The first few years of the 19th century then saw extinctions in many areas. The Ruff bred for the last time in Huntingdonshire

before 1810. Around the decoys on Holderness and the carrs along the Hull in the East Riding of Yorkshire it was not recorded breeding after 1807. By 1825, it had ceased to breed in the Durham marshes about the Tees, Yorkshire (the old sites around Selby, Doncaster and Wetherby were drained) and the Lincolnshire fenland, the final reclamation work being completed at this time. In W Suffolk it bred for the last time at Mildenhall in 1825 and it possibly bred in the Tollesbury Marshes in Essex into the 1820s.

This period saw the increase in that other form of persecution of rare birds—the 19th century collector. As the Ruff became rarer, so the value placed upon specimens of eggs and skins increased. Males in breeding plumage were particularly valued, and not just by the collector. A case containing a stuffed male with its 'ruff' decorated many ordinary drawing rooms of the period.

In the years up to the middle of the century, the Ruff was lost as a breeding species from Cambridgeshire, where it was formerly common in the fens, last breeding near Ely in the 1840s. Near to Yarmouth, just over the Suffolk border, it was last recorded breeding in 1844 and it bred for the last time in the fenland area of Norfolk around Feltwell sometime during the 1840s.

By 1850 the Ruff bred in only three counties. In Northumberland it bred commonly on Prestwick Carr at least up to 1853, at which time two nests and eggs were collected, and nested occasionally until around 1865. In Lincolnshire it was still breeding on the heaths of the northwest; the last eggs were taken from Scotton Common in 1882. In its former stronghold in Norfolk, it had declined to the point where breeding was known only at Hickling; regular breeding ceased in 1871.

Sporadic breeding occurred in Norfolk until 1890 and in Suffolk in 1898, the only remaining records of the 19th century and the point of effective extermination. Further sporadic breeding occurred in Norfolk, Durham and Lancashire up to 1922, but then in 1963 the first breeding in Britain for 41 years was proven in the Ouse Washes following both increases in wintering birds through the 1950s and suspected breeding there for several years. This was the advent of a recolonisation that led to 21 Reeves breeding there in 1970. Numbers have declined somewhat since but breeding has spread to other English counties. Displaying males were observed in Wales and Scotland during the *88–91 Atlas* survey period.

Number of counties in which recorded:

Period	Probable breeding		Confirmed breeding		Combined		
	Br	Ir	Br	Ir	Br	Ir	Both
1875–1900	0	0	2	0	2	0	2
1968–1972	1	0	5	0	6	0	6
			change		4	0	4
					200%		200%

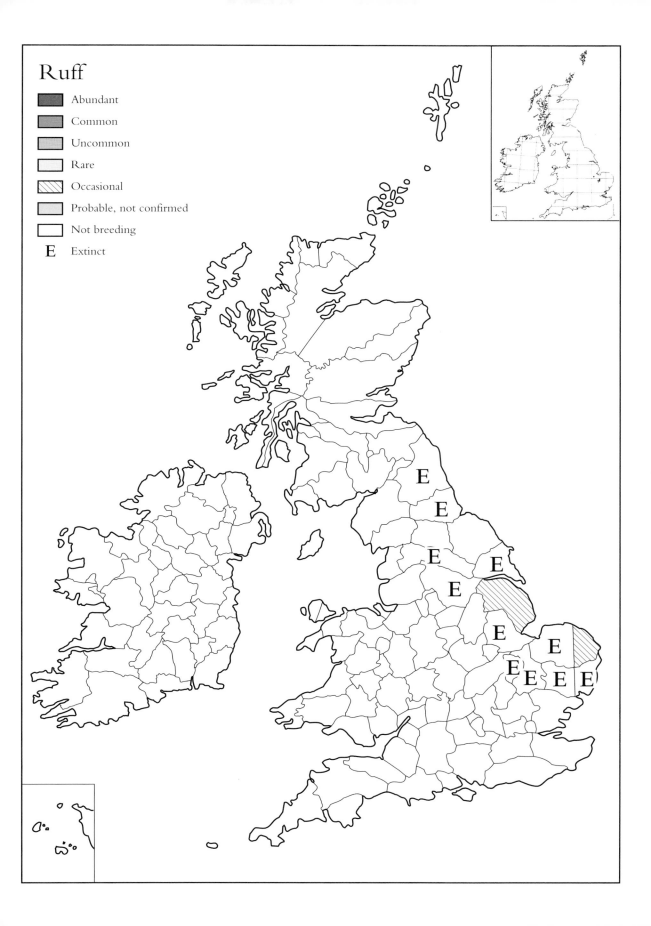

Ruff

- **Abundant**
- **Common**
- **Uncommon**
- **Rare**
- **Occasional**
- **Probable, not confirmed**
- **Not breeding**
- **E** Extinct

Snipe (Common, Whole or Full Snipe)

Gallinago gallinago

The Snipe bred widely throughout Britain and Ireland between 1875 and 1900, being absent from only a few counties in the SW Midlands and around London. It was particularly common in parts of Wales, Scotland and Ireland. Large numbers of Snipe also visited Britain and Ireland during the winter from NE Europe (R. Green in litt.). Its marsh and wet meadow breeding habitat requirements in the lowlands unsurprisingly meant that the Snipe was already recorded diminishing in numbers through the 19th century as drainage of these lands took place and reclamation and enclosure ensued. This effect was widespread and was mentioned as having affected the numbers breeding from Essex to Wiltshire in the south to the Tweed and Forth regions in the north. Breeding ceased during the last quarter of the 19th century in several counties, notably Oxfordshire and some surrounding areas, and had declined substantially in the lowlands of N Wales. Numbers in the uplands were probably not affected because

there the species breeds mainly on peat bogs and flushes on moorland—sites largely unaffected by agricultural changes at that time. Vast numbers were both shot, particularly after the widespread introduction of the breech-loading shotgun, and trapped in winter, leading some to speculate that this may have been responsible for some local reductions in N Scotland and Ireland. In the winter of 1880–81, for example, enormous bags were recorded, many sportsmen claiming bags of over 1,000 Snipe each. In Orkney and elsewhere severe winters, especially between 1878 and 1881, were also said to have reduced numbers for some years following.

In the early years of the 20th century Snipe numbers appeared to recover somewhat, particularly in the English Midlands. This increase accelerated until the 1930s in most areas, and the early 1940s in a few others. The population remained stable for some 10–15 years but then started a slow decline. Breeding ceased in Middlesex again in 1956 but elsewhere the species was still breeding in all counties, albeit irregularly in some. The *68–72 Atlas* confirmed the losses. Areas of the Midlands and S and SW England were wholly without breeding birds. Perhaps the most striking thing about the map in the *68–72 Atlas* is its broad resemblance to the map opposite suggesting that by the *68–72 Atlas* study period the distribution of the Snipe was similar to that at the end of the 19th century. The *88–91 Atlas* documented the continuing fall in lowland breeding numbers in Britain and also those on the upland margins and in Ireland.

From the evidence of the 19th century naturalists it is probable that an underlying gradual decline has been apparent since their time due to drainage and land use changes but that the added pressure from winter shooting caused accelerated losses. The recovery of the Snipe populations between 1900 and 1940 was probably due to two factors: first, the depression in British agriculture, which was accompanied by a reduction in arable land and an increase in pasture and rough grazing land, and second, a reduction in shooting of Snipe. This relief, however, was not enough to balance the breeding habitat losses for very long and, so, eventually numbers reverted to their declining trend with both summer and winter habitat losses continuing to the present day. A striking recent development has been the decline of Snipe breeding populations in Ireland, almost certainly because of drainage, intensification of grassland management and exploitation of peat bogs (R. Green in litt.).

Number of counties in which recorded:

Period	Probable breeding		Confirmed breeding		Combined		
	Br	Ir	Br	Ir	Br	Ir	Both
1875–1900	2	0	99	34	101	34	135
1968–1972	2	0	106	34	108	34	142
			change		7	0	7
					7%		5%

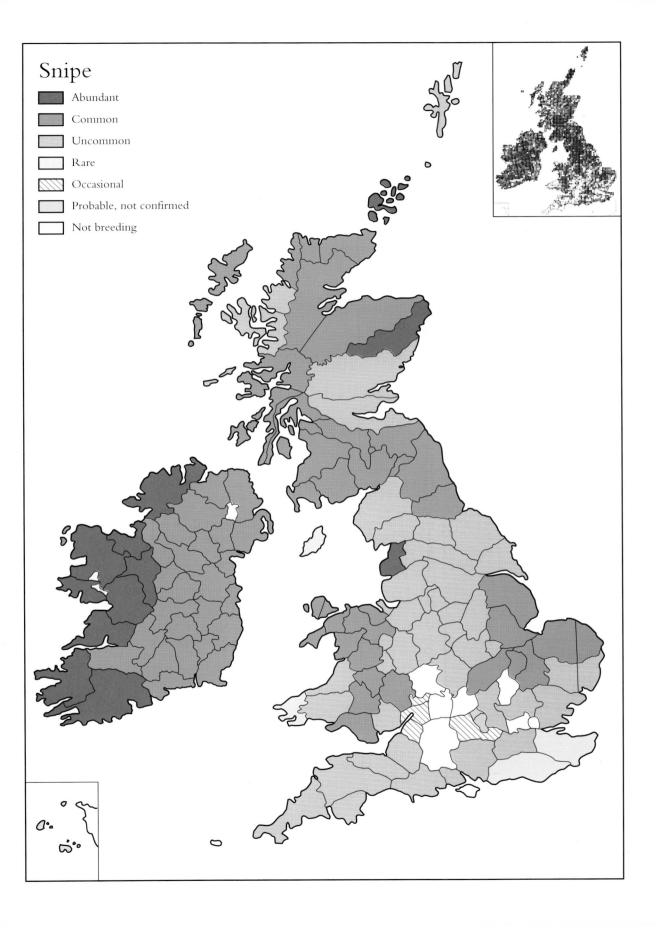

Snipe

- Abundant
- Common
- Uncommon
- Rare
- Occasional
- Probable, not confirmed
- Not breeding

Woodcock

Scolopax rusticola

The Woodcock was an esteemed bird of the table and a favourite of the sportsman and, hence, most early references referred to its occurrence in the winter when it was most often sought out and shot. Hence, until about the middle of the 19th century, there were few breeding records. It seems that, particularly relative to the number of naturalists studying there, there were far more records from the northern half of Scotland than elsewhere before 1850, although both Latham (1785, 1821–28) and Daniel (1807–13) state that they did not know of any instance of the Woodcock breeding in Scotland. Morris (1855) hinted that between about 1830 and 1850 far more records from the Midlands and southern counties of England had come to light and this, in addition to his own records, led More (1865) to suggest that 'many more birds remain to breed now than formerly; and this increase appears to be owing to the great extent of country which has been covered with plantations during the past few years'. Yarrell (1837–43) wrote that the Woodcock's nest or young had been found in almost every county in England and in several of those in Scotland and more frequently of recent years than formerly.

In Ireland there were several items of circumstantial evidence that showed that the Woodcock did not breed (or did so extremely rarely and sporadically) before the late 18th century. The earliest cases of breeding known to Thompson (1849–56) took place during the 1830s but their wide distribution over the country suggests that Woodcock had been breeding there for some years. The species evidently increased from this point and, by about 1860, were recognised to breed throughout the country. By the end of the century Woodcock bred in most woodlands and, in some well-wooded counties, occurred in large numbers. It was said that the increase in Woodcock numbers was due to the increase of tree planting that had taken place although it was suspected that the parallel increase in Britain indicated some other cause (Ussher and Warren 1900). Climatic changes have been suspected (Gibbons *et al.* 1993).

More's (1865) investigations showed that the Woodcock bred occasionally in all counties of England and Scotland other than Cornwall and those of S Scotland, not at all in Wales but more commonly north from the Forth/Clyde valleys. By the last quarter of the 19th century breeding had evidently become more regular in most English counties, particularly in the north; Cornwall had been colonised but breeding records were still scant in many southeastern counties. The species remained scarce in Wales, particularly in the south, and the added detail available during this period proved that the Woodcock bred less commonly in N Scotland than was previously apparent.

This establishment of a regular breeding population in Britain and Ireland seems to have taken place in nearly all areas, except Wales and the extreme west, simultaneously in about the 1820s. The subsequent build-up of numbers, particularly in Scotland and Ireland, and the spread westward from the 1830s were strikingly rapid. New plantations undoubtedly created new breeding habitat but it was probably the fact that most of them were Pheasant coverts and, hence, were protected that really allowed the Woodcock to increase so successfully. Following research of the old literature Alexander (1945–47) was able to demonstrate the 19th century range expansion of the Woodcock up to 1886 and the map that accompanies this account shows the continuation of the expansion up to the end of the century.

The decrease noted in N Scotland continued into the 20th century and a decline began in S England (particularly in the southwest) and Ireland. These were not extensive, however, and the 20th century conifer plantings have encouraged local increases, especially in N Wales, East Anglia and SW Scotland. Since the late 1970s a decline has begun that has accelerated since about 1980 and may be related to the condition, particularly the state of maturity, that the post-1939–45 war conifer plantations have reached (Sharrock 1976).

Number of counties in which recorded:

Period	Probable breeding		Confirmed breeding		Combined		
	Br	Ir	Br	Ir	Br	Ir	Both
1875–1900	2	0	96	34	98	34	132
1968–1972	1	1	99	33	100	34	134
			change		2	0	2
					2%		2%

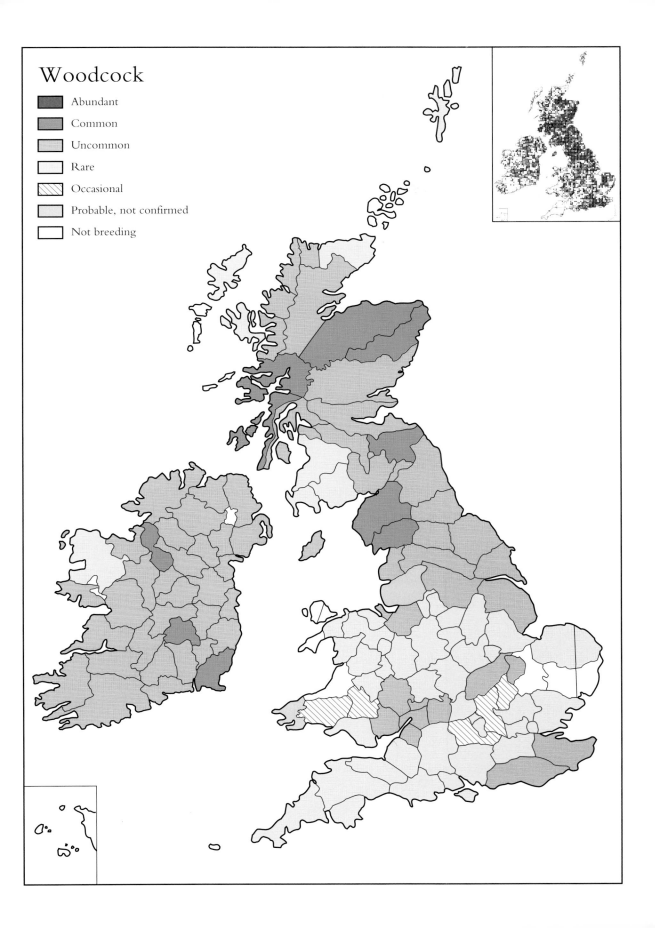

Woodcock

- ■ Abundant
- ▨ Common
- ▨ Uncommon
- ☐ Rare
- ▨ Occasional
- ▨ Probable, not confirmed
- ☐ Not breeding

Black-tailed Godwit

Limosa limosa

There has evidently been some confusion concerning how far into the 19th century the Black-tailed Godwit bred in Britain. It seems clear that regular breeding ceased before the middle of the century but it is possible that sporadic nesting took place a little later in its traditional East Anglian haunts and very occasionally into the last quarter of the 19th century.

More (1865) expressed the belief that Norfolk was the 'only county in which there is a possibility that a pair or two may linger occasionally'. From other evidence it appears that this, indeed, may have been the case around the middle of the 19th century. The Black-tailed Godwit apparently formerly bred in abundance in the East Anglian marshes but its extinction as a regular breeding species, owing primarily to the drainage of the grazing marshes and their eventual conversion to arable land, the bulk of which took place during the 18th century, occurred sometime between 1829 and 1835. In Norfolk it had bred in its greatest numbers around Buckenham, Thurne and Horsey but was evidently very rare by 1825. In 1829 a nest was found at Horsey and breeding probably persisted there for a few years subsequently. The species was recorded at sporadic intervals over the next 20 years or so in the spring but was shot wherever it appeared. A sale of a collection of eggs in 1858 contained three, purportedly of this species, taken at

Reedham in 1857. There is little to add to this account concerning the species' status in Suffolk. It appears to have been accepted that the accounts of breeding in the Norfolk Broads also applied to the parts of this district over the border into Suffolk as an egg taken from near Yarmouth in 1821 was claimed for that county (Babington 1884–86). The last nests were found in Cambridgeshire about 1829 and no birds (either breeding or on passage) were seen in the county after 1850 until the 20th century. Although there are no specific records it was believed that the Black-tailed Godwit bred in the adjoining Huntingdonshire fens up to about the same date. An egg was bought in the Cambridge market in 1847 but with no information of its origin. It seems probable that the Black-tailed Godwit became extinct in the Lincolnshire fens at around the same time as other areas of the East Anglian fens (say between 1829 and 1847) and potential breeding pairs were shot for a few years later. The latest 19th century breeding record was of a nest found and eggs taken from near Wainfleet in 1885. There is little supporting information for this record but it was considered to indicate probable breeding by later writers (Blathwayt 1915, Witherby et al. 1938–41, Smith and Cornwallis 1955).

The Black-tailed Godwit evidently bred on the edge of Hatfield Moor in Yorkshire during the early years of the 19th century but there are no specific records. Nelson et al. (1907) believed that it probably bred in the carrs of the East Riding.

Nesting was first suspected again in Moray in 1914 (perhaps of the islandica race—Bannerman 1953–63), but absolute proof was wanting. The Black-tailed Godwit did not breed, or attempt to breed, again in England until the 1930s. A pair was present at a site in Norfolk in 1934 and breeding was suspected but not proven. An increasing number of passage birds were noted throughout E England (although these may have been both limosa and islandica races) from 1890 until 1937 and may have led to four breeding attempts between 1937 and 1942 (Bannerman 1953–63). These were most notably in the S Lincolnshire fens—the recolonisation of East Anglia took place from this point—especially on the Ouse Washes (from 1952) but, latterly, also on the nearby Nene Washes (from the late 1970s). In 1946 two young and an adult of the islandica race were photographed on a Caithness moor, the first confirmed breeding record from Scotland. In the following years breeding was recorded from several sites in Scotland, most often from Shetland (in most years from 1949), in Orkney (irregularly since 1956), but also down into the southeast of the country (J. Cadbury in litt.). Black-tailed Godwits nested on the Somerset Levels in 1963 and increased up to six pairs before drainage lowered the water table and since 1985 only a single pair has attempted to breed (Baxter and Rintoul 1953, Parslow 1973, Sharrock 1976, J. Cadbury in litt.).

Number of counties in which recorded:

Period	Probable breeding		Confirmed breeding		Combined		
	Br	Ir	Br	Ir	Br	Ir	Both
1875–1900	1	0	0	0	1	0	1
1968–1972	5	0	9	0	14	0	14
			change		13	0	13
					1300%		1300%

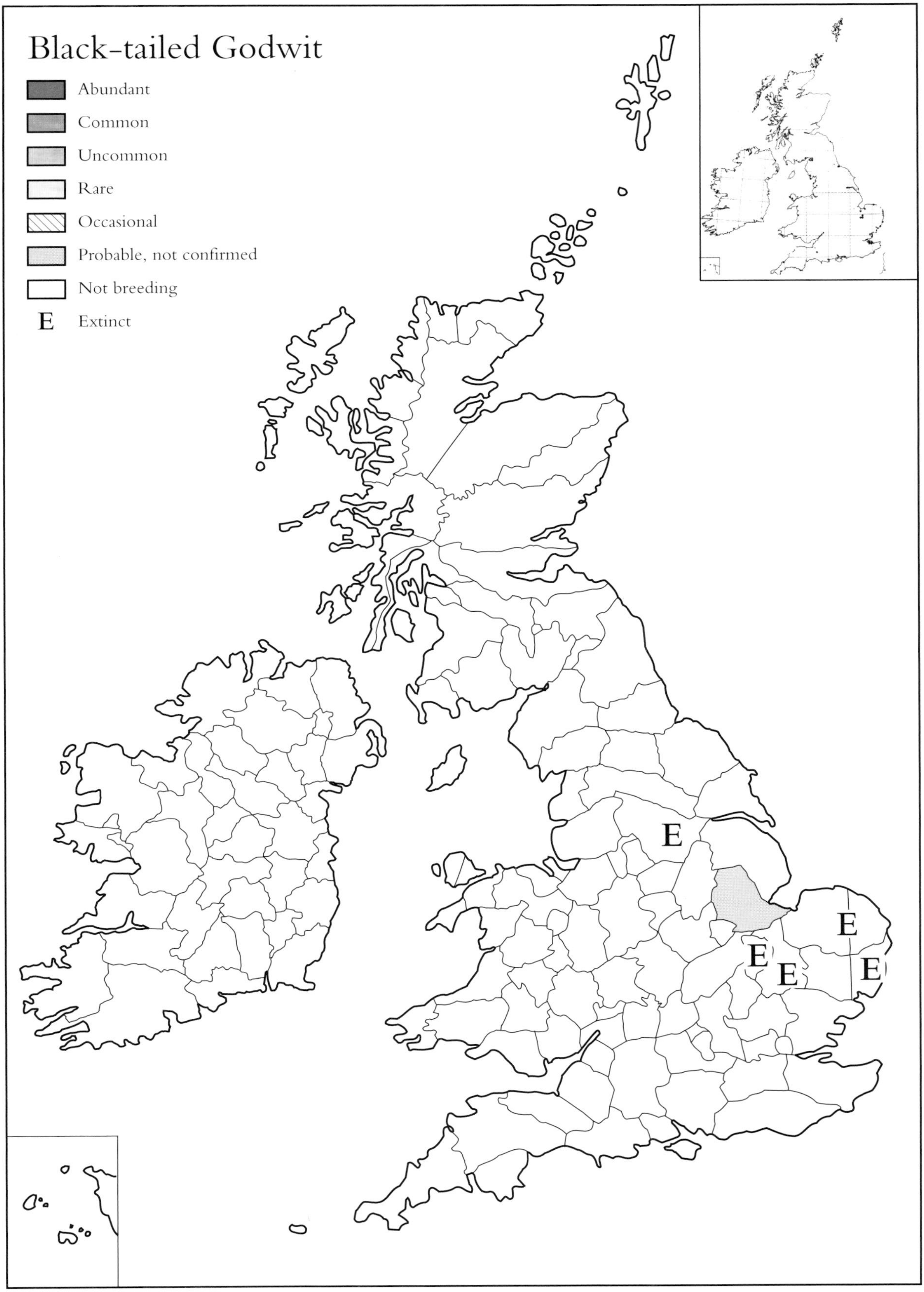
Black-tailed Godwit
Abundant
Common
Uncommon
Rare
Occasional
Probable, not confirmed
Not breeding
E Extinct
E
E
E
E
E

Whimbrel

Numenius phaeopus

The Whimbrel was well known as a passage migrant throughout Britain and Ireland during the 19th century but the only places where it bred, were in Orkney and Shetland.

It had been known to breed in Shetland for much of the 19th century and an account of a collecting trip there in 1832 recorded nests on Yell and Hascosay but included the observation that they were rapidly decreasing (Saxby 1874)—the eggs were gathered regularly by the islanders as they were regarded as particularly delicately flavoured. It was said that Hascosay held the majority of the breeding pairs in Shetland but this seems unlikely given the number of other localities at which the species was known or believed to breed (M. Grant in litt.). It may have been, however, the largest (or most dense) concentration of breeding Whimbrel recorded at that time. Between 1887 and 1894 it was reckoned that seven or eight pairs bred on the island; however, 22 pairs were noted there in 1897 and 16 nests were said to have been found, although that year was evidently exceptional as not nearly so many pairs were recorded in subsequent years. It should be noted that Chislett (1923) doubted this record and it does seem unlikely in view of the much lower numbers on the island in the years immediately preceding and following and the Whimbrel's high degree of site fidelity (M. Grant in litt.). Other islands upon which nests were found were Unst (at Hermaness and near Belmont), Uyea Island off Unst, Yell (around the lakes of Lumbister, Colister and Gossawater

amongst other places), north of Mainland (especially around Esha Ness), an island near Whalsay, Noss, North Roe and Urie Lingey near Fetlar. Pairs were seen in a number of other localities during the breeding season. At the end of the 19th century it was estimated that 30 pairs bred in Shetland, although this may have been an underestimate, and they occurred in similar numbers to the Curlew.

The Whimbrel was confused with the Curlew during the early years of the 19th century on Orkney, but breeding of Whimbrel was first recorded on Hoy in 1831 when, evidently, a few broods were seen. It bred in far fewer numbers than the Curlew during the second half of the century and, indeed, was decreasing. By 1889, although occasionally seen on other islands, its only positive breeding site was on a small marshy area on Hoy. This record is one of the last from Orkney. Occasionally breeding has been suspected since but was not confirmed until 1968, since when a few pairs have bred regularly. Interestingly, the moorlands on Eday and N Mainland where the Whimbrel now breeds are not the areas where breeding previously occurred (M. Grant in litt.).

One other record of possible breeding in Scotland exists; that of a pair exhibiting a distraction display on North Rona in 1885.

Low numbers continued to breed on Shetland through the 20th century until 1930 after which an increase in numbers (to 50–55 pairs in the 1950s) culminated, in the 1960s, in the recolonisation of islands that had not seen breeding for many years. Here, as on Orkney, the distribution of breeding Whimbrel is different to that in the 19th century. For example, according to Grant (1991), on the island of Unst, whilst a few pairs of Whimbrel do currently nest at Hermaness and near Belmont, neither of these locations is thought of as a major Whimbrel nesting area on this island today, although these are two areas specifically mentioned in the earlier records. Also, whilst these early records mention nesting on small islands close to Fetlar (e.g. Hascosay and Urie Lingey), there is no mention of actual nesting on Fetlar. Today, Fetlar is probably the most densely colonised island in Shetland. The disappearance of Whimbrel from certain localities where they nested in the late 19th century is associated with increases in numbers of large gulls or Great Skuas (Richardson 1990). The increase in Shetland may have been associated with changing climatic factors (Richardson 1990) whilst the production of fledglings appeared to be in excess of that required simply to balance adult mortality (Grant 1991). Batten et al. (1990) suggested that the recent trend towards colder springs and cooler summers may have suited the species. From 1957 one or two pairs have bred on Lewis in the Outer Hebrides and sporadic breeding has taken place elsewhere in Scotland.

Number of counties in which recorded:

Period	Probable breeding		Confirmed breeding		Combined		
	Br	Ir	Br	Ir	Br	Ir	Both
1875–1900	0	0	2	0	2	0	2
1968–1972	2	0	5	0	7	0	7
			change		5	0	5
					250%		250%

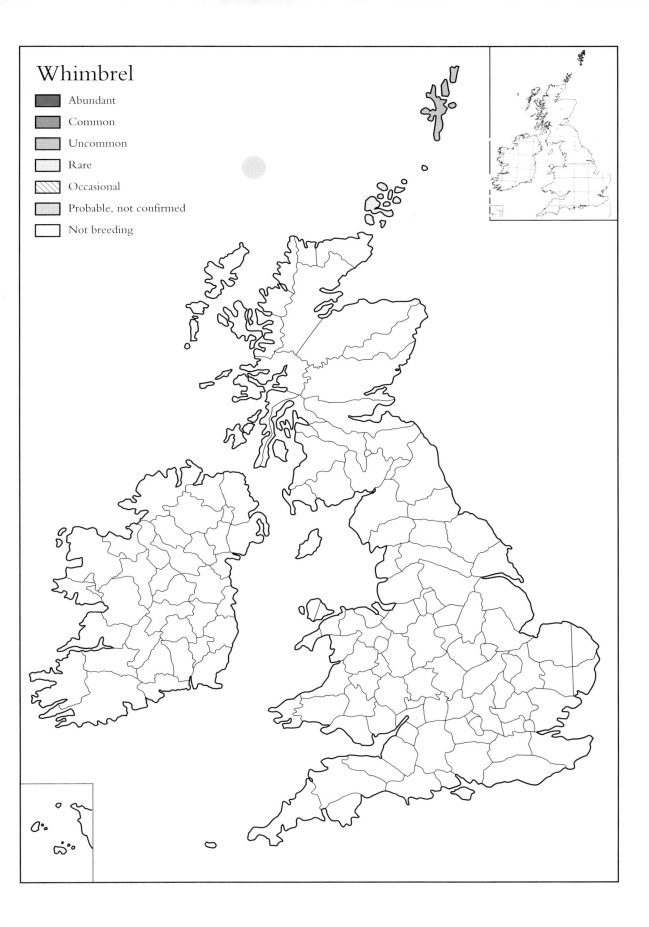

Whimbrel

- Abundant
- Common
- Uncommon
- Rare
- Occasional
- Probable, not confirmed
- Not breeding

Curlew
(Common Curlew)

Numenius arquata

Up to about the 1860s the Curlew's breeding range encompassed the moors and uplands of Devonshire and Cornwall, Wales, the Shropshire uplands and, from the lower Pennines, northwards through N England and Scotland to Shetland.

From about that point the spread to lower areas began. By the end of the 1860s a few pairs had begun breeding on the Somerset part of Exmoor and Dunkerry Beacon, and by the end of the century Curlews were breeding in other hilly districts of the west of the county. The first recorded eggs in Wiltshire were taken on Ashbourne Down in 1876, although many sportsmen asserted that the Curlew bred here, and on other downs, some years earlier (Smith 1887). Peirson (1959) was of the opinion that these early records referred to the Stone Curlew but the 19th century naturalists were quite able to distinguish the two species. Indeed Smith wrote that Curlews 'though not so regularly as [the Stone Curlew], breed in the more retired districts of our Wiltshire downs'. The earliest record of breeding in Dorset concerns a clutch of eggs taken from the Poole estuary in 1873. The Curlew evidently increased slowly from this point but never bred far from the coast. During the 1880s the Curlew was suspected of breeding in Hampshire. By 1890 it had become clear that a pair or two bred on some heaths in the New Forest, where they subsequently increased. In Cheshire the Curlew was breeding in several places by 1900 but had already withdrawn from a few low-lying mosses following reclamation. Evidently, it had started to breed, or to breed regularly, in Lancashire from about 1870 and several new breeding sites were noted from the 1880s. The Curlew bred extensively in Ireland, chiefly on the flat bogs and the mountain moors, but was least frequent in Munster and absent from some southeastern counties.

The evidence for the Curlew breeding in the Outer Hebrides was confusing. Macgillivray, in his early writings, considered it a common breeding species whereas later, in 1841, he said that he did not find it breeding there. There were a few other records of birds seen in the summer in the Outer Hebrides but just as many notes of its absence. It was considered by later writers to have probably (but only occasionally) nested during the 19th century (e.g. Baxter and Rintoul 1953).

In the Curlew's traditional upland haunts there was little evidence of any change, although, in some localised areas of Scotland, the conversion of grouse moor to deer forest was creating new, suitable breeding habitat. This habitat change was believed to have benefited Curlews since there were associated increases in numbers (Harvie-Brown and Buckley 1895). The areas of moor denuded of heather (such as large areas of Assynt) were said to have encouraged Curlews to colonise as did the new forests for a short period after planting. There are too few data, however, to confirm such statements (M.Grant in litt.). Perhaps the high levels of predator control exercised by gamekeepers during the second half of the 19th century allowed some of the increases in Curlew numbers and distribution.

A change of breeding habit, hinted at during the end of the 19th century, was confirmed from the beginning of the 20th. Several areas began to record breeding in new lowland sites, for instance in river valleys and on low-lying moors, particularly in N and W England. From the 1940s this increase accelerated and the species spread into almost all parts of E England. This was accompanied by an expansion into agricultural habitats, first into lowland pastures and rough meadows prior to 1939 and then into arable crops, when these fields were ploughed up during the 1939–45 war (Parslow 1973). Ireland was completely colonised by 1948 when breeding was first noted in Armagh. In England, particularly, however, there was some indication that the period of expansion was slowing by the late 1950s. The *88–91 Atlas* confirmed that the expansion had ended. It also revealed a decline, particularly in S and E Ireland, but also in W Scotland, the Midlands, Pembrokeshire, Devonshire and Dorset caused perhaps by habitat losses resulting from agricultural changes, although very high levels of nest predation could be causing declines in Northern Ireland, even in some locations where little loss of suitable breeding habitat has taken place (M. Grant in litt.).

Number of counties in which recorded:

Period	Probable breeding		Confirmed breeding		Combined		
	Br	Ir	Br	Ir	Br	Ir	Both
1875–1900	2	0	75	29	77	29	106
1968–1972	1	0	94	34	95	34	129
			change		18	5	23
					23%	17%	22%

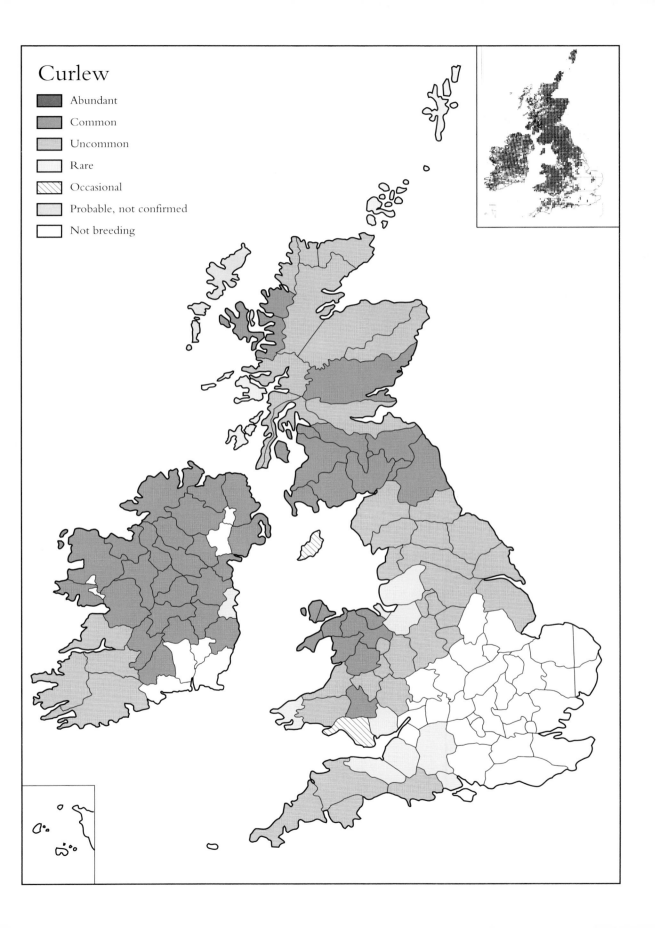

Curlew

- **Abundant**
- **Common**
- **Uncommon**
- **Rare**
- **Occasional**
- **Probable, not confirmed**
- **Not breeding**

Redshank (Common Redshank)

Tringa totanus

Numbers of Redshanks, particularly in England, fluctuated somewhat during the 19th century. The expansion of cultivation and continuing drainage destroyed much ideal habitat and decreases in numbers were already apparent by the middle of the century in southern coastal counties (especially Kent and Essex). By this time Redshanks had almost deserted the East Anglian fens and had bred for the last time in Pembrokeshire, probably during the 1840s.

There was an apparent recovery during the second half of the century, seen first of all on the coast, but then increasingly inland. Norfolk had historically been a stronghold of the species and numbers began to increase in this and neighbouring counties. After ceasing to breed in Lincolnshire during the 1850s or 1860s it returned to breed along the Humber during the 1880s or 1890s. In southern counties it increased on the coast; this was especially apparent in Kent, and by the close of the century it was breeding commonly far inland in that county along the river valleys. In Cambridgeshire, numerous accounts attested to its scarcity around the middle of the century but by the close it was breeding commonly again, especially on the Ouse

Washes. Another sizeable group bred along the Trent valley in Nottinghamshire and Derbyshire, once again having increased after the 1870s. The Redshank bred sparingly in N England and N Wales, mainly on the coast. In S Scotland it was uncommon, but north of the Forth/Clyde valleys it bred more plentifully.

There is some confusion concerning the status of the Redshank in the Outer Hebrides. More (1865) regarded it as particularly common but Harvie-Brown and Buckley (1888) could find little evidence of breeding, and Hartert *et al.* (1912) stated that it bred rarely there at that time. Other evidence suggests that the Redshank underwent the same decline and subsequent recovery in the Outer Hebrides that occurred over other parts of its Scottish range (Baxter and Rintoul 1953), although the timing may have been a little later than elsewhere. The Redshank was also said to breed in relatively high numbers in Orkney.

Its main habitats in Ireland were on the marshes, lakes and rivers, in similar sites to that of the Common Sandpiper. It was absent from some counties in the southwest and southeast and, overall, was scarce in Munster. It was similarly scarce west of the Galway and Mayo lakes.

The 19th century increase continued during the 20th century. By 1925 every British county held breeding pairs except for Pembrokeshire and Cornwall. It became clear that the main period of expansion occurred from about 1893 until 1915 when 26 counties in S England and Wales were occupied for the first time. Corresponding increases were noted throughout N England and S Scotland; however, the expansion remains largely unexplained. The apparent increase ceased about 1940 (although Cornwall, Wexford and Kerry were colonised after 1940) and a decline set in. This decline was most apparent in S and SE England (particularly in the inland counties of Wiltshire, Middlesex, Hertfordshire, Essex and Suffolk) but also took place locally elsewhere and was attributed to further habitat losses. A parallel contraction of range has occurred in Ireland away from the south of the country. Further losses occurred during the severe winters of the early 1960s and this led to the proposition that the mild climatic period before the 1940s may have assisted the increase then (Parslow 1973). This seems likely as adult Redshank are considered not to survive cold winters well (Thompson and Hale 1993).

Number of counties in which recorded:

Period	Probable breeding		Confirmed breeding		Combined		
	Br	Ir	Br	Ir	Br	Ir	Both
1875–1900	0	2	66	28	66	30	96
1968–1972	5	2	97	22	102	24	126
			change		36	−6	30
					55%	−20%	31%

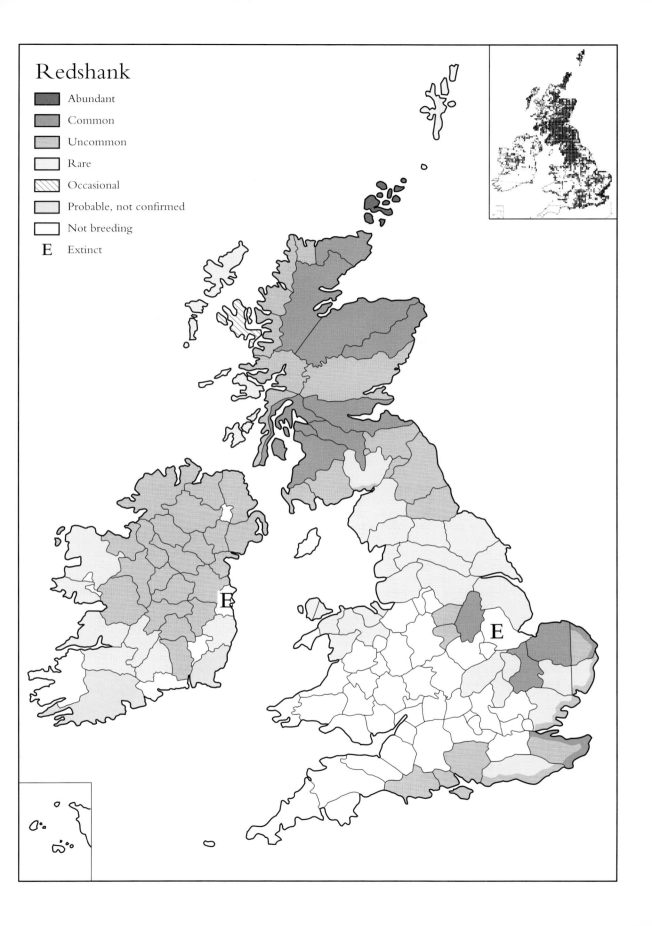

Redshank

- Abundant
- Common
- Uncommon
- Rare
- Occasional
- Probable, not confirmed
- Not breeding

E Extinct

Greenshank

Tringa nebularia

The Greenshank was little known in summer during the first half of the 19th century. The first record of breeding in Britain was of a nest found by Macgillivray on Harris, Outer Hebrides probably between 1822 and 1834. In the 1830s eggs and chicks of a further three nests were found in Argyll and Sutherland. Once it was known that Greenshanks and their eggs were to be found in Scotland, collectors started to make efforts to procure them. From the 1840s eggs were found throughout NW Scotland, Sutherland providing the bulk of the spoils. Many records detailing time and place of collection exist from the period around the middle of the century as more and more collectors took to the hills. Later naturalists, however, took great care to limit the amount of intelligence, printed, and described the distribution of the Greenshank in much more general terms than earlier.

In the last quarter of the 19th century, the Greenshank was described as breeding throughout Sutherland, particularly commonly around the headwaters of the rivers Helmsdale, Brora and Shin in the southeast and widely, but far more thinly, over the rest of the county. In Caithness it was regarded as less plentiful than in Sutherland and its stronghold was said to be in the northwest of the county. Between 1868 and 1903 records of nests found in West and NW Ross suggest that it was a reasonably common species there—as an example there was a record of six pairs breeding on a small estate in Ross. The distribution of the Greenshank in the Moray region was confusing. Harvie-Brown maintained that there was evidence of a redistribution of the population during the second half of the century (Harvie-Brown and Macpherson 1904). From 1865 he often travelled the hills around Laggan and Dalwhinnie and had never come across Greenshanks. In 1873 he was aware of two or three pairs breeding in that area and argued that this colonisation was of birds from the Moor of Rannoch, even though it was not recorded breeding there until the late 1870s. Following this discovery, however, it increased in numbers until, by 1903, it bred not uncommonly in a few areas. In Rothiemurchus in the Spey Valley, Invernessshire little was recorded of breeding Greenshanks, although a few nests had been found from the 1880s. Before this date collectors appear not to have recognised that this type of habitat provided breeding sites and apparently did not search there. However, there is a suggestion that some parts of the Spey Valley were colonised only after forest fires and timber felling had partially cleared some areas (P. Thompson in litt.). Nethersole-Thompson (1951) further speculated that Greenshanks spread into the Spey Valley as a consequence of years of successful breeding, partially attributable to the high level of predator control exercised on estates in N and W Scotland. Breeding had been irregularly recorded from N Argyll since the first nest in 1853 and was probably sporadic as the area was so far from the primary breeding groups.

In the Outer Hebrides it bred both on Harris and on Lewis. Few of the Inner Hebrides provide suitable breeding habitat and it is perhaps unsurprising that it bred only on Skye in any numbers, whilst breeding had been reported from Tiree and the Island of Pabbay, off Skye. Nethersole-Thompson (1951), however, considered both the Pabbay record and Saxby's assertion that it had bred in Shetland in 1871 unlikely.

Little widespread change has occurred in the Greenshank's mainland distribution through the 20th century. Locally, upland conifer planting has made some sites uninhabitable by Greenshanks, particularly in the flows of Caithness and Sutherland, and in the 1950s losses occurred when the forest marshes of Speyside and Deeside dried out (Nethersole-Thompson and Nethersole-Thompson 1979). The major changes have occurred in the Outer Hebrides (where the Greenshank has increased and spread to the south islands although the reason for this is unknown, P. Thompson in litt.) and Shetland (where breeding was first proven in 1980 on Mainland).

Number of counties in which recorded:

Period	Probable breeding		Confirmed breeding		Combined		
	Br	Ir	Br	Ir	Br	Ir	Both
1875–1900	0	0	12	0	12	0	12
1968–1972	1	0	14	1	15	1	16
			change		3	1	4
					25%		33%

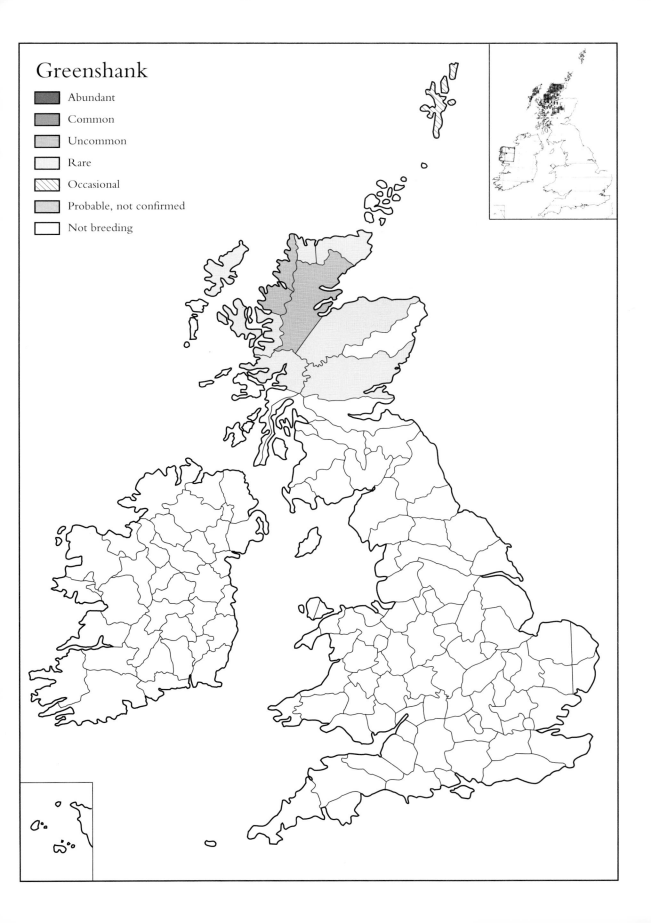

Greenshank

- ██ Abundant
- ▓▓ Common
- ░░ Uncommon
- □ Rare
- ▨ Occasional
- ▒ Probable, not confirmed
- □ Not breeding

Common Sandpiper (Summer Snipe)

Actitis hypoleucos

The Common Sandpiper is commonly considered a bird typical of upland water. Far more uncommonly, in Britain, it is found breeding on the shores of lowland rivers and gravel pits. In Ireland this situation is often reversed: Common Sandpipers breed in higher densities alongside lowland water than upland streams and rivers (Sharrock 1976). This habit in Ireland may give a clue to the lowland distribution of the Common Sandpiper (especially in the S and Midlands of England) evident during the 19th century.

In SW England the Common Sandpiper was clearly a common breeding species. In Cornwall it bred on streams and rivers throughout the county and in Devonshire it apparently preferred breeding on the moors, often far from water. In Dorset the Common Sandpiper apparently declined during the 19th century: Yarrell (1837–43) wrote that it bred in the county, but More (1865) seemed to indicate that it bred rarely and, although there were many summer records, Mansell-Pleydell (1888) was not aware of any proven records of breeding. In Lincolnshire there was a record of two pairs that bred at Saltfleet Haven in 1893. In N Wales it was regarded as equally common at all elevations and nests were recorded from almost 600m to the mouths of rivers. Notably, it was found breeding com-

monly throughout Anglesey. Elsewhere in Britain its distribution during the last quarter of the 19th century is similar to that of the present day. It was common throughout the uplands of N England and its distribution extended throughout the Scottish mainland. It bred commonly on many of the western islands but in Orkney and Shetland it was a more local breeding species.

The breeding habits of the Common Sandpiper in Ireland, described by Ussher and Warren (1900), confirm its preference for the shores of lowland rivers and lakes. It was apparently nowhere more common than along the inland reaches of the Shannon and the shores of the larger sheets of water such as the Loughs Derg, Corrib, Erne and Neagh but breeding records from the southeastern counties, especially Waterford, Kilkenny, Carlow and Wexford, were scarce.

It is unclear when the Common Sandpiper began to withdraw from lowland areas. It ceased to breed in Cornwall before about 1940 and probably 20–25 years earlier than that, and, during the first decade of the 20th century, it was declining in Devonshire. Breeding ceased, or became only occasional, in many other southern and Midland counties during this period. In S Wales a decline became most marked during the late 1940s and 1950s and in N England during the 1950s and 1960s (Parslow 1973). The extent of the, apparently almost total, withdrawal of breeding pairs from lowland England and Wales since the last quarter of the 19th century appears not to have been appreciated by 20th century ornithologists. The decline may have been caused by pollution of streams and rivers, for which there is ample evidence, especially near the new industrial areas and close to mines (Mitchell 1885, D'Urban and Mathew 1892, Nelson *et al.* 1907). Increased disturbance by people (Yalden 1992) and the sanitisation of river banks, particularly in combination with flood control measures, however, are more probable causes (D. Yalden in litt.). On the other hand, the northwestward retreat of the Common Sandpiper in Ireland and the proliferation of superficially suitable, but little used, new breeding sites in the English lowlands (e.g. gravel pits) suggest that some other reason (perhaps climate linked) may be involved. Breeding adults are long lived and site faithful but production and recruitment of young are low (Holland and Yalden 1991, 1994). Hence, the retreat may simply reflect insufficient recruits to maintain the population over the whole range, the survivors concentrating further away from people and agriculture (D. Yalden in litt.).

The *88–91 Atlas* confirms the continuing decline. The Common Sandpiper's retreat in Ireland has developed further (it is now most common in the higher areas of the west and north) and there has also been a withdrawal from parts of NE Scotland.

Number of counties in which recorded:

Period	Probable breeding		Confirmed breeding		Combined		
	Br	Ir	Br	Ir	Br	Ir	Both
1875–1900	0	0	84	34	84	34	118
1968–1972	4	3	58	24	62	27	89
	change				−22	−7	−29
					−26%	−21%	−25%

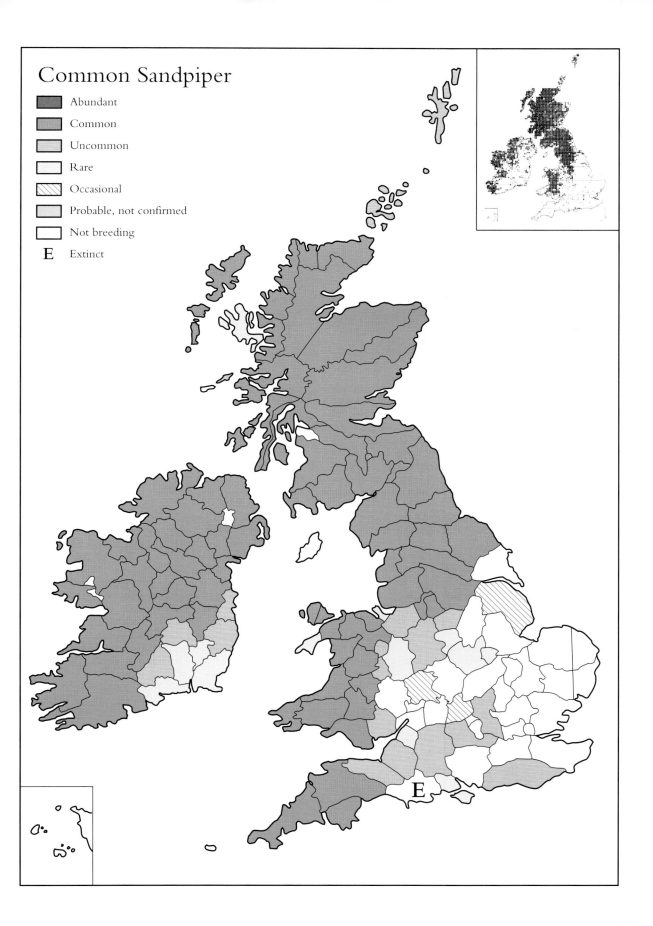

Common Sandpiper

- Abundant
- Common
- Uncommon
- Rare
- Occasional
- Probable, not confirmed
- Not breeding
- **E** Extinct

E

Red-necked Phalarope

Phalaropus lobatus

The Red-necked Phalarope may have bred at several localities on the Scottish mainland in the early years of the 19th century. Col. Drummond Hay asserted that it bred on the Moor of Rannoch in Perthshire in around 1830 and a single bird seen in the same area during the summer of 1875 or 1876 indicated that it may have bred there. It was stated, on the authority of Dewar, that it had bred in Inverness-shire (More 1865). St John's record of a pair seen at Altnaharrow, at the head of Loch Naver, in June 1848, suggested to some that it bred there. These records led Harvie-Brown (1906) and others to consider that the Red-necked Phalarope may have had a wide mainland distribution up to the early 19th century.

Pennant, in 1769, was the first to recognise the Red-necked Phalarope as a British breeding species, from a specimen sent him from Stronsay in Orkney. The first breeding record was made by Simmonds whilst accompanying Robert Stevenson, the engineer, during an inspection tour of the northern lighthouses in about 1803. He shot a number of birds in Sanday and North Ronaldsay and, upon dissection of six females and two males, noted that they had recently bred. From the 1830s collectors almost caused the extinction of the species in Orkney. Red-necked Phalaropes had been recorded breeding in Sanday, Westray, North Ronaldsay and Mainland but by the 1880s were probably confined to the first island and may have briefly become extinct during the 1860s and 1870s.

The Red-necked Phalarope was not recorded from Shetland until Saxby (1874) was informed of its occurrence in 1864. He was told that phalaropes were seen in the marshes on Unst every summer but it was not until 1867 that he visited the locality. He found two nests of four eggs each and a third with one egg. Saxby and the landowner evidently afforded some protection to the birds here as they persisted stably during Saxby's residence on the island; however, after he left Shetland in the early 1870s their numbers fluctuated and they deserted Unst for a short period. In 1887 an inspection of the same marshes (by now widely known) revealed between nine and 18 pairs. Most of the nests found had been destroyed and in 1890 a number of nests were again found, only one of which contained undamaged eggs. Evidently the colony was being preyed upon by something in addition to collectors. No further nests were found in that area during the 19th century and the last pair of birds was shot in about 1897. A second colony was discovered in Dunrossness, Shetland in 1890 when about six nests were found. In 1897 and 1898 there were estimated to have been 15 pairs.

In the 1860s 30–40 pairs were said to breed in four or five small colonies throughout the Outer Hebrides. Benbecula was evidently the stronghold here with 10–20 pairs; the remaining pairs were distributed throughout North and South Uist. Small breeding colonies were noted on North Uist in 1883 and sporadic pairs were noted on South Uist throughout the last quarter of the 19th century. Numbers evidently fluctuated and most of the blame was placed on egg collectors.

The fortunes of the Red-necked Phalarope during the 20th century have been mixed. As egg collecting decreased numbers increased to a limited extent. A small colony of the species was found in Mayo in 1900 and breeding was first proven there, the first in Ireland, in 1902 although it may have been in existence during the 19th century (M. O'Brien in litt.). The colony increased to 50 pairs in 1905 and in the same year the species was first found breeding on Tiree although it may well have done so earlier (Everett 1971). In the 1920s around 100 pairs bred in Britain and Ireland. Following this recovery numbers again began to decrease in Ireland and Orkney during the 1930s and the Outer Hebrides during the 1960s. By 1990 there were no more than 20 pairs breeding in Scotland and one or two in Ireland. Factors affecting the decline still include the depredations of egg collectors but the main reason has been habitat loss (Sharrock 1976, Gibbons *et al.* 1993).

Number of counties in which recorded:

Period	Probable breeding		Confirmed breeding		Combined		
	Br	Ir	Br	Ir	Br	Ir	Both
1875–1900	0	0	4	0	4	0	4
1968–1972	1	0	4	1	5	1	6
			change		1	1	2
					25%		50%

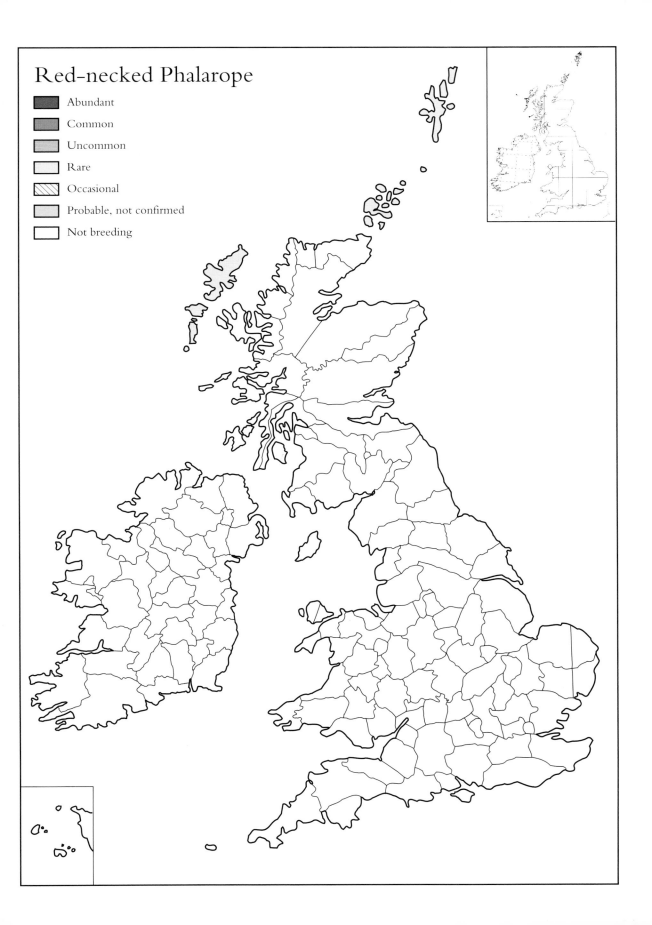

Red-necked Phalarope

- Abundant
- Common
- Uncommon
- Rare
- Occasional
- Probable, not confirmed
- Not breeding

Arctic Skua

Stercorarius parasiticus

Gray (1871) wrote that this was probably the most common species of skua throughout Scotland. Its stronghold at that time was believed to be the Outer Hebrides. The breeding grounds here were host to colonies of up to around 40 or 50 pairs and locations noted were Stuala island off South Uist, Wiay, Benbecula and North Uist. There were also one or two breeding places on Lewis. Harvie-Brown (1888) did little to shed further light on breeding there apart from a record of an egg taken at Loch Eoin in the islands in 1871. Further locations were omitted to avoid persecution; 'indiscriminate slaughter' was apparently carried out by proprietors and shooting tenants of breeding grounds because of their belief that Arctic Skuas preyed on gamebirds. In Sutherland only one pair was known to breed and this regularly; in Caithness, however, the Arctic Skua bred in considerable numbers on the inland moors and marshes. Persecution by gamekeepers of one colony in Caithness finally eradicated it, 80 Skuas being shot in the first year of clearance. The largest Shetland colony was considered to be that on Noss, although the colonies on Fetlar and Hermaness in Unst closely approached it in size. The Hermaness colony numbered 200–300 birds. It was noted that although most Arctic Skuas nested in colonies, scattered pairs bred throughout the islands. Dunn (1837) gave Eday as the principal breeding site of the species in Orkney but Buckley and Harvie-Brown (1891) could neither find evidence of breeding nor of when this had ceased. Cultivation of Eday and clearance of the heather there may have led to the total disappearance of the Arctic Skua. It disappeared from the south end of Sanday some years prior to 1881 and the only breeding pairs remaining at the end of the 19th century were those in mixed colonies with gulls in North Walls parish on Hoy. A few other pairs bred elsewhere alone. It was specifically mentioned as not breeding in Islay in 1852 or Jura in 1867, although Pennant knew it as a breeding species in Islay in the 18th century. It was certainly common on both islands during the last quarter of the 19th century and Harvie-Brown (1892) mentioned two other large scattered colonies, probably on Coll, one of which consisted of over 100 pairs.

The decline of the Arctic Skua during the 19th century at the hands of its human persecutors was reversed in the early part of the 20th century following protection of some colonies. The population in Orkney was limited to a small, but increasing colony on Hoy and small colonies on two other islands in 1941, in total about 80 pairs. By 1961 it had increased to about 200 pairs on Hoy and was nesting on ten further islands. The population declined to 1 pair in 1905 but none bred until the 1920s. Breeding recommenced on Fair Isle in the early 1920s and increased slowly—between 1948 and 1962 it increased from 15 to 70 pairs. Elsewhere, however, local decreases have taken place. In Shetland, numbers were not maintained in the proximity of Great Skua colonies, such as at Hermaness, Noss and Foula.

The British population in 1969–70 was recorded at 1,090 pairs by an 'Operation Seafarer' census. At this time the Orkney population was 230 pairs but subsequently increased to 622 in 1974. At the time of the *68–72 Atlas* the breeding range of the Arctic Skua differed little from that of the 19th century. Between the *68–72 Atlas* and the *88–91 Atlas* the population increased further. The increases were most apparent on Orkney and in Caithness, but a welcome addition to the range is the spread of breeding to the Sutherland coast. The population of the Arctic Skua in 1985–87 was 3,350 pairs. Its fortunes follow closely that of its host species, such as Arctic Terns, Puffins and Kittiwakes, and recent declines in the breeding success and survival of these species have had similar effects on the Arctic Skua—the 1985–87 population estimate is now thought likely to be over-optimistic.

Number of counties in which recorded:

Period	Probable breeding		Confirmed breeding		Combined		
	Br	Ir	Br	Ir	Br	Ir	Both
1875–1900	0	0	7	0	7	0	7
1968–1972	1	0	8	0	9	0	9
			change		2	0	2
					29%		29%

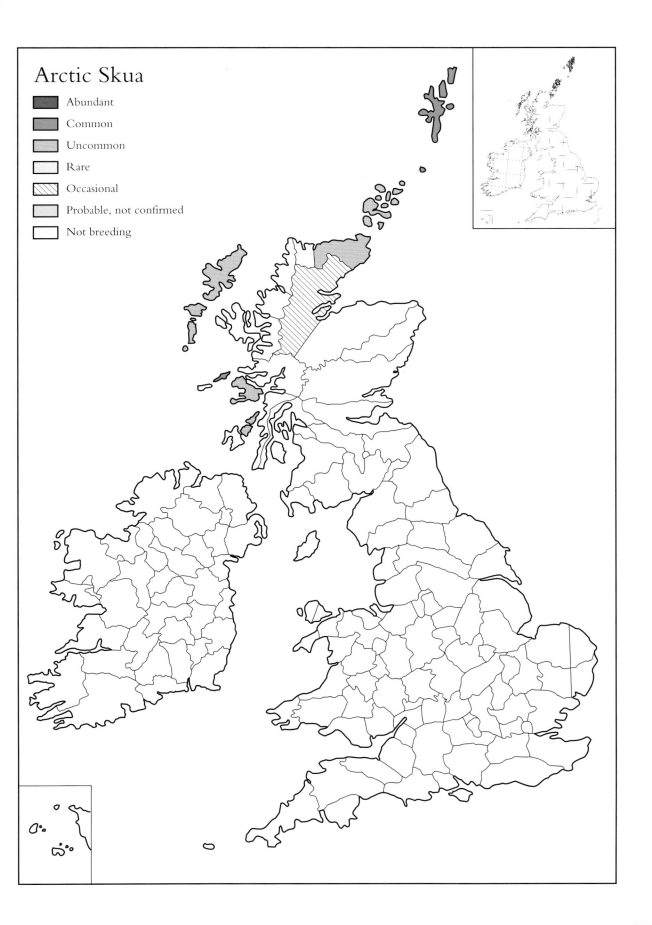

Arctic Skua

- ■ Abundant
- ■ Common
- ■ Uncommon
- □ Rare
- ▨ Occasional
- ▨ Probable, not confirmed
- □ Not breeding

Great Skua (Common Skua)

Catharacta skua

Furness (1987) argued that the Great Skua colonised Shetland a short time before the Reverend George Low published an account of his observations of these birds following his visit to the Northern Isles in 1774. The record of three pairs on Saxavord on Unst and six or seven pairs on the island of Foula were the first published records of breeding Great Skuas in Britain (Low 1879). Most writers prior to this record did not include it in their list of British or Scottish birds and those that did described it from specimens shot or observed during passage. The fact that no Great Skua remains have been found in the many middens dating from between the Bronze Age and Viking periods examined by archaeologists in N Scotland suggests that they were not present there and other etymological and traditional evidence supports the proposition that the colonisation of Scotland occurred during the 18th century (Furness 1987). If this is correct then Low observed the very beginning of this colonisation. The gradual expansion of numbers and colonisation of new sites can be traced with some accuracy through the remaining years of the 18th century to the present day.

Throughout the 19th century intense persecution by English collectors served to limit Great Skua numbers despite pleas from the Shetland islanders that they be spared; its aggressive behaviour towards predators was valued as protection for lambs, particularly from White-tailed Eagles. This persecution, and its consequent reduction in Great Skua numbers, apparently forced colonies to move and this may have been the reason for the colonisation of new areas. The Saxavord colony was eliminated before the middle of the 19th century but the formation of another colony on Unst, at Hermaness around 1830, may have been by birds displaced from Saxavord. This thrived until around 1850 when it may have reached 50 or 60 pairs but persecution took its toll so that it declined towards the end of the century to fewer than ten pairs. The Foula colony fared slightly better because of its isolation—whilst Skuas were accessible near to the mainland, the Foula colony was little troubled. By the middle of the 19th century, as the Unst colonies were harried near to extinction, collectors were motivated to make the trip to Foula and numbers began to fall there. Great Skuas colonised Ronas Hill, on Mainland, in the 1820s and 1830s but were exterminated by Dunn during a sporting tour. They recolonised Ronas Hill around 1880 and, with fluctuating success, increased slowly. In 1896 a pair attempted to breed on Bigga in Yell Sound and about the same time another pair attempted to breed elsewhere in Yell (Evans and Buckley 1899, Furness 1987).

The Shetland population, the only Great Skuas breeding in Britain, was rapidly becoming extinct in the 1890s but considerable effort was expended in encouraging protection by some of the most respected Scottish naturalists, including Harvie–Brown and Clarke, which prevented the species' extermination.

Up to 1970 the population doubled every decade and during the 1970s numbers increased most in absolute terms. It seems likely that overfishing of herring, mackerel and predatory fish has allowed an increase in sandeel stocks in the northern North Sea and the huge amounts of discarded fish at Shetland has benefited the Great Skua and other seabirds. Breeding has spread to Orkney, the Western Isles and parts of the N and NW Scottish coast during the 20th century but since the 1970s new colonisations have been to the north (into the Arctic and east into the Barents Sea) suggesting that the southward expansion of the 1960s and early 1970s is now over (R. Furness 1987).

Number of counties in which recorded:

Period	Probable breeding		Confirmed breeding		Combined		
	Br	Ir	Br	Ir	Br	Ir	Both
1875–1900	0	0	1	0	1	0	1
1968–1972	1	0	7	0	8	0	8
		change			7	0	7
					700%		700%

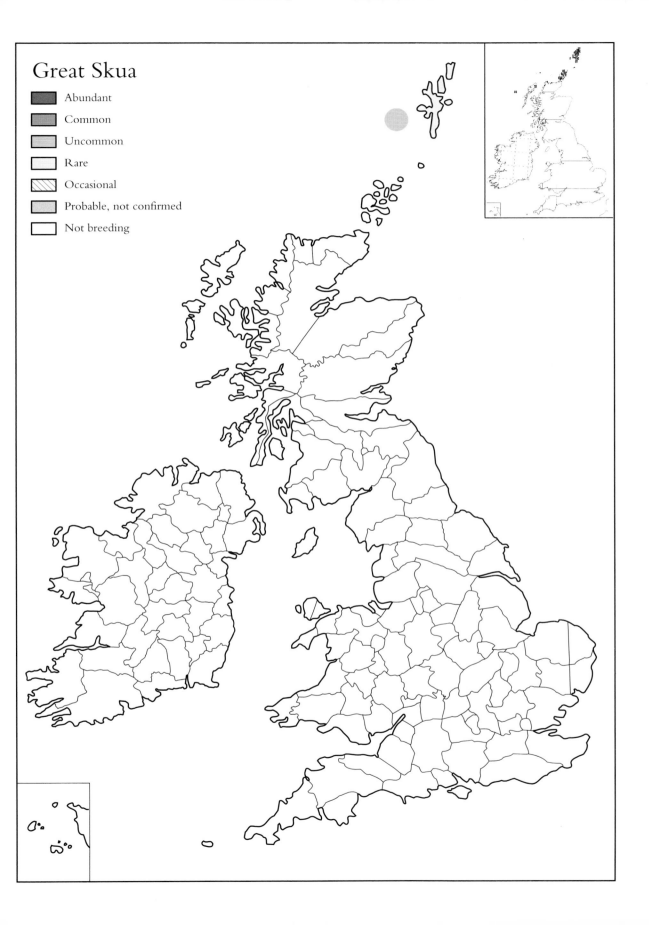

Great Skua

- Abundant
- Common
- Uncommon
- Rare
- Occasional
- Probable, not confirmed
- Not breeding

Black-headed Gull (Brown-headed Gull)

Larus ridibundus

Many of the early accounts of the Black-headed Gull concerned the harvesting of its eggs for food. Evidently, in E England particularly, it was an important economic resource and many eggs were collected there for sale in the markets of the East Anglian towns. The colony on Scoulton Mere in Norfolk was evidently ancient, being mentioned in the 16th century. The eggs would be harvested in May and up to 1000 were taken a day. A measure of the size of the colony, and its apparent resilience, can be given by examination of the economics of the egg gathering venture. The rights to collect the harvest there cost £15 a year and the eggs were sold for between three-pence per dozen and fourpence a score. The collection of between 14,000 and 18,000 eggs each season was necessary to break even and evidently this was achieved by clearing the first clutch and harvesting the second but leaving one or two eggs to hatch. Notwithstanding the enormous number of eggs taken, the colony was still thriving in the 1880s and one other survived in Norfolk, at Hoveton. A great many others in the county had, however, become extinct during the 18th and early 19th centuries. The cause of the extinctions, in most cases, was the drainage and enclosure of the breeding marshes. The history of the Black-headed Gull throughout E England followed a similar pattern of early extinctions following agricultural changes but with some, harvested, colonies thriving; locally, however, uncontrolled egg taking reduced numbers considerably (Nelson *et al.* 1907). The Sea Birds Preservation Act of 1869 evidently assisted the species' survival whilst breeding and the apparent stability of the population throughout Britain during the last quarter of the 19th century was probably partly a consequence of this protection. For instance, after the Act was passed a number of colonies became established in Dorset.

The Black-headed Gull bred in its greatest, and most stable, numbers in the remote uplands of N England and Wales and in Scotland. These areas were not subject to the same habitat modification pressures as the English lowland sites and the colonies suffered far less human predation. Suitable breeding sites were evidently scarcer in the rugged W Scotland uplands but, where sites existed, the Black-headed Gull bred in large numbers.

It bred extensively throughout Ireland except for the eastern and southern coastal counties. No colonies were known between Kerry and Down but elsewhere the great red bogs and reed fringed lakes afforded ideal breeding sites (Ussher and Warren 1900). There was no indication of any change in numbers or distribution apart from the often mentioned habit of this species to shift sites periodically.

The apparent stability noted in some of the English counties towards the end of the 19th century following the earlier decrease turned into a recovery shortly before 1900. The recovery was demonstrated by the results of a survey carried out in 1938 (Hollom 1940). By this time the number of colonies in S and E England had increased and breeding colonies had become established in mid and S Wales and in some N Midlands counties. Overall the number of colonies had more than doubled since the turn of the century and 158 colonies were located in England and Wales (Witherby *et al.* 1938–41). A further survey confirmed the continuing, but uneven, increase in Britain and, although no survey was organised, the Black-headed Gull was believed to have similarly increased in Ireland. The population has continued to grow and spread (from *ca* 35,000 pairs in 1938 to *ca* 100,000 in 1973 in England and Wales) and colonies have been established throughout the English Midlands and in E Ireland. In the period between the *68–72 Atlas* and the *88–91 Atlas* a decrease has taken place particularly in Scotland and NW Ireland. There is new evidence that American mink has arrived in these areas in the last 15–20 years with fairly devastating effects on some ground and water nesting bird species, including the Black-headed Gull (M. Tasker *in litt.*).

Number of counties in which recorded:

Period	Probable breeding		Confirmed breeding		Combined		
	Br	Ir	Br	Ir	Br	Ir	Both
1875–1900	0	0	53	24	53	24	77
1968–1972	3	2	81	30	84	32	116
			change		31	8	39
					58%	33%	51%

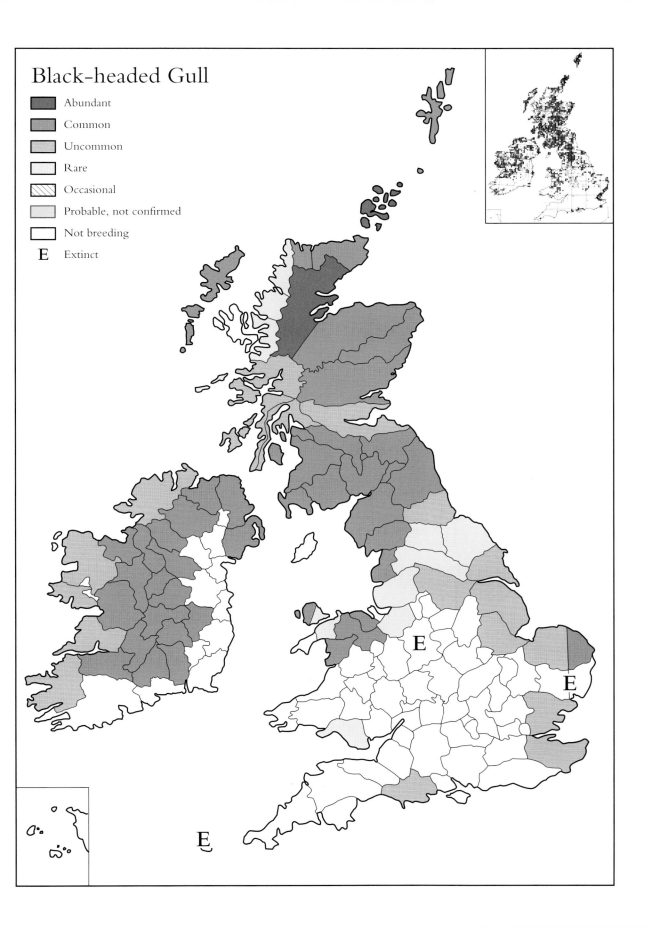

Black-headed Gull

- Abundant
- Common
- Uncommon
- Rare
- Occasional
- Probable, not confirmed
- Not breeding
- **E** Extinct

Common Gull

Larus canus

The status of the Common Gull in Britain confused the early 19th century naturalists. Although he gave no specific examples, the presence of these gulls all around the coast, and all through the year, led Yarrell (1837–43) to hint that he believed that it bred from Wales anticlockwise round the coastline, to Sussex and, perhaps, elsewhere in England. He was able to instance a few Scottish breeding records but his record of a very large colony at St Abbs Head in Berwickshire is interesting in view of later, conflicting evidence. Morris (1851–57) gave an account of the distribution of this species that was very similar to that of Yarrell.

The late 19th century naturalists disagreed over whether Common Gulls bred on St Abbs Head; if they did, they would be the most southerly breeding members of the species known in Britain during that century. In one paper, Selby said he found it breeding on 'the upper ledges and recesses of the precipices, and was observed in great numbers'. In another paper, he noted that they were breeding in great numbers in 1833 although this time he identified a rock to the south of the Head as the specific breeding locality. Curiously, he later mentioned the Common Gull only as a winter visitor (Selby 1841). Hepburn (1851) could find no Common Gulls breeding on the Head but did note that an extensive colony inhabited the Ernesheugh 'about two

miles' (3km) to the west. This was the last record of breeding in this area. All criticism of these records, particularly by Evans (1911) and Baxter and Rintoul (1935, 1953) places great doubt on the accuracy of Selby's and Hepburn's identification. In a letter to Muirhead in 1887 Hepburn added that several pairs bred on the Bass Rock at the time that he saw the Ernesheugh colony. During the second half of the 19th century it was clear that the Common Gull did not breed outside of Scotland and Ireland. Saunders (Yarrell 1871–85) firmly stated that there was no proof that it bred on any part of the English (or Welsh) coast or that it bred on the Berwickshire coast at least during the previous 20 years. This finally settled the arguments surrounding the true breeding places of this species.

The Common Gull was recorded breeding in SW Scotland on cliff sites on the Mull of Galloway, Ailsa Craig and the Scaur rocks in Ayrshire and beside inland lochs in Wigtownshire. It bred through the west of the Clyde district into the rest of N Scotland. Its E Scotland distribution began in S Perthshire, where it bred commonly from the Moor of Rannoch northwards, and a colony on the Coreen Hills, Aberdeenshire, is adjacent to what is now the largest known colony in the world. It bred in its largest numbers in the Northern Isles during the 19th century, especially in Orkney. Then, as now, the largest Common Gull colonies throughout its British and Irish range were inland, with relatively small groups on the coast. In Ireland its breeding range was restricted to the coastal regions of the west and north. The colonies were most frequently located on low islands in both freshwater and saline loughs although they also bred on some of the marine islands off the west coast.

There is little reliable evidence to support the assertion that the Common Gull was increasing in numbers during the 19th century (Alexander and Lack 1944). The confusion over the correct identification of this species, the fact that this species, the Black-headed and Herring Gulls were all called the Common Sea-mew in the 18th and early 19th centuries and the presence of non-breeding birds seen in summer throughout Britain all serve to place doubt on any Common Gull record prior to the 1870s. As accurate recognition of this species developed during the late 19th century an increase in numbers may well have become apparent; however, this is just as likely to have been an artefact of improving recognition. On the other hand there is no doubt that it increased both in numbers and breeding range in Scotland and Ireland and into England during the 20th century. This increase lasted at least until the 1950s but locally it is probably increasing to the present day (*88–91 Atlas*).

Number of counties in which recorded:

Period	Probable breeding		Confirmed breeding		Combined		
	Br	Ir	Br	Ir	Br	Ir	Both
1875–1900	0	0	24	5	24	5	29
1968–1972	1	1	39	17	40	18	58
			change		16	13	29
					67%	260%	100%

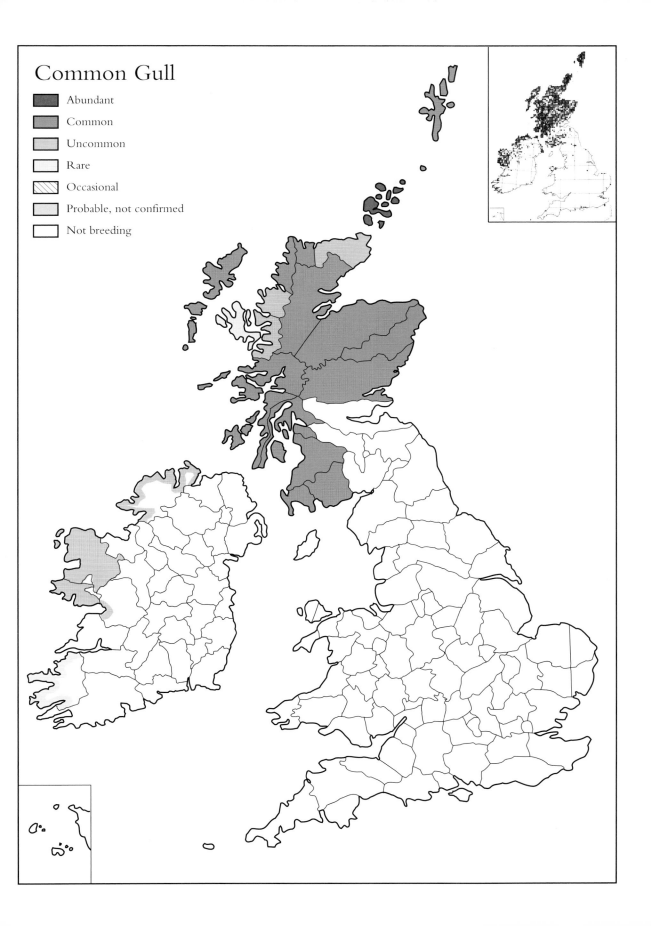

Common Gull

- **Abundant**
- **Common**
- **Uncommon**
- **Rare**
- **Occasional**
- **Probable, not confirmed**
- **Not breeding**

Lesser Black-backed Gull

Larus fuscus

The earliest record of a Lesser Black-backed Gull collected in Britain was shot by Pennant in the middle of the 18th century in Anglesey. He believed, however, that it was a small type of Greater Black-backed Gull and it was Montagu (1802) who was the first to describe the distinguishing features of the specimen and give it species status as the Lesser Black-backed Gull. It took a number of years before the species' breeding range was fully understood and so it is difficult to determine how stable or otherwise the population was during the 19th century.

Its presence on the English south coast was confined to a few that bred at Newhaven (but ceased to do so some time before 1890) and a very few (perhaps one pair by 1909) in the Isle of Wight. It bred in small numbers around the Cornwall and N Devonshire coasts and in the Isles of Scilly and on Lundy. It bred more numerously in Wales. Most of the colonies there were small although one on Puffin Island may have been substantial and an inland colony on Cors Caron, Cardiganshire consisted of about 50 pairs in 1893, whilst a pair bred on Cors Fochno, another inland site, in the same county. In all no more than 500 pairs bred in

Wales at the end of the 19th century (Lovegrove *et al.* 1994). Five colonies existed in Lakeland by the 1890s but some small ones on, for instance, Windermere and Ullswater, had broken up. Those that remained were, in the main, substantial and were located on the grouse moors of Foulshaw Moss, Roudsea, Butterburn Flow (the only truly inland colony), Solway Moss and Bowness Moss. The only substantial east coast colony was that on the Farne Islands where it was the most ubiquitous bird of the islands, breeding on all but the Islestone Shad. In the east and inland parts of Scotland and in Orkney it had decreased markedly because of persecution from shepherds and gamekeepers particularly on the islands and shores of the Caithness and Sutherland lochs. It had been recorded breeding on the peat mosses of Abernethy Forest and sparingly on the Culbin Sands. It was far more common on the Scottish west coast and on nearly all of the marine islands of both the west and north. The largest breeding group on the Scottish mainland was probably on the islands of Loch Maree, where 'thousands' bred and were apparently increasing in 1888.

In Ireland it bred locally, never in very large colonies, and in far fewer numbers than the Herring Gull, with which it often shared colonies. The Lesser Black-backed Gull's largest breeding group was on the Saltees, Wexford. The inland sites recorded were on a bog in Kildare (where about 100 pairs bred), at several sites in Westmeath and Galway, probably on Lough Derg, and in Clare. The Loughs Corrib and Mask held many scattered pairs, an island in Lough Erne, Fermanagh held at least 15 pairs, while a colony of about 20 pairs was noted on a mountain bog in Antrim. Many of the inland colonies had been exterminated by egg gathering or by gamekeepers by the closing decades of the 19th century.

The decrease noted in Scotland during the 19th century continued in the 1900s but, as keepering declined, numbers stabilised and, locally, increased again from about the 1930s. A general increase took place in W England and Wales although a number of southern colonies were plundered for eggs during the 1939–45 war and recovered very slowly. On the whole it has increased in Ireland but there have been many local fluctuations involving shifts of populations, evidently to coastal colonies in Northern Ireland. The *68–72 Atlas* demonstrates the increase in the number of colonies that had become established, particularly in S and NE England and E Scotland and the apparent decrease in inland breeding sites in N Scotland. In strong contrast to the Herring Gull, breeding numbers of the Lesser Black-backed Gull have continued to increase on most coasts of Britain and Ireland, although the overall trend at inland colonies remains less clear (Lloyd *et al.* 1991). The reasons for this difference in trends are not clear.

Number of counties in which recorded:

Period	Probable breeding		Confirmed breeding		Combined		
	Br	Ir	Br	Ir	Br	Ir	Both
1875–1900	0	0	35	13	35	13	48
1968–1972	6	2	53	18	59	20	79
			change		24	7	31
					69%	54%	65%

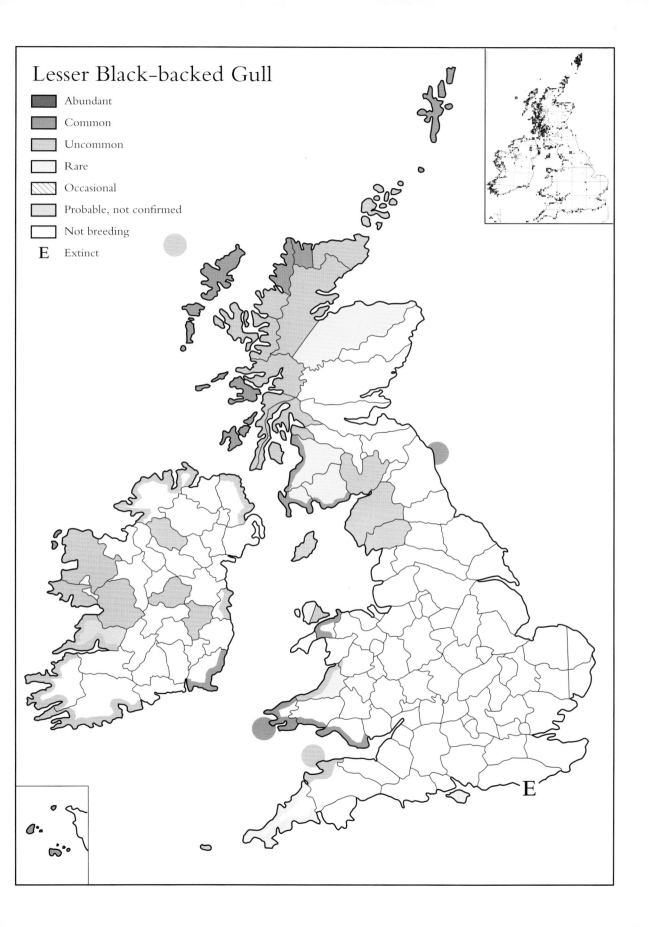

Lesser Black-backed Gull

- Abundant
- Common
- Uncommon
- Rare
- Occasional
- Probable, not confirmed
- Not breeding
- **E**   Extinct

E

Herring Gull

Larus argentatus

The population of the Herring Gull appears to have been largely stable during much of the 19th century. Little mention was made of any change in numbers or distribution apart from some local decreases on the most heavily shot cliffs, particularly along the E and S coasts of England, in the second half of the century. It was a numerous species breeding on all of the coastline of Britain and Ireland where suitable cliffs existed and on most of the islands, but in England and Wales it was recorded inland only rarely during the spring and autumn and uncommonly in the winter and, in most cases, was not seen to alight (e.g. Aplin 1889). In N Scotland it bred regularly inland. In Sutherland it bred on hill sides and on the shores and islands of inland lochs and, in the 1880s, bred on the hill of Tain in increasing numbers. It had been occasionally recorded breeding on Rannoch Moor.

In Ireland it was considered the commonest of the gulls. Although never breeding in such large colonies as the Kittiwake, it was more widespread and nested wherever there were suitable sites on the coast (although no inland colonies were known) (Ussher and Warren 1990). The largest colonies were in the west and south although it was fairly evenly distributed throughout the coasts of counties from Wexford to Antrim. The colonies on the Cliffs of Moher in Clare and the Great Saltee Island off the Wexford coast were said to have been particularly extensive.

It seems likely that the cessation of the persecution of seabirds, combined with the increase of edible refuse at fish-docks, rubbish tips and sewage outfalls that followed the movement of the human population from the countryside to towns and cities, allowed the increase in the Herring Gull population that became apparent in the early 20th century (Parslow 1973). The increase may have started earlier but details of population changes among abundant species are difficult to discern from the 19th century literature. Notes of increases this century came from many sources but it seems notable that the largest increases have occurred in colonies in the neighbourhood of areas of high human populations. The most spectacular was the growth of the colony at Walney Island, Lancashire: 35 pairs bred there in 1934, 120 in 1947, ca 9,500 pairs in 1965 and a peak of 20–25,000 pairs in the 1970s (Dean 1990). Since then sand and gravel extraction and, perhaps, avian botulism have reduced numbers substantially; only ca 8,000 pairs were estimated in 1988. Many other notable increases occurred elsewhere and were generally believed to have accelerated following the 1939–45 war. In England and Wales, the total population was estimated to have doubled between the war and the late 1960s (Parslow 1973). Other changes took place amongst the Herring Gull population as it increased, including widespread nesting on buildings since the 1939–45 war (Monaghan and Coulson 1977) and, especially in Ireland, more inland sites have been colonised.

The *68–72 Atlas* survey probably recorded the Herring Gull population near its zenith. The 'Operation Seafarer' survey in 1969–70 suggested that some colonies may still have been increasing at up to 15% per annum (Cramp *et al.* 1974) but between then and the late 1980s large declines have been recorded (Lloyd et al. 1991). In some regions these amounted to more than a halving of the population and only a few regions recorded stable or increasing populations. The reasons for these changes are still being investigated but the factors involved may include an increased incidence of botulism, possible changes in food availability and, locally, increased predation by foxes (Gibbons *et al.* 1993).

Number of counties in which recorded:

Period	Probable breeding		Confirmed breeding		Combined		
	Br	Ir	Br	Ir	Br	Ir	Both
1875–1900	0	0	43	12	43	12	55
1968–1972	1	0	66	26	67	26	93
			change		24	14	38
					56%	117%	69%

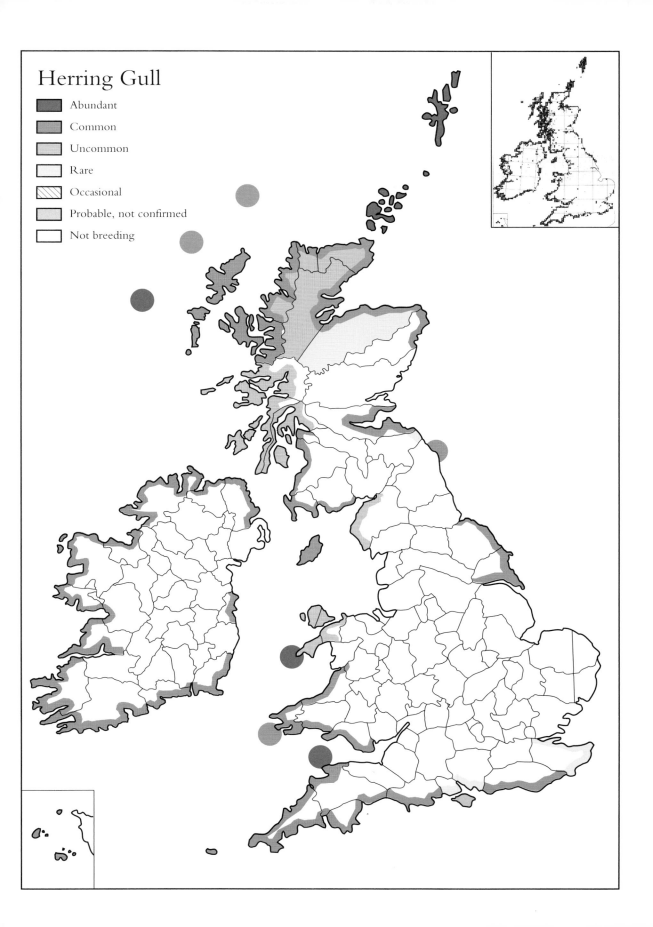

Herring Gull

- **Abundant**
- **Common**
- **Uncommon**
- **Rare**
- **Occasional**
- **Probable, not confirmed**
- **Not breeding**

Great Black-backed Gull

Larus marinus

The Great Black-backed Gull in Britain during 1875–1900 bred mainly on the coasts and islands of W and N Scotland but even here it had declined in some areas. In Caithness, for instance, it had been persecuted heavily and had declined substantially from a common species after the middle of the 19th century to one only occasionally encountered by the 1880s (Harvie-Brown and Buckley 1887). It bred at few sites in England and Wales. In Ireland it was distributed along the rocky coasts of the western and southern counties and the colony on the Bills Rocks, Mayo was considered by Ussher and Warren (1900), at over 50 pairs, to be the largest in Britain and Ireland. Although this assertion appears to modern ornithologists to be very surprising and, perhaps, unlikely, there are no published counts of colonies larger than this.

During the early decades of the 19th century the Great Black-backed Gull was said to have bred in the marshes of the Thames estuary on both the Essex and Kent sides and was apparently still doing so in 1843 (Yarrell 1837–43) but writers at the end of the 19th century had little knowledge of its history there and none of the date of its extinction (Christy 1890, Ticehurst 1909). Both Glegg (1929) and Harrison (1953) mentioned the records without comment

but the species is generally considered to prefer to nest on rocky promontories and the summits of coastal islands. Inland colonies are rare this century in comparison with Herring or Lesser Black-backed Gull. It is now only possible to speculate on the fate of these lowland colonies. Those inland or on coastal marshes would have been easily accessible to humans and, in S Britain, disturbance may have caused their abandonment during the 18th and early 19th centuries but it seems possible that habitats such as estuarine marsh may have been favoured. Where it was little disturbed its breeding sites remained more or less stable throughout the 19th century, notwithstanding the number of eggs taken for human consumption, but overall the population remained at a low level until the closing years of the century. After about 1850 large numbers were shot by the shore-gunners—the smaller gulls were shot remorselessly for little more than target practice but the Great Black-backed Gull was a prize worth displaying.

It is likely that human persecution was responsible for the almost total lack of non-coastal breeding records of this species during the last quarter of the 19th century and their withdrawal from many coastal cliffs in S England and Wales. The only mention of inland sites were of a few on the Scottish isles, especially those with few human inhabitants. Persecution, which in all its forms had kept the Great Black-backed Gull's population low throughout the 19th century, lessened somewhat following the Sea Birds Preservation Act of 1869 and subsequent Wild Birds Protection Acts. It may have been this influence that led to the apparent increase in the numbers of this species that took place from the 1880s, particularly in England and Wales. This is not clear, however, as the 1869 Act was not a complete success in its aims and few of the later Acts specifically mentioned the Great Black-backed Gull. It seems probable that the relaxation in persecution combined with the Gull's exploitation of the edible refuse at dumps, docks and sewage outfalls (the result of the increase in the human population and its movement into towns and cities) allowed the increase.

The population of Great Black-backed Gulls has increased throughout the 20th century from its nadir in the 1870s. Special enquiries into this species' status in England and Wales were undertaken in 1930 (by when the species had recovered from near-extinction to between 1,000 and 1,200 pairs) and 1956. The population in some areas (notably on islands) had almost trebled in the intervening period and during 1985–87 *ca* 2,380 breeding pairs were counted (Parslow 1973, Lloyd *et al.* 1991). Scotland (*ca* 16,300 pairs) and Ireland (*ca* 4,500) hold the bulk of the present-day population, however, and the British and Irish population as a whole has shown little change between 1969 and 1987 (Lloyd *et al.* 1991).

Number of counties in which recorded:

Period	Probable breeding		Confirmed breeding		Combined		
	Br	Ir	Br	Ir	Br	Ir	Both
1875–1900	0	0	31	9	31	9	40
1968–1972	0	0	49	20	49	20	69
			change		18	11	29
					58%	122%	73%

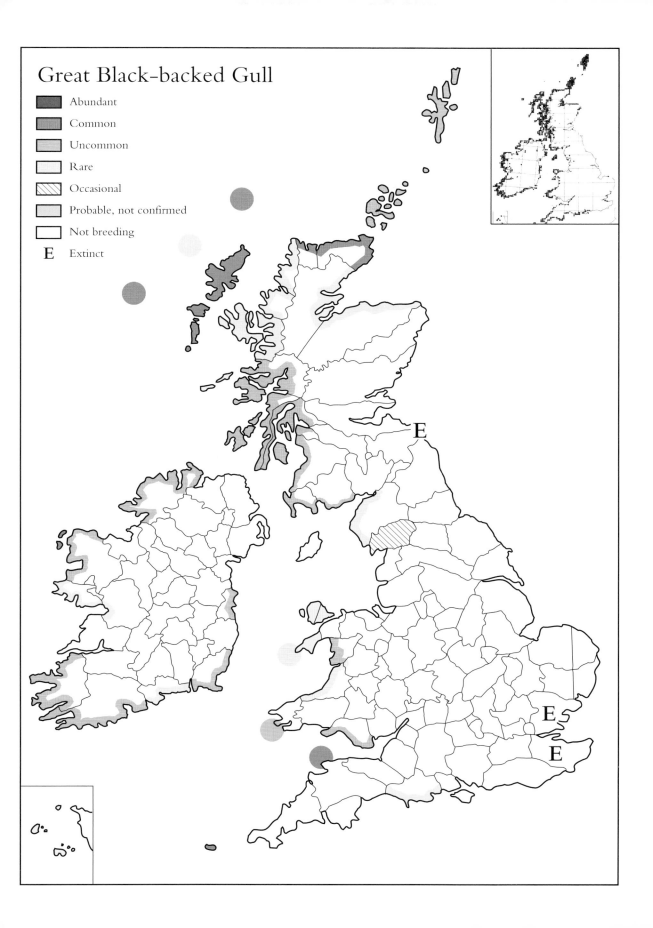

Great Black-backed Gull

- ■ Abundant
- ■ Common
- ▨ Uncommon
- ▢ Rare
- ▨ Occasional
- ▨ Probable, not confirmed
- ▢ Not breeding
- **E** Extinct

Kittiwake (Kittiwake Gull)

Rissa tridactyla

The broad pattern of the Kittiwake's distribution in Britain appears to have changed little through the 19th century; although some colonies were abandoned, there were still colonies on most coasts. During the early years of the 19th century the Kittiwake was said to have been a regular and common breeding species from the Isle of Wight westwards and around the coast of the southwest peninsula (Yarrell 1837–43). This assertion, however, must be considered carefully in the light of Montagu's (1802, 1813) statements that it was rare on the southern coast and that writers of the late 19th century could give no, or few, instances of breeding (Mansell-Pleydell 1888, Kelsall and Munn 1905).

Numerous testimonies spoke of the huge slaughter of birds of the year for their barred wings, a fashionable millinery adornment, of the numbers shot at many colonies from boats by weekend sportsmen as target practice and, in the Borders and N England especially (at St Abbs Head, Berwickshire and Flamborough Head, Yorkshire, for instance), large numbers of young were harvested for food. This persecution certainly lessened substantially following the 1869 Sea Birds Preservation Act but did not cease entirely as shooting resumed as soon as the close season ended at the beginning of August. The Kittiwake's breeding sites in England and Wales were few by the last quarter of the 19th century and numbers fell markedly at many of those that survived. It had ceased breeding on the Isle of Wight before 1858 (Kelsall 1909), in the Isles of Scilly it had decreased markedly by the end of the century so that only three nests were recorded (on Gorregan) in 1900 (Coulson 1963) and in Cornwall only a few nested on the cliffs of Land's End although 'large numbers' bred on Lundy, Devonshire. In Wales the species bred on some of the Pembrokeshire islands and cliffs and was the most numerous of the local gulls there. A few pairs bred at the foot of the Little Orme's Head, in colonies at Nevin and Cilan Head and there were one or two other small colonies on Lleyn, all sites in Caernarvonshire. In Anglesey there was a 'good sized colony' on Puffin Island and a few on the adjacent headland of Penmon. The Kittiwake was first recorded breeding on the Isle of Man by More (1865) and there was one small colony of 30 or 40 pairs on the Calf of Man, a little east of the stack, in 1905. Colonies in E England existed on the Pinnacles and adjacent cliffs in the Farnes and those on the Yorkshire cliffs at Bempton and Speeton were gradually increasing because of the Sea Birds Act but in 1907 had still not yet reached their former numbers.

The Kittiwake bred around much of the Scottish coast and on many islands, in particular Ailsa Craig, Skye, Handa, Bulgie Island, Bass Rock, Staffa, Rum, Tiree, Canna, Hysgeir off Canna, Eigg, Horse Island, Muck, Treshnish Isles, Mull, Islay, Mingulay, North Rona and St Kilda. It bred on most of the islands of Orkney, one of the largest colonies being on Copinsay, and in Shetland it bred abundantly. The largest Shetland colonies were in Burra Firth, Unst, Foula, the Noup of Noss and Ramna Stacks. The most notable mainland colonies were on the Rowans near Wick and Duncansby Head in Caithness, on the Kincardineshire and Aberdeenshire coasts and around St Abbs Head (although this was much smaller than it had been at the end of the 18th century).

The Irish Kittiwake colonies were many, although there were only three sites on the east coast, and a number of them evidently held vast numbers—one of the largest was apparently at Horn Head. Rathlin Island, Antrim was said to have held 'enormous numbers' (Patterson 1880) and Ussher and Warren (1900) singled out Tormore, Donegal, Aughris Head, Sligo and the Cliffs of Moher, Clare as having particularly large numbers—the latter colony being probably the largest in Ireland.

The 20th century has seen a steady increase in both numbers of Kittiwakes and the number of new colonies following the cessation of persecution. Between 1920 and 1969 both increased at about 3–4% annually (Coulson 1963, 1974) although the overall rate of increase has since slowed (Lloyd *et al.* 1991). As shown in the *68–72 Atlas*, the most striking change since the 19th century has been the extension of breeding in England and Wales.

Number of counties in which recorded:

Period	Probable breeding		Confirmed breeding		Combined		
	Br	Ir	Br	Ir	Br	Ir	Both
1875–1900	0	0	35	11	35	11	46
1968–1972	0	0	44	14	44	14	58
			change		9	3	12
					26%	27%	26%

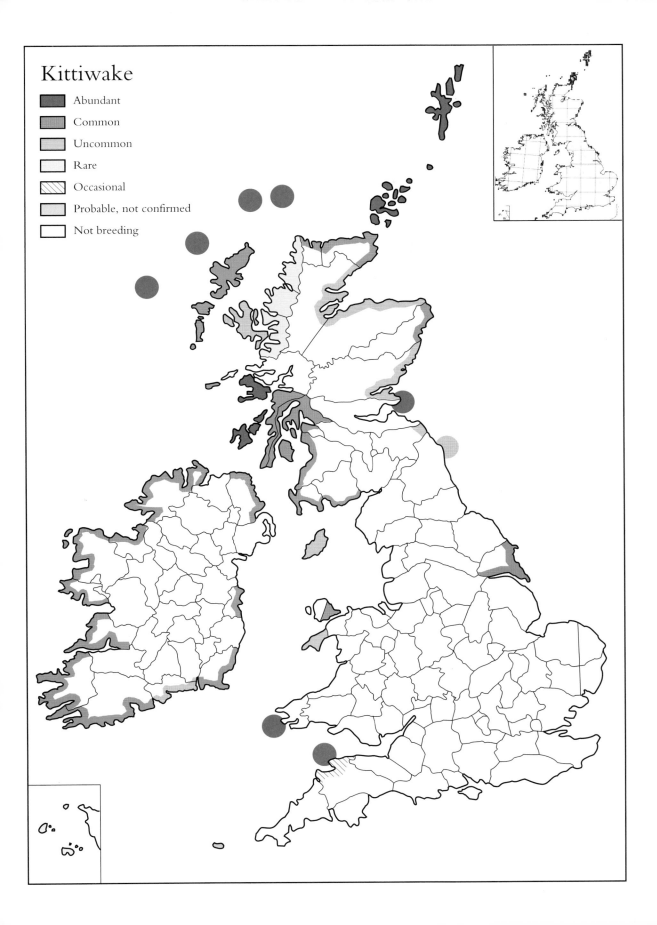

Kittiwake

- Abundant
- Common
- Uncommon
- Rare
- Occasional
- Probable, not confirmed
- Not breeding

Sandwich Tern

Sterna sandvicensis

The Sandwich Tern was first collected in 1784 by Boys at Sandwich, Kent and the record was published by Latham in 1785. Initially it was recognised only from the SE coasts of England, from Kent to Suffolk, and the first proof that it bred elsewhere came with Selby's discovery of a colony on the Farne Islands prior to 1826. The chief colony on the Farnes was on the Knoxes and remained so throughout the 19th century; around 300 pairs were estimated to have bred there in 1896. Smaller numbers bred on the Wideopens and the Brownsman. The protection afforded to the breeding birds of the Farnes from the end of the 19th century allowed the Sandwich Tern to thrive there and this colony appears to have been stable. This was not the case elsewhere off the Northumberland coast. Selby had recorded it breeding on Coquet Island but persecution and egg collecting eradicated the species there probably during the 1870s. The islets around Holy Island saw many attempts at colonisation but egg gatherers thwarted most of them. Attempts were made to rear young at the Snook, Holy Island and on nearby Black Law between 1883 and 1901.

The history of the Scottish colonies is just as depressing. Breeding had been reported from the Isle of May, Bass Rock and other Forth islands up to the 1840s but ceased on most of these prior to 1850—egg collectors were clearly responsible.

A few Sandwich Terns continued to breed regularly on the latter islands into the 1870s but then ceased. The only breeding records during the last quarter of the 19th century were of pairs in 1881 and a single egg found in 1887 on Inchmickery in the mouth of the Forth. Breeding around Findhorn in Moray and Nairn was sporadic; some said that the number remaining to breed was correlated with how much persecution they received during the spring passage. The largest colony, of up to 36 pairs, was reported off the Culbin Sands in 1887. An egg was taken from the SE Sutherland coast in 1878 but no other records exist of breeding there to the end of the century. A small group was found breeding on North Ronaldsay in Orkney in 1893 amongst a colony of Arctic Terns but had disappeared prior to 1910. Gray (1871) recorded a small colony on the island of Inchmoan in Loch Lomond but, if they were identified correctly, no more was heard of them there.

The colony on Walney Island, Lancashire was heavily persecuted. It was located, in the main, amongst Black-headed Gulls on the north end. It reached 40 pairs in 1880 but in 1889 breeding switched to the south end of the island where six pairs bred in 1890 (Macpherson 1892). It was suggested that the rapid augmentation of numbers noticed at Ravenglass in 1891, from 34 nests early in the season to 71 later, was the result of birds escaping the persecution on Walney.

The breeding colonies on the beaches around Dungeness, Sandwich, the Blackwater estuary in Essex and the Suffolk coast were all eliminated before 1850 by dealers who sold the eggs of many species in the London markets as those of the Lapwing. Evidence of impending recolonisation of these areas became apparent around 1890 when one or two pairs may have bred in Kent and Essex.

It was last recorded breeding in the Isles of Scilly in 1879.

The Sandwich Tern may have bred on the Rockabill off the Dublin coast amongst other terns and on a Donegal lough in small numbers in the mid 19th century. The only persistent colony was that on Rathroeen Lake, Co. Mayo which under protection, rose to 150 nests by 1886.

The decline of the Sandwich Tern appears to have resulted from human persecution. Once this persecution was relaxed and protection was provided, the population quickly returned to, what was probably, its former level. The population has shifted during the present century and individual colonies have waxed and waned but, in Britain, the main population remains along the eastern and southern coasts. Despite the fluctuations the total population has slowly increased and the breeding range has expanded (Parslow 1973) but persecution in the Sandwich Tern's wintering grounds remains a threat (Gibbons *et al.* 1993).

Number of counties in which recorded:

Period	Probable breeding		Confirmed breeding		Combined		
	Br	Ir	Br	Ir	Br	Ir	Both
1875–1900	0	0	5	1	5	1	6
1968–1972	1	0	22	13	23	13	36
			change		18	12	30
					360%	1200%	500%

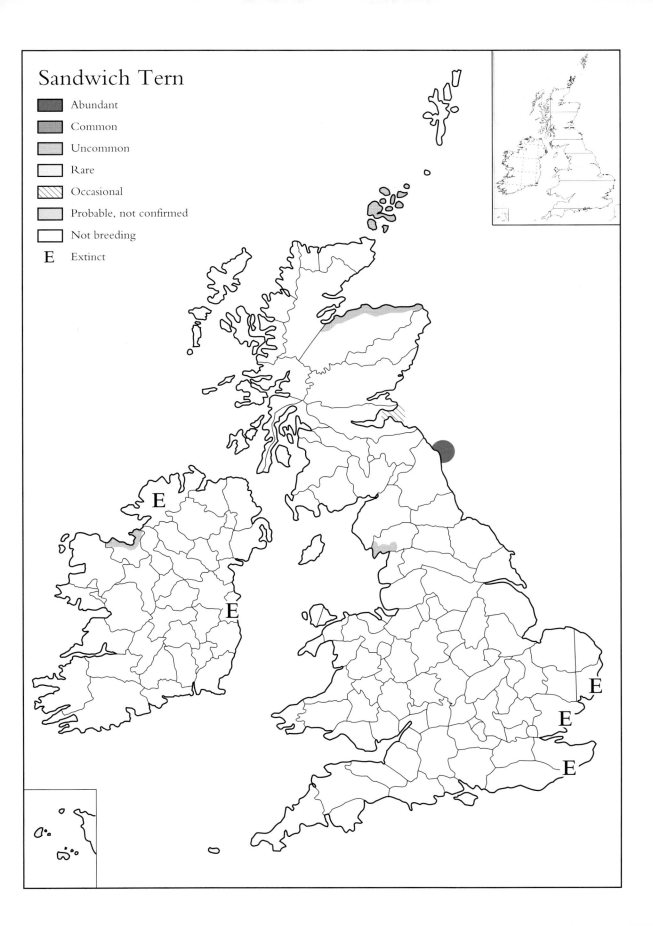

Sandwich Tern

- **Abundant**
- **Common**
- **Uncommon**
- **Rare**
- **Occasional**
- **Probable, not confirmed**
- **Not breeding**
- **E** Extinct

Roseate Tern

Sterna dougallii

The histories of all the known 19th century Roseate terneries are recounted individually.

Isles of Scilly. Very few records exist of this colony. When Mitchell discovered it in 1840 he was able to collect a number of eggs but it was abandoned before 1865, probably because of persecution from egg and skin collectors.

Walney and Foulney Islands, Lancashire. Hancock was the first to recognise the Roseate Tern in the Common Tern colony on Foulney in 1840. Persecution from egg collectors appears to have caused the tern's decline there. In 1864 several birds were seen but, in 1865, Saunders could locate only one pair, this time on Walney. Later records indicate that no Roseate Terns bred here after 1876 until the recolonisation of the 1920s.

The Skerries, Anglesey. It is not known when this colony was first discovered but Forrest (1907) noted that it had been well known for many years. It was described as 'very large' in 1892 and nine clutches of eggs were taken in 1896 but Forrest noted that the colony was preyed upon by egg collectors and numbers had declined considerably as a result. The colony was abandoned a few years after this date possibly because of the presence of rats on the islands, first noted in 1905.

Llanddwyn Island, Anglesey. The first reference to this colony was in 1902 when Coward recorded several pairs of terns, the majority of which were Commons but many were Roseates. Forrest (1907) believed that the colony may have been established in 1900. This colony was apparently increasing during this period as from 1910 at least 250 pairs bred. Llanddwyn seems to have been colonised from The Skerries in about 1900.

The Pembrokeshire Islands. Mathew (1894) recorded the possibility that the Roseate Tern had once bred on Skokholm Stack along with other tern species. Lockley et al. (1949) noted that it had been recorded breeding on Grassholm ca 1885.

Farne Islands, Northumberland. The lighthouse keeper first distinguished Roseates in an Arctic Tern colony on The Brownsman in about 1815. At that time, and into the 1830s, it bred commonly but soon after that numbers declined. From the 1860s only one to three pairs bred annually, latterly mainly on Knoxes Reef.

The Islands of the Firths of Clyde and Forth. The Roseate Tern was first collected in Britain from a colony on the Cumbraes in 1812 and described by Montagu (1813). This colony evidently died out shortly afterwards as Jardine, when describing a large colony on the Isle of May in 1843, did not record breeding on the Cumbraes. Turnbull (1867) mentioned the Isle of May colony but Harvie-Brown (1888) stated that it had not bred there for many years.

Kilbrannon Sound, Kintyre. Gray discovered a large colony on an islet between Arran and Kintyre in 1853. It was still healthy in the late 1860s when he took 'a basketful' of eggs for his collection but was not noted subsequently.

Loch Lomond, Argyll. Gray (1871) recorded a few breeding in a mixed tern colony on Inchmoan but no mention was made of it subsequently.

Findhorn, Moray. Gray (1871) noted the existence of a well-established colony here. Several nests were discovered in 1887 but this site was evidently occupied erratically as subsequent searches failed to find any evidence of breeding Roseate Terns.

Mew Island, Down. Roseate Terns here were first recorded by Thompson following a visit in 1827. Wholesale persecution and slaughter had reduced numbers by 1833 and the terns abandoned the island by 1850.

Rockabill, Dublin. 'Hundreds' bred here when the colony was first recognised in 1844. Shooting by egg collectors reduced numbers to fewer than 40 pairs by 1850. They were extinct here shortly after this date.

The accounts of the Roseate Tern's decline during the first half of the 19th century were almost always linked with human predation of both eggs and birds, and perhaps this was the cause of this species' near extinction; in 1900 probably only a handful of pairs remained to breed in Britain (Witherby et al. 1938–41). The first decade of the 20th century saw the beginning of the Roseate Tern's recovery in Britain and its recolonisation of Ireland. The population increased further during and after the 1939–45 war but crashed in 1969. The decline has affected most colonies in Britain, Ireland and France, suggesting a common cause. Persecution at its wintering grounds has been suggested (Avery and del Nevo 1991).

Number of counties in which recorded:

Period	Probable breeding		Confirmed breeding		Combined		
	Br	Ir	Br	Ir	Br	Ir	Both
1875–1900	0	0	4	0	4	0	4
1968–1972	1	0	9	11	10	11	21
			change		6	11	17
					150%		425%

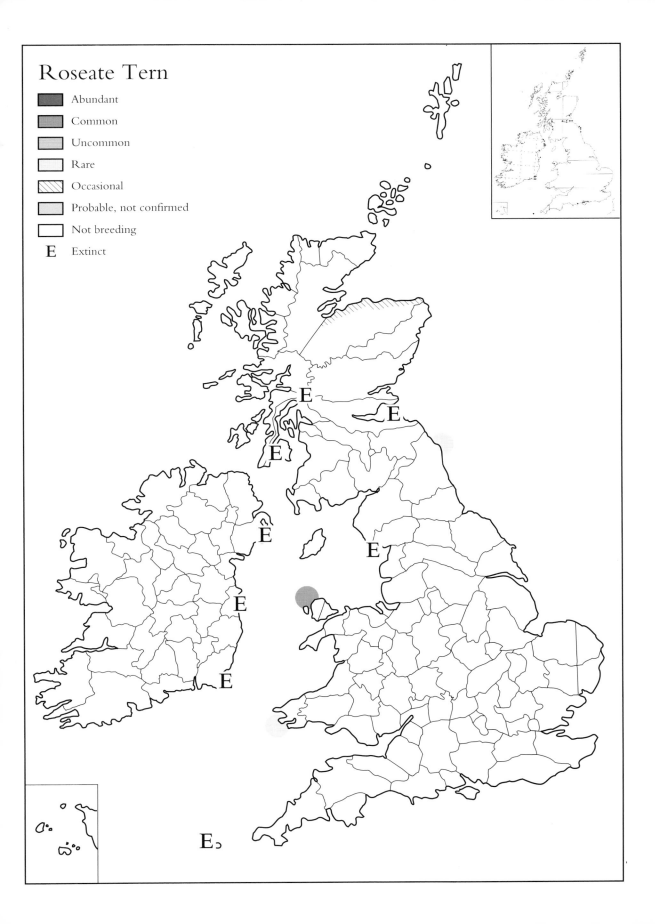

Roseate Tern

- ■ Abundant
- ▨ Common
- ▨ Uncommon
- □ Rare
- ▨ Occasional
- ▨ Probable, not confirmed
- □ Not breeding
- **E** Extinct

Common Tern

Sterna hirundo

This species was long considered more common than it actually was before it was recognised that the similar looking Roseate and Arctic Terns, first described in 1813 and 1819, respectively, often bred in the same colonies. Even after they were discriminated from each other it was very difficult to identify the species in the field, particularly without the aid of modern optics, and most records from the first half of the 19th century must be treated with caution. After that time, great care was taken to authenticate records of breeding terns, often with the assistance of a shotgun, and so, if selected carefully, can be considered more reliable than earlier records.

The Common Tern colonies known during 1875–1900 in Britain and Ireland are as follows.

Isles of Scilly: bred but in declining numbers. Dorset: bred commonly on Chesil Bank. Sussex: although had bred in some numbers on the beach between Rye Harbour to beyond Winchelsea it had declined and, by the 1890s, only a few still bred. Kent: Dungeness had a long history of breeding terns but they had declined substantially because of the vast numbers of eggs that were taken for food; around the turn of the century protection began and numbers began to increase. Suffolk: a large colony existed at

Aldeburgh and a smaller one at Orford Ness. Norfolk: egg collecting had substantially reduced numbers here but it still bred in a few places; in 1901 the Blakeney Point ternery held about 140 nests. Lincolnshire: nested in scattered colonies along the coast. Lancashire: 20 nests were counted in S Walney in 1864 and 12 in 1905. Cumberland: colonies were recorded at Ravenglass, Rockcliffe marsh and, occasionally, elsewhere on the Solway coast. Northumberland: the main colony in the Farnes was on the Inner Wideopens and a few pairs probably also bred on the Knoxes. The Common Tern was apparently attempting to colonise the mainland and was seen in summer far inland. It bred for the first time on Holy Island in 1900.

The authority for the statement that it bred regularly in Glamorgan is not clear. About 20 pairs bred on Skokholm Stack, Pembrokeshire in 1884. The largest group in Wales was in Anglesey in Llanddwyn Bay between the island and Aber Menai Point and also on the adjacent Caernarvonshire shore. It also bred on Dulas Island and Ynys Moelfre off Anglesey.

In Scotland it nested in greater numbers than the Arctic Tern northwards to Loch Broom, Sutherland into SE Sutherland. Colonies were recorded from many of the Inner Hebrides; a particularly large one existed on Islay but in the Outer Hebrides there were only a few, small colonies. It bred for the first time in Orkney in 1860 and by the 1880s there were five modest colonies. Shetland was probably colonised about 1890.

Although probably less numerous than the Arctic Tern the Common Tern bred locally around much of the coast of Ireland and in smaller colonies. It bred on more inland waters than the related species.

Although always an erratic breeding species and difficult to census, numbers increased, particularly in England, from the end of the 19th century following protection, although this may have been an extension of a steady range expansion apparent during the second half of the 19th century (see the notes on Orkney, Shetland and Holy Island above). From the 1930s a slow decline set in and, following the 1939–45 war, an increasing number of pairs began breeding inland in E England and, later, in E Scotland. This inland increase is a result of an increasing number of new suitable waters created by gravel pit and reservoir expansion. The decline in Ireland has been most marked, especially inland, but a number of coastal colonies have been abandoned during the 20th century.

Number of counties in which recorded:

Period	Probable breeding		Confirmed breeding		Combined		
	Br	Ir	Br	Ir	Br	Ir	Both
1875–1900	0	0	37	21	37	21	58
1968–1972	0	0	61	26	61	26	87
			change		24	5	29
					65%	24%	50%

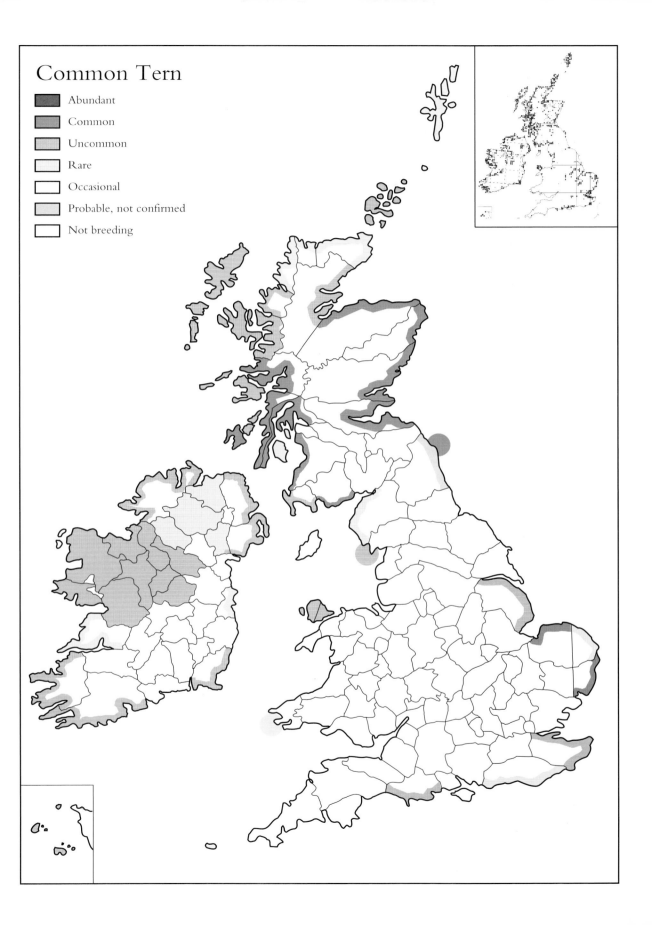

Common Tern

- **Abundant**
- **Common**
- **Uncommon**
- **Rare**
- **Occasional**
- **Probable, not confirmed**
- **Not breeding**

Arctic Tern

Sterna paradisaea

All breeding tern species were confused with each other during the 18th and early years of the 19th centuries, particularly in mixed breeding colonies. They were not fully and separately described until the second decade of the 19th century. The Arctic Tern colonies recorded during 1875–1900 in Britain and Ireland are as follows.

Isles of Scilly: the commonest tern breeding in the islands although in fewer numbers than formerly. Sussex: the assertion, quoted by Borrer (1891), that they still bred in small numbers on a beach near St Leonards and in considerable numbers at Pevensey was ignored by Witherby *et al.* (1938–41). Lincolnshire: small colonies had established themselves from time to time on the coast but did not seem to have survived for many years; in 1872 four pairs nested at North Cotes and in 1883 and 1884 a small colony was reported on Friskney Flats. Lancashire: four nests were noted by Harting (1864) on N Walney but the following year they had increased to about 40 nests; they had moved to the south end by 1891 and in 1905 50 pairs bred there. Isle of Man: Ralfe (1906) seems not to have been certain of the identity of the terns breeding at the north end; it has become clear that these were Arctic Terns and had decreased from 'hundreds' to eight birds in 1862; during the last 20 years of the century about 30 pairs bred at two adjacent sites. Northumberland: it was one of the predominant species breeding in the Farne Islands and was increasing under protection there; it had become extinct on

Coquet Island and bred for the first time on Holy Island in 1900; in 1879 a nest was found on Ross Links.

In Wales, the large colony on the Skerries, off the northwest of Anglesey, and that on the stacks off Rhoscolyn on Holy Island, had been known for many years.

Scotland. Solway: a colony shifted from year to year between Southerness and Heston, Kirkudbrightshire. Clyde: it is possible that the colonies noted by Paton and Pike (1929) on Lady and Horse Islands were established before 1900. Inner Hebrides: bred in large numbers on the Ascribs; bred at Dunvegan Loch and Loch Bracadale on Skye and Raasay, the Colbost and Skinidin Isles off Skye. Outer Hebrides: here, in its main breeding haunt, it bred in scattered colonies around the islands especially in the Sound of Harris and the islets of the west; in 1886 about 30 pairs bred in North Rona. NW Mainland: it bred in a few sites in Assynt, Eddrachillis and Durness but Loch Broom and the Summer Isles were the most southerly colonies; in these latter colonies they had decreased substantially following persecution by the local crofters. Sutherland and Caithness: bred in scattered colonies around the coasts of both counties, very often some distance from the sea; one site mentioned was on the bank of a moorland loch 6km inland from Wick; it bred commonly on the Pentland Skerries. Orkney: was described as breeding very abundantly, more so on the smaller, uninhabited holms than on the larger islands. Shetland: it bred more commonly on the western coasts than the east and in several localities colonies existed some distance from the shore, but overall it was a common breeding species. E Scotland: there were very few breeding sites between E Sutherland and the Farne Islands; there were a few scattered colonies along the N Grampian and around the Aberdeenshire coasts, but none on the Ythan estuary; it bred occasionally on the East Lothian coast and the Isle of May.

The Arctic Tern was the most numerous of the terns breeding in Ireland and bred around much of the coast. The largest colony was on Roanish, a low rocky island in Gweebarra Bay, Antrim. It bred extensively on the rocky shores and islands of freshwater lakes in Connaught including Loughs Corrib, Mask and Carra. There was a colony on Lough Melvin, Leitrim and, possibly, on an island off the Tyrone shore of Lough Neagh. Ussher and Warren (1900) mentioned 27 sites by name and hinted at several others.

It seems likely that, apart from the abandonment or decline of the southern English and Welsh colonies, numbers in Britain have remained stable during the 20th century. In Ireland there has been a dramatic decline at most colonies, particularly from the 1930s. The well publicised overfishing of sandeels in Scottish waters has led to the concern that it is to blame for reduced Arctic Tern breeding success after the late 1980s (Parslow 1973, Gibbons *et al.* 1993).

Number of counties in which recorded:

Period	Probable breeding		Confirmed breeding		Combined		
	Br	Ir	Br	Ir	Br	Ir	Both
1875–1900	0	0	19	11	19	11	30
1968–1972	1	2	38	13	39	15	54
			change		20	4	24
					105%	36%	80%

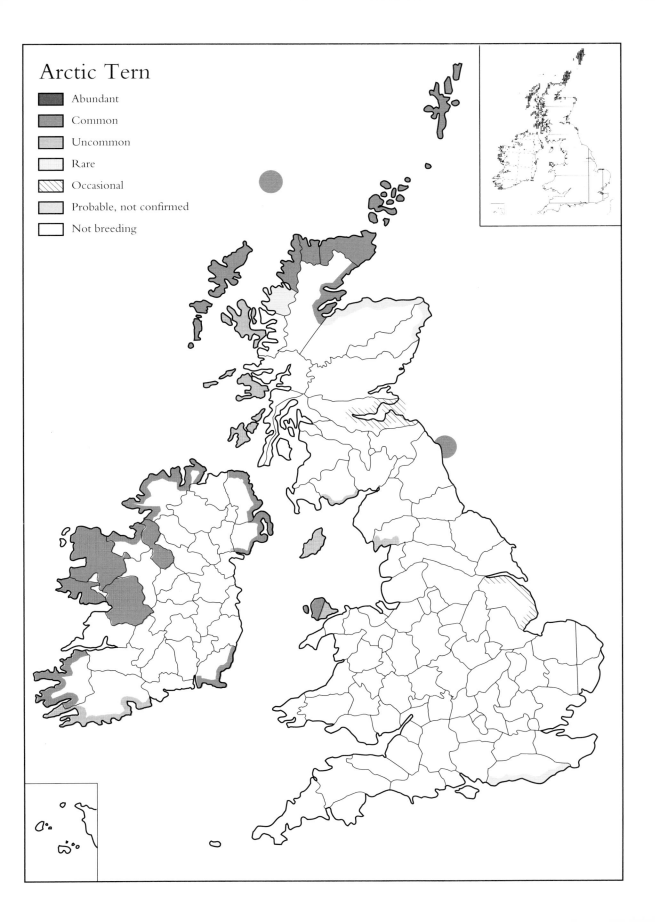

Arctic Tern

- ■ Abundant
- ■ Common
- ■ Uncommon
- □ Rare
- ▨ Occasional
- ▨ Probable, not confirmed
- □ Not breeding

Little Tern
(Lesser Tern)

Sterna albifrons

The Little Tern was declining rapidly as a result of persecution, for its feathers and eggs, disturbance and habitat destruction at the end of the 19th century. In Kent coastal developments by the military and of bungalows caused the abandonment of several colonies. It must be remembered, however, that Little Terns tend to move between colonies from year to year and periodic abandonment of colonies is to be expected (J. Sears in litt).

The Little Tern colonies that were recorded during 1875–1900 are as follows.

Sussex: bred 'not very plentifully' in a few places, particularly in the east of the county; the only site mentioned was that at Rye. Kent: colonies formerly (before 1909) existed on Yanlet Island, the Isle of Grain, near Reculvers and between Sandwich and Deal; one colony remained, in 1909, on the north coast, and a fairly large colony between Hythe and Dymchurch and a series of colonies around Dungeness still existed. Essex: the only colony still existing in 1890 was between Harwich and Walton on the Naze; 'great numbers' bred here but the Osea Island colony became extinct some years earlier. Suffolk: a large colony bred at Aldeburgh and 'considerable numbers' at Orford; a colony on Southwold beach became extinct shortly after 1850 and on Landguard Point during the 1880s.

Norfolk: a few pairs still bred at Breydon but not at Hickling and Horsey. Lincolnshire: at least three sites held four colonies; there were two colonies at Gibraltar Point and a few bred on the Humberston foreshore and at Cleethorpes. Yorkshire: it had bred at Spurn for many years; in 1861 40–50 pairs bred there: despite persecution, the colony persisted and in 1900 about 100 young were raised. Lancashire: colonies had been exterminated near the lighthouse at Lytham and on Foulney and numbers at its only remaining colony, that on Walney, had declined. Cumberland: the protected colony at Ravenglass was thriving in the 1890s but sites that had held large colonies earlier in the century held only occasional pairs; in 1890 a pair nested near Skinburness and a couple of pairs raised young at Dub Mill in 1891. Isle of Man: a colony of about 20 nests was found in 1898 probably at Rue Point.

The N Wales colonies were not molested to the same degree as those in England. A colony became established at Ynyslas, Cardiganshire about 1896 and 12 pairs were breeding in 1903. Colonies of up to 60 pairs were scattered from the Dovey estuary to Pwllheli in Merioneth, and the largest here was near Criccieth. A few small colonies were recorded between Bangor and the Conway estuary in Caernarvonshire but they bred nowhere on the north coast except for the Point of Air. In Anglesey colonies were recorded at Rhosneigr, Aber Menai, Malldraeth, the mouth of the Alaw and Llugwy Bay. A colony in Glamorgan was declining quickly—40–50 nests were found in the 1880s but only six in 1899.

In W Scotland the Little Tern was only recorded breeding on Tiree but had bred on Loch Lomond, Argyll. In the Forth it bred at Gullane Point and Tyne Mouth and was once recorded breeding on Inchmickery in the mouth of the Forth. It bred in several places on the Tentsmuir coast and was evidently increasing and spreading in that area. It bred in several localities on the Aberdeenshire coast and between there and the Moray Firth, in its largest numbers at Findhorn and Culbin Sands.

In Ireland the species bred locally on the coasts of Leinster, Ulster and Connaught and in its largest numbers in Donegal.

Under protection the Little Tern population perhaps increased slightly in places from the end of the 19th century. Numbers probably peaked around 1930 but disturbance at the breeding colonies, shortage of suitable (undisturbed) alternative sites, predation and flooding are currently the main limiting factors (*88–91 Atlas*). The most significant changes in distribution between 1875–1900 and the *68-72 Atlas* survey have been the reduction in the N Grampian coastal distribution, the increase on the East Anglian coast (where around 40% of the British and Irish population now breed), the increase in W Scotland from one to 36 colonies and the late 19th century absence of records from the Solent.

Number of counties in which recorded:

Period	Probable breeding		Confirmed breeding		Combined		
	Br	Ir	Br	Ir	Br	Ir	Both
1875–1900	0	0	26	10	26	10	36
1968–1972	1	1	36	11	37	12	49
			change		11	2	13
					42%	20%	36%

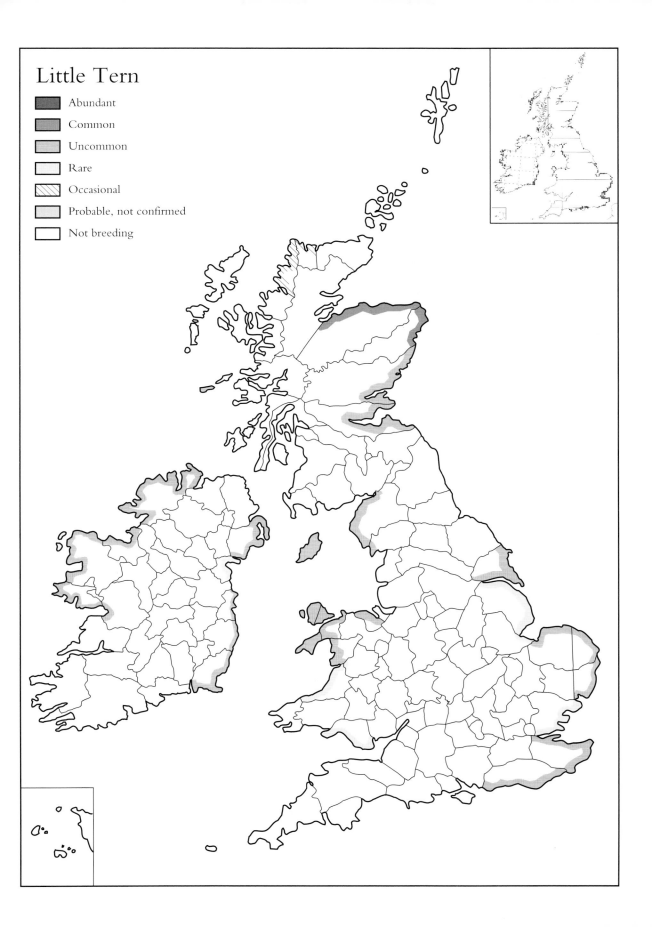

Little Tern

- **Abundant**
- **Common**
- **Uncommon**
- **Rare**
- **Occasional**
- **Probable, not confirmed**
- **Not breeding**

Black Tern

Chlidonias niger

The Black Tern evidently bred in large numbers in the marshes of E England during the 18th century. The species, however, ceased to breed regularly by about the middle of the 19th century although it occasionally bred later. The only breeding record during the last quarter of the 19th century was in Kent in 1884 and no further records were made until those of the 1940s in Sussex.

A description of a visit to a fen in SE Lincolnshire in 1769 by Pennant included the following: 'The pewit gulls [probably the Black-headed Gull which bred commonly in the fens at that time] and black terns abound; the last in vast flocks almost deafen one with their clamours'. From the end of the 18th century, however, the Black Tern decreased quickly. This was clearly coincident with the widespread drainage taking place at that time but it is not clear whether this was the only cause of the Black Tern's extinction in England. There seems to have been a lot of apparently still suitable marsh surviving into the second half of the 19th century in which it had formerly bred. In contrast, on a couple of occasions after the Black Tern had ceased to breed regularly, after 1850, it was encouraged to breed again after the sites were flooded. It is not evident that many were shot for food and at least one early account noted that the eggs were not good to eat. It is likely that this species, having declined following habitat loss during the end of the 18th century, then became a valuable target of the collectors. From the first decade or so of the 19th century the decline accelerated and before 1850 it ceased to breed regularly in Britain (Stevenson 1866–90).

It evidently bred in the East Riding of Yorkshire in the early years of the 19th century but it is not clear when it became extinct. According to Strickland (Nelson *et al.* 1907) it had bred 'near some of the streams at Driffield' but had not done so for some years prior to 1844. In Lincolnshire there was, perhaps surprisingly, no record that it had ever bred in the marshy heaths of the northwest but it

definitely did in the southeastern fens. It probably ceased breeding when the East Fen was drained in the early 19th century although eggs were recorded taken at Crowland Wash about 1845.

In Norfolk the Black Tern bred at Feltwell near Brandon, Upton and Winterton. It ceased to breed in the broads during the 1830s, hung on a little later in the eastern fens but became extinct there before 1850. There was little evidence of breeding in Suffolk but Babington (1884–86) felt that Black Terns must have bred in the adjacent parts of Suffolk to the Norfolk breeding sites, say near Brandon and Mildenhall. A nest found following an unusually large influx of the species in 1824 near Bottisham, Cambridgeshire, was the only one recorded in the county. Christy (1890) stated that the species had bred in Essex but provided no evidence.

After 1850 there were a few sporadic records of breeding. The Little Ouse in Norfolk flooded in 1852 and the following year, as the flood receded, four pairs were seen on Hockwold Fen and three nests were taken on nearby Feltwell Fen. The last nest found in Norfolk was in 1858 at Sutton. Both eggs were taken and the adults shot. In Oxfordshire, Mathew was informed that it bred on Otmoor between 1855 and 1860. There were a couple of assertions that it had bred in Cumberland. The only dated record was that of a clutch of eggs taken from a nest on the Solway in 1855. In Suffolk a pair was supposed to have bred at Oulton but Ticehurst (1932) felt that the evidence was not very satisfactory.

The longest history of breeding took place on Romney Marsh in Kent. The Black Tern had never bred anywhere else in the county but, up to the 1840s, it gradually declined and ceased breeding regularly before 1850. In 1884, Austin was employed as a 'watcher' at Dungeness and waded into the marsh to collect Black-headed Gull's eggs. Whilst there he saw five or six pairs of Black Terns and two nests. The eggs were all taken.

The Black Tern was not suspected of breeding again in Britain until the wartime records at Pett Level, Sussex. The area was flooded as part of the south coast defences in 1940 and, in 1941 eight nests were said to be found there. In 1942 five pairs were said to breed at the same location (Cooke 1946). These records, however, are not now accepted (J.Sharrock in litt).

The Black Tern nested in the Ouse Washes, after flooding, in 1966. A pair bred on an islet in Lough Erne, Fermanagh in 1967 and raised a single young, but another attempt at the same site in 1975 was unsuccessful. It may have bred on the Tayside coast in 1970 and another breeding attempt was made on the Ouse Washes in 1975. The eggs of a pair that bred in Nottinghamshire that year were taken by a collector.

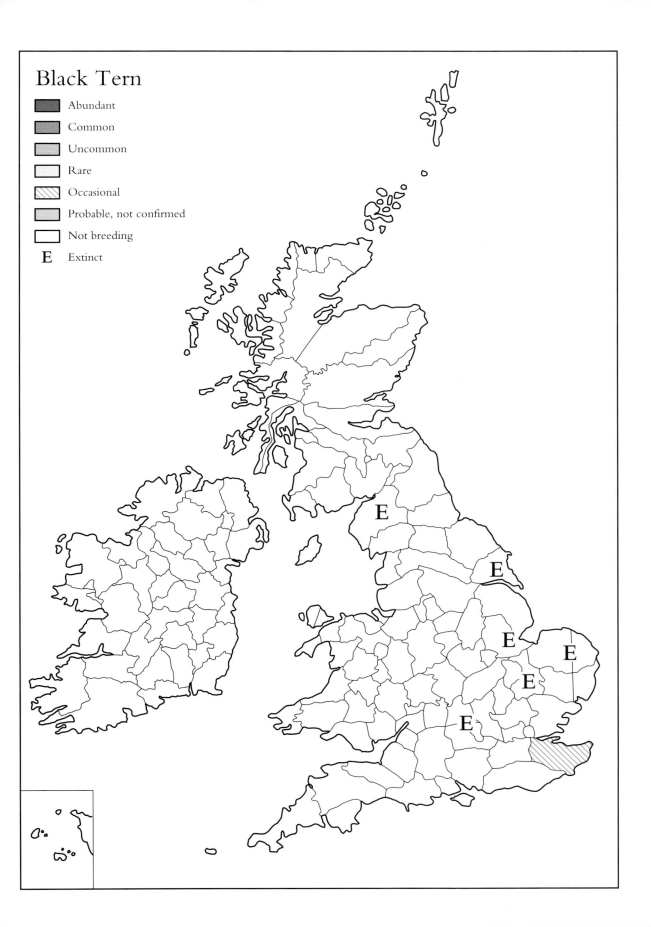

Black Tern

- ■ Abundant
- ▨ Common
- ▨ Uncommon
- ☐ Rare
- ▨ Occasional
- ▨ Probable, not confirmed
- ☐ Not breeding
- **E** Extinct

Guillemot (Common Guillemot)

Uria aalge

The distribution of the Guillemot in Britain and Ireland during the 19th century was very similar to that apparent today. Its breeding site requirements, the ledges, sheer cliffs or boulders at their bases and the tops of isolated stacks, are of habitats that are the least changed over many centuries; humans have had little influence over these sites. Where suitable cliffs exist, close to suitable fishing areas, Guillemot colonies have been established for many years and many of those specifically mentioned in the 19th century accounts still exist today (Thom 1986, Hutchinson 1989, Lloyd *et al.* 1991, Lovegrove *et al.* 1994). Human influence, however, was responsible for a diminution of numbers at some colonies. Guillemots had formerly (prior to 1891) bred abundantly on Beachy Head in Sussex but only two or three pairs remained because of the persecution (often in the form of sport shooting from boats) that had taken place. Numbers on the cliffs between Dover and St Margaret's Bay, Kent were severely reduced by persecution from fishermen and shore-gunners but they began to recover after the passing of the Wild Birds Protection Acts of the 1880s

and 1890s. Cliff falls, however, also reduced the number of suitable ledges along this part of the Kent coastline; Guillemots bred in 'considerable numbers' before the middle of the century and about 60 pairs bred in 1895 but further cliff falls caused breeding to cease before the 1914–18 war.

The colony along the cliffs between Flamborough Head and Speeton was host to Guillemots 'in such vast quantities as to be practically innumerable'. It was first mentioned by Willughby in 1678 and Guillemots and their eggs had been harvested since about that time. Areas of the cliffs that were of easy access, particularly to fishermen, were abandoned by the birds during the first half of the 19th century. Up to 140 eggs were taken in a single climb, 1,700 a day and about 130,000 annually by up to four teams but, during the period when many birds were shot on the cliffs by tourists and gunners, egg gathering was abandoned until the Sea Birds Preservation Act of 1869 which banned the shooting of seabirds during the breeding season. Numbers then recovered sharply, egg gathering was resumed and was organised so that the harvest was sustainable by ceasing collecting on 1st July and leaving heavily worked cliffs 'fallow' for a year or two.

The Scottish colonies for which estimates of population size exist are as follows (Baxter and Rintoul 1953). St Abbs, Berwickshire: in 1885 500–600 pairs bred. Kennivara Head, Tiree: *ca* 400 pairs in 1891. Isle of May, Forth: 300 pairs in 1888.

In Ireland the Guillemot bred wherever the cliffs were suitable. Those of Moher in Clare held the largest numbers whilst other large colonies existed at Loop Head, Clare, the Blaskets, Skelligs and Bull and Cow Rocks off Kerry and Cork, Rathlin Island off Antrim and Horn Head, Donegal.

As the 20th century opened the Guillemot population in Britain and Ireland continued to thrive in the post-Protection Act years. By about the 1930s, however, a marked decline became evident in the southernmost colonies of England and Wales that then accelerated, and was locally apparent elsewhere, from about the 1940s. This decline has been attributed to oil pollution, especially in the south, but, as the trend has been of long duration, may be related to the warming of the sea around the British coasts during the 20th century (Parslow 1973). Guillemots breeding in S British are a relatively small part of the total population, however, and numbers may have been increasing in N Britain and Ireland (*68–72 Atlas*). This optimism was confirmed during the 1970s and 1980s when numbers increased, since the *68–72 Atlas* by, for instance, 380% in SW Scotland and 130% in Wales (*88–91 Atlas*).

Number of counties in which recorded:

Period	Probable breeding		Confirmed breeding		Combined		
	Br	Ir	Br	Ir	Br	Ir	Both
1875–1900	0	0	40	10	40	10	50
1968–1972	0	0	37	12	37	12	49
			change		−3	2	−1
					−8%	20%	−2%

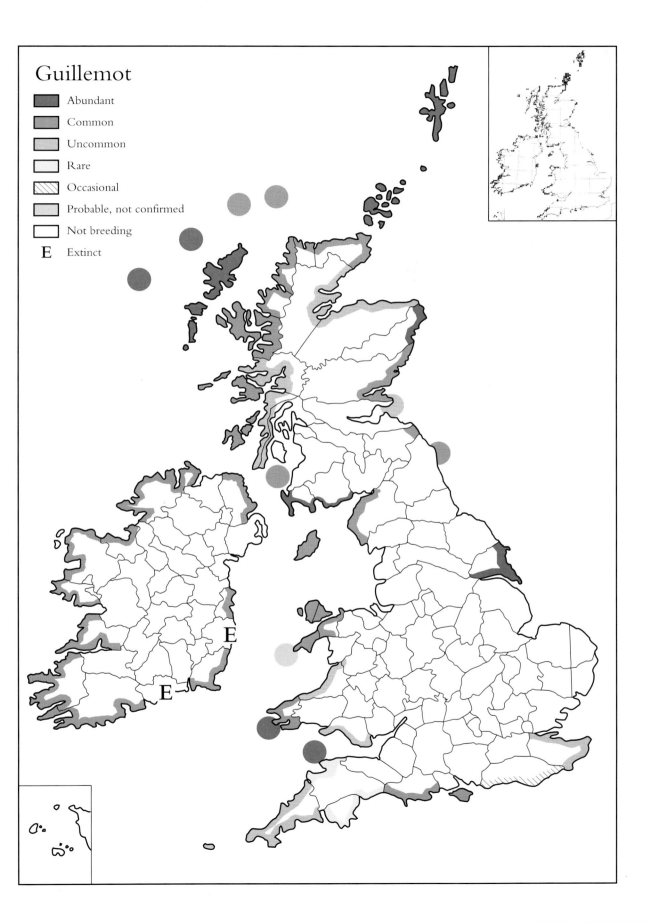

Guillemot

- ■ Abundant
- ■ Common
- ▨ Uncommon
- □ Rare
- ▨ Occasional
- ▨ Probable, not confirmed
- □ Not breeding
- **E** Extinct

Razorbill

Alca torda

Overall the Razorbill was considered to be scarcer than the Guillemot in Britain at the end of the 19th century, although, in Ireland, the Razorbill was the commoner species (Hartert *et al.* 1912). It bred in its largest numbers in W Scotland and Ireland, and in far fewer numbers in Wales. In England, there were only a few colonies and some of these were on the point of abandonment at this time. Estimates of numbers were, in the main, highly speculative. Even today this is one of the hardest species to census adequately.

The Farne Islands, Northumberland, colony is of ancient origin. Razorbills bred on The Pinnacles amongst the Guillemot colony but, by 1896, had decreased markedly. Fewer than ten pairs bred there and those not every year. The only other English colony in the east was at Flamborough Head, Yorkshire where 'thousands' were noted on the cliffs in 1884. Large numbers of eggs were taken but there is no indication of any decrease in numbers. In 1901 Walpole-Bond noted Razorbills flying into a Guillemot colony below South Forelands lighthouse on the Dover cliffs in Kent; breeding was never confirmed at the time and this remains an intriguing record. The colony at Beachy Head in Sussex was the last to survive on the SE English coast; this was probably never large but was abandoned during the 1880s. On the Isle of Wight the Razorbill bred commonly at Freshwater and in small numbers on the Culver Cliffs. From the Dorset coast around the south-west peninsula it was generally distributed. In Dorset and Cornwall it was said to have bred in large numbers. Far smaller colonies were dotted around the Devonshire cliffs, although, in the Isles of Scilly and on Lundy, there were substantial colonies. The only other English colony recorded was that at St Bee's Head in Cumberland which held a 'considerable number' of pairs.

In Wales Worm's Head, Gower in Glamorganshire, the Pembrokeshire islands of Caldy, St Margaret's, Skokholm, Skomer, Grassholm and Ramsey were specifically mentioned as Razorbill breeding sites and it bred on a number of mainland cliffs. A few pairs bred in the Guillemot colony at New Quay Head, Cardiganshire. It bred in colonies around the Caernarvonshire coast from Llanbedrog to Nevin, including both Orme's Heads. It also bred on islands such as St Tudwal's and Bardsey. In Anglesey it bred on Puffin Island and the cliffs opposite and, in diminishing numbers, at South Stack.

The Scottish population was distributed mainly on the islands, of both the west and north and, near the mainland, on stacks and islets. Between the Mull of Galloway, Wigtownshire and Cape Wrath, Sutherland, isolated pairs or very small colonies bred in many places on the mainland cliffs but on the E Scottish coast it was more sporadically distributed. Colonies existed around Cromarty Firth, on Troup Head in Banffshire, the Rock of Dunbuy, Fowlsheugh in Kincardineshire, the Isle of May and St Abbs Head, Berwickshire.

The major Irish colonies of the time were on the cliffs of Moher, Clare, the Blaskets and Skelligs off Kerry and the Bull Rock off the Cork coast. Lambay and Ireland's Eye, off the Dublin coast, were the only colonies in the east between Wexford and Antrim. Elsewhere it bred generally along the coast.

Notwithstanding the persecution by humans that the Razorbill endured during the 19th century, when many were killed and their eggs taken, there were few indications of any widespread decline. The Razorbill does, however, seem to have declined during the 20th century. Counts at 25 of 32 colonies for which records of numbers are available between the 1800s and 1969 showed a decrease (Cramp *et al.* 1974). This decline has been most pronounced in S England and Wales but the population has remained broadly stable elsewhere. Several reasons have been suggested for this decline, including changes in the availability of the Razorbill's food, mortality caused by fishing nets and deaths from oil pollution.

Number of counties in which recorded:

Period	Probable breeding		Confirmed breeding		Combined		
	Br	Ir	Br	Ir	Br	Ir	Both
1875–1900	0	0	38	11	38	11	49
1968–1972	0	0	39	13	39	13	52
			change		1	2	3
					3%	18%	6%

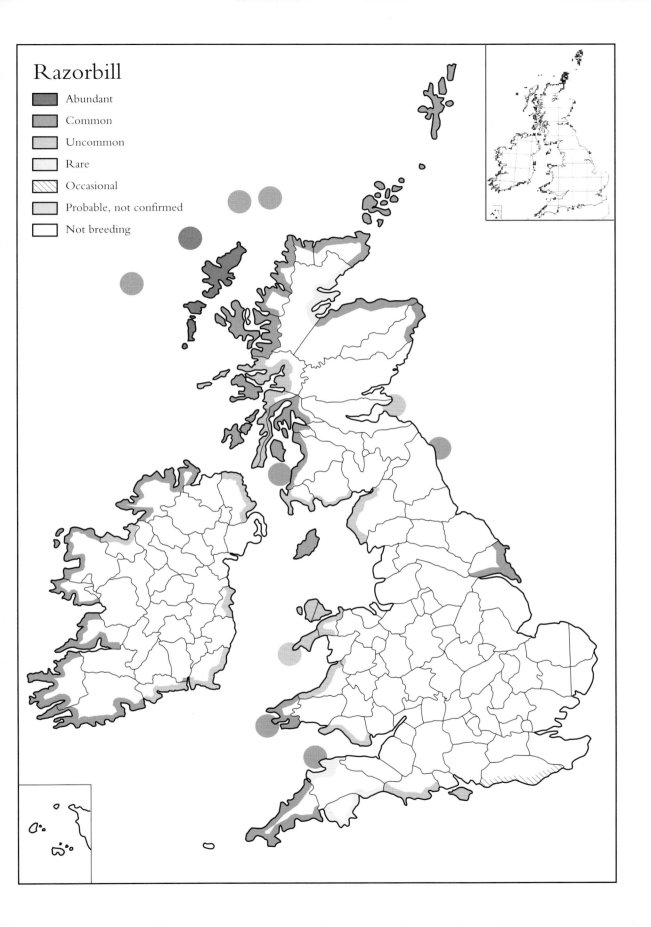

Razorbill

- **Abundant**
- **Common**
- **Uncommon**
- **Rare**
- **Occasional**
- **Probable, not confirmed**
- **Not breeding**

Black Guillemot

Cepphus grylle

During the last quarter of the 19th century the only British breeding site of the Black Guillemot remaining outside Scotland and Ireland was on the Isle of Man. It bred at six or seven sites on the island but was considered to have decreased there since, at least, the 1880s. It was said to breed near Tenby, Pembrokeshire until about the end of the 18th century and to the same period on Llanddwyn Island, Anglesey. It may have bred to a slightly later date on the Great or Little Orme's Head, Caernarvonshire. It was mentioned as breeding at Flamborough Head, Yorkshire in the 1760s and suspected of doing so in about 1810 but not later. The note that it bred at St Bee's Head, Cumberland (More 1865) was not repeated by later writers. Most of these English and Welsh records are from one writer, Pennant (1771, 1778). No other original records of breeding Black Guillemots exist for N Wales and the only other Yorkshire record was of an adult on the cliffs in summer. In all, records of breeding Black Guillemots in England and Wales other than on the Isle of Man came from just three writers and must be treated with caution. On the other hand it is interesting to speculate on the apparent almost simultaneous extinction of such widely spaced colonies. This occurred before the popular pastime of sport shooting of seabirds and, in Wales at least, widescale collection of eggs for food did not take place. It is possible that climatic conditions adversely affected Black Guillemots, although the period in which the extinctions took place was in the middle of the 'Little Ice Age' and could have suited this Arctic species. Perhaps there was some adverse change in fish stocks but this is unlikely to have been so widespread.

The Black Guillemot, in Britain in 1875–1900, was most common in W and N Scotland. On the Scottish mainland it may have bred on some cliffs in S Ayrshire and one or two pairs bred on an island off the tip of the Mull of Kintyre. Just two or three sites were known on the coasts of mid and N Argyll although it was more common on the west coast further north. There were only a few colonies known on the cliffs of N Scotland. Of the larger Inner Hebridean islands, Mull probably held relatively high numbers and some bred on Canna, Rum and Eigg. It bred commonly on Skye and the nearby islands and, in the Outer Hebrides, it bred throughout the group, mainly on mainland Lewis and mainly on the east coast there. It bred on most of the Orkney islands, most commonly on Eynhallow, and was common in Shetland. Evidence of breeding on the Scottish east coast is meagre and not conclusive. It is probable that it bred at Troup Head and near Longhaven in Aberdeenshire.

In Ireland it was much more frequent on the north and west coasts than elsewhere. The impression is given that there were no large colonies but, on suitable parts of the coast, for instance in W Galway and Mayo, it bred on every suitable stretch of the cliffs.

The 20th century saw an increase in Black Guillemot numbers on the Irish Sea coasts and the establishment of several new colonies. Birds recolonised but then abandoned the Great Orme before the 1939–45 war. It was probably these birds that bred in various places in the adjacent southeastern cliffs of Anglesey, particularly from the early 1950s. Several new colonies have been formed on the E Irish coast, most of them in artificial sites—in holes in piers and old harbour walls. The *68–72 Atlas* shows the extent to which breeding had spread around the coast of Anglesey and in SW Scotland and the development of the population in E Ireland during the 20th century. Since then, the number of breeding sites has been increasing in W (especially SW) Scotland but decreasing in W Ireland (Lloyd *et al.* 1991).

Care should be taken when considering records of this species as, especially when breeding at low densities, it can be very secretive and, unless searched for in the right season, is easily overlooked. This is likely to have happened on the NE Scottish coast in the 20th century. The actual breeding site also often moves and it is quite likely, for instance, that N Welsh and Anglesey birds were overlooked in the 18th and 19th centuries if they moved to remote areas (M. Tasker in litt.).

Number of counties in which recorded:

Period	Probable breeding		Confirmed breeding		Combined		
	Br	Ir	Br	Ir	Br	Ir	Both
1875–1900	1	0	14	10	15	10	25
1968–1972	0	0	24	15	24	15	39
			change		9	5	14
					60%	50%	56%

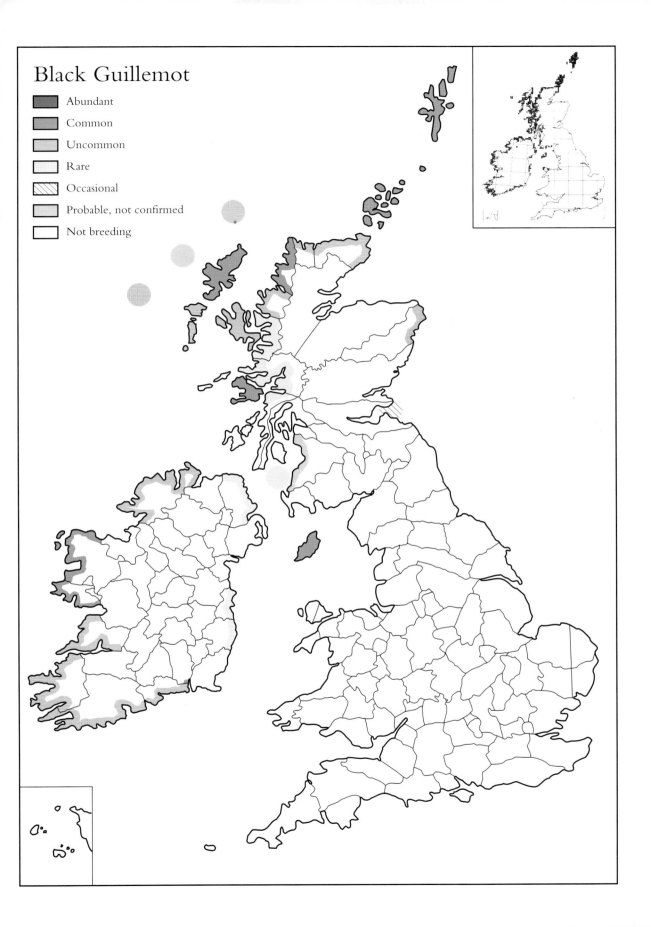

Black Guillemot

- Abundant
- Common
- Uncommon
- Rare
- Occasional
- Probable, not confirmed
- Not breeding

Puffin

Fratercula arctica

The distribution of the Puffin in Britain and Ireland during the 19th century was recorded quite clearly but great care should be taken of the records of numbers inhabiting the colonies. Colonies existed in the largest numbers on the cliffs and islets of NW Scotland, Orkney and Shetland; further south the colonies became more widely spaced and smaller. The largest of these, then as now, were those on St Kilda. Visitors to the islands were often overwhelmed by the numbers put to flight whilst walking through the colonies. Many people described the scene of the incredible flights darkening the sky. Rev. Macaulay (1764) likened the spectacle to that of a swarm of locusts whilst Mackenzie (1905), during his period as minister to the islands between 1829 and 1843, estimated that the colonies held three million birds. His estimates of the numbers of other species in the islands have been demonstrated as being substantially over optimistic so his estimate of the number of Puffins must also be treated with doubt. Sands (1877) and Steele-Elliott (1895) calculated that the annual harvest of Puffins, killed for their feathers, from the islands amounted to up to 90,000 and that when this market weakened by 1900 and far fewer were taken the numbers breeding increased substantially. Other colonies throughout the Outer Hebrides were described in similar terms. Harvie-Brown and Buckley (1888) described the four largest colonies of those that

they had seen as St Kilda, the Shiant Isles, the Sutherland coast from Cearvaig Bay to the point opposite Garbh Island and Ailsa Craig. Puffins bred abundantly around Orkney and Shetland. The largest colonies in Shetland were those in the north of Unst, on Noss and Foula; those in Orkney were far smaller and were spread throughout most of the islets.

In England the Puffin bred in large numbers on the Farne Islands, although a decrease had been recorded to the 1830s from which it subsequently recovered. The Puffin had been recorded breeding on the Flamborough cliffs for many years and at the end of the 19th century was breeding in very large numbers. The accounts from the first 40 years of the 19th century of breeding on the Dover cliffs were accompanied by some confusing detail but it remains likely that Puffins bred there. Elsewhere in England and Wales the largest colonies were on Lundy, the islands of Pembrokeshire, some of the islands of N Wales and the Calf of Man. In Ireland many islands were noted as having large colonies especially those off Kerry and Cork but the largest was on the mainland at Horn Head, Donegal. The population in Ireland was said to be increasing at the end of the 19th century.

Although no reliable numbers exist of the size of the Puffin population in Britain and Ireland at the end of the 19th century, the impression is gained that it bred very widely in Scotland, where it was regarded the commonest of the 'rock birds', and many colonies were very large and considered to be increasing. Local changes certainly occurred with shifts of colonies from some sites that apparently became unsuitable for various reasons such as introductions of the brown rat, or erosion of soil cover.

As the 20th century began, a decline had become evident, particularly in W Britain. This accelerated between about 1920 and 1950 and has been most evident outside Scotland where many of the formerly huge colonies are now extinct or nearly so. A recent stabilisation of numbers has given hope of a recovery, but Harris (1984) discussed the likelihood that recent sea temperature changes have reduced the amount of available fish prey that has been further depleted through fishing. The marine changes are part of a natural cycle and will probably recover; the industrial harvest of small fish for processing into fish meal will need human intervention to correct.

Number of counties in which recorded:

Period	Probable breeding		Confirmed breeding		Combined		
	Br	Ir	Br	Ir	Br	Ir	Both
1875–1900	0	0	31	8	31	8	39
1968–1972	0	1	27	8	27	9	36
			change		−4	1	−3
					−13%	13%	−8%

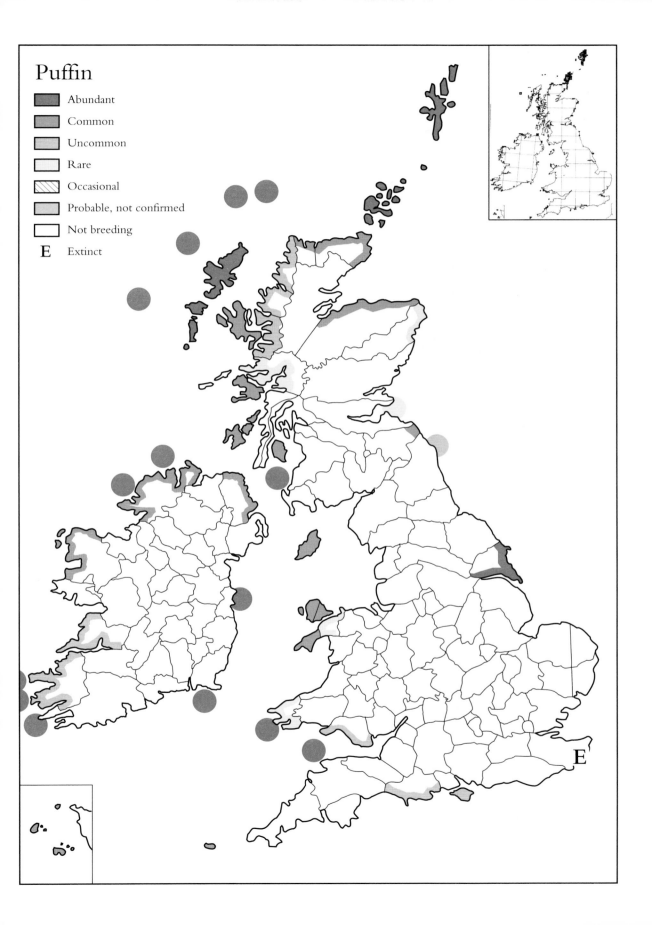

Puffin

Abundant

Common

Uncommon

Rare

Occasional

Probable, not confirmed

Not breeding

E   Extinct

Pallas's Sandgrouse

Syrrhaptes paradoxus

The first recorded occurrence of Pallas's Sandgrouse in Britain was in early 1859 when one was shot at Walpole St Peter's, Norfolk. Others were shot in Wales and in Kent in the same year but, in 1863 and continuing into 1864, the first extraordinary irruption took place in Europe. Nearly 300 Pallas's Sandgrouse were recorded in Britain, most along the east coast as far north as the Dornoch Firth, but they also occurred in the Outer Hebrides and in Ireland from Dublin to Donegal. Small groups were noted in 1872 (Ayrshire) and 1876 in nine counties mainly on the English east coast. In 1888 the largest invasion in Britain and Ireland took place. Pallas's Sandgrouse were seen throughout the region and amounted to several thousand individuals in Britain and over 100 in Ireland; breeding took place at two localities. A large number of Sandgrouse frequented the Culbin Sands on Findhorn, Elginshire from May of that year and in early June two eggs were collected by a local rabbit-catcher. Later on in the month young Sandgrouse were found in the same area. In May large numbers arrived along the entire Yorkshire coast. On 15th June 1888 a nest with two eggs was reported on Newbald Lodge Farm near Beverley by a local rabbiter and another, again with two eggs, was found at High Gardham in the same locality on 5th July. Breeding was suspected to have taken place in Suffolk (Ticehurst 1932) and in Norfolk (Riviere 1930). A number of naturalists judged that the darker colour of the late 1888 specimens indicated that fresh arrivals found their way to Britain. Whatever their origin, Sandgrouse appeared to overwinter and 1889 saw many more records. They appeared to remain in Elginshire until the spring of 1889 and, once again, a young bird was found on Culbin Sands on 8th August of that year. Further invasions occurred in 1890, 1891, 1899, 1904, 1906 and in 1909 (the 1909 records followed another major irruption into Europe in 1908) but no further breeding was recorded. A record of this species in Kent in December 1964 was the first since

1909 and three were recorded in 1969. The large invasions evidently took place in years when snow lay late in the E European and Asian steppes and prevented breeding there (Sharrock and Sharrock 1976). The reasons why there have been no further major irruptions of Pallas's Sandgrouse since that of 1908 are not clear. Perhaps a contraction of the species' W Siberian range has occurred or possibly there was a short-lived expansion during the second half of the 19th century (Cramp 1977–94) and early 20th century (Kirkman 1910–13).

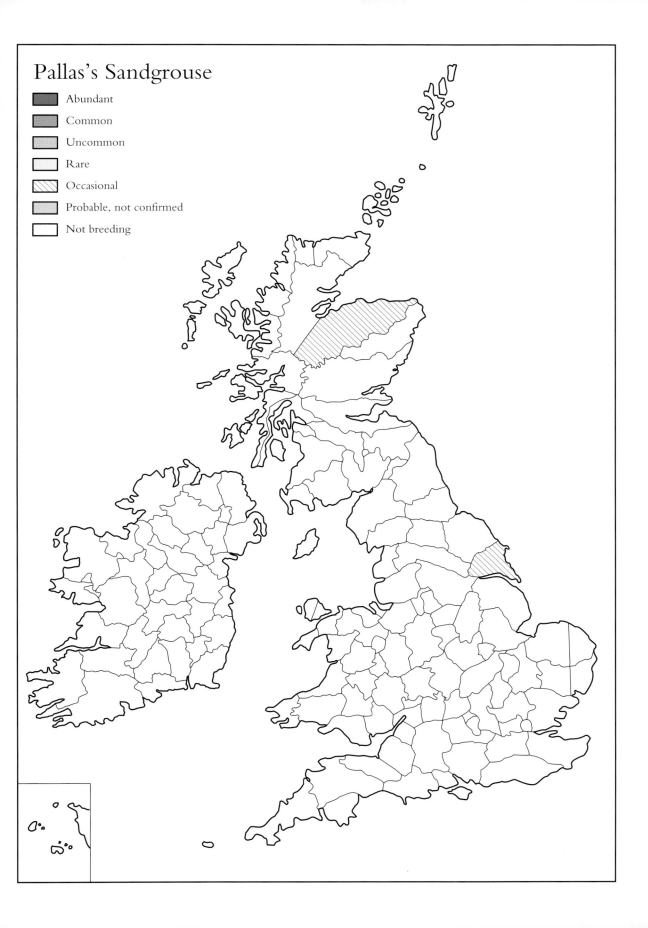

Pallas's Sandgrouse

- **Abundant**
- **Common**
- **Uncommon**
- **Rare**
- **Occasional**
- **Probable, not confirmed**
- **Not breeding**

Rock Dove

Columba livia

The problems associated with the late separation of this species from the Stock Dove and the resulting confusion over their status, especially during the first half of the 19th century, are discussed under the account of the latter species. These difficulties were confounded by the problems concerned with determining whether groups of rock-dwelling pigeons were of these two species or of feral 'house pigeons'. Feral Pigeons had penetrated almost everywhere that people lived by this time; the arrival of a pair of Rock Doves was noted amongst the Feral Pigeons of remote Inchnadamph in Assynt in 1877 but, generally, little note was made of the status of the Feral Pigeon and so it is not possible to determine the degree to which it had colonised Britain and Ireland at this time. Feral Pigeons have been a feature of London's birdlife since at least the 14th century and the practice of keeping pigeons for food was widespread then (London Natural History Society 1964). It can only be assumed that flocks of Feral Pigeons occurred in many of the towns and villages of Britain during the 19th century. It is also difficult, partly for this last reason and partly because of identification difficulties, to judge from the early 19th century records which of them refer to pigeons of the ancestral Rock Dove stock. This account, therefore, records, without modification, the accumulated opinions of the naturalists of the end of the 19th century and draws from the conclusion of the Rock Dove's status published in *A Handlist of British Birds* (Hartert *et al.* 1912). The confusion of earlier writers means that no attempt has been made to determine the counties where it had bred in the past but from which it was extinct by the end of the 19th century. It is clear, however, that it was probably more widespread formerly and bred along parts of the S English coast, in far greater numbers in the counties of the southwest and, possibly, inland in Wales and the S Pennines.

The Rock Dove bred, mainly, on the W and N coasts of Britain and throughout most of the coast of Ireland in around 1900. In England it bred commonly on the coast of Yorkshire, very sparingly in Devonshire and Cornwall and at one locality in Cumberland. It bred at a number of sites on the Welsh coast and was widespread throughout the mainland coasts and islands of Scotland and Ireland. In more detail, the species bred locally, but still in considerable numbers, in the caves of the Flamborough and Bempton cliffs and thence northwards to the Cleveland coast. The Devonshire and Cornwall populations were apparently almost extinct around the end of the century but a few still bred on the north coast of the former county and the south coast of the latter. After much argument it became generally accepted that the blue pigeons nesting on St Bee's Head were Rock Doves; however, those that bred in the Lakeland hills were believed to have been Feral Pigeons. The Welsh population appears to have been distributed around the rocky headlands and islands of Caernarvonshire and Anglesey in the north and the Gower, Carmarthenshire and Pembrokeshire coast and islands. The latter county probably held the bulk of the population and those on Ramsey lasted well into the 20th century.

In SW and E Scotland the pure ancestral form still bred but was clearly being rapidly contaminated by the feral stock. Over the north and west of the Scottish mainland and on the islands the Rock Dove existed in its purest form, and greatest numbers. They were, however, decreasing here. Many were shot for food or their eggs and young taken for food or domestication. Harvie-Brown and Macpherson (1904) believed that the growing practice of overwintering cattle indoors, particularly in the islands, was resulting in less winter food being available. In Ireland persecution had caused the extinction of much of the east coast population, but in general numbers appeared broadly stable.

The Rock Dove rapidly died out as a pure race in England and Wales during the 20th century. The W, N and islands of Scotland and the W and S of Ireland remain the species' stronghold at the present day (*88–91 Atlas*).

Number of counties in which recorded:

Period	Probable breeding		Confirmed breeding		Combined		
	Br	Ir	Br	Ir	Br	Ir	Both
1875–1900	0	0	35	14	35	14	49
1968–1972	1	0	14	10	15	10	25
			change		−20	−4	−24
					−57%	−29%	−49%

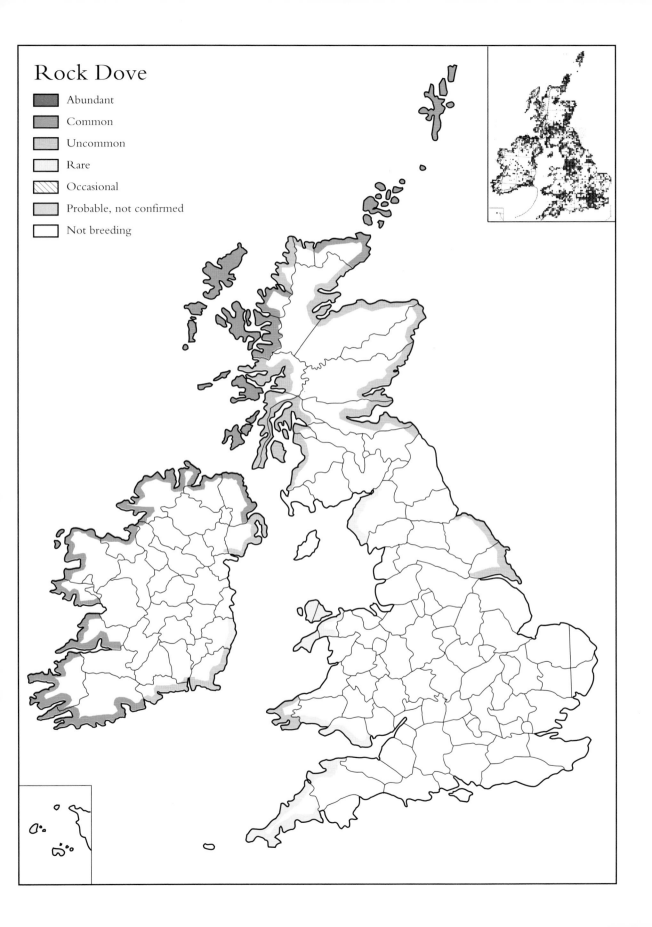

Rock Dove

- Abundant
- Common
- Uncommon
- Rare
- Occasional
- Probable, not confirmed
- Not breeding

Stock Dove
(Bush Dove)

Columba oenas

The Stock Dove and Rock Dove were not separated until late in the 18th century, the Stock Dove being first scientifically described by Linnæus in 1758 and the Rock Dove by Gmelin in 1789. Neither Bewick (1797–1804), Montagu (1802, 1833) nor Fleming (1828), however, distinguished the two species. Nevertheless at around this time recognition that both species inhabited Britain, and that the Rock Dove was the true ancestor of domesticated pigeons, began to emerge. Selby (1821), Gould (1832-37) and Jenyns (1835) described the two species correctly and other naturalists of the time began to ascertain each species' status in Britain and Ireland.

By the middle of the 19th century the distribution of the Stock Dove was imperfectly understood. Yarrell (1837–43) knew of specific breeding records only in Suffolk and Norfolk. He had received general comments that it was rare in the south, but not uncommon in some of the midland and eastern counties of England; no mention was made of Wales, Ireland or N England and it was not recorded breeding in Scotland. Eyton (1838–39) believed that it probably bred in N Wales at that time. Morris (1851–57),

only ten years later, was able to add records from Yorkshire, Lincolnshire, Hertfordshire, Essex, Oxfordshire, Buckinghamshire, Cornwall and Scotland north to Caithness. The writers of the accounts during the last quarter of the 19th century then set about disentangling the records of the two species. It is likely that the rapid increase in range apparent in the 19th century was partly an artefact of this improved understanding of the Stock Dove's status and was not entirely a real increase in numbers. It is also possible, however, that changes in the countryside during the 19th century, such as the increase in arable farming and an increase in the number of trees during the industrial revolution, as coal rather than wood became more widely used as fuel, would have suited the species. It is clear that the accounts at this time still contained some errors. Bull (1888), for instance, recorded that Rock Doves bred in rocky outcrops in Herefordshire—these were probably Stock Doves, a fact confirmed by later naturalists. Notwithstanding the fact that Morris was aware of the Stock Dove breeding in Cornwall in the 1840s, Rodd (1880) initially gave no indication that it had ever done so but found it nesting not uncommonly only six years later (Morris 1851–57; Rodd 1880).

In Ireland it was said to have been an introduced species with the first nest discovered in Co. Down in 1875, although introduced by whom and when was not mentioned by Ussher and Warren (1900). It seems likely, however, that this is another indication of increasing familiarisation with a species that would appear to be of 'no use' and an unlikely candidate for introduction (C. Mead in litt). After 1875 a rapid expansion was said to have taken place until two discrete populations were evident—one in the northwest, the other in the east mainly in Co. Wicklow.

In England, Wales and Scotland the Stock Dove's distribution appears to have changed little during the 20th century. Local exceptions to this were recorded up to the mid 1950s (e.g. in Sutherland and Cheshire), and the decline of the horse, and the consequent decrease in the amount of spilt grain, from the 1920s probably caused some redistribution of the species. Expansion of range has clearly taken place in Ireland. By about 1957, however, a marked decrease was apparent particularly in E and SE England. This was probably the result of poisoning by pesticides but by 1965–66 the decline probably halted. This was relatively short-lived as the results of the two *Atlases* (*68–72* and *88–91*) suggest further declines took place in the intervening period. Changing agricultural practices have been blamed for these recent decreases.

Number of counties in which recorded:

Period	Probable breeding		Confirmed breeding		Combined		
	Br	Ir	Br	Ir	Br	Ir	Both
1875–1900	1	1	98	10	99	11	110
1968–1972	0	1	94	31	94	32	126
			change		−5	21	16
					−5%	191%	145%

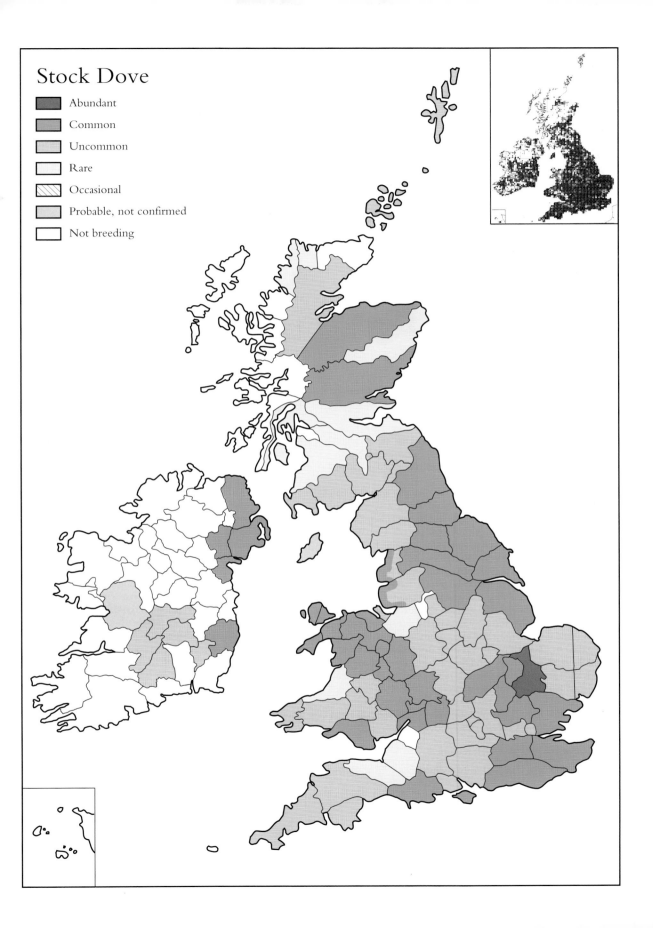

Stock Dove

- Abundant
- Common
- Uncommon
- Rare
- Occasional
- Probable, not confirmed
- Not breeding

Woodpigeon (Ring Dove)

Columba palumbus

The Woodpigeon was considered common 'in all the wooded and enclosed parts' of Britain by Yarrell (1837–43), but he noted that it was less common in the 'higher, northern regions' from which it withdrew in the winter. Just a few years later it was evident that it had increased somewhat in Scotland, although it did not breed in the Outer Hebrides or the Northern Isles. The recent increase in the Lothians was particularly noteworthy (More 1865).

By the last quarter of the 19th century the increase had clearly accelerated and the Woodpigeon was now breeding in more general habitats. The increase had been noted in Kent, for example, especially 'during recent years'. The Woodpigeon had spread out of woods and plantations and had developed a tendency to nest in isolated trees and, significantly, to move into the gardens and squares of the expanding towns. In Middlesex and London the Woodpigeon had evidently spread into the suburbs of the City and was increasing there. Harting (1866) had found only a few nests in the country districts of Middlesex whereas Swann (1893) recorded it from most of the woods at the City margins and also commonly from the London parks. In Oxfordshire it was increasing 'slightly' and was breeding in hedgerow trees and isolated thorn bushes as well as woods and spinneys. In Bedfordshire, in contrast, the increase was noted particularly in the winter; a number of examples were given of huge flocks passing over the county during the winters of the 1890s. The Woodpigeon's increase had been particularly rapid in Worcestershire and Shropshire.

The expansion in Scotland was far more extensive than that of other parts of Britain. It also appears to have begun much earlier. As an example Gray (1871) cited the change in status of the Woodpigeon in East Lothian; although it evidently became particularly abundant here, the timing of the increase was the same as in other areas of Scotland (Baxter and Rintoul 1953). Gray asserted that at the time of writing it was perhaps more numerous there than in any other part of Britain despite extraordinary slaughter—over 130,000 were recorded killed by the county Agricultural Society between December 1862 and June 1870 and in Haddingtonshire between 15,000 and 29,000 were killed each year—yet it was absolutely unknown in the area in 1790. Up to the 1860s in Scotland there was little indication that it bred outside of woods and plantations. The species continued to increase in SE Scotland throughout the rest of the 19th century. Another early recognition of the increase of the Woodpigeon took place in Solway. Gray and Anderson (1869) noticed that it had been increasing for some years and that it was particularly destructive in the ripening cereals of Ayrshire and the turnip shoots in Wigtownshire. Gray (1871) regarded this species as only a straggler to the Outer Hebrides; however, Harvie-Brown believed that it bred in the Glen of Rodel on Harris in 1879 and subsequently.

In Ireland it was distributed throughout except in those districts devoid of tree cover. It was, however, spreading westwards during the last years of the 19th century, apparently facilitated by the increase in woodland planting.

Many of the counties that are marked on the accompanying map as 'common' rather than 'abundant' had good woodland cover. This gives an indication of the increase that the species was still undergoing during the last quarter of the 19th century. When compared with the map in the *68–72 Atlas*, it seems that the species was less abundant in western counties in the 19th century.

The Woodpigeon undoubtedly became a serious pest species amongst the developing agricultural crops during the 19th century. This growth in arable crops (both spring and autumn grown and including such green crops as clover grown for winter livestock feed) was the major contributor to the increase in the Woodpigeon but other reasons were also suggested by the naturalists of the 1800s. The increase of conifer plantations provided new nesting sites and the destruction of raptors and corvids removed many of its natural predators.

The slow spread northwards continued during the 20th century although it was not until after the 1939–45 war that the Woodpigeon bred in Shetland. Local declines in numbers, particularly in towns and cities, became evident with the decline of the horse from the 1920s but this is set against numbers of unusually tame Woodpigeons associating with Feral Pigeons in city centre flocks.

Number of counties in which recorded:

Period	Probable breeding		Confirmed breeding		Combined		
	Br	Ir	Br	Ir	Br	Ir	Both
1875–1900	0	0	105	34	105	34	139
1968–1972	0	0	106	34	106	34	140
			change		1	0	1
					1%		1%

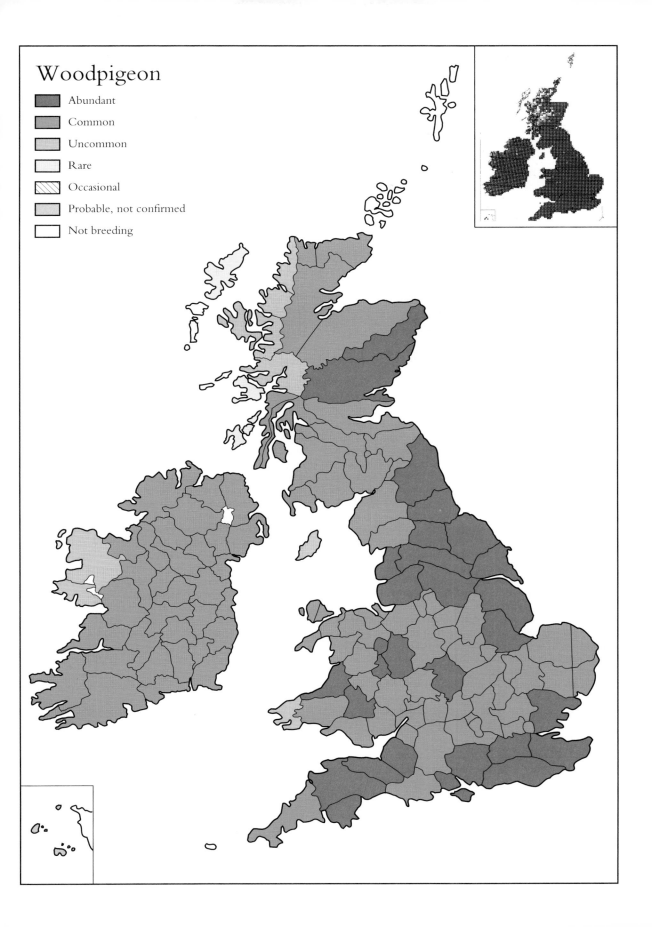

Woodpigeon

- Abundant
- Common
- Uncommon
- Rare
- Occasional
- Probable, not confirmed
- Not breeding

Turtle Dove

Streptopelia turtur

The Turtle Dove apparently underwent a westerly and northerly expansion during the 19th century. In the first half of the century its stronghold was in the counties of East Anglia and others on the SE coast of England. In Norfolk an increase in numbers was attributed to the increase in conifer plantations there (Stevenson 1866–90) but this seems unlikely as the species is normally associated with open, agricultural land and not extensive woodland (A. Evans in litt.). It also bred not uncommonly as far as the English counties on the Welsh border, throughout the Midlands and all other counties south. Occasional breeding had taken place as far north as Lancashire and, perhaps, on two occasions in Ireland. More (1865) could only record the species probably breeding in N Wales but it was recorded as a regular summer visitor in the locality of Llandudno on the N coast of Wales in 1861. Thenceforth a spread from the English border counties became apparent. By 1890 it was regarded as common in the eastern Welsh counties such as Montgomery and E Radnor. It bred less commonly in the counties further west, and not at all on the west coast, but by the end of the 19th century it had bred in all Welsh counties except Anglesey. Many writers during the last quarter of the century noted an apparent recent increase in the numbers of the Turtle Dove. This increase was most noticeable in the Midland counties and supported the Welsh colonisations and a northward expansion. After an increasing number of summer records in Lincolnshire during the 1870s and 1880s, the first nest was found in 1887 in the north of the county. Its expansion in Yorkshire took place through the 1880s and 1890s. In the northwest, Cheshire was colonised in the 1860s and 1870s. Occasional breeding was taking place further north, for instance, in 1885 near Carlisle in Cumberland.

Few major changes apparently took place in the first half of the 20th century. The south of Lancashire recorded first breeding in 1904 and numbers increased steadily until about 1930; further sporadic records took place further north on the west side of England. In 1912 breeding was first proven in Northumberland. Breeding consolidated here until a small colony was established by the 1930s. In Ireland a pair bred in Dublin in 1939 and possibly on two or three other occasions elsewhere in Ireland.

From the mid 1940s several changes took place. The small population established by this time in NE England fuelled an expansion here. A few now bred in Durham, whilst breeding was first proven in Berwickshire in 1946, Roxburghshire in 1951 and East Lothian in 1958. Breeding had been suspected in the Dumfries and Galloway region from 1955. Apart from this population in NE England and Scotland, the northern limit of regular breeding of the main population at this time was in S Lancashire. Also at this time a decrease was noticeable in Wales. Breeding did not, apparently, take place in Cardiganshire, Merioneth, Caernarvonshire or Radnor in the late 1950s and early 1960s. The *68–72 Atlas* recorded little further change apart from, perhaps, the fluctuating western edge of the population moving back into Wales a little. Turtle Dove numbers were probably at an all time high at this point.

In the period between the *68–72* and *88–91 Atlases* a substantial decline occurred. A reduction in breeding range is clear (the results of the *88–91 Atlas* survey indicate about 25% in Britain) with most losses occurring on the western, southwestern and northern edges. The CBC index fell to about 40% of its 1970 level by the end of the 1980s. The reasons for the Turtle Dove's decline probably include losses of the species in its wintering range caused by the Sahel drought and persecution during migration, as well as the use of improved herbicides and inorganic fertilisers, and changes in the timing of harvesting, which have reduced the availability of the seeds that make up most of its diet.

Number of counties in which recorded:

Period	Probable breeding		Confirmed breeding		Combined		
	Br	Ir	Br	Ir	Br	Ir	Both
1875–1900	0	0	67	0	67	0	67
1968–1972	11	0	70	4	81	4	85
			change		14	4	18
					21%		27%

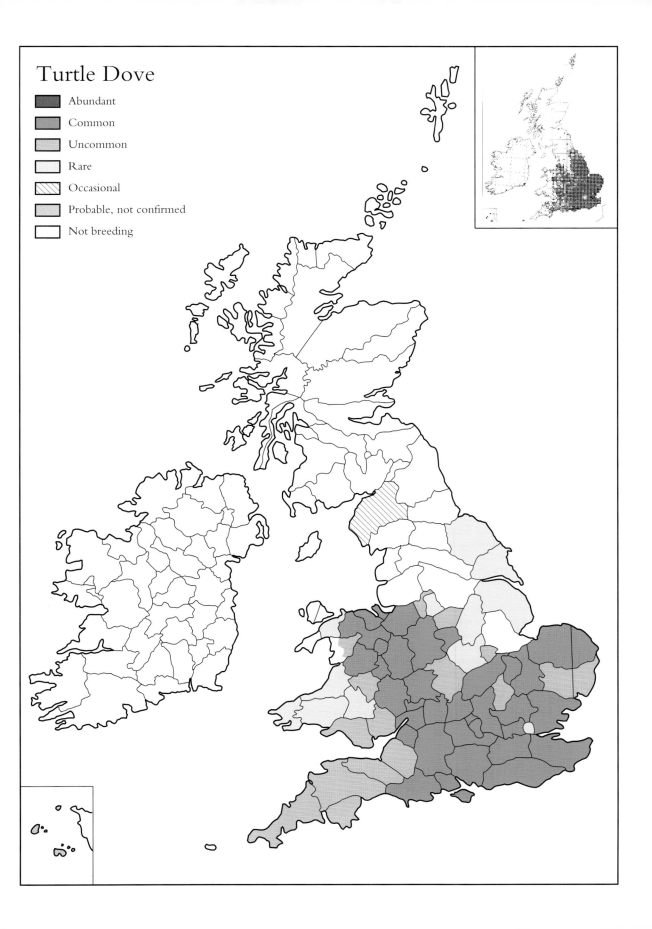

Turtle Dove

- Abundant
- Common
- Uncommon
- Rare
- Occasional
- Probable, not confirmed
- Not breeding

Cuckoo

Cuculus canorus

The Cuckoo was distributed throughout Britain and Ireland at the end of the 19th century and was the subject of much research. There were a number of aspects of the Cuckoo's biology that caused interest and controversy amongst 19th century naturalists. The popularity of recording the date of the first Cuckoo in local and national newspapers continues to the present day and was supported by the detailed records of some naturalists. The records of arrival and departure dates (of all summer migrants) represented the first, widescale attempts at quantifying aspects of the biology of birds and led to a wider interest in migration, which became an important area of study around the turn of the century. The published data of average arrival dates of the Cuckoo suggest that it reached southern counties between the 10th and 14th April. By the end of the third week in April it had spread north along the eastern counties and had reached the Scottish Borders and during the final week of the month it spread into the rest of England, Wales and S Scotland. Although data for much of Scotland were scant, during early May it evidently spread throughout the rest of that country. There were many records of March birds but most of these claims were dismissed.

Another aspect of the Cuckoo's biology that was regularly recorded was the range of host species. These included, not uncommonly, the Red-backed Shrike, but the most common victims were the Dunnock and Pied Wagtail, followed by the Robin and Meadow Pipit. In the uplands the Meadow Pipit and Pied Wagtail were most commonly victimised. It is apparent that the Reed Warbler has assumed more importance as a host species in the 20th century (the number of nests parasitised has doubled since 1939 whilst the parasitism of other hosts has declined, Brooke and Davies 1987) but care must be taken to consider that, in the absence of special studies, the 19th century records of Cuckoos' eggs found will reflect the number of host species' nests discovered.

The 19th century naturalists were still arguing about how the eggs were transmitted into the host's nest. The weight of opinion at the end of the 19th century favoured the assertion that the egg was laid on the ground and carried to the nest in the Cuckoo's beak. This belief was based on accounts of birds shot with egg yolk on their bills, of Cuckoos' eggs found on the ground and the records of their eggs found in domed nests (Wren, Chiffchaff) or nests in cavities (Redstart). The argument was not completely settled until Chance's observations after the 1914–18 war fully established that Cuckoos lay directly into their hosts' nests (Chance 1922).

The subject of egg mimicry also created a lot of interest. Many naturalists gave examples of Cuckoos eggs that both did and did not resemble those of their host and led some to carry out experiments to determine the tolerance of hosts to foreign eggs. One of the most substantial was carried out in 1882 (Beckwith 1887–93). Beckwith placed foreign eggs into 50 nests with many combinations of size and colour and found that in only seven cases were the eggs either deserted or thrown out. Extremes such as eggs of the Rook and Stock Dove in the nests of the Blackbird seemed to have been accepted.

The status of the Cuckoo through the 19th century appears to have been stable and remained so until the 1950s. Although not quantified, a decrease then began, probably particularly in lowland regions and mainly in the eastern counties of England; however, it was also apparent elsewhere (Parslow 1973). The decline continued between the *68–72* and *88–91 Atlases*, especially in Ireland, and has been linked to the fortunes of its host species, especially the Meadow Pipit, habitat losses and fluctuations in food availability (Gibbons *et al.* 1993).

Number of counties in which recorded:

Period	Probable breeding		Confirmed breeding		Combined		
	Br	Ir	Br	Ir	Br	Ir	Both
1875–1900	0	0	108	34	108	34	142
1968–1972	0	0	108	34	108	34	142
			change		0	0	0

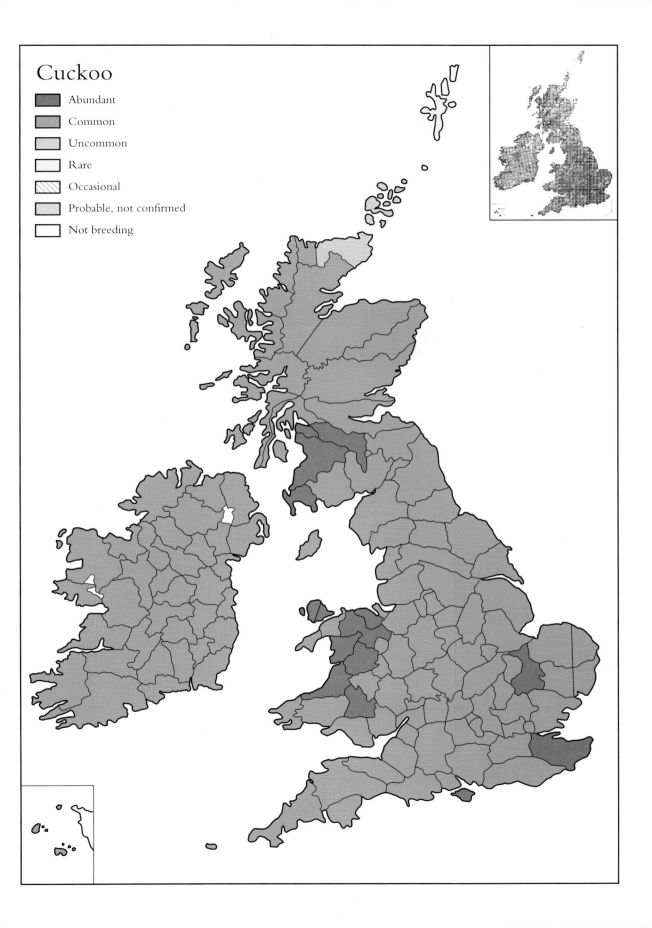

Cuckoo

- Abundant
- Common
- Uncommon
- Rare
- Occasional
- Probable, not confirmed
- Not breeding

Barn Owl

Tyto alba

For many years Barn Owls were, at the very least, tolerated, and often actively protected by farmers in recognition of their effectiveness in clearing barns and farmyards of rats and mice. Indeed, barns were often built with an 'owl hole' to provide access for them. Through the 18th and much of the 19th centuries the Barn Owl was generally regarded as the commonest owl throughout most of Britain and Ireland. From the middle of the 19th century, however, it was becoming clear that the decline, first expressed as a national problem in the 20th century, was already underway. This decline was noted from counties throughout England and S Scotland, particularly in the west. The blame for the decline was placed at the feet of gamekeepers and other human persecutors. Appreciation of the species' usefulness dwindled as the agricultural depression progressed and grain storage (and the attendant rats and mice) declined. The castigating words of D'Urban and Mathew (1892) summarise the change in attitude to the Barn Owl and the disgust felt by most naturalists of the time at the massacre. 'In every little bird-stuffer's shop the Barn Owl may be numbered by the half dozen distorted and caricatured, his face and wings, perhaps, converted into fire screens; too often we find him rotting with crows and weasels in a keeper's larder, having

been murdered by the cruel pole trap to which, having caught his mouse, he has unsuspiciously betaken himself to devour it at leisure; while the guns of those who, if they knew their own interests would best strive to protect him, are too often pointed at him.'

In some counties (for instance in Wiltshire, Sussex and Bedfordshire) it was believed that Barn Owls predated young gamebirds and so they were destroyed by gamekeepers. In Sussex, Barn Owls were shot because it was claimed they disturbed the sleep of the increasing number of holidaymakers and fruit-pickers lodging in barns. The decline may have been exacerbated by a high frequency of severe winters during 1860–1900. A decline in numbers was noted in Devonshire, Wiltshire, Sussex, Bedfordshire, Worcestershire, Warwickshire, Shropshire, Glamorganshire, Lincolnshire, Lancashire, Northumberland, Cumberland, Westmorland, Tweed and Clyde.

North of the Forth/Clyde valley the Barn Owl was very local and there were few records of breeding. It is possible that a number of sight records, particularly in E Scotland, referred to winter immigrants and, in addition, birds purchased in England were liberated here. The Barn Owl had evidently increased from about the 1840s—in 1844, an owl taken alive in Speyside was completely unknown to the local people but by the 1890s there had been a number of reports throughout the area south of the Great Glen. North of the valley firm breeding records had occurred only along the west coast.

In Ireland Barn Owls were most common in the counties of the southeast quarter but they bred throughout the country. Here too they were persecuted for no better reason than that they were infrequently seen and the demand for a mounted specimen in the house was as great here as in Britain.

During the early 1900s concern was expressed by ornithologists at the decline of the Barn Owl which led to an ambitious early census in 1932 (Blaker 1934). The status of the species during the late 19th and first half of the 20th century was complex. A decline was apparently underway in many parts of its range (Bunn *et al*. 1982) during this period although a recovery was taking place in S Scotland (Baxter and Rintoul 1953). The reasons for the long-term decline are complex. Intensification of agriculture and loss of suitable habitat have been blamed but, during the period in question (say, 1870 to the 1930s), the agricultural depression was underway and the landscape changed little relative to the decades both preceding and following. Perhaps the rate of decline fell during this inter-war period with the decline in keepering because there was little further widespread concern expressed until the disappearance of birds from their normal haunts attracted the attention of ornithologists in the 1950s. This coincided with the beginning of the organochlorine scares and has continued to the present day. The *88–91 Atlas* reveals the extent of the decline since the *68–72 Atlas* survey.

Number of counties in which recorded:

Period	Probable breeding		Confirmed breeding		Combined		
	Br	Ir	Br	Ir	Br	Ir	Both
1875–1900	0	0	103	34	103	34	137
1968–1972	2	1	106	17	108	18	126
	change				5	−16	−11
					5%	−47%	−8%

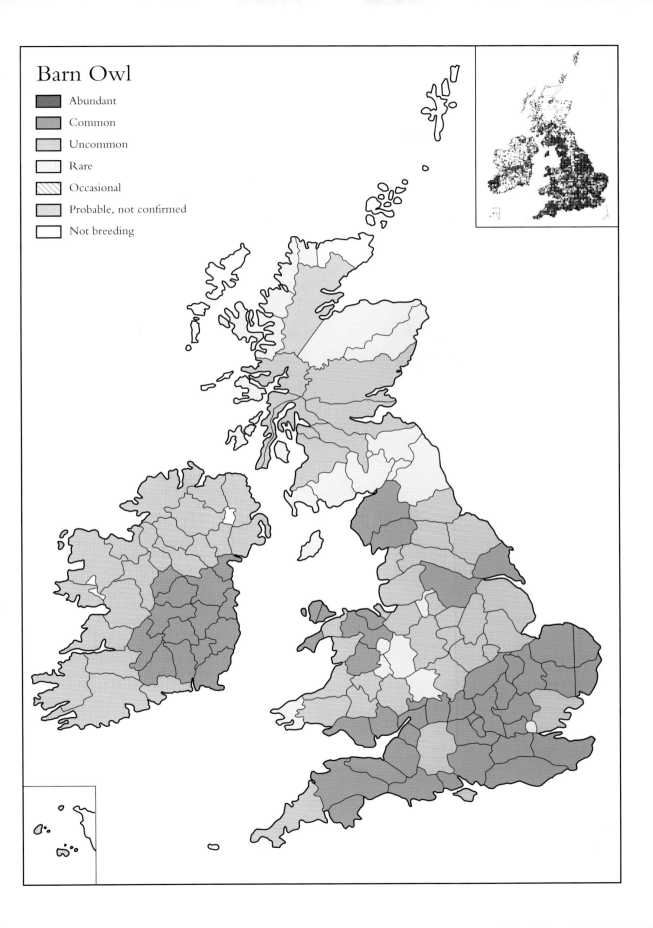

Barn Owl

- **Abundant**
- **Common**
- **Uncommon**
- **Rare**
- **Occasional**
- **Probable, not confirmed**
- **Not breeding**

Little Owl

Athene noctua

The Little Owl was considered an occasional visitor to Britain from the Continent throughout the early years of the 19th century and had been recorded from most of England and Wales, although it seems likely that some such early records may have related to translocated individuals (D. Glue in litt). From the 1840s, however, it was not possible to discriminate at all between natural occurrences and released birds. Just why so many attempts were made to naturalise the Little Owl in Britain has never been satisfactorily explained. It is entirely possible that they were released for no other reason than that they were considered an ornamental addition to the British countryside or the fact that they were common on the other side of the English Channel may have been reason enough. Whatever the reason, the Little Owl happily occupied the vacant niche for a small nocturnal predator on lowland agricultural land in Britain (Glue and Scott 1980).

One of the earliest attempts at introduction was that by Charles Waterton in 1843 who released five imported birds, from Rome, in Walton Park, Yorkshire. They apparently did not survive. Many other Little Owls were turned down during the second half of the 19th century. Further attempts in Yorkshire, in 1890 and 1905, were unsuccessful as were attempts in Hampshire (the attempt in the New Forest in the 1860s may have led to one or two breeding attempts and another in 1888 by Meade-Waldo was one of many attempts that he made) and near Tring, Hertfordshire. Two concerted efforts at naturalising the species, from the 1870s in Kent and in the 1880s in Northamptonshire, are thought to have led to the successful colonisation of Britain.

Lord Lilford released a number of birds over several years in the grounds of the family seat near Oundle, Northamptonshire. During this period Little Owls were commonly available from London dealers for sale as pets (they were renowned cockroach killers when kept in the house) and Lilford used to obtain chicks from the markets annually. The first nest was found at Lilford in 1889 and from that year the owls evidently increased and spread rapidly. In 1890, and in subsequent years, several nests were found on the estate and in 1892 the first nest was recorded on the Woburn estate in Bedfordshire. Although it was often assumed that these were the result of releases on the latter estate, this was later proven not to be the case. At the same time the Little Owl was apparently expanding its range out of Northamptonshire north into Rutland and southwest into Buckinghamshire (although this may have been aided by unrecorded releases on other estates). During the final five years of the century it expanded throughout S Nottinghamshire, most of Hertfordshire and, probably, into N Oxfordshire and Huntingdonshire. Before 1908 it had reached S Oxfordshire, much of Lincolnshire, parts of Norfolk and Suffolk, Essex, Staffordshire (and possibly Shropshire), S Derbyshire, Leicestershire, E Berkshire and Cambridgeshire.

The initial introductions in Kent, at Stonewall Park near Edenbridge, by Meade-Waldo, comprised about 40 birds released between 1874 and 1880. The first nest was found in the park in 1879 and this was followed, in 1896 and 1900, by the release of a further 25 birds. The spread from this centre of the introduction was not as rapid or as widespread as that resulting from the Lilford introduction and probably had not expanded beyond Kent by the turn of the century. Nevertheless, before 1908 Little Owls had spread into Surrey and Sussex (Witherby and Ticehurst 1908).

The rapid spread continued in the early years of the 20th century. Most of England south of Harrogate and Wales was colonised by 1925. Most remaining parts of England and NW Wales were colonised by the 1950s and breeding was first confirmed in SE Scotland in 1958. By this time the expansion and increase in numbers had slowed substantially. Losses in the 1960s followed the severe winters of that period and other local declines have coincided with habitat loss and the reduction in the number of safe nesting sites in timber, especially in the most intensively farmed areas (Parslow 1973, Gibbons *et al*. 1993). The Little Owl has yet to colonise the Isle of Man or Ireland.

Number of counties in which recorded:

Period	Probable breeding		Confirmed breeding		Combined		
	Br	Ir	Br	Ir	Br	Ir	Both
1875–1900	4	0	7	0	11	0	11
1968-1972	2	0	81	0	83	0	83
			change		72	0	72
					655%		655%

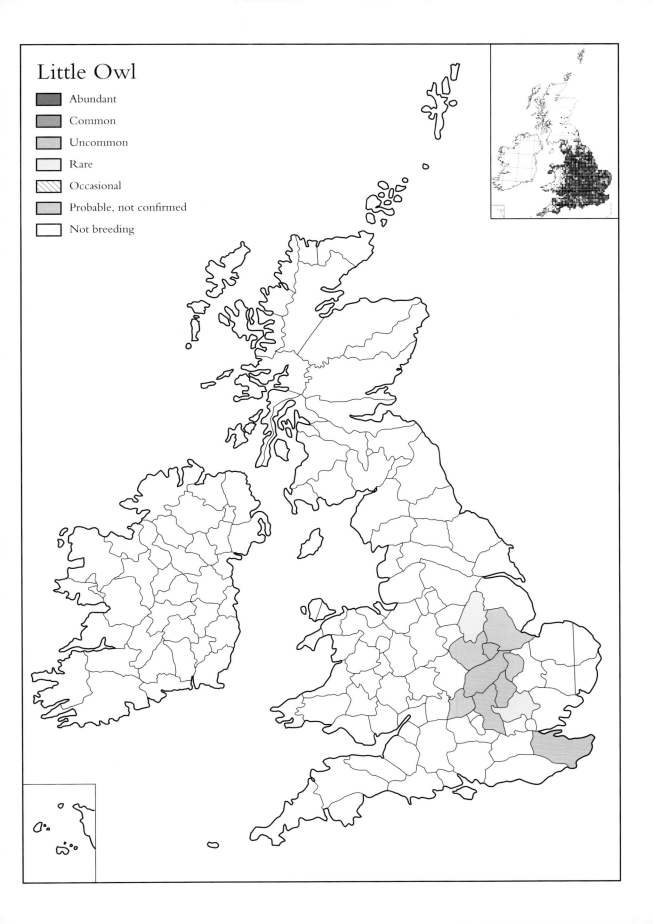

Little Owl

- Abundant
- Common
- Uncommon
- Rare
- Occasional
- Probable, not confirmed
- Not breeding

Tawny Owl (Brown Owl, Wood Owl)

Strix aluco

The status of the Tawny Owl was often expressed in comparison with the Long-eared Owl during the 19th century. As a general rule, by the last quarter of the century, the Long-eared Owl was said to be the commoner species of the two in much of N England whilst the Tawny occurred in greater numbers than the Long-eared over the rest of England, Wales and Scotland. In some counties (for instance Bedfordshire and Shropshire) the Barn Owl was believed to have been the commonest of the three. In Ireland, of course, the Tawny Owl was absent—no authentic record of its natural occurrence existed in the 19th century. Records from the 1890s and 1900 were proven to be of escaped or released birds.

In many counties of England numbers of the Tawny Owl were apparently decreasing. In most cases this was attributed to the merciless persecution meted out by gamekeepers and sportsmen (it was grudgingly accepted that the species rarely preyed on gamebirds but was persecuted for its predations on young rabbits and leverets—an important economic resource in the 19th century). Tawny Owls were also very popular cased exhibits and many were killed to satisfy this demand. In some counties, there was also a paucity of nesting holes, resulting from the increased tidying of park and farmland that left few old trees with suitable cavities. Decreases in numbers were noted from as early as the 1860s and were reported from Devonshire, Sussex, Essex, Norfolk, Bedfordshire, Shropshire and Lancashire. In contrast, in Wiltshire, the Tawny Owl was said to have been rapidly increasing in the 1880s. Although seen and heard on a few occasions on the Isle of Wight it had never been recorded breeding.

The Tawny Owl was reported to have increased its range northwards in Scotland during the late 19th century. It was not known from Assynt on the West Ross/Sutherland border before 1885 but in that year a pair of Tawny Owls bred in a dovecote at Assynt Lodge and, in 1890, an adult bird and a brood of three young were seen at Scourie, Sutherland. This range extension was said to have followed an unusual invasion into W Scotland (N Argyll, W Inverness and West Ross) between the spring of 1889 and the winter of 1891. The Tawny Owl was always extremely scarce in Caithness. It was known to breed on Mull, Jura and Islay but not on any of the other Western Isles. Low's (1813) assertion, in the early 19th century, that it bred in Orkney was almost certainly a record of an accidental bird (Buckley and Harvie-Brown 1891)—the species did not breed in either Orkney or Shetland.

A widespread increase took place over much of England, Wales and S Scotland between 1900 and 1930 (Witherby *et al.* 1938–41). This may imply that the decrease noted earlier in this account in some counties due to human persecution may, in fact, have been severe and that the decline in game preservation in the 20th century, particularly from the 1914–18 war, caused a reduction in the number of gamekeepers, allowing the Tawny Owl to recover. The recovery continued in some areas until the early 1950s. This was particularly noted in S Wales, Lancashire and Suffolk but it probably continued in other counties from Hampshire to N England and, especially, parts of S Scotland (Parslow 1973). Since that time the Tawny Owl population in Britain has been broadly stable, apart from small fluctuations that have occurred following fluctuations in rodent populations, the use of organochlorine pesticides and severe winters (*88–91 Atlas*). As conifer plantations have matured in the uplands Tawny Owl numbers have increased there.

Number of counties in which recorded:

Period	Probable breeding		Confirmed breeding		Combined		
	Br	Ir	Br	Ir	Br	Ir	Both
1875–1900	0	0	102	0	102	0	102
1968–1972	0	0	104	0	104	0	104
			change		2	0	2
					2%		2%

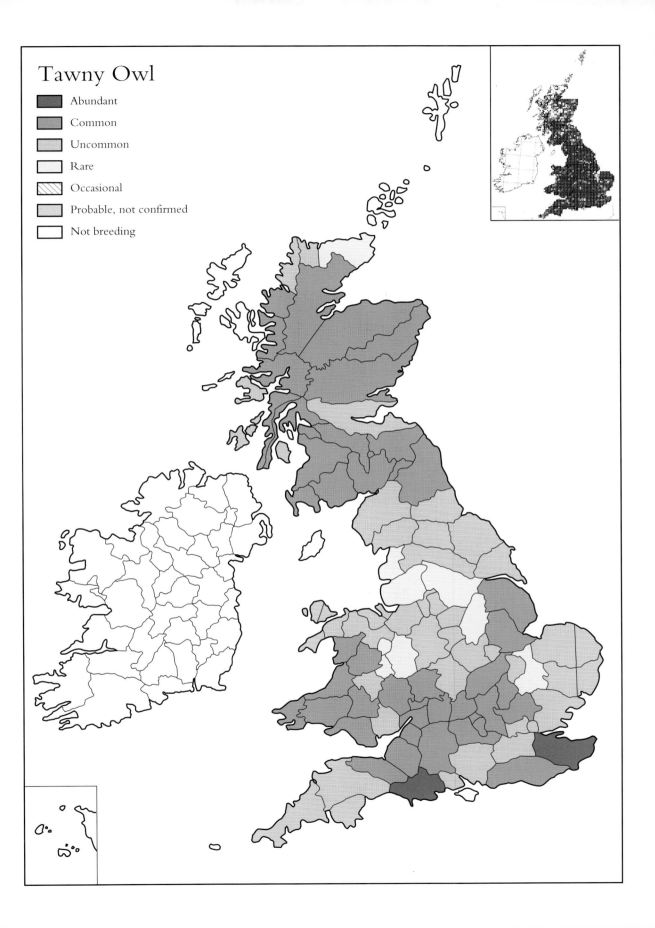

Tawny Owl

- Abundant
- Common
- Uncommon
- Rare
- Occasional
- Probable, not confirmed
- Not breeding

Long-eared Owl

Asio otus

The Long-eared Owl was unknown as a breeding species in a number of counties in S England and Wales up to the middle of the 19th century, and in many other counties it was scarce (More 1865). It is probable that this elusive owl was under-recorded where it occurred at low densities. It is fairly certain, however, that the second half of the century saw an overall increase in Long-eared Owl numbers and an increase in its breeding range in S England. Curiously, this increase (if real), was not recognised as such by the 19th century writers, and it took place against a background of persecution (mainly from game-conservers and gamekeepers but also because, along with Short-eared Owls and Barn Owls, Long-eared Owls were collected widely by Victorian taxidermists for decorative purposes). By the end of the century the Long-eared Owl had been recorded breeding throughout S England and N Wales.

It is possible that this increase was facilitated in two ways. Firstly, there is speculation that the distribution of the Long-eared Owl in the 20th century is affected by interspecific competition for nest and feeding sites with the larger Tawny Owl (D. Glue in litt) and that the decline of the former species, coincident with the 20th century increase of the Tawny Owl, is evidence of the Long-eared

Owl's inability to compete effectively with it (Mikkola 1983). If this is so, then the persecution of the Tawny Owl during the 19th century (e.g. Bull 1888) may have allowed the Long-eared Owl to replace it.

Secondly, plantations of both exotic and native conifers were maturing during the later years of the 1800s and these were quickly inhabited by Long-eared Owls; in those counties that were not inhabited before the 1860s they were considered to have occurred exclusively in the new plantations. This was especially true in Kent, Sussex, Norfolk and Hampshire although, in the absence of conifers, they will breed elsewhere, for example in chalk scrub, coastal thickets, farmland with tall hedges and copses, and shelter belts on upland pasture and on the fringes of moorland. In N Wales there are very few records of the Long-eared Owl prior to the 1870s but records increased after that, and by the end of the century they apparently bred most numerously where coniferous woodland existed (such as in Snowdonia) although they were clearly not confined to them. Although widespread throughout much of Scotland anyway, new plantations allowed the Long-eared Owl to expand into previously uninhabited areas. This was considered particularly true in the extreme north—in Sutherland and Caithness and on Orkney—but the spread here may have had other causes as the owl will nest on the ground in the absence of trees.

In Ireland the Long-eared Owl was more common than the only other species of owl to breed there (the Barn Owl) and was widely distributed, being absent only from the western seaboard where there were few trees. It was believed that it had recently increased because of the extension of tree plantings.

Locally, the 19th century population level was not maintained in the 20th century. From around the turn of the century a decline began, particularly in S England and Wales. The Long-eared Owl had become very scarce in many of these counties by the 1930s. After this point the decline became apparent more widely, being recorded from other parts of England and S Scotland. In S England and Wales many counties had been abandoned and this coincided with the beginning of the Tawny Owl's range expansion into areas and habitats where it would have become more of a potential competitor (D. Glue in litt). In other parts of Scotland up to the 1960s, however, the Long-eared Owl may have bred more stably in the extending conifer plantations and, similarly, it apparently held its former numbers in Ireland.

The *88–91 Atlas* shows how the decline has extended throughout Britain and Ireland. In both Scotland and Ireland the largest losses have been in the west.

Number of counties in which recorded:

Period	Probable breeding		Confirmed breeding		Combined		
	Br	Ir	Br	Ir	Br	Ir	Both
1875–1900	2	0	100	34	102	34	136
1968–1972	7	1	83	31	90	32	122
			change		−12	−2	−14
					−12%	−6%	−10%

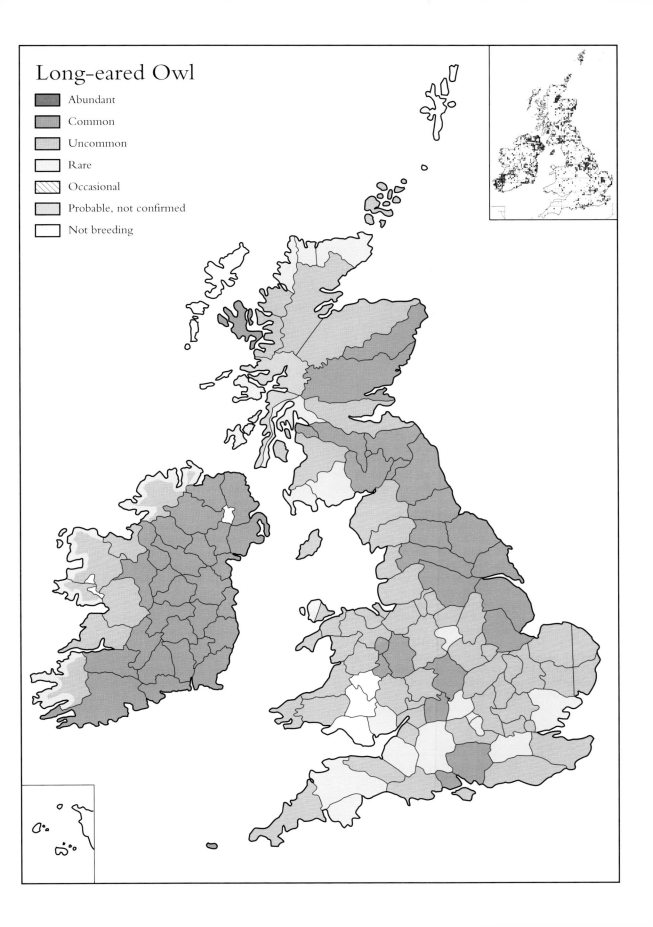

Long-eared Owl

Abundant
Common
Uncommon
Rare
Occasional
Probable, not confirmed
Not breeding

Short-eared Owl (Woodcock Owl)

Asio flammeus

Two discrete, more or less regular, breeding populations of Short-eared Owls existed during 1875–1900 in Britain, namely those breeding in N England and Scotland and the other in SE England. That in SE England was centred around the East Anglian fen counties in Norfolk, Cambridgeshire and Suffolk as far east as the coast and probably became extinct, or nearly so, during the 1870s or 1880s. Nests were found irregularly but consistently throughout the period in such places as Tuddenham Fen in Suffolk. Here, as elsewhere in East Anglia, the Short-eared Owl was clearly on the decline, as drainage and persecution and disturbance by humans took their toll. It rarely bred farther south, but did so in Essex in 1884, and on the Walton Marshes in Essex in that year and in 1889. In Kent nests were occasionally found following years of vole plagues. Outlying records include a nest found in the Hampshire New Forest in the vole plague year of 1892 while breeding was regular on the mosses of Cheshire, such as that at Carrington, where it bred until 1893. In Wales records of birds seen in suitable habitat in summer abounded, but with few instances of confirmed nesting. A pair bred on a moor in N Cardiganshire in 1874, several pairs were known to breed on Plynlimon,

Montgomeryshire about 1896 and Short-eared Owls were believed to breed on the island of Skomer, off Pembrokeshire. At the southern extremity of the Pennines the owl bred occasionally, as for instance in Derbyshire where it was said to 'breed annually on the moors of the Peak'. Further north in England breeding was progressively more regular. In Lancashire it bred annually in the vicinity of the Ribble estuary, less regularly on some of the moors and mosses and once, in 1884, on the island of Walney. Breeding was regular in NW Yorkshire, Cumberland, Westmorland, Durham and Northumberland.

Throughout Scotland the Short-eared Owl bred locally and sparingly. It was recorded breeding in all areas except the Dee drainage area, although it was considered rare in Shetland and on some of the Inner Hebrides. The Outer Hebrides and Orkney consistently supported the nucleus of the British population and breeding occurred there regularly, especially on Benbecula and North Uist, despite many eggs being taken from the latter island by collectors.

The overall status of the Short-eared Owl changed slowly through the first half of the 20th century. In some areas of England and Wales breeding became regular, precipitated by the afforestation programme. The removal of the larger grazing herbivores (such as rabbit, sheep and deer) and the application of fertilisers during tree planting increase the number of voles in these areas and this assisted the establishment of owl populations that were probably able to breed very productively. Lockie (1955), for example, recorded very large increases in clutch and brood sizes, from territories less than 20% of the normal size, in areas of high vole populations. These gains were short-lived, however, the owls being unable to use the forest areas once the canopy had closed. In the East Anglian and adjacent counties breeding became more regular with the establishment there of a population in coastal areas where new suitable nesting grounds were provided on coastal grazing marshes, often after flooding, and created through reclamation of saltings (D. Glue in litt). Here, as in the new forests, refuge from persecution has allowed numbers to increase.

During much of the remainder of the 20th century, the Short-eared Owl consolidated its increase aided by further conifer plantings, though losses have been detected in some areas, such as central Wales, and have been attributed to the loss of suitable nesting habitat in over-mature conifer forests (Gibbons *et al.* 1993). Historically Short-eared Owls have consistently over-wintered in Ireland with breeding attempted on only a very few occasions and occasionally on the Isle of Man but only since the 1970s have a few irregular cases of nesting been confirmed (Gibbons *et al.* 1993). It is unlikely that new areas of conifer woodland, on the scale that happened in earlier years, will be planted in the future. It remains to be seen whether the clear-felling and re-stocking activities in the forests will provide suitable breeding habitat.

Number of counties in which recorded:

Period	Probable breeding		Confirmed breeding		Combined		
	Br	Ir	Br	Ir	Br	Ir	Both
1875–1900	2	0	43	0	45	0	45
1968–1972	4	0	50	0	54	0	54
			change		9	0	9
					20%		20%

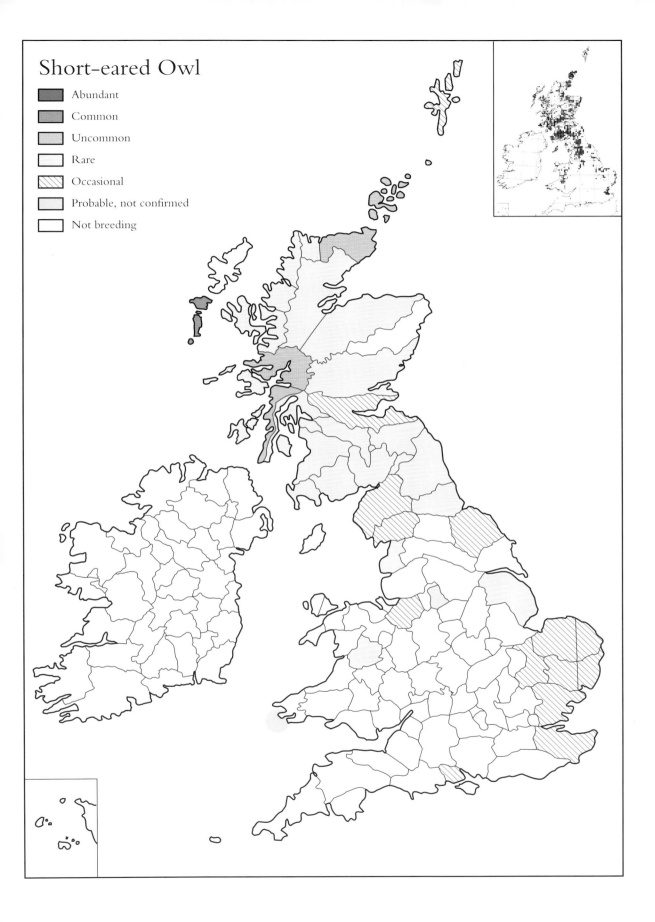

Short-eared Owl

- Abundant
- Common
- Uncommon
- Rare
- Occasional
- Probable, not confirmed
- Not breeding

Nightjar (Fern Owl)

Caprimulgus europaeus

In Britain, only the smaller off-shore islands and the Outer Hebrides, Orkney and Shetland did not record breeding Nightjars at the end of the 19th century. Otherwise, breeding took place in every other British county and region. The Nightjar was especially common in the counties of the English south coast, Wales and the Marches. In Ireland it bred in almost all counties, being particularly common throughout Munster, but was scarce in W Connaught and most inland counties of Ulster. Its breeding habitat then, as now, was described as moors, heaths, commons and areas of recently planted wood. In general, Nightjars were described breeding in most unenclosed scrubby areas and mention was often made of their taking to the new conifer plantations, especially in Scotland where some estates were planting these species. During the last quarter of the 19th century the Nightjar was noted to be decreasing slightly in some local areas especially where suitable habitat was lost to urbanisation around the largest towns (especially London as well as the manufacturing towns in the Midlands, Lancashire and Yorkshire). Although not a large influence, the Nightjar was shot regularly in some areas, being suspiciously similar in looks and nocturnal habits to the owls. The evidence of authors throughout the 19th century,

however, gives the impression that the distribution and population of the Nightjar appears to have been stable.

Throughout the first 20 years or so of the 20th century there appears to have been no marked change in the distribution of the Nightjar. The losses to urbanisation noted above that certainly continued during this period may well have been balanced in some areas by the start of the widespread planting of conifers begun after the 1914–18 war. This temporary respite, however, began to lose influence as the plantations matured and loss of suitable habitat continued, and it is evident that by the 1930s a general decline was underway. The decline appears to have started earliest, and thence most deeply, in W Britain. In Wales especially the species was lost from some counties by the 1950s or 1960s. Its distribution was apparently thinning in most other areas of Britain and Ireland and more counties had lost the Nightjar as a breeding bird by 1970. Oxfordshire and Cambridgeshire were among these as were many areas in Scotland, particularly in the W Highlands. It is apparent that, even at this time, although the Nightjar was lost from the areas mentioned, its general distribution had not altered significantly, despite the widespread impression of a decline in numbers—the species was clearly breeding far more locally than in earlier years.

At the point of the *68–72 Atlas* survey the Nightjar had been lost from much of Scotland, NE England, much of the Midlands, central Wales and large areas of Ireland. Estimates of 3,000–6,000 pairs at this time, 2,100 churring males in Britain in 1981 and over 3,000 churring males in 1992 suggest that there was a marked decline between the *68–72 Atlas* and 1981 and a considerable increase between 1981 and 1992. Over 50% of the 1992 birds were found in forestry plantations in clearfell areas or areas of recent restocking. As the forests planted during the first wave of afforestation in Britain following the 1914–18 war matures, it is likely that more of this habitat will be generated. Following restocking, these areas remain suitable for Nightjars for up to 15 years, particularly if growing conditions are poor and canopy closure is delayed. The overall reason for the long-term decline is likely to be habitat loss (through housing development and degradation due to recreation and lack of management) although climatic change and loss of insect prey through the use of pesticides may have played a part (Morris *et al.* 1994). Of habitat loss, the decline in the amount and quality of heathland through housing development, mineral extraction, farming, forestry and scrub invasion is considered to be a major reason for the decline prior to 1981 (38% of churring males were associated with heathland in 1992, A. Evans in litt.).

Number of counties in which recorded:

Period	Probable breeding		Confirmed breeding		Combined		
	Br	Ir	Br	Ir	Br	Ir	Both
1875–1900	0	2	104	28	104	30	134
1968–1972	13	6	71	6	84	12	96
change					−20	−18	−38
					−19%	−60%	−28%

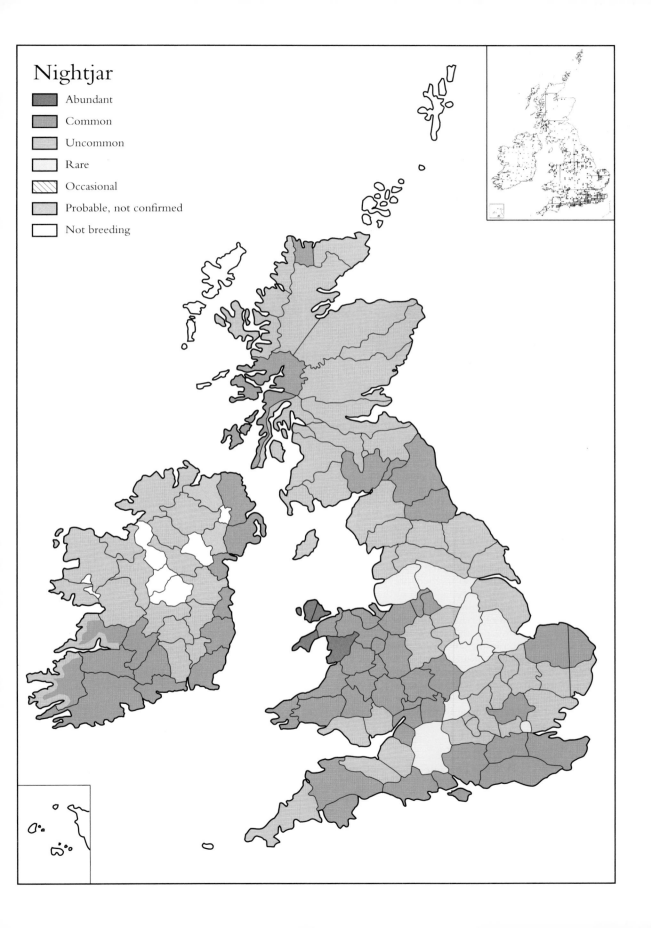

Nightjar

- Abundant
- Common
- Uncommon
- Rare
- Occasional
- Probable, not confirmed
- Not breeding

Swift

Apus apus

The Swift was a widespread and common bird during the 19th century, although several writers of the middle of the century had noted a reduction in numbers during the first half (Yarrell 1837–43, Morris 1851–57). It is difficult to determine now how real this was but, notably, these comments concerning the decline were not followed later in the 19th century by notices of increases. The inference is that numbers at the end of the century were reduced from those at the beginning. The Swift bred more or less commonly throughout Britain and Ireland being absent only from the Western and Northern Isles and NW Scotland. In some areas it was scarce, notably in the exposed and thinly peopled areas in W Ireland and the Scottish Highlands. It was also scarce in the manufacturing areas of the Midlands and N England and, by the turn of the century, had disappeared from the centre of London. Airborne pollution in these industrial towns and the largest cities had been blamed for a reduction in the amount of flying insects and thus for the disappearance of the Swift but this is likely to have been an oversimplification as Swifts are able to feed many miles from the nest site (C. Perrins in litt.).

Mention was made by some writers at the beginning of the 20th century of an increase in numbers of the Swift, especially in Ireland, but no quantitive evidence is available and so how extensive this was is not clear. Overall distribution throughout Britain and Ireland changed little from that in the 19th century. As the 20th century progressed, however, local increases occurred. The suspected increase in the coastal districts of W Ireland was regarded as 'definite' after 1932 and the Swift was believed to be increasing over the country as a whole by the 1950s and 1960s (Ruttledge 1966). In Yorkshire the assertion that the Swift had been driven from the industrial towns of the southwest appears to have reversed early in the 20th century and following the 1939–45 war it returned to breed in the centre of London.

The *68–72 Atlas* recorded no further recent changes although breeding in S Scotland appears to be less widespread than in the 19th century when Gray and Anderson (1869) wrote that in Ayrshire and Wigtownshire it was extremely abundant 'frequenting all the old ruined towers of castles'. The Swift was common in Ayrshire in 1908, but Paton and Pike (1929) felt that they could not call it common in that county at that time and that it had decreased.

The *88–91 Atlas* brought attention to the fact that numbers nesting in Britain and Ireland and the dynamics of the population are amongst the least understood of any of our breeding species.

Number of counties in which recorded:

Period	Probable breeding		Confirmed breeding		Combined		
	Br	Ir	Br	Ir	Br	Ir	Both
1875–1900	0	0	101	34	101	34	135
1968–1972	0	0	95	34	95	34	129
			change		−6	0	−6
					−6%		−4%

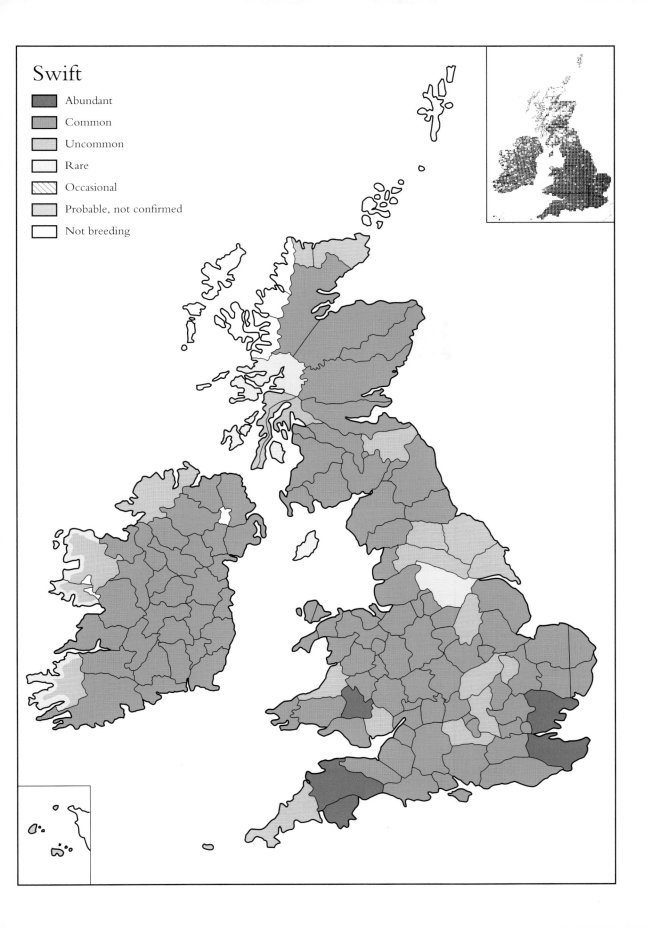

Swift

- Abundant
- Common
- Uncommon
- Rare
- Occasional
- Probable, not confirmed
- Not breeding

Kingfisher

Alcedo atthis

The Kingfisher (the Halcyon of the ancients) has long been surrounded by myths. Sailors still believed in the early 19th century that, when the Kingfisher was raising young, the seas calmed and would afford ships a safe passage—hence the term halcyon days (Yarrell 1837–43). Another early belief gave the first reason for its destruction. Many cottages up to the early 19th century had a Kingfisher suspended from the ceiling in the belief that it turned to face the prevailing wind (Smith 1887). Thenceforward, the history of the Kingfisher is one of almost ceaseless destruction. Every schoolboy attempted to kill a specimen for his collection (Morris 1851–57) and it was in great demand by the bird stuffers. As early as the 1860s it was decreasing in numbers. The decline was blamed on the collectors, the popularity of using the feathers, wings or the whole bird as fashion accessories, and anglers who killed birds to use their plumage to make fishing flies or in the belief that they ate trout and salmon fry. In addition to this it suffered because it was shot, as some other species were, just because it was beautiful or unusual. It is likely, too, that Kingfishers would have abandoned many watercourses as they were polluted during the Industrial Revolution and this may explain the lack of birds in parts of Yorkshire (C. Mead in litt.). This decline was noted in most English counties from Surrey to Lancashire and Shropshire to Norfolk. The reasons given for it were always one, or a combination, of the above although heavy mortality during cold weather was well understood as a factor that caused the population to fluctuate (Steele-Elliott 1897–1901). Accounts written from the late 1890s began to record a recovery in numbers. This increase was noted in Brecon, Nottinghamshire and Kent where the Wild Birds Protection Acts and a series of mild winters were held to aid the recovery (Ticehurst 1909).

The Kingfisher's northern breeding limit was reached in mid Scotland. In the west it was considered not uncommon in Ayrshire, Renfrewshire and Lanarkshire and, a little further north, had been recorded breeding at Inveraray, Argyll, and on Loch Lomond on the Argyll/Stirlingshire border. It bred regularly into mid Perthshire and, further east, it reached its northern breeding limit in Fife (in Forfarshire a specimen seen in spring near Auchenblae was considered a notable record but a nest was found in Stuartfield, Aberdeenshire in 1903).

In Ireland it had been recorded breeding in every county but, nevertheless, was considered a scarce and local species over much of the country. In some counties with suitable streams and stream banks it bred particularly commonly and in a few others along the eastern side of the country it probably bred more or less regularly. There were no contemporary notes of significant persecution (apart from the usual schoolboy egg collections) and, hence, no notice of a decline in Ireland (Ussher and Warren 1900). Kennedy *et al.* (1954), however, hinted that the persecution in Ireland in the 19th century was as severe as in Britain.

The 20th century saw local increases following a reduction in the persecution that the Kingfisher had suffered through the 19th century. The recovery, however, was set back on a number of occasions following a number of hard winters. That of 1946/47 marked the beginning of a general decrease in Scotland and was compounded by the severe winter of 1962/63. By the 1960s only in Dumfriesshire and Kirkcudbrightshire did breeding take place annually; river pollution elsewhere in Scotland had probably served to halt any recovery that may have taken place after the harsh winters. Canalisation of many watercourses is an additional modern problem and means that there are fewer nesting banks available (C. Mead in litt.). The *68–72 Atlas* gives the first hint of a recovery in Scotland that was confirmed by the *88–91 Atlas*. In Ireland Kennedy *et al.* (1954) described a 20th century recovery, confirmed by the results of the *68–72 Atlas*, but there was a dramatic, unexplained, decline in breeding records during the *88–91 Atlas* survey.

Number of counties in which recorded:

Period	Probable breeding		Confirmed breeding		Combined		
	Br	Ir	Br	Ir	Br	Ir	Both
1875–1900	0	0	89	34	89	34	123
1968–1972	1	0	86	34	87	34	121
			change		−2	0	−2
					−2%		−2%

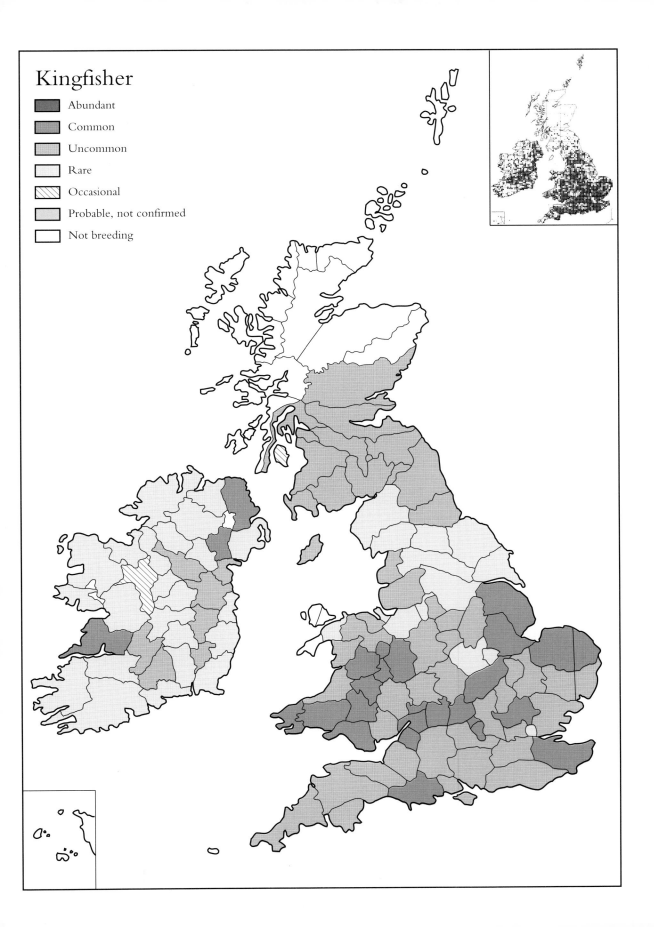

Kingfisher

- Abundant
- Common
- Uncommon
- Rare
- Occasional
- Probable, not confirmed
- Not breeding

Hoopoe

Upupa epops

The 19th century naturalists were absolutely clear that many more Hoopoes would have bred if they were not molested. Their striking appearance and obvious rarity made them a sought after specimen. Time and again accounts were given of their collection during the spring and autumn passage and, indeed, of 163 records of passage Hoopoes between 1850 and 1900 fewer than 20 appear to have been sight records; at least 145 were shot.

Evidence suggests that a warm, dry summer is required to encourage the Hoopoe to attempt to breed in Britain. The frequency of nesting attempts appears not to have changed through the 20th century, although clusters around a series of warm summers were evident. For instance, the 1950s provided four records, including two in 1955, the same year in which Bee-eaters bred in Sussex.

The Hoopoe was recorded regularly throughout Britain and Ireland during the 19th century, predominantly during the spring passage along the S coast of England and during the autumn passage in N England and Scotland. The number of Hoopoes on passage in Britain and Ireland appears to have been cyclic; for instance, the period 1850–1890 provided almost 90% of the 19th century records in Suffolk. Proven breeding, however, was a very rare occurrence. The published literature cites no more than 12 records of proven breeding in all years up to 1900 and just six proven breeding attempts were recorded during 1875–1900. These are detailed below.

1. Near Dorchester, Dorset, a nest was found a few years prior to 1892.
2. Near Christchurch, Hampshire, two eggs were collected from a nest in 1886.
3. In the New Forest, Hampshire, young were reared from nests in the same locality in 1897, 1898 and 1900.
4. Near Salisbury, Wiltshire, a brood of young was collected in 1877.
5. In Pontrhydyrhun Wood, Monmouthshire, an adult, nest and eight eggs were collected around 1890.
6. In addition, in the 1880s and 1890s some records of, apparently, recently fledged young exist for Kent.

Number of counties in which recorded:

Period	Probable breeding		Confirmed breeding		Combined		
	Br	Ir	Br	Ir	Br	Ir	Both
1875–1900	1	0	4	0	5	0	5
1968–1972	0	0	2	0	2	0	2
			change		−3	0	−3
					−60%		−60%

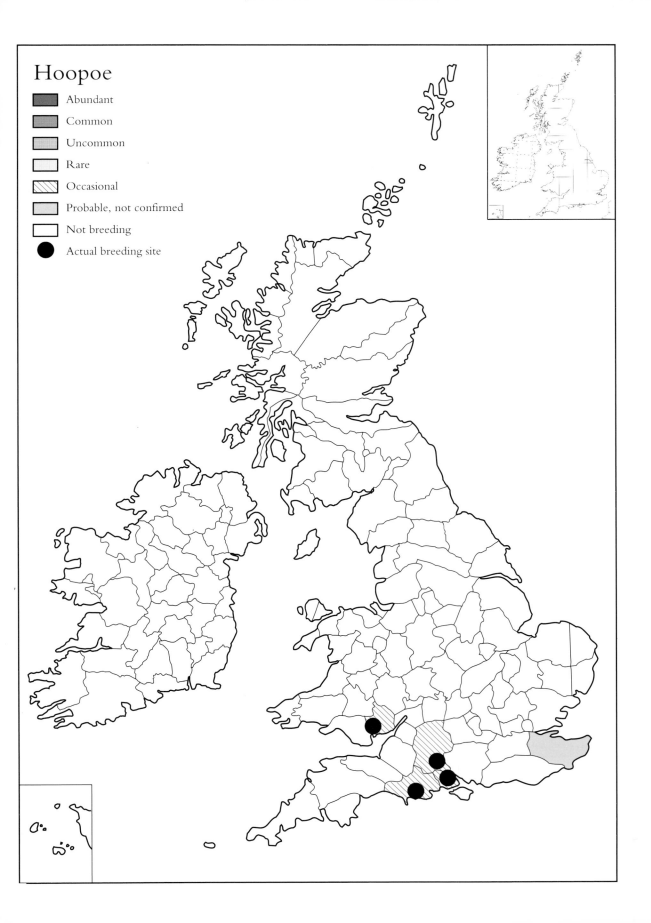

Hoopoe

- ▤ Abundant
- ▤ Common
- ▥ Uncommon
- ▨ Rare
- ▨ Occasional
- ▨ Probable, not confirmed
- ☐ Not breeding
- ⬤ Actual breeding site

Wryneck

Jynx torquilla

At the end of the 19th century the Wryneck bred over most of lowland England. It was common in much of SE England, becoming rarer towards the north and west, and bred as far as the foothills of the Pennines and the Cambrian mountains. Along the south coast and in some of the southeastern counties (e.g. Isle of Wight and Suffolk) it was considered the commonest of the woodpeckers. The only positive exceptions to this southerly distribution were outlying clusters of breeding Wrynecks in Cumberland and Durham. Here, at the end of the 18th century, it was met with annually and bred very locally through the first half of the 19th century from Kendal to Carlisle (the last nest was taken at Rickerby in 1863) and in Durham the last dated record was of eggs taken in 1872 although it may have bred into the 1890s. Other records from N England appear unreliable. It is unlikely that the Wryneck bred in any other northern counties within the lifetime of the late 19th century writers but it is probable that it bred more commonly and was more widespread in Lancashire, Yorkshire, Cumberland and Durham and probably in Northumberland and Westmoreland in the 18th and, possibly, early 19th centuries. In N Wales the most recent acceptable breeding records were of eggs taken in Llandinam, Montgomeryshire

in 1860 and in Denbighshire in 1866. Even at this time declines were noted in some counties. This decline appears to have affected populations throughout the species' range in Britain. No explanation was given for this decrease but it does appear to have begun in the main breeding range no earlier than around the 1870s.

The account by Witherby *et al.* (1938–41) confirmed the decline. The Wryneck may have provided one of the few documented examples of the effects on birds of the deterioration of grassland during the agricultural depression (Peal 1968). Wrynecks feed extensively on the ant *Lasius flavus* but these insects are scarce in neglected and ungrazed areas, because tall vegetation inhibits the foundation of their colonies (Potts 1970). By the 1930s the Wryneck was no longer breeding regularly in N England and the Isle of Wight and was very scarce in the W and N Midlands. By inference, it was probably absent from many of the Welsh border counties. Breeding was finally proven in Devonshire in 1925 but had ceased again only a few years later. During the war years the Wryneck ceased to breed in Devonshire, Somerset, Worcestershire and Warwickshire and during 1950–54 it ceased to breed in the counties of the south coast, some of the S Midlands, Essex and other counties neighbouring London, Northamptonshire, Huntingdonshire and Shropshire. At this point it bred only in Oxfordshire, Buckinghamshire, Berkshire, Surrey, Norfolk, Suffolk and Kent. The decline then appears to have accelerated in the 1960s so that by 1965 only two proven breeding attempts were made, both in Kent. Including records of possible breeding, most notably in Surrey, and most interestingly in the Spey Valley in Inverness-shire, the population in 1965 was estimated to have been 25–30 pairs. The decline between 1939 and 1966 was attributed to the spread of arable farming and forestry during that period and the consequent loss of grassland and its ant populations (Peal 1968).

The *68–72 Atlas* recorded only 14 instances of confirmed breeding—one in the New Forest, five in Kent, two in Surrey, one in Herefordshire, one in Cambridgeshire, two in Suffolk and two in the Spey Valley—and those over the four year study period. Hope was expressed at that time that the breeding of birds of Scandinavian stock in Scotland may be the salvation of the Wryneck in Britain. This was not borne out by the *88–91 Atlas*. Only a single breeding attempt was confirmed and three defined as possible in Scotland during the four study years. The Wryneck is now effectively extinct in Britain.

Number of counties in which recorded:

Period	Probable breeding		Confirmed breeding		Combined		
	Br	Ir	Br	Ir	Br	Ir	Both
1875–1900	1	0	54	0	55	0	55
1968–1972	4	0	8	0	12	0	12
			change		−43	0	−43
					−78%		−78%

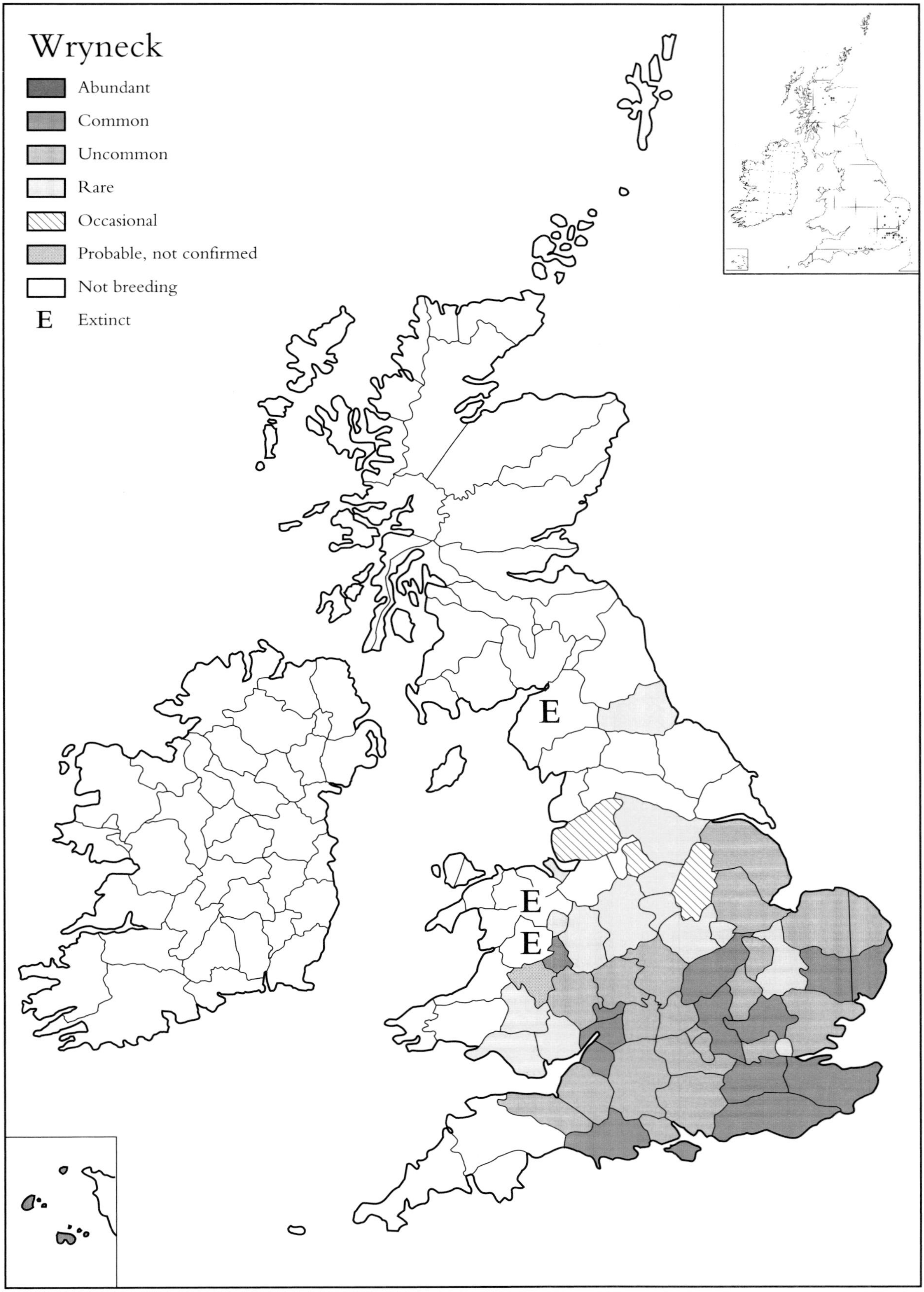
Wryneck
Abundant
Common
Uncommon
Rare
Occasional
Probable, not confirmed
Not breeding
E Extinct
E
E
E

Green Woodpecker

Picus viridis

The Green Woodpecker was common and widely distributed throughout England and Wales at the end of the 19th century, breeding almost up to the Scottish border; indeed, over much of its range it was considered the commonest woodpecker. Its bright plumage, however, made it a target of the collectors and, in some areas, its numbers had been appreciably reduced through collection. Its northern breeding limit in the east was around Morpeth in S Northumberland and, in the west, regular breeding took place no further north than Preston in Lancashire, although a nest had been taken near Carlisle in 1840 and breeding was asserted to have taken place near Penrith in 1887. This scarcity in N England and absence from Scotland was possibly not always so. In Lancashire around 1700 it had been regarded as a very common bird, certainly not the case in 1885. Yarrell (1837–43), on the authority of Selby, believed that it was 'common and well-known in the wooded districts of England and Scotland'. This contention follows the inclusion by many 18th and early 19th century writers on British and Scottish zoology of the Green Woodpecker as a Scottish species, breeding as far north as Blairgowrie, Perthshire in 1798 and in Forfarshire before 1812. More evidence exists to support the presumption that it was a familiar Scottish bird in the 18th and early 19th centuries in that a Gaelic name was recorded for it, *Lasair choille*. It must be added, however, that Harvie-Brown (1906) and Baxter and Rintoul (1928, 1953) were very suspicious of these early records.

The colonisation of the Isle of Wight probably took place some time after 1905, the first nest being found near Ryde in 1910. Apart from fluctuations in numbers following severe winters little other change occurred over most of England and Wales throughout the 20th century. In N England, however, an increase in numbers and distribution became apparent around 1920 in the east and the 1940s in the west. The increase was very rapid in Northumberland and Durham, its status changing from a rare, occasionally breeding species in 1920 to being common only 15 years later. The increase in Lancashire, Westmorland and Cumberland was not apparent until later but was fully underway by about 1945. In 1951 breeding was proven in Scotland for the first time for over 100 years. From this record in Selkirk the Green Woodpecker spread throughout the Scottish lowlands.

The *68–72 Atlas* shows the recolonisation of some coastal areas of Scotland, into Dumfries and Galloway and up the E coast of Scotland as far as the Forth/Clyde valley. Breeding at this time had extended as far north as Angus. The expansion was thought to be associated with the spread of conifer plantations and the attendant increase in the population of wood ants, an important prey species of the Green Woodpecker (Sharrock 1976). This now seems unlikely, however, as the species is apparently occupying deciduous woodland on policy estates rather than conifer woodland (Thom 1986).

The *88–91 Atlas* placed on record the continuing spread, especially northwards up the east coast as far as the Moray Firth. Suitable habitat exists even further north and it is expected that the spread will continue. Fewer Green Woodpeckers, however, were breeding in areas of SW England, W Wales, areas of the E coast of England north from the Wash and SW Scotland. These declines have been linked with land use changes, particularly those that involve the destruction of areas of short, close cropped turf that supports the dense colonies of the ant-prey species of the Green Woodpecker. Local reductions of the rabbit following myxomatosis outbreaks have also affected this habitat but anecdotal evidence suggests that rabbit numbers are currently (1994) very high (K.Smith in litt).

Number of counties in which recorded:

Period	Probable breeding		Confirmed breeding		Combined		
	Br	Ir	Br	Ir	Br	Ir	Both
1875–1900	0	0	77	0	77	0	77
1968–1972	4	0	86	0	90	0	90
			change		13	0	13
					17%		17%

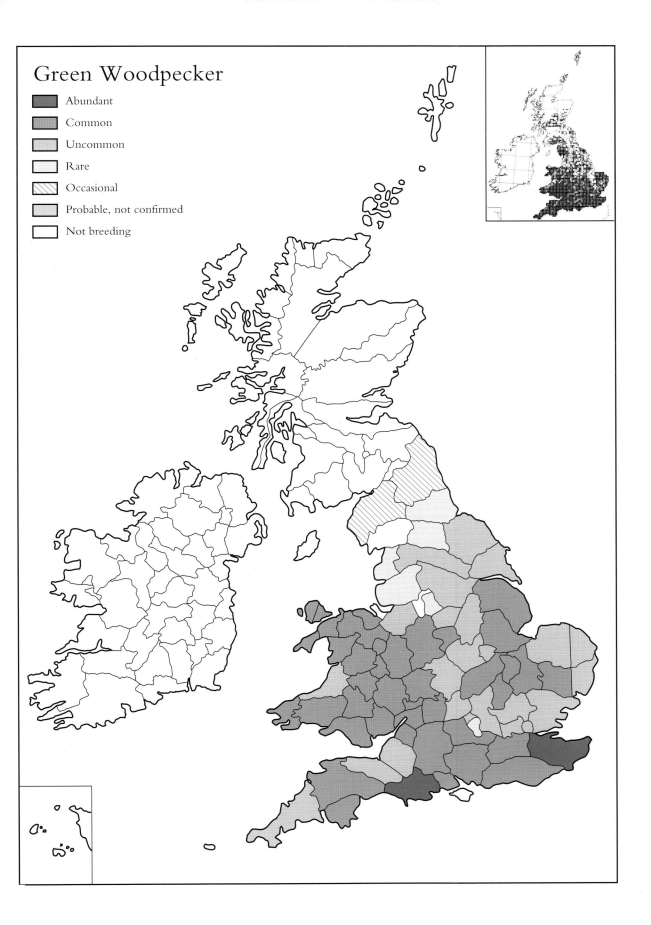

Green Woodpecker

- Abundant
- Common
- Uncommon
- Rare
- Occasional
- Probable, not confirmed
- Not breeding

Great Spotted Woodpecker

Dendrocopos major

The major change in the distribution of the Great Spotted Woodpecker between 1875–1900 and the late 20th century has been its expansion into N England and Scotland. Harvie-Brown (1880) provided evidence of a large scale withdrawal of the Great Spotted Woodpecker from Scotland during the end of the 18th and the first half of the 19th centuries. Its stronghold then was in the ancient forests of Rothiemurchus, Darnaway and Spey, and of Strathglass and other parts of Inverness-shire, along the banks of the Caledonian canal and Loch Ness. These are areas where interestingly, the species now occurs at its greatest densities in Scotland (Gibbons *et al.* 1993). The last records of possible breeding concerned individuals collected in the 1867, 1868 and 1869 seasons. Until the 1890s Harvie-Brown only received records of winter birds. He could find little evidence of a widespread decline prior to the 1860s and the inference is that it must have been fairly rapid. Some possible causes for the disappearance were recorded including the loss of nest sites caused by smugglers burning dead trees as a means of communication, competition for nest sites with Starlings (whose numbers were

inceasing rapidly at the time), and predation of eggs and chicks by Red Squirrels (whose numbers were also recovering), but the case for none of these possible causes was proven. Harvie-Brown concluded that the destruction of the forests and the clearing of dead trees in the remaining woods probably caused the bulk of the losses of this species.

The Great Spotted Woodpecker also became extinct in N England, N Cheshire and Yorkshire during the early years of the 19th century which suggests that its extinction here and in Scotland may have been caused by a more widespread agent than the local effects suggested by Harvie-Brown. In retrospect, it seems likely that these losses were the result of the intensive management of woodlands at that time: either clear felling or highly managed coppice systems (K. Smith in litt). Great Spotted Woodpeckers occur at their highest breeding densities in mature deciduous woodland (Gibbons *et al.* 1993) and do not nest in young woodlands at all. The Great Spotted Woodpecker's recolonisation of Scotland was probably of birds spreading from the repopulation of N England. The spread in N England appears to have begun during the 1870s and, in 1887, the first record of breeding since the middle of the 19th century in Scotland was of a nest at Duns, Berwickshire. The following year Great Spotted Woodpeckers bred at Canonbie, Dumfriesshire and, by 1890, had bred in both Annandale and Eskdale. Before 1897 they had bred at one Perthshire locality and in 1898 they nested at Halmyre, Peeblesshire. Throughout this period pairs were noted in summer in parts of their old Moray haunts and this led to the belief that a very few pairs of the old breeding stock managed to hold out there.

In other parts of England the Great Spotted Woodpecker was more or less generally distributed (although absent from W Cornwall and rare in the east) with an indication that numbers increased from about 1890 here and in E Wales. The most striking feature of its English distribution was its comparative scarcity in southern counties. It seems likely that intensive woodland management was, here too, responsible for its thin distribution (K. Smith in litt). It bred regularly west to the Cambrian mountains but further west in Wales it bred very rarely and, indeed, was absent from Pembrokeshire, Anglesey and Lleyn.

The increase in N England continued at least until the 1950s, and possibly later, and this was associated with further northwards expansion in Scotland culminating with the (sporadic) colonisation of Caithness in the 1940s. The increase in other parts of England and in Wales has also continued. The latest jump in numbers has coincided with the decay of elms suffering from Dutch elm disease that has provided an increase of insect prey (Parslow 1973, Sharrock 1976) but other factors may be involved as the population has not declined again as the diseased trees have been cleared (Gibbons *et al.* 1993, K. Smith in litt).

Number of counties in which recorded:

Period	Probable breeding		Confirmed breeding		Combined		
	Br	Ir	Br	Ir	Br	Ir	Both
1875–1900	3	0	75	0	78	0	78
1968–1972	0	0	101	0	101	0	101
			change		23	0	23
					29%		29%

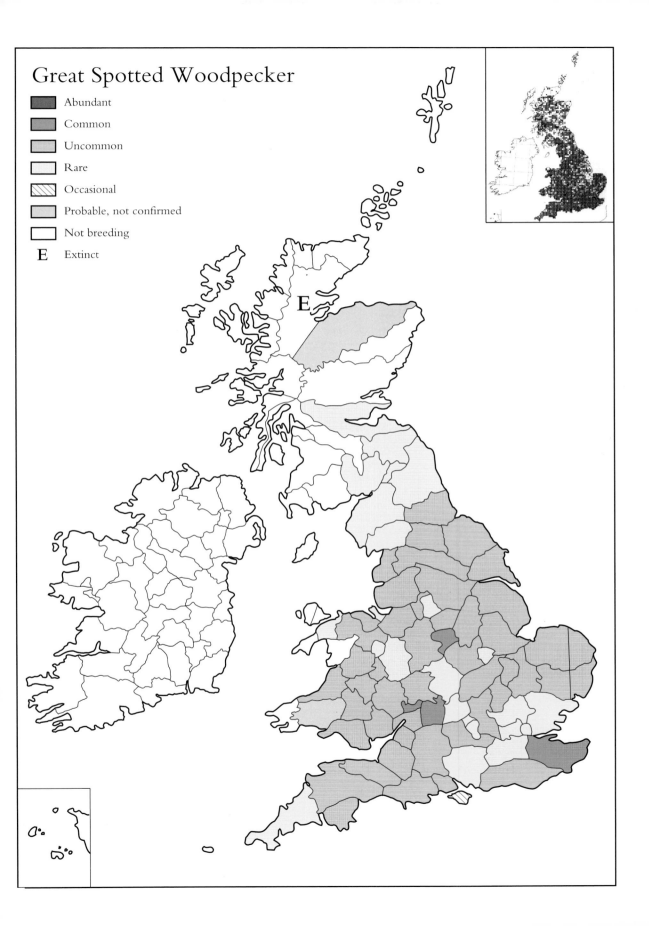

Great Spotted Woodpecker

- Abundant
- Common
- Uncommon
- Rare
- Occasional
- Probable, not confirmed
- Not breeding
- **E** Extinct

Lesser Spotted Woodpecker

Dendrocopos minor

During the 19th century, the Lesser Spotted Woodpecker was most common in SW England, although it was apparently absent from Cornwall. Elsewhere in England, particularly in the eastern counties, it was common in places but bred far more locally than in the southwest. It bred very occasionally in S Cumberland but had not been recorded from Westmorland or Furness; evidently Lakeland lay outside the range of regular breeding. The northern limits of regular breeding were, in the west, in Lancashire, where it had bred near Morecambe and, in the east, in Yorkshire up to the Durham border. It also bred in Wales apart from the extreme west. It did not breed in Scotland or Ireland and little evidence exists to suggest it had ever done so; however, its inclusion in an account of the natural history of Dublin in the late 18th century led some to suggest that it may have bred in Ireland before that country was deforested. The status of the Lesser Spotted Woodpecker does not appear to have altered throughout the 19th century and may have been stable for many years previously. Locally, however, some losses were noted from areas cleared of dead and decaying trees.

Little widespread change in numbers occurred in the first 60 years or so of the 20th century. Locally, however,

decreases have occurred, sometimes on a severe scale. One cause of the decline in SW England was the loss of old orchards. At the end of the 18th century in Devonshire, and a little later in Herefordshire and Somerset, the method of manufacture of cider was proven to cause lead poisoning; sales of the liquor ceased abruptly, and the orchards that were planted during the Napoleonic wars when imports of continental wines ceased, fell into disuse but for many years were left standing. After the 1914–18 war particularly, these decaying trees provided ideal breeding habitat for Lesser Spotted Woodpeckers. By the end of the 1939–45 war, however, almost all of these old orchards were grubbed up and clearances of old parkland elsewhere in England led to an almost complete disappearance of the Lesser Spotted Woodpecker from these areas (Gilbert and Walker 1954). To this day, the population of the species appears lower in the west than was apparent during the 19th century and, furthermore, it is entirely absent from large parts of SW England (Gibbons *et al*. 1993). Other decreases, quickly recovered from, were noted following the severe winters of 1946/47 and 1962/63 (Gilbert and Walker 1954, Marchant *et al*. 1990). From around 1970, coincident with the spread of Dutch elm disease, an increase in this woodpecker's numbers became apparent. The increase was fuelled by the increase of invertebrate prey under the bark of the dead and dying elms and led to an expansion of the Lesser Spotted Woodpecker population out of traditional woodland sites to the ailing elm trees of farmland hedgerows. As the affected elms fell, or were felled, and were cleared and the effect of the Dutch elm disease outbreak diminished, then numbers of Lesser Spotted Woodpeckers fell. By 1988 the gains of the 1970s had almost completely disappeared.

Number of counties in which recorded:

Period	Probable breeding		Confirmed breeding		Combined		
	Br	Ir	Br	Ir	Br	Ir	Both
1875–1900	1	0	68	0	69	0	69
1968–1972	1	0	75	0	76	0	76
			change		7	0	7
					10%		10%

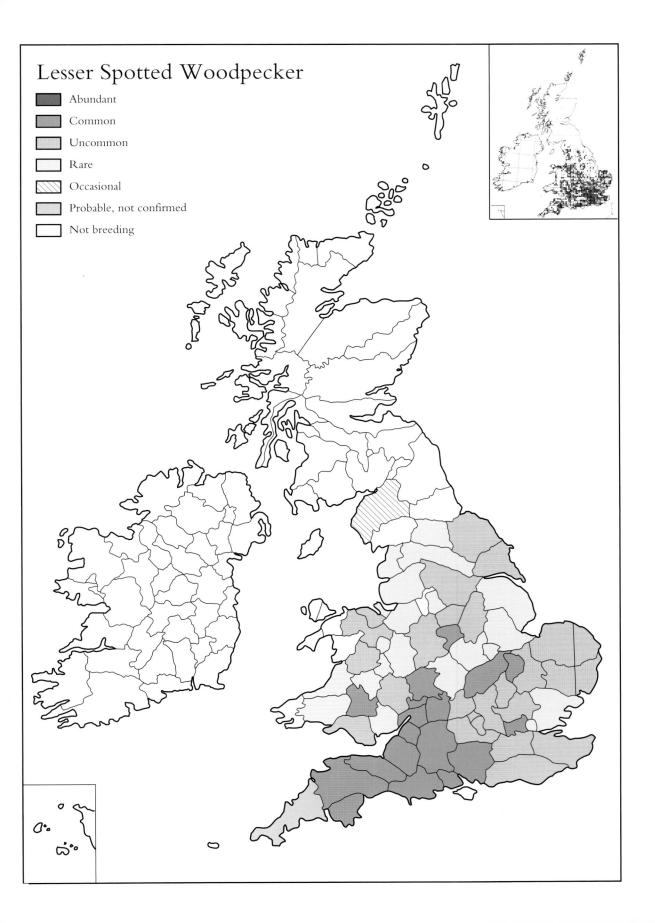

Lesser Spotted Woodpecker

- Abundant
- Common
- Uncommon
- Rare
- Occasional
- Probable, not confirmed
- Not breeding

Woodlark

Lullula arborea

The status of the Woodlark during the 19th century was complex and is difficult to unravel. It was clearly fluctuating substantially at that time and, as it was a species that was not generally well known to the layman or sportsman (it was often confused with the Tree Pipit), recognition of changes may have occurred very slowly. It is also possible that the accounts used during this survey have emphasised different stages of what may have been short-term fluctuations, although it is probable that these fluctuations were taking place against a background of an overall decrease in Woodlark numbers and distribution after the 1850s. Nevertheless the information published suggests that some counties were colonised during this period.

Analysis of the data published by More (1865) indicates that the Woodlark was common in Wales and in England north to the S Pennines and he stated that it bred less commonly in Essex, Yorkshire, Lancashire and Westmorland. The Woodlark was recorded as absent in Lincolnshire and some counties of S Wales, although More had few correspondents in this latter area.

By the end of the 19th century the Woodlark bred in its greatest numbers south of a line drawn between the Severn and Thames estuaries, along the lower Teme, Avon, Severn and Wye valleys, and in Norfolk and Suffolk. It was not common in any county but on warm, sheltered hillsides it was sometimes said to have bred in some numbers, for example in Devonshire and W Kent. The high price obtained by bird catchers for males in good song led to the extermination of the species in several places in SW England (D'Urban and Mathew 1892). Outwith these areas it bred occasionally or regularly but in small numbers and had withdrawn from some counties of E England. In Essex, it appears to have died out soon after 1840. In contrast, however, it was recorded breeding on the heaths of NW Lincolnshire around the turn of the 19th century and, from the 1880s, it evidently bred in Glamorgan.

Although it had been recorded breeding in several widely spaced Irish localities in the 19th century, it bred in Dublin only into the 1850s and in Down was absent after 1874. The last nest found in Ireland was in 1894 in Wicklow.

The decrease continued into the early 20th century but the 1920s saw a turning point and numbers began to increase, particularly in SE England but also in some western counties such as Somerset and Brecon. During the 1940s the increasing population began to expand its range, recolonising Yorkshire in 1945 after an absence of 40 years, becoming particularly numerous in Nottinghamshire in the same year and spreading into new areas of Lincolnshire from about 1946. Woodlark numbers peaked in about 1951, remained stable for a few years but then declined again from 1954. The fall accelerated from about 1960 and, following the severe winter of 1962, plummeted to the point that only 100 occupied territories were known throughout the entire country (Parslow 1973). The breeding range contracted correspondingly to the point that by the *88–91 Atlas* survey the population had become concentrated in only five areas: SW England, Dorset and S Hampshire, the Surrey/Hampshire border, Breckland and the Suffolk coast.

Although climate changes may be responsible for some of the fluctuations, habitat losses and changes (such as the loss of areas with short grass/bare soil that has taken place with the reduction in grazing pressure on much of the remaining heathland) have caused the recent decreases (Gibbons *et al.* 1993; R. Fuller in litt.). There is an intriguing suggestion that the breeding habitat preference of the Woodlark has altered since the 19th century. In counties from Devonshire to Kent it was considered to breed primarily in the vicinity of woodland, copses and plantations, from which it gained its common name (Smith 1887, Mansell-Pleydell 1888, D'Urban and Mathew 1892, Kelsall and Munn 1905, Ticehurst 1909) but modern ornithologists find that the only 'woods' it is associated with are young (less than five years old) conifer plantations (R. Fuller in litt.).

Number of counties in which recorded:

Period	Probable breeding		Confirmed breeding		Combined		
	Br	Ir	Br	Ir	Br	Ir	Both
1875–1900	3	1	58	2	61	3	64
1968–1972	7	0	21	0	28	0	28
			change		−33	−3	−36
					−54%	−100%	−56%

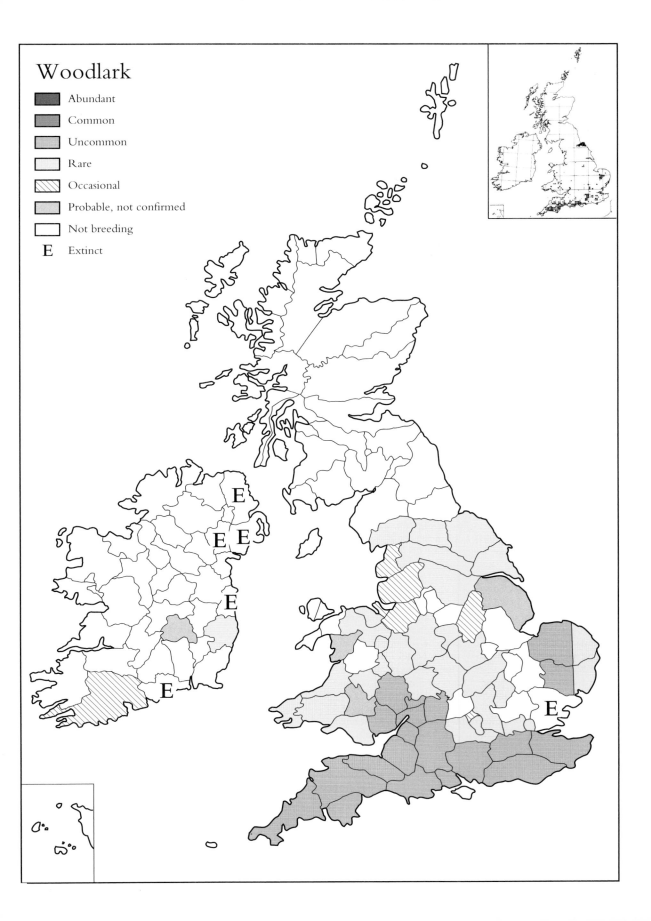

Woodlark

- ■ Abundant
- ■ Common
- ■ Uncommon
- □ Rare
- ▨ Occasional
- ▦ Probable, not confirmed
- □ Not breeding
- **E** Extinct

Skylark

Alauda arvensis

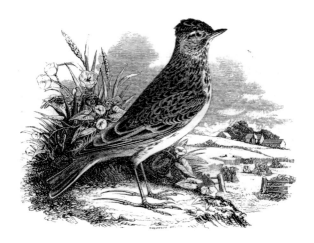

The Skylark bred widely and commonly in Britain and Ireland at the end of the 19th century. It bred on most of the Irish off-shore islands, even the exposed Blaskets, as it did in the Scottish Inner Hebrides, and only a few of the most remote islands did not sustain breeding pairs. The Skylark was not widespread in the uplands, many areas of moor and hill being devoid of the species, especially over much of Scotland north of the Forth and Clyde valleys. It was common in the Scottish lowlands up to the 1860s and 1870s but as the 19th century drew to a close changes in agricultural practices, involving the decline of arable farming and the increase of livestock on the land, served to destroy Skylark breeding habitat there. It is clear that in other areas of Britain, Skylarks were breeding freely on arable land, the transition from natural pastures and grasslands having been accomplished many years previously. In Scotland this change of land use was still developing throughout the Highlands and, as traditional Skylark breeding habitat was ploughed, contemporary writers saw decreases in the species' populations. In addition, in Scotland, it was said that the new practice of turning sheep and cattle out to grass earlier in the season as stock rearing intensified churned up otherwise suitable grassland (Harvie-Brown and Buckley 1895, Harvie-Brown 1906).

The Skylark was also subject to other pressures. In the early years of the 19th century the male was a very popular cage bird and many were taken in the winter for sale in the larger cities of Britain, France, Italy and, especially, Germany. They fetched high prices alive, but the major markets for captured Skylarks were those that sold birds for food. The numbers taken were astonishing. Around 400,000 were said to have been sold in 1854 in the London markets alone, on some days single deliveries of 20,000 to 30,000 Skylarks were received there (Smith 1887), and at the dinner that was held to celebrate the opening of the Forth railway bridge in 1890, a pie of 300 larks was served (Harvie-Brown and Buckley 1892). These British winter larks were caught in drag nets throughout, especially, the S England downlands. This practice had more or less ceased by the end of the 19th century, but it was not until the 1940s that Skylarks started to breed again in any numbers in the Highlands (Baxter and Rintoul 1953, Parslow 1973).

Other than this, little widespread change in numbers appears to have taken place in Britain through the 20th century until recent times, although changes in availability of preferred breeding habitats following local agriculture changes have led to local fluctuations. A decline was noted in Ireland during the 1960s (Ruttledge 1966) but was not evident later (Hutchinson 1989). However, between 1980 and 1991 the British population on farmland has halved (Marchant *et al.* 1990), with similar declines over much of W Europe (e.g. Hustings 1988). The causes are likely to be complex, but probably reflect a number of aspects of agricultural intensification. For example, population densities and breeding success are known to be especially high in young grass leys (O'Connor and Shrubb 1986), but the area of leys has been declining for 25 years as mixed farming has been superseded by farms specialising in either arable production or stock rearing on long-term leys. Furthermore, although Skylarks can nest successfully in cereals and other arable crops, the autumn-sown cereal varieties that have replaced spring-grown crops and now dominate arable landscapes may often grow too tall and dense for Skylarks to use for nesting (Schlapfer 1988, Wilson and Browne 1993). The trend towards early sowing has also reduced the availability of overwinter stubbles which provide important seed food resources for Skylarks during winter (Green 1978). Despite the recent population declines, there is as yet little evidence of any distributional change (Gibbons *et al.* 1993).

Number of counties in which recorded:

Period	Probable breeding		Confirmed breeding		Combined		
	Br	Ir	Br	Ir	Br	Ir	Both
1875–1900	0	0	108	34	108	34	142
1968–1972	0	0	108	34	108	34	142
			change		0	0	0

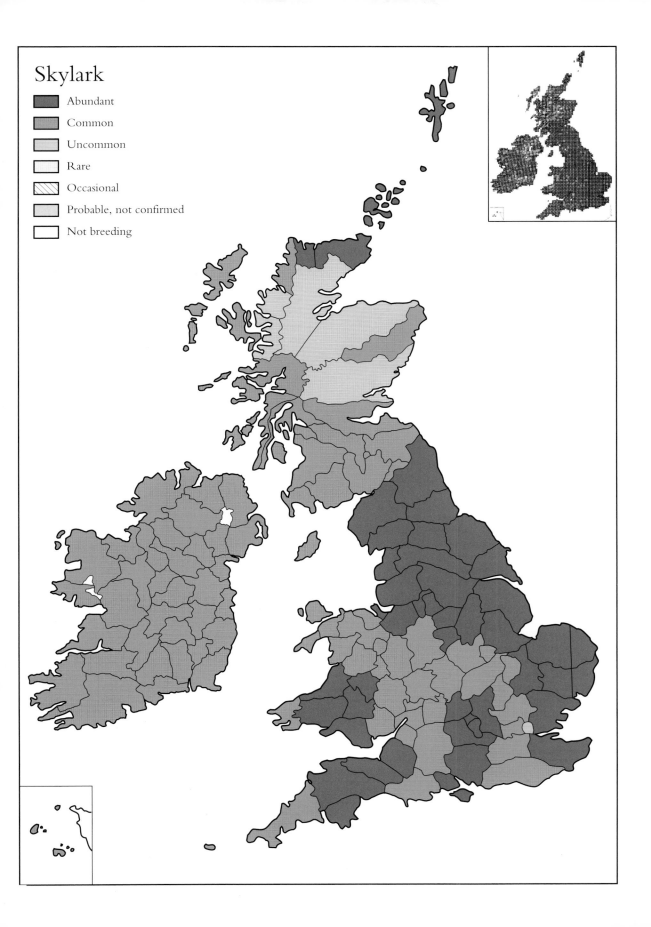

Skylark

- ■ Abundant
- ▨ Common
- ▨ Uncommon
- □ Rare
- ▨ Occasional
- ▨ Probable, not confirmed
- □ Not breeding

Sand Martin
(Bank Martin)

Riparia riparia

The Sand Martin was absent only from some of the off-shore islands of Britain and Ireland during the last quarter of the 19th century. Its distribution was considered to be largely restricted by the availability of nesting sites, soft banks in the vicinity of water being generally required. Because this usually meant the banks of lowland rivers and sandy cliffs, Sand Martins were generally described as breeding locally. Other nesting sites were recorded, however. For example, the low, earthy sea-cliffs of the W coast of Wales were used, commonly in places, and in other areas, notably Orkney, Sand Martins bred amongst rabbit burrows where the sandy soil was exposed. In Ireland, the faces of exposed peat banks were often used. The expansion of road and rail building at this time opened up new quarries and gravel-pits and thus provided suitable nesting banks; new railway cuttings were also used in some places.

Some writers had noted the variability in numbers of Sand Martins arriving in the spring, but a population crash on the scale that happened in recent years in the 20th century had not been recorded in the previous century. There were local decreases, particularly in Orkney, however,

which were blamed on the increase of the brown rat. No widespread change in distribution appears to have taken place throughout the 19th century; earlier writers described the population as distributed widely over the whole of Britain and Ireland although in Shetland only one instance of breeding had been recorded, this from near Lerwick in 1887. In the first quarter of the 20th century the Sand Martin was described in similar terms, attention only being drawn to its apparent scarcity in the extreme north of Scotland (although in the absence of modern censusing techniques it is difficult to determine any changes in the species' status). No further breeding had been recorded from the Outer Hebrides, Shetland or Orkney.

Later 20th century writers suspected a slow decline in numbers of Sand Martins in Britain and Ireland but the evidence for this does not appear to be definite (Alexander and Lack 1944, Parslow 1973). First mentioned at the end of the 19th century (Aplin 1889, Ticehurst 1909), the move to nesting in man-made habitats accelerated through the middle and later parts of the 20th century and, by the 1960s, the great majority of the species nested in sand and gravel pits. In central and E England the considerable growth in the number of gravel pits since the end of the 1939–45 war led to growth in Sand Martin numbers in those areas. Conversely, the numbers nesting in natural sites have declined, particularly so in areas of Scotland, the Lake District and Cornwall. In retrospect, the net result of these changes in nest site preference probably did not affect the total size of the Sand Martin population in Britain and Ireland up to the late 1960s.

The *68–72 Atlas* noted the effects of the first recorded crash to occur in the Sand Martin population. This took place at the same time as that of the Whitethroat between the breeding seasons of 1968 and 1969. The crash was attributed to the same cause; the failure of the rains in the Sahel region of West Africa caused massive mortality in the Sand Martin's wintering area. Early estimates of the losses suggested that three quarters of the breeding population in Britain and Ireland had been wiped out and this was confirmed later when it was calculated that a pre-1968 population of between 250,000 and 500,000 had fallen to between 40,000 and 160,000 by the early 1970s (Marchant *et al.* 1990). The number breeding in 1985, following the 1983/4 crash, was probably even smaller. This crash was attributed to the same winter drought effects, but since 1985 the numbers of Sand Martins in Britain and Ireland have recovered to the point where the *88–91 Atlas* estimated a maximum total of 400,000 nests. The losses following the two crashes appear to be fairly evenly distributed throughout Britain and Ireland, although locally, for instance in central England and parts of S Ireland, the losses were more severe.

Number of counties in which recorded:

Period	Probable breeding		Confirmed breeding		Combined		
	Br	Ir	Br	Ir	Br	Ir	Both
1875–1900	0	0	108	34	108	34	142
1968–1972	0	0	104	34	104	34	138
	change				−4	0	−4
					−4%		−3%

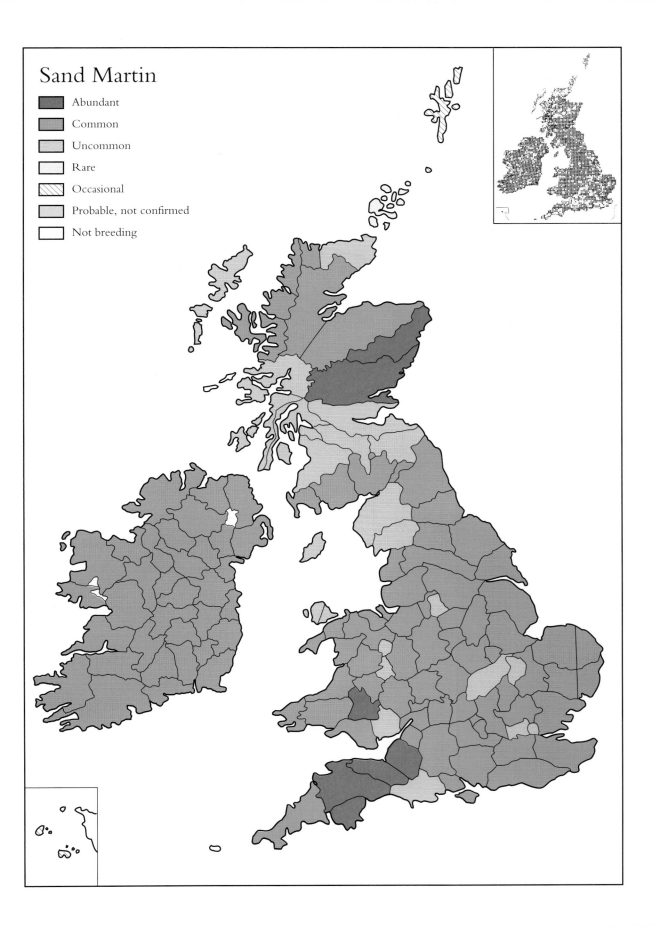

Sand Martin

- Abundant
- Common
- Uncommon
- Rare
- Occasional
- Probable, not confirmed
- Not breeding

Swallow (Chimney Swallow)

Hirundo rustica

The Swallow was as familiar and popular in the 19th century as it is today. Its close association with people has a very long history and there are a number of references to the species' use of man-made structures for nest sites in Roman and Greek literature. The transition from natural to artificial sites is so complete and occurred so long ago that it is now very rarely that natural nest sites are found. Turner and Rose (1989) noted a few examples of natural nesting sites: nests have been found in caves, crevices in cliffs, holes in banks and, perhaps, also in hollow trees. It has been speculated that the Swallow had a much more local and restricted range in the past before human structures were available for nesting sites, only finding natural sites around coasts and in upland areas. Some of the early 19th century literature may help in identifying the original nesting preferences of the Swallow and thus help understand its historical range.

The Swallow's commonly used name at the time was the Chimney Swallow. Yarrell (1837–43), in describing nest sites, stated that the most frequently used location was 'a few feet down an unused chimney, the bird taking advantage of any angle or depression to obtain support for the intended structure'. Moreover, he recorded other artificial sites and, specifically, in N England, mine shafts or old

wells were habitually used. Other artificial sites that are more familiar today were noted but, apparently, were used by Swallows far less frequently than those mentioned above. The practice of nesting in chimneys and mine shafts appears to have declined somewhat towards the end of the 19th century as writers then noted chimney nests as an occasional and local habit and occurring only in old houses. Presumably the modern, narrower design of chimneys did not allow access or did not supply suitable ledges. Is it possible, then, that a commonly used nest site in the past, before humans provided an alternative, and before humans cut down the forests, was the interior of hollow trees? Certainly the chimneys, mine shafts and wells used would emulate an old hollow tree. Is it possible, therefore, that the distribution of the Swallow may have been widespread in the days of extensive forest cover more than is generally supposed today?

There is little evidence to suggest that Swallow numbers have changed substantially throughout the 19th and 20th centuries. Local fluctuations have taken place such as in NW Scotland. There are decreases in some English counties during the 1950s and 1960s and increases in W Ireland in the second half of the 20th century. Where decreases have been noted they were usually linked with agricultural changes, modernisation of farm buildings that led to no access to Swallows or fewer nesting ledges and improved farmyard hygiene, and perhaps the decline of the horse, led to less aerial insect prey. Although, as stated, there is little evidence in support, it seems possible that urbanisation, generally replacing farmland, would have virtually eliminated pairs in this habitat as Swallows do not breed in urban sites. It is likely, too, that the change from mixed farming, with its livestock and consequent airborne insect population, to arable farming that took place up to the 1870s and again during, and following, the 1939–45 war, has caused a decline in Swallow breeding density (D. Bryant in litt).

The *68–72 Atlas* recorded regular breeding in the Outer Hebrides where it had been sporadic in the past. It also showed the uniform distribution across Ireland that would have been unfamiliar to the 19th century naturalists. Otherwise little further change appears to have occurred since the end of the 19th century. The *88–91 Atlas* revealed a few local changes when compared with the earlier Atlas. Breeding has certainly increased in the Western and Northern Isles of Scotland whilst a gap has opened up in the Swallow's distribution in the upland Nevis range. CBC declines during the 1980s may be linked to increased wintering range mortality (Marchant *et al.* 1990) during periods of drought.

Number of counties in which recorded:

Period	Probable breeding		Confirmed breeding		Combined		
	Br	Ir	Br	Ir	Br	Ir	Both
1875–1900	0	0	106	34	106	34	140
1968–1972	1	0	107	34	108	34	142
		change			2	0	2
					2%		1%

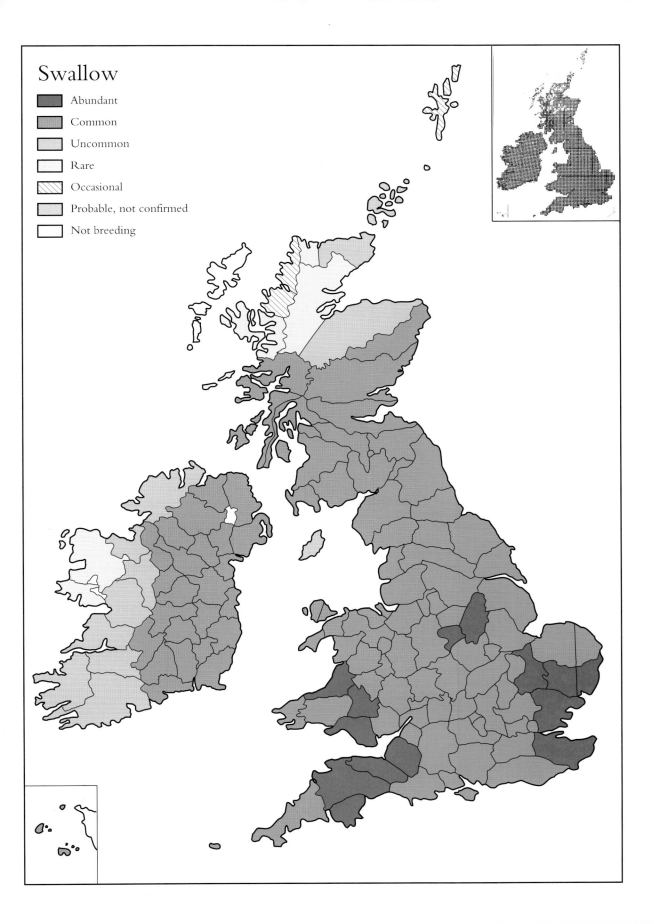

Swallow

- Abundant
- Common
- Uncommon
- Rare
- Occasional
- Probable, not confirmed
- Not breeding

House Martin
(The Martin)

Delichon urbica

The House Martin's habit of nesting on man-made edifices developed from its ancestral nesting habitat of cliffs and caves, both coastal and inland (Clark and McNeil 1980). Although often noted on natural features, by the 19th century the vast majority of nests were found on artificial structures and it can be surmised that this habit facilitated a much more widespread breeding distribution than would have existed prehistorically (Marchant *et al.* 1990). In the 19th century it was often noted as a bird of the towns and villages, in contrast to the Swallow which was considered to be typical of more isolated dwellings. Urbanisation during the past few hundred years may also have aided more widespread nesting, especially in the suburbs although the heavily polluted inner cities may well have been sparsely populated by House Martins (D. Bryant in litt). In some parts of Scotland it was said that the building of many new farmhouses in the Highlands was providing new nesting sites (Harvie-Brown and Buckley 1892). The now well known feature of the House Martin's biology for numbers to wane and increase locally, and for traditional colonies to be abandoned periodically, was noted in a number of areas but not generally understood.

One commonly proposed explanation for the decline of House Martins blamed the House Sparrow (for instance, Mitchell 1892). The House Sparrow increased dramatically during the 18th and 19th centuries, especially in the vicinity of human habitation, and increasing numbers were seen to usurp House Martins from their nests. A vitriolic paper on the 'injurious nature' of Sparrows published in the *Journal of the Proceedings of the Essex Field Club* gave an account of the results of an attempt to eradicate all House Sparrows from the vicinity of an Essex country house (quoted in Christy 1890). It considered that a huge increase in the numbers of House Martins nesting on the house was related to the decline of the sparrows. At the start of the campaign in 1870 the house held seven martins' nests, by 1877 there were 110 and the maximum number reached was 130 during the 1880s apparently in inverse proportion to the number of sparrows around the house (Christy 1890).

Other reasons proposed to explain decreasing numbers included the sanitising of towns and villages (improved sewerage disposal, new metal roads and the decline of the horse on the streets) which probably reduced the number of airborne insect prey and the amount of nesting material available, and agricultural changes that increased the amount of land under crops and hence reduced the number of insects that gather around farm livestock (Rintoul and Baxter 1935). The House Martin was said to have become extinct in many manufacturing districts and large towns because of the decline in insects caused by aerial pollution (Nelson *et al.* 1907). It has been suggested that fluctuations in the number of cliff and cave nesting colonies might fall and rise with the occurrence of cold and warm climatic periods (Clark and McNeil 1980) and, especially in areas of sparse human habitation, that colonies may shift from natural to artificial nesting sites periodically (Thom 1986). Thus the decrease noted in the number and size of maritime cliff colonies in Scotland at the end of the 19th century perhaps did not reflect an overall, long-term diminution in House Martin numbers but rather was part of a natural cycle.

A number of studies during the 20th century have identified declines and increases in numbers of House Martins. Some of them had clear attributable causes, for example the increases that occurred in the larger cities following the Clean Air Act of 1956, but most were local changes that demonstrate the natural mobility of the House Martin nesting population (Marchant *et al.* 1990).

Number of counties in which recorded:

Period	Probable breeding		Confirmed breeding		Combined		
	Br	Ir	Br	Ir	Br	Ir	Both
1875–1900	0	0	103	34	103	34	137
1968–1972	1	0	106	34	107	34	141
			change		4	0	4
					4%		3%

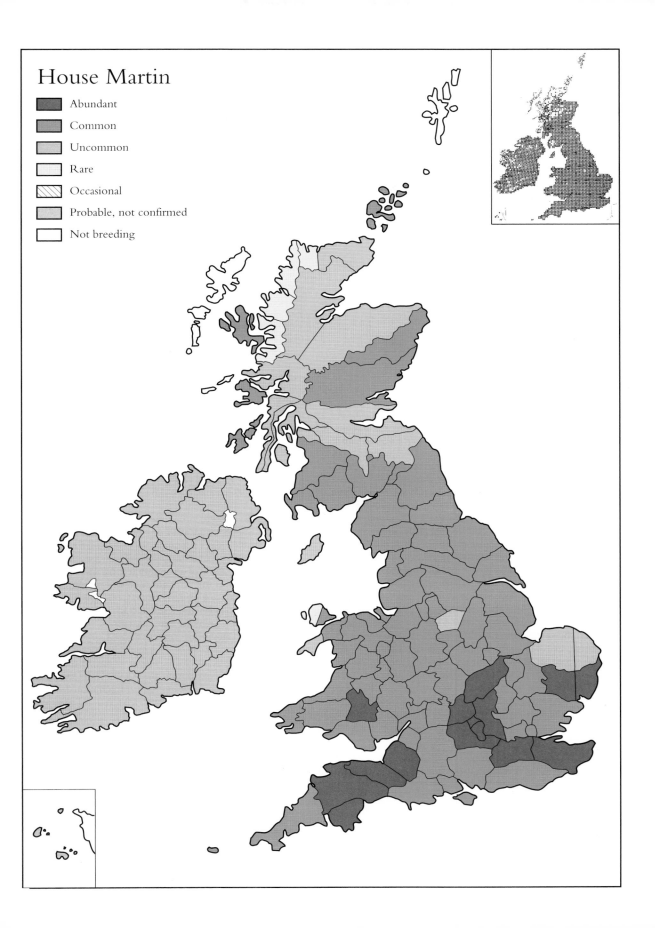

House Martin

- Abundant
- Common
- Uncommon
- Rare
- Occasional
- Probable, not confirmed
- Not breeding

Tree Pipit

Anthus trivialis

In the 19th century the Tree Pipit was a common bird over much of England, Wales and S Scotland but was uncommon in parts of E, SW and, especially, NW England and E Scotland, whilst over much of W Scotland it bred very locally. Only one nest had been found in the Isle of Man, in 1890, and the Tree Pipit was absent from the Hebrides, the Northern Isles and Ireland. Indeed, in Ireland, there existed only four old records of Tree Pipit observations and none had ever been collected there.

The history of the species is especially interesting in Scotland. Early 19th century evidence of breeding there was conflicting. Yarrell (1837–43) made no mention of the Tree Pipit breeding any further north than Northumberland but, by the time Morris (1851–57) wrote his account of British birds, it had been recorded breeding in East Lothian. From around 1860 records in S Scotland became far more frequent and in the central Highlands and E Scotland, by the mid 1860s, breeding was being recorded with increasing frequency. By around 1870 the Tree Pipit was being recorded as common in Scotland south of the Forth/Clyde valley and breeding regularly in many areas north of that. The assumption is that an increase, if not an expansion of range, had taken place in Scotland from the middle of the 19th century onwards, if the contemporary

records can be taken at face value. Care must be taken, however, to understand the confusion that existed about this species amongst non-naturalists. All three species of breeding pipits in Britain were known familiarly by the name 'titlark', and occasionally the Tree Pipit by the name 'wood lark'. Clearly, most people did not distinguish between the species, although naturalists knew quite clearly the features that differentiated, especially, the Meadow Pipit and Tree Pipit. Over much of England there were many naturalists able, and keen, to determine the avifauna of their own area and to substantiate their local correspondents' records but in Scotland, many of the early records were received from local people or visiting sportsmen, and so are less reliable. This situation changed somewhat after the middle of the century, however, when more naturalists took an interest in the Highlands.

In Wales, the Tree Pipit was considered rare up to the middle of the 19th century, but by the end of the century was considered common almost everywhere. Caution must be taken in considering this as a record of a range expansion in Wales because of the identification problem.

The population north of Inverness certainly increased from around 1900 to the point where the Tree Pipit was regarded as one of the commonest breeding birds in the mature birchwoods of Sutherland by the 1950s. After sporadic summer records, breeding was finally proven again on the Isle of Man in 1959 and has increased since. Elsewhere, at this time, numbers in England, and especially the southeast, appeared to have decreased generally, although newly established conifer plantations are attractive to this species.

The first proven breeding in Caithness occurred during the *68–72 Atlas* survey suggesting that the Tree Pipit population was still expanding slightly. Overall, at this time, distribution over England was remarkably similar to that at the end of the 19th century, although some local differences did exist.

The *88–91 Atlas* recorded the continuing decline in central and S England that had been suspected for many years. It is probable that a combination of many factors is involved in this decline, but especially important are likely to be the maturation of many conifer forests over the last 30 years or so and the intensification of farming leading to the loss of marginal rough ground. Comparison of the 1875–1900 map with the 1988–91 abundance map (Gibbons *et al.* 1993) suggests that the species has declined in numbers over much of central and SE Britain perhaps reflecting the prevalence of coppicing during the 19th century and its decline since (R. Fuller in litt.). Breeding was first proven in Ireland during the *88–91 Atlas* survey after being suspected since, at least, 1975 (Hutchinson 1989).

Number of counties in which recorded:

Period	Probable breeding		Confirmed breeding		Combined		
	Br	Ir	Br	Ir	Br	Ir	Both
1875–1900	0	0	101	0	101	0	101
1968–1972	2	0	101	0	103	0	103
			change		2	0	2
					2%		2%

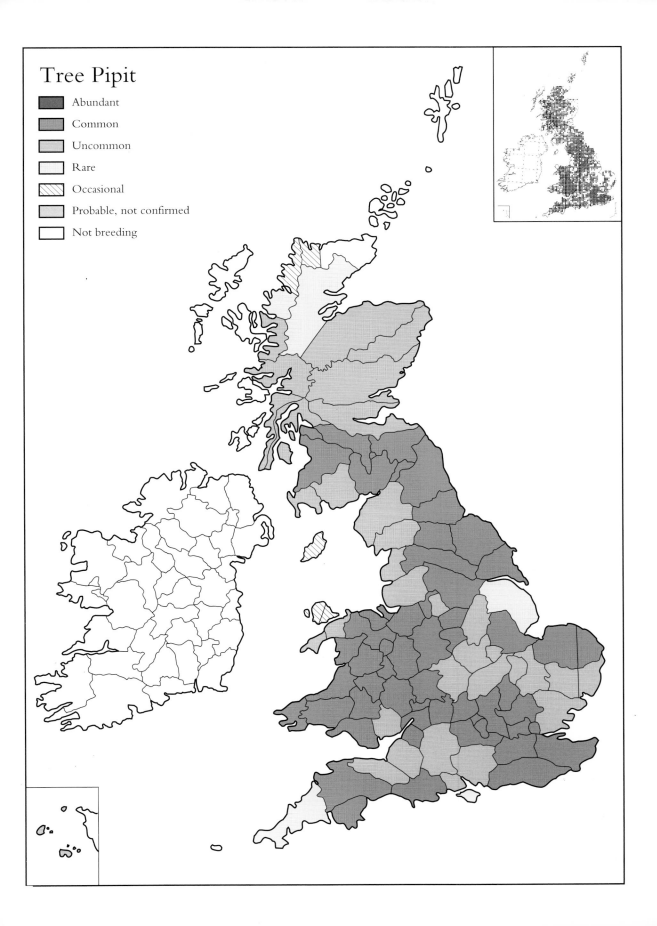

Tree Pipit

- Abundant
- Common
- Uncommon
- Rare
- Occasional
- Probable, not confirmed
- Not breeding

Meadow Pipit

Anthus pratensis

The Meadow Pipit bred throughout open habitats in Britain and Ireland in the 19th century. In many counties this pipit was considered to be the most ubiquitous bird of all upland areas and especially abundant in the west and north. Usually considered a bird of heaths and moors, it bred over a wide range of elevations and habitats, from coastal saltmarsh and saltings and reclaimed land to hill pasture and moorland, while even small patches of coarse, tussocky grasses in the corners of cultivated fields in the most intensively farmed areas provided sufficient food and safe nesting sites. In some counties of the S and E Midlands, however, it bred very locally and, although it was seen in the spring and summer, no nests were found in Northamptonshire or Huntingdonshire. In Bedfordshire, Hertfordshire, Buckinghamshire and S Oxfordshire breeding had been proven on very few occasions during the 19th century.

Through the first half of the 20th century little apparent change in numbers or distribution occurred but a decrease identified later in the century in S England may well have had its genesis in changes in agriculture in the lowlands, possibly from the end of the 19th century. The evidence for this decline is confusing, as is often the case when considering a common and widespread species. In the 1930s Ticehurst (1932) made no suggestion of a decrease in Suffolk but, later, loss of habitat for feeding and nesting was blamed for the decrease there (Parslow 1973). Numbers

breeding on the Isles of Scilly during the early 20th century remained stable; breeding was still taking place commonly there in the 1940s (Ryves and Quick 1946) but ceased before the 1960s (Parslow 1973). Degradation of lowland heath, and to a lesser degree moorland, has limited Meadow Pipit nesting possibilities (D. Glue in litt.). Also, the extent to which pressures such as parasitism by Cuckoos and severe winters have affected Meadow Pipit numbers is largely unknown (D. Glue in litt.). By the 1960s decreases were being noted in many counties of S England and the Midlands and a horseshoe shaped area of thin distribution was identified from S Lancashire into the Midlands over heavy clay soils (Sharrock 1976). In Scotland, at this time, local increases were associated with new conifer plantations (Thom 1986). A decline in 1985 and 1986 cannot be explained by agricultural changes alone as it was too steep and widespread; however, a combination of cold weather in the Meadow Pipit's wintering area and cool, wet summers in Britain in the 1980s may well have influenced the population (Gibbons *et al.* 1993).

Number of counties in which recorded:

Period	Probable breeding		Confirmed breeding		Combined		
	Br	Ir	Br	Ir	Br	Ir	Both
1875–1900	2	0	106	34	108	34	142
1968–1972	0	0	108	34	108	34	142
			change		0	0	0

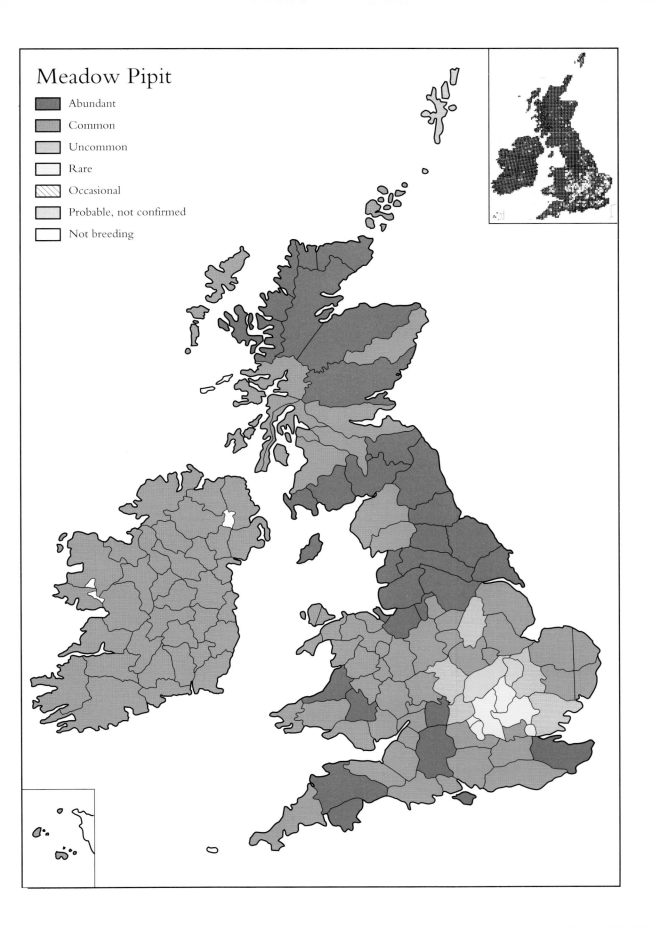

Meadow Pipit

- Abundant
- Common
- Uncommon
- Rare
- Occasional
- Probable, not confirmed
- Not breeding

Rock Pipit

Anthus petrosus

The coasts of Britain and Ireland are thought to be among some of the places least changed by human activities during the 19th century. The Rock Pipit population was stable where its preferred habitat of rocky shores and islands was abundant. It bred commonly in all those counties with a coastline (in Hampshire it was dismissed as 'common along the coast'), the exceptions being in the east coast counties stretching from Kent to Lincolnshire, though it had apparently withdrawn from the Sussex cliffs after 1891. The bias towards the western coasts was associated with the more rugged, rocky igneous and metamorphic rocks there as opposed to the low sedimentary material of other coastlines (D. Glue in litt.).

The Rock Pipit was first separated from the Meadow Pipit in 1789 and described by Latham in 1790 from a specimen collected on the N Kent marshes. It remained a common winter visitor to the county throughout the 19th century but breeding records were scant. Several times breeding was said to have taken place on the grass-covered sea-wall at Romney Marsh but Ticehurst (1909) did not feel that sufficient evidence was available to support the records, though More (1865) evidently did. The first record for Kent that Ticehurst felt able to admit was that by Walpole-Bond who followed an adult to a nest of young on the Dover cliffs in 1901. In Yorkshire the Rock Pipit's chief breeding places were the cliffs around Flamborough Head although it was recorded from elsewhere, including Spurn. The north shore of the Severn estuary provided few nesting places and Rock Pipits were considered rare there as a consequence. The same was true of the Wirral coast where breeding was recorded only on the rocky islets of Hilbre. The Rock Pipit was thinly scattered along the Lancashire coast, but was not frequent anywhere. It bred in small numbers on Walney Island. The main breeding place on the Lakeland coast was around St Bees Head, and along the southern shore of the Solway estuary a small marsh was the only breeding place. On the N Solway coast it bred on the saltings, particularly between Caerlaverock and Annan in Dumfriesshire.

A few local changes in distribution have been described during the 20th century but little evidence has been collected to quantify densities or the changes. Walpole-Bond (1903) recorded an unusual inland breeding attempt from the hills above Llanfaredd, Radnor in 1902; nests have also been found a kilometre or more inland on some Scottish islands (Williamson 1964). By the 1920s the Rock Pipit appears to have withdrawn from Dumfriesshire and there were no further records from the S Yorkshire coast. Between 1905 and 1963 there were only two breeding records from Hampshire (in 1951 and 1955). However, Rock Pipits returned to the Sussex cliffs in 1932 and numbers subsequently increased quickly (Parslow 1973). To what extent this seemingly resilient small passerine is prone to cold winter losses is unknown, though it is not thought to be great in the generally mild maritime environment of Britain, especially on the west coast (D. Glue in litt.). In the period between the *68–72* and *88–91 Atlases* there was some evidence of decreasing numbers, perhaps caused by the destruction of cliff-top feeding habitat and other inland summer foraging areas with the increasing intensification of agriculture. It is evident that the biggest losses have occurred throughout the S coasts of Britain, particularly in Sussex, Devonshire and Cornwall (Gibbons *et al.* 1993). The impact of marine pollution may not be so important for the Rock Pipit as it has been for numbers of large seabirds but disturbance and pollution at sea-side settlements may be a cause for their absence in places (D. Glue in litt.).

Number of counties in which recorded:

Period	Probable breeding		Confirmed breeding		Combined		
	Br	Ir	Br	Ir	Br	Ir	Both
1875–1900	0	0	57	17	57	17	74
1968–1972	1	0	49	19	50	19	69
			change		−7	2	−5
					−12%	−12%	−7%

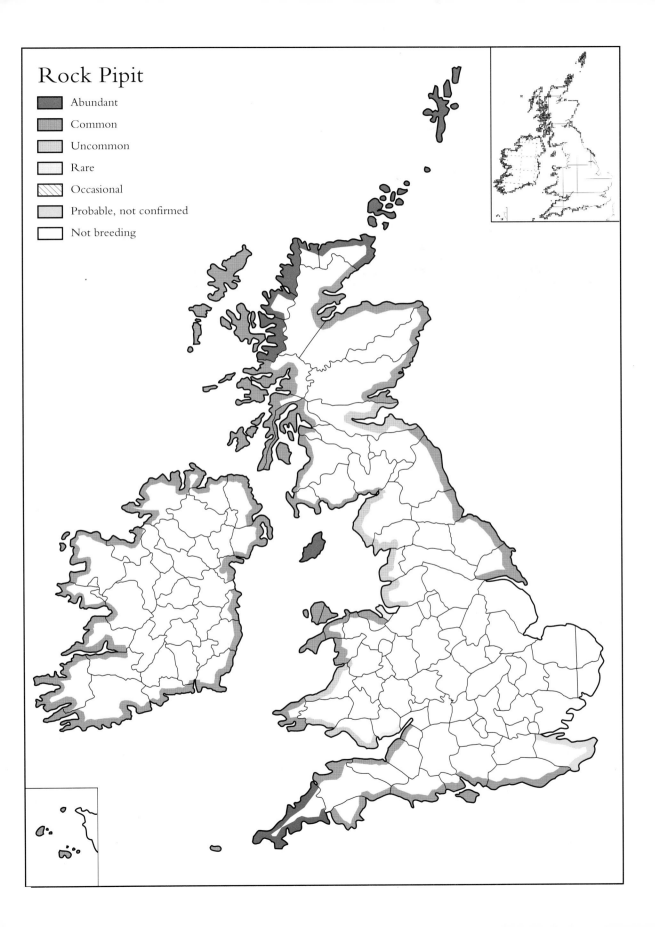

Rock Pipit

- **Abundant**
- **Common**
- **Uncommon**
- **Rare**
- **Occasional**
- **Probable, not confirmed**
- **Not breeding**

Yellow Wagtail (Ray's Wagtail)

Motacilla flava

After Gould separated the Yellow Wagtail *M. f. flavissima* from the Blue-headed Wagtail *M. f. flava* in 1832 much effort was made to determine accurately the breeding distribution of the former race in Britain. At the end of the 19th century it was considered to breed most commonly in S England, especially in the lower Severn and Avon valleys and on the east and southeast coasts. Further west and north it was rare. It had not been recorded breeding in Cornwall and bred very rarely in Devonshire; it was mainly a passage migrant. To the west of the Cambrian mountains it was extremely scarce although it bred locally (for instance along the Dyfi estuary and on Tregaron Bog on the Teifi in Cardiganshire). North of the Pennines it was a rare bird breeding locally in small numbers. The race *flavissima* had been known from Northumberland and Durham since it was first recognised, so too in Lakeland although there is some indication that numbers there fluctuated substantially through the second half of the 19th century. Thus, in the 1850s it was common locally in Cumberland but had evidently decreased by the end of the century.

In SW Scotland it was common in places (for instance in some parts of Ayrshire, Renfrewshire and Lanarkshire) but was very locally distributed. It was far less common in SE Scotland where few records exist of breeding; there are no records in Tweed. North of the Clyde/Forth river valleys breeding took place sporadically. There were few areas where breeding was sustained for any length of time, the lengths of coast in E Scotland, from the rivers Don to Newburgh and from Peterhead to Fraserburgh, all in Aberdeenshire, being notable exceptions. An exceptional outlying record is of two pairs that bred annually between 1896 and 1902 on Raasay, off Skye.

The distribution of breeding Yellow Wagtails in Ireland followed an interesting. The species was known only from two sites in Ireland, separated by about 200km (although in 1868 a nest with young was found on the west side of Dublin). These two colonies were fairly substantial and, at least during the 19th century, stable. The most extensive of the two was that around the Connaught loughs of Carra, Mask and Corrib on the borders of the counties of Galway and Mayo. The first Yellow Wagtail nest was found nearby by Lord Lilford on the Corrib above Galway in 1853 or 1854 and the species was subsequently found to breed along the complete length of that river and Lough Corrib. Breeding on Lough Carra was confined to the shores adjacent to Lough Mask. Ussher and Warren (1900) described the Yellow Wagtail breeding in tufts of coarse grass on the many small, rocky islands, and later ornithologists found it on the lake shores, but it did not frequent the pastures adjacent to the loughs. The second colony was around Lough Neagh in Ulster and Yellow Wagtails bred on the shores of Lough Neagh in counties Tyrone, Armagh, Antrim and Londonderry (but with no records of birds breeding in Down). The colony appeared divided, with pairs breeding commonly both along the Bann between Toome Bridge and Lough Beg on the Londonderry and Antrim border and also on the south shores of the lake in Armagh and Tyrone. Yellow Wagtails at this colony were not confined to the lakeside to the same extent as at the Connaught colony, as they had been seen foraging up to 3km inland in Armagh.

Both Irish colonies declined rapidly in the early 20th century, disappearing from the Connaught site during the 1920s and from Ulster in the 1940s. These extinctions are unexplained. Similarly, the Yellow Wagtail's range contracted in Britain at this time, particularly at its northern and western edges but also along the south coast counties. Since the 1939–45 war the decline has continued steadily (Parslow 1973, Sharrock 1976). Loss of breeding habitat, through drainage, the intensification of agriculture and the replacement of grasslands with cereals, appears to be the main cause of the declines (Gibbons *et al.* 1993).

Number of counties in which recorded:

Period	Probable breeding		Confirmed breeding		Combined		
	Br	Ir	Br	Ir	Br	Ir	Both
1875–1900	0	0	87	7	87	7	94
1968–1972	2	1	75	1	77	2	79
			change		−10	−5	−15
					−11%	−71%	−16%

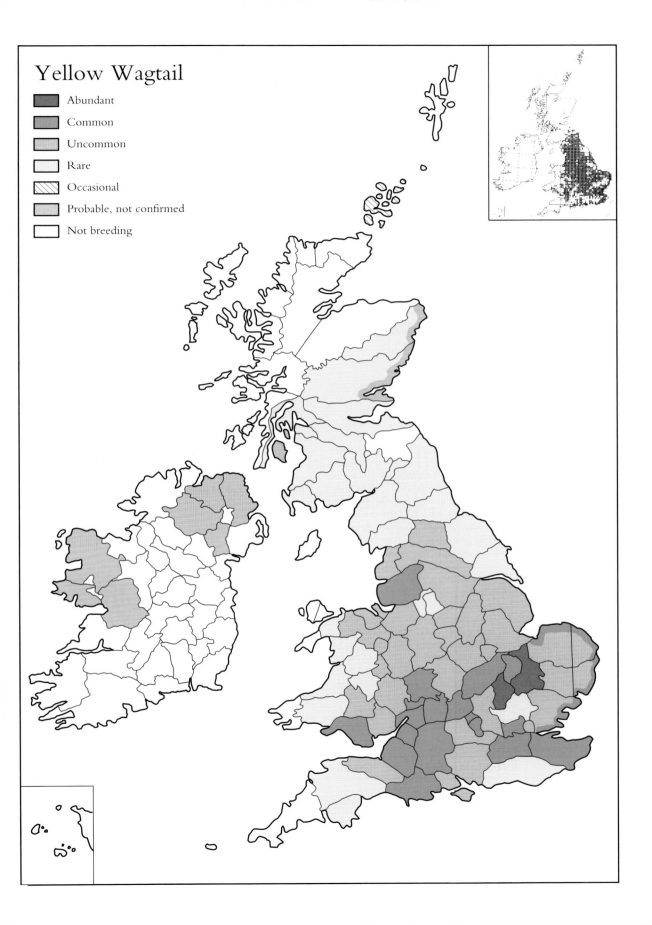

Yellow Wagtail

- Abundant
- Common
- Uncommon
- Rare
- Occasional
- Probable, not confirmed
- Not breeding

Grey Wagtail

Motacilla cinerea

The preferred breeding and feeding habitat of the Grey Wagtail is fast-flowing shallow watercourses with rocks, riffles and shingle, bordered by broadleaved trees (Ormerod and Tyler 1987). Such streams were reasonably stable habitats, only subject to local changes, at least until the end of the 19th century. Acidification of watercourses has little effect on the breeding abundance of the Grey Wagtail because it will take a wide range of insect prey, some of non-aquatic origin (Ormerod and Tyler 1987). This may mean that it may be able to cope with mildly polluted waters, a feature of many 19th century streams, and, indeed, even with water more grossly polluted. In Lancashire, note was made of the abundance of Grey and Pied Wagtails in the vicinity of towns and villages in the winter, especially where there were streams in which sewage flowed. These streams, it was asserted, were rich in insect life and, in addition, rarely froze (Mitchell 1885). Increasing numbers of artificial habitats and features have been created that are suitable for the Grey Wagtail such as millstreams, weirs, artificial waterfalls and canal locks, especially on the lowland streams and rivers; these features may have helped it to colonise some of these lowland areas.

At the end of the 19th century the Grey Wagtail bred widely over SW and N England, Wales, Scotland (but not in many of the Western Isles or Shetland) and Ireland. In the Midlands and S England it bred more sparsely and was evidently in the process of spreading into these areas. In Hertfordshire it had been first recorded breeding in 1879 but within ten years or so it was breeding commonly, albeit very locally. Although suspected for some years, breeding was not proven in Kent until 1885 and in Surrey it bred extremely irregularly, if ever, until about the same period. The spread, evident at this time, into S and E England was a continuation of an expansion in range that probably began sometime before the middle of the 19th century. Thus in the 1830s it was recorded breeding only in N England, Scotland and Ireland (Yarrell 1837–43). It was not known to breed in N Wales then (Eyton 1838–39), nor possibly anywhere in the Principality (Morris 1851–57), very occasional breeding had been recorded in Hampshire and Devonshire (Yarrell 1837–43). The expansion had occurred throughout Europe, with breeding in central Europe after about 1850; in the 20th century it continued northwards into NW Europe (Voous 1960 in Parslow 1973).

The expansion into SE England continued into the 20th century (breeding was first proven in Cambridgeshire in 1934) and breeding became more regular in those counties where previously it had been irregular. The increase in numbers and extension of range accelerated during the 1950s and breeding was recorded for the first time in Essex and Leicestershire in 1951 and in Nottinghamshire and Huntingdonshire in 1955. In several counties (for example Suffolk, Northamptonshire and Kent) the Grey Wagtail became well established after breeding erratically, and in others (for example Berkshire and Oxfordshire) it increased (Parslow 1973). The population suffered a set back following the hard winters of the early 1960s but recovery followed and numbers of the Grey Wagtail increased slowly until the middle of the 1970s when a further series of harsh winters then and in the 1980s cut back the population.

Number of counties in which recorded:

Period	Probable breeding		Confirmed breeding		Combined		
	Br	Ir	Br	Ir	Br	Ir	Both
1875–1900	0	0	88	34	88	34	122
1968–1972	3	0	97	34	100	34	134
			change		12	0	12
					14%		10%

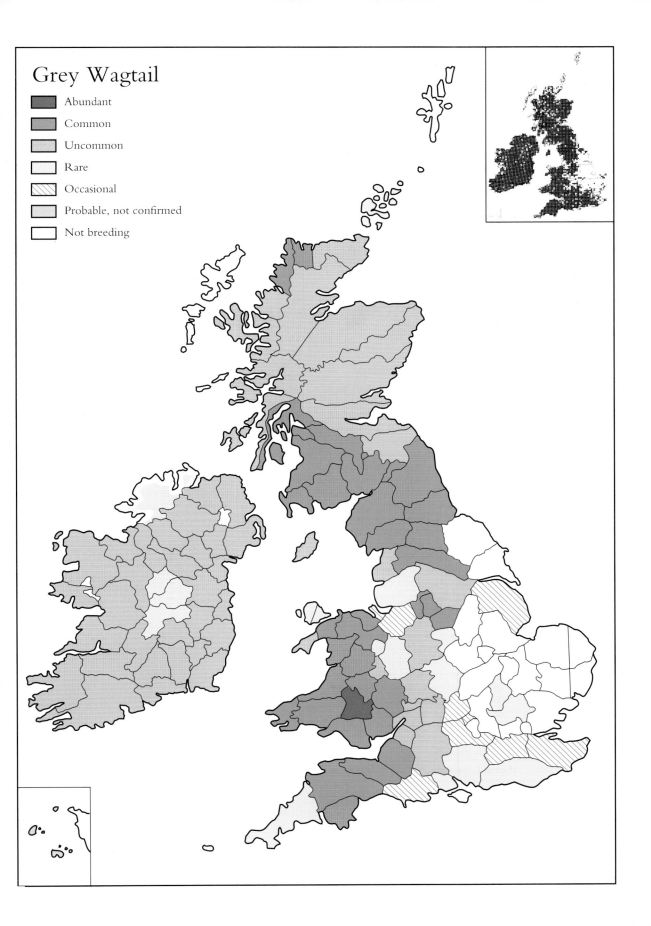

Grey Wagtail

- Abundant
- Common
- Uncommon
- Rare
- Occasional
- Probable, not confirmed
- Not breeding

Pied Wagtail

Motacilla alba

The Willy Wagtail was a common and familiar bird throughout Britain and Ireland in the 19th century. Over much of England south of the Pennines, Wales, lowland Scotland and Ireland it was common and widely distributed. The only part of Ireland where it was not very common was the extreme west in Connaught and the Aran Islands. In the lowlands of N England it was common and widespread but on the higher land it bred more locally. Its status north of the Great Glen was a little confused but suggested a decline. To take Sutherland as an example, prior to 1887 it was regarded as an abundant species both here and in Caithness (Harvie-Brown and Buckley 1887). By the 1890s no special mention was made of its status and it bred throughout the county, and in the N Moray region, in small numbers (Harvie-Brown and Buckley 1895). By the end of the century it was becoming rare in Sutherland with only one record of a pair possibly breeding in the north of the county (Harvie-Brown and Macpherson 1904). In Shetland the evidence for breeding was scant up to the end of the century, coming only from an undated record of eggs taken from near Scalloway and a nest and eggs collected from Clickhimin Loch in *ca* 1881 (Evans and Buckley 1899). Local decreases were reported throughout Scotland during the latter half of the 19th century, but were largely unexplained. The increasing 'sanitisation' of farms, towns and villages, through changes in farming practice, and the development of underground sewerage, will have resulted in local reductions in insect prey (Ticehurst 1909, Tomes 1901).

The race normally breeding in Britain and Ireland is the Pied Wagtail *M. a. yarelli* but during the 19th century there were many records of breeding of birds exhibiting characteristics of the continental White Wagtail *M. a. alba*. Most of these records came from S and E England. The most likely are as follows. Devonshire: bred for many years near Topham prior to 1890. Isle of Wight: a pair and their nest were collected *ca* 1865. Middlesex: a pair was present and possibly bred on the canal in Harrow in 1890. Kent: although no nest was found, several records exist of pairs seen in the breeding season from the 1840s onwards. Suffolk: about five records of *alba* X *alba* and *alba* X *yarelli* pairs were recorded nesting around the village of Tostock during the 1880s and 1890s. Interestingly, there were no records from Scotland.

The Pied Wagtail population decreased in Scotland in the first half of the 20th century (Parslow 1973) but at the same time pairs were recorded breeding for the first time in the Outer Hebrides. The Pied Wagtail first bred, on South Uist, in 1923 and then near Stornoway in 1932, and has bred there regularly since, the population slowly increasing. In Ireland it was said to have increased in numbers substantially from the 1920s, especially in the counties of the west coast and had become, by the 1960s, one of Ireland's commonest birds (Kennedy *et al.* 1954, Kennedy 1961, Ruttledge 1966). This is interesting as it was described as also very common there at the end of the 19th century (Ussher and Warren 1900), suggesting that the decrease in Scotland in the early 20th century may have occurred in parallel with the increase in Ireland. No further widespread changes have occurred up to the present date. Local, or temporary, declines have occurred following severe winters but, in contrast, there has been a spread and an increase in numbers in the Scottish Northern and Western Isles since the early 1970s (Thom 1986).

Number of counties in which recorded:

Period	Probable breeding		Confirmed breeding		Combined		
	Br	Ir	Br	Ir	Br	Ir	Both
1875–1900	0	0	105	34	105	34	139
1968–1972	0	0	108	34	108	34	142
			change		3	0	3
					3%		2%

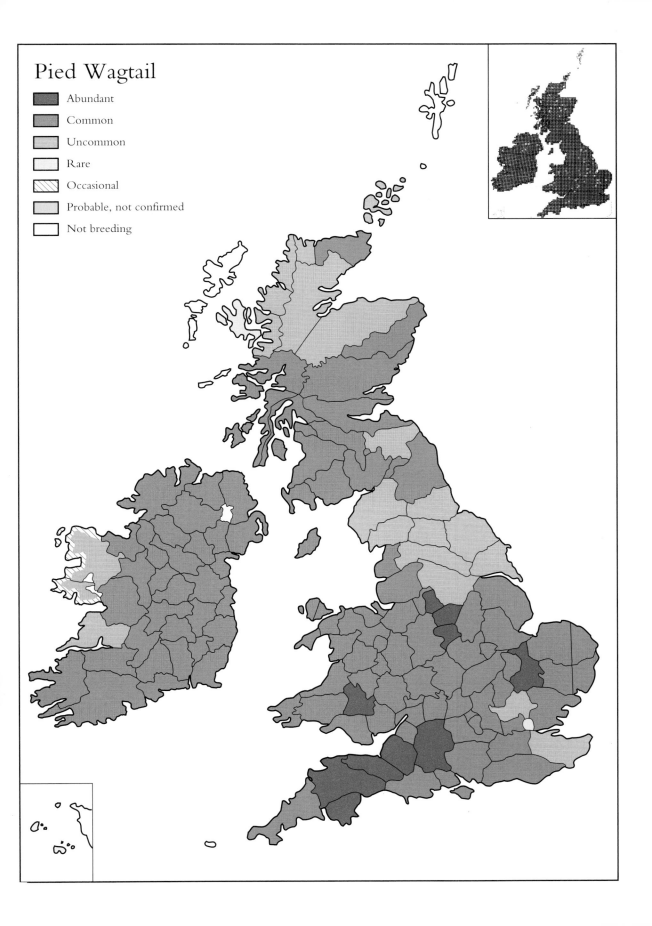

Pied Wagtail

- Abundant
- Common
- Uncommon
- Rare
- Occasional
- Probable, not confirmed
- Not breeding

Dipper

Cinclus cinclus

The Dipper was distributed throughout the uplands of Britain and Ireland during the 19th century. It was, however, decreasing locally, especially on the northern trout and salmon streams. It was suspected of eating fresh ova and young fish (later evidence shows that this is, indeed, the case although the impact on fish stocks is likely to be small, S. Tyler in litt.) and, hence, was persecuted by anglers. Evidently many streams in, especially, E and N Scotland had completely lost their Dippers; there is a record of 548 destroyed in three years in one Scottish district (Morris 1851–57). Elsewhere, declining numbers followed the pollution of the breeding streams and the consequent loss of pollution-sensitive invertebrates such as mayfly nymphs and caddis larvae upon which the Dipper feeds (Gibbons *et al.* 1993). This was particularly true of W Cornwall and parts of Devonshire where the streams had been polluted by tin mining activities. By inference, Dippers had also declined in the growing manufacturing districts of N England as a result of the river pollution there. A decline in the industrialised parts of S Wales, however, was not noted until later.

Elsewhere, an outlying breeding group of Dippers almost died out in Leicestershire during the second half of the 19th century. In the northwest of the county they were often seen during the 1840s and 1850s but by the 1880s they were only occasionally taken. There were records of sightings and of specimens taken in Oxfordshire through the 19th century. In 1876 at Claydon, in the north of the county, a nest and four eggs were found and the adults killed; in 1888 a pair was observed near Woodstock; and breeding was recorded at the mill at Mapledurham in 1899 in the southeast of the county.

The Dipper was recorded on very few off-shore islands, particularly outside Scotland. It was common on Mull and Rum, though less frequent on Eigg, and was included on a list of the birds of Jura.

In only a single county in Ireland were there no records of breeding Dippers. They did not breed in Longford and were considered scarce in Westmeath and Armagh but elsewhere were common and widespread. The Dipper was particularly mentioned as occurring down to sea-level in Ireland where ravines ran steeply to the coast. In Devonshire, too, nests had been recorded amongst rocks on the shore at Torquay.

Dippers favour steep upland streams for breeding (Tyler and Ormerod 1994) but will occur on streams at lower altitudes and with shallower gradients, particularly in the vicinity of weirs and mill races. The Dipper's habit of building nests on artificial structures (such as under bridges and in mill walls) may have been a recent development of the late 18th or early 19th century. Neither Bewick (1797–1804), Mudie (1834) nor Yarrell (1837–43) gave any examples of artificial breeding sites in their accounts, and examples seem to have been infrequent enough for Morris (1851–57) to mention specifically those that had come to his attention. Most of the writers of the late 19th century avifaunas, however, seemed familiar with the habit.

There had been no widespread change in either distribution or numbers of Dippers in Britain and Ireland up to the *68–72 Atlas*. Locally, however, numbers declined, for instance, as mentioned previously, in S Wales (although they have recovered on streams that have since been cleaned up). Orkney and the Isle of Man were briefly colonised but had been abandoned again by the 1950s. The *88–91 Atlas* revealed that the area in the centre of Ireland from which Dippers are absent may be increasing in extent and that losses were apparent from many areas of Britain, most noticeably on the eastern fringe of its Palearctic range in W and SW England. Many of the areas of sparse distribution, or where Dippers are absent, contain acidic watercourses and poor invertebrate and fish communities; some of the recent losses of Dippers from previously inhabited streams have been associated with increasing acidification of the water following the afforestation of their catchments (Ormerod and Tyler 1987).

Number of counties in which recorded:

Period	Probable breeding		Confirmed breeding		Combined		
	Br	Ir	Br	Ir	Br	Ir	Both
1875–1900	2	0	85	33	87	33	120
1968–1972	0	0	74	34	74	34	108
			change		−13	1	−12
					−15%	3%	−10%

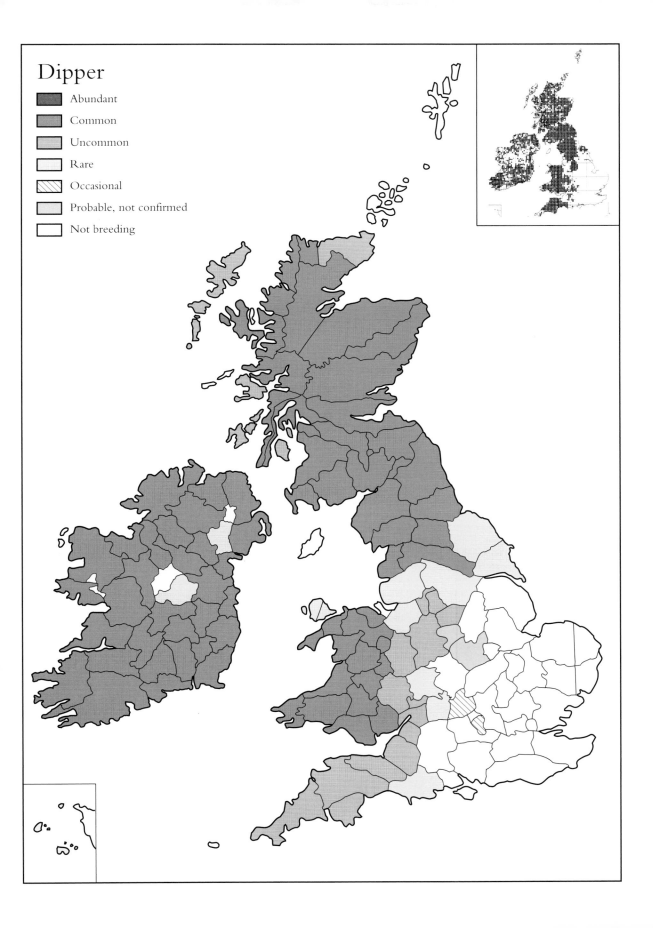

Dipper

- ■ Abundant
- ▨ Common
- ▨ Uncommon
- ▢ Rare
- ▨ Occasional
- ▨ Probable, not confirmed
- ▢ Not breeding

Wren

Troglodytes troglodytes

The Wren was commonly and widely distributed over the whole of Britain and Ireland in the 19th century. It was distributed universally from lowland homesteads and plantations to the most exposed mountain moorlands and sea cliffs. The degree of the Wren's ubiquity was beautifully described by Ussher and Warren (1900) when they wrote that it bred even on 'uninhabited island rocks, where its lively song relieves the awful solitudes'. It was recorded on all of the larger Scottish islands; the only significant exception was Tiree where it was only noted during the winter.

The geographical variant, the celebrated St Kilda Wren *T. t. hirtensis*, was first proposed in *The Zoologist* (Seebohm 1884) as a discrete species *T. hirtensis*. Ornithologists disagreed at the time as to the true specific status of the St Kilda Wren but, despite the confusion, the Victorian collectors immediately went to work attempting to add examples to their collections snared on their behalf by the islanders. The female collected by R. W. Chase in July 1886 was recorded by Harvie-Brown (1888) in the expectation that this would prove to be the last of its race collected from the main island of the group, such were the depredations waged upon the species following its separation from the mainland race. Although Harvie-Brown considered that the St Kilda Wren fared a little better on the

smaller islands of the group (for example on Dun), he was sufficiently concerned by the extent of the collecting to warn that by 1888 it had been almost exterminated. This subsequently proved not to be the case and his words may have stung the consciences of many of his colleagues for collection of skins rapidly diminished. Heathcote (1900), however, remarked that at that time the eggs of the St Kilda Wren still had considerable market value and that local islanders supplemented their meagre income by supplying clutches to collectors and dealers and the species was still decreasing in numbers.

In Shetland recognition of the distinct characters of the local Wrens encouraged Barrington, in a letter to Newton in the 1890s, to try to give them specific status, or to place them with the Faeroese and Icelandic populations, then recognised as a separate species, *T. borealis*. Newton rejected this idea but, later, the Shetland form was described by Hartert in 1910 as a distinct race *T. t. zetlandicus*. Perhaps we can thank Newton for the continuing existence of the darker and larger Shetland race! Two further races were described later, those of the Outer Hebrides and Fair Isle, *T. t. hebridensis*, 1924, and *T. t. fridariensis*, 1951, respectively.

Little change has occurred throughout the 19th and 20th centuries in the distribution of the Wren. The species, however, suffers huge losses in the coldest winters, often taking many years to recover its numbers. We can imagine that the cold winters of the 19th century (especially those of the first half and towards the end) would have had a significant effect on the numbers of Wrens at that time. Breeding was first recorded on Tiree in 1952 but did not occur during the *68–72 Atlas* survey. The Wren had, however, returned by the time of the *88–91 Atlas* survey.

Number of counties in which recorded:

Period	Probable breeding		Confirmed breeding		Combined		
	Br	Ir	Br	Ir	Br	Ir	Both
1875–1900	0	0	108	34	108	34	142
1968–1972	0	0	108	34	108	34	142
			change		0	0	0

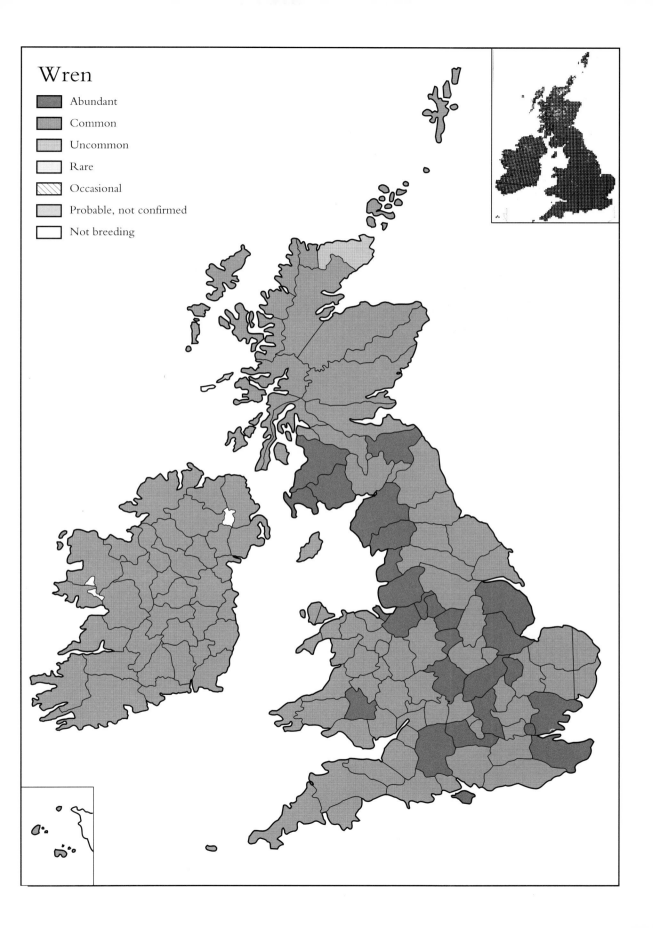

Wren

- Abundant
- Common
- Uncommon
- Rare
- Occasional
- Probable, not confirmed
- Not breeding

Dunnock
(Hedge Sparrow)

Prunella modularis

Harvie-Brown and Buckley (1892) described the status of the Dunnock in W Scotland thus, 'Abundant wherever man has settled, even in the smaller isles, and wherever there may be only a shepherd's house and garden, or, at most, one or two dwellings'. It was clearly less common in barer areas with little human population, and other general statements in the 19th century literature give the impression that much of the rest of upland Scotland was only thinly populated by Dunnocks. Following the interest in sheep farming in the Highlands, and the consequent notorious Clearances between 1782 and 1854, the human population in the uplands and moorlands of Scotland fell dramatically and it is likely that the Dunnock withdrew from some of these areas at this time. In contrast, however, in Ireland it was found commonly even in bleak, treeless areas and on some islands where other passerines were absent. A nest was even taken on the Tearaght, a precipitous rock on the outermost edge of the Blasket group off Kerry. Its date was not recorded by Ussher and Warren (1900) but it must have been during the second half of the 19th century.

There were very few early records of the Dunnock from the Outer Hebrides. Macgillivray (1837–52) did not mention it at all; however, by 1841 it had been recorded in the Glen of Rodel in Harris. More (1865) did not include the Outer Hebrides in the breeding distribution of the Dunnock but Gray (1871) wrote 'Well known on all the Hebrides, except the bleakest islands'. From that point it was recorded from widely spaced localities in Harris and Lewis and, apparently, slowly spread throughout the islands.

A Dunnock shot in Orkney in 1862 was considered to have been a notable record and More (1865) did not know of any breeding records; it seems probable then, if it bred here at all, it did so very occasionally up to the 1860s. In 1887 it was considered 'now more common' and, thenceforward, it was recorded breeding in a number of areas on Mainland.

Throughout the remainder of Britain and Ireland the Dunnock bred commonly and was widespread. It is an early coloniser of scrub and clearings, and prospered where coppice management of woodland encouraged vigorous growth of ground vegetation such as brambles, wild rose and other woody shrubs. Coppicing is an ancient activity and will have allowed the Dunnock to spread to newly opened parts of the dense forests of early Britain. This prepared it for an expansion into the newly created hedgerows (a linear form of coppice) resulting from the enclosure activities of the 18th and early 19th centuries. This was not the only human-induced change in the landscape of which the Dunnock took advantage. As noted above, it was associated with human habitation and throughout the 19th century it was noted that it moved into the yards, gutters and drains of towns and villages as hard weather approached and in the spring moved back to parks and gardens to nest (Mudie 1834, Yarrell 1837–43, Morris 1851–57). The association with humans is likely to have had a long history. The landscape that humans created apparently suited the Dunnock and it is likely that its distribution during the 19th century was the most complete that the population had reached in its history in Britain.

Up to the 1939–45 war there were no recorded changes in the Dunnock's numbers or distribution. After that point it appears to have increased in some areas, particularly in E and SE England. These increases were particularly noted in and around towns (a marked increase was noted in the London parks from the early 1950s) and may have been a result of the growth and proliferation of ornamental suburban gardens (Parslow 1973). CBC data reveal a slow decline in numbers from the early 1970s, which remains largely unexplained (Marchant *et al.* 1990).

Number of counties in which recorded:

Period	Probable breeding		Confirmed breeding		Combined		
	Br	Ir	Br	Ir	Br	Ir	Both
1875–1900	0	0	107	34	107	34	141
1968–1972	0	0	107	34	107	34	141
			change		0	0	0

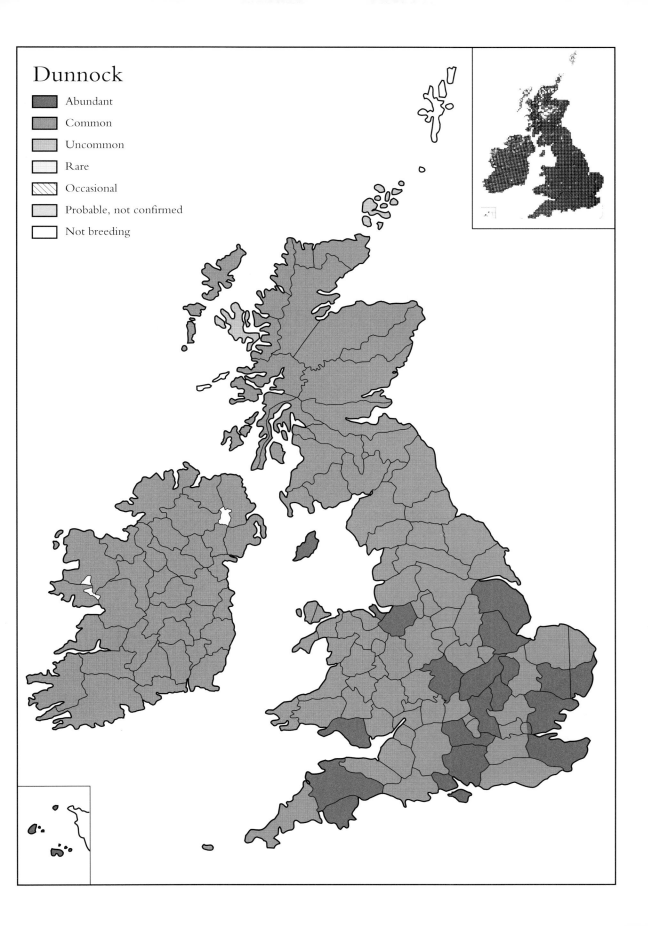

Dunnock

- Abundant
- Common
- Uncommon
- Rare
- Occasional
- Probable, not confirmed
- Not breeding

Robin (Redbreast)

Erithacus rubecula

The Robin was a widespread species during the 19th century. It bred on most marine islands except the Shetlands, although it occurred there on passage, most often in autumn, and as a winter visitor, and was apparently increasing as such towards the end of the century. Similarly, in Orkney it was said to be increasing overall through the second half of the 19th century (both on passage and sparingly as a breeding species), although the population had been devastated by a severe frost in around 1878 and took some years to recover—it was still scarce ten years later. It may have increased substantially in the Outer Hebrides. In around 1840 it was regarded as an occasional breeder and then only in the Glen of Rodel, the only wood of any size in the islands at the time. By 1865 Robins were found breeding in the wood near Stornoway; by 1871, and thereafter, it apparently bred in many other localities. It occurred throughout the year on the smaller wooded Scottish islands but was absent from those that were bare, for instance Hysgeir off Canna and Tiree; it was recorded on this latter island only during winter. In Ireland it bred commonly throughout the country and was absent or rare only in the bleakest districts and on some of the barest islands.

The Robin, through both superstition and familiarity, was little molested. This respect weakened somewhat during the height of the epicures' reign after the middle of the century. The Robin was esteemed for the table and some local decreases in numbers occurred as a result. The newspapers of the early 1890s that announced, firstly, 'wings will be all the rage' and then that whole birds would be worn on the head drove the fashion trade of the time to organise the slaughter of many small British and foreign bird species to satisfy the resultant demand. The Robin was particularly popular as a millinery adornment but also provoked some disquiet because of its familiar association with the gardener and householder (Turner 1964). Otherwise the species was common and there is little evidence of any widespread changes in numbers or distribution throughout the 19th century.

It is apparent that the only significant influence on Robin population changes is winter weather (Marchant *et al.* 1990). The only widespread fluctuations in numbers during the 20th century have followed the most severe winters, although it is probable that, on farmland, recent agricultural changes have affected the attractiveness of this habitat to this species. It is also likely that anything that adversely affects the quality or extent of farmland hedgerows will also affect Robin numbers in this habitat. As an illustration, since the winter of 1962–63, when CBC data collection began, the Robin has apparently become more characteristic of pasture, sheep and dairy farms with their associated hedges and shelter belts than of the more open arable and cereal farms (Marchant *et al.* 1990).

Number of counties in which recorded:

Period	Probable breeding		Confirmed breeding		Combined		
	Br	Ir	Br	Ir	Br	Ir	Both
1875–1900	0	0	107	34	107	34	141
1968–1972	0	0	107	34	107	34	141
			change		0	0	0

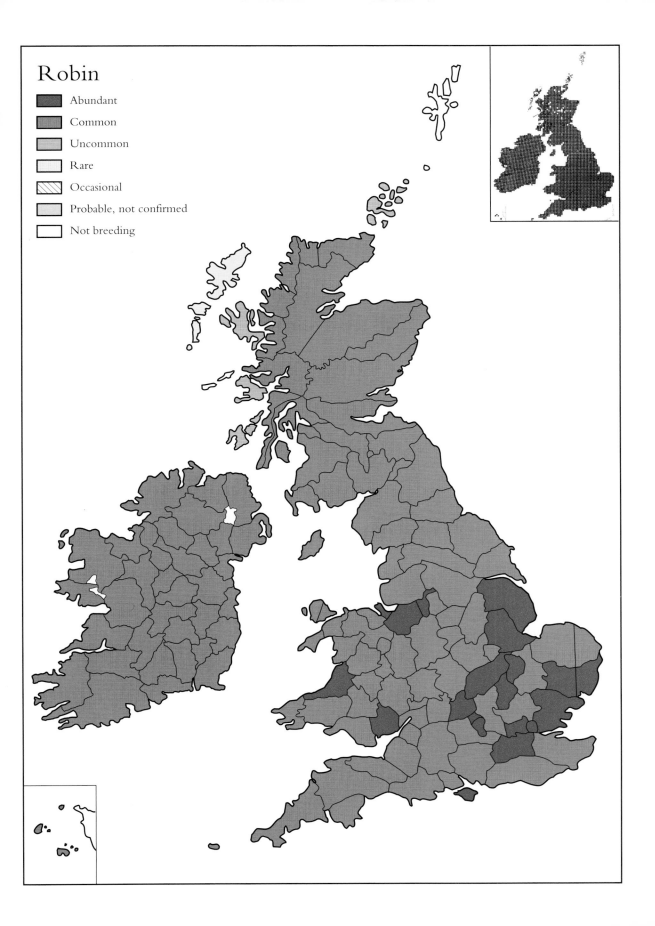

Robin

- ■ Abundant
- ■ Common
- ▨ Uncommon
- ▢ Rare
- ▨ Occasional
- ▨ Probable, not confirmed
- ▢ Not breeding

Nightingale

Luscinia megarhynchos

The Nightingale was a favourite bird of the Victorians. Notice was published in local newspapers of the time when territorial males were located, especially in areas of Britain where breeding was not regular, and day trips were organised for people to visit these sites to listen to the song. Considerable confusion existed, however, concerning the true identity of the singer which, regularly, proved to be a Sedge Warbler, Garden Warbler or Blackcap. Fluctuations in the numbers found each year were often commented upon and may have been affected to some extent by shifts in the breeding sites following the coppicing cycle (A. Henderson in litt.) and weather conditions. Occasionally they were so numerous in some places that their nocturnal singing was considered a nuisance. One landowner was so inundated by coachloads of sightseers that he eventually ordered that the bird be scared away from his property (Coward and Oldham 1900).

Breeding took place most commonly and regularly south and east of a line drawn between the Severn and Humber estuaries, although it had not been recorded in Cornwall, and in Devon was only local in the south. Northwest of that line breeding occurred regularly, but very locally in the Severn and Wye valleys and into Wales, but not west of the Cambrian foothills. The Nightingale's northernmost breed-

ing limit was reached in Yorkshire, at Boroughbridge, *ca* 26km NW of York and it has never bred in Ireland or Scotland. Evidence suggests that the Nightingale may not have bred further north than Doncaster or anywhere in N Wales in the early years of the 19th century and may have been undergoing an expansion of range during the latter half of that century. During the 19th century nightingales were subject to tremendous persecution from bird-catchers who took many males for sale as cage birds (for instance Ticehurst 1909). They were valued highly for their singing prowess. They sang continuously throughout the breeding season but few lasted beyond their first autumn in captivity; most died dashing themselves against the bars of their cages trying to follow their migratory instincts (D'Urban and Mathew 1892). By the turn of the century declining numbers were noted throughout their British range, particularly near the largest cities and on the northern and western fringes.

The main breeding range of the Nightingale in the early years of the 20th century had changed little from that in the 19th. However, breeding north and west of the Severn–Humber line was now only isolated and sporadic. As the 20th century progressed an overall decline in numbers was apparent. This was not a steady decline and populations in many areas appeared to increase in the mid 1930s; thereafter a relatively high population existed but a sharp fall was noticed in many southern and eastern counties from the 1950s. These changes may have been related to the varying fortunes of agriculture over this period (A. Henderson in litt.).

The *68–72 Atlas* described a breeding range that had changed little from the main breeding range of the 19th century or, indeed, throughout the 20th century. Breeding numbers were still apparently falling, although few quantitive data were available to support this. The *88–91 Atlas* demonstrated clearly the receding front of regular breeding towards the south and east. Although there were losses throughout the range those from the northern and western edges were most apparent.

A number of reasons have been suggested for the decline. The Nightingale's preference for coppiced woodland is well documented. Losses of that habitat and clearances of other scrubby land will have made some areas unsuitable. Other, less dramatic changes of habitat, such as the thinning of the lowest shrub layer, have occurred in some previously populated woodlands (A. Henderson in litt.). Climatic change, however, is likely to be at the root of this decline, indicated by the retreat towards the south-east and the fact that many apparently suitable habitats still exist in areas where the Nightingale has bred in the past but from which it has subsequently withdrawn.

Number of counties in which recorded:

Period	Probable breeding		Confirmed breeding		Combined		
	Br	Ir	Br	Ir	Br	Ir	Both
1875–1900	0	0	55	0	55	0	55
1968–1972	2	0	48	0	50	0	50
			change		−5	0	−5
					−9%		−9%

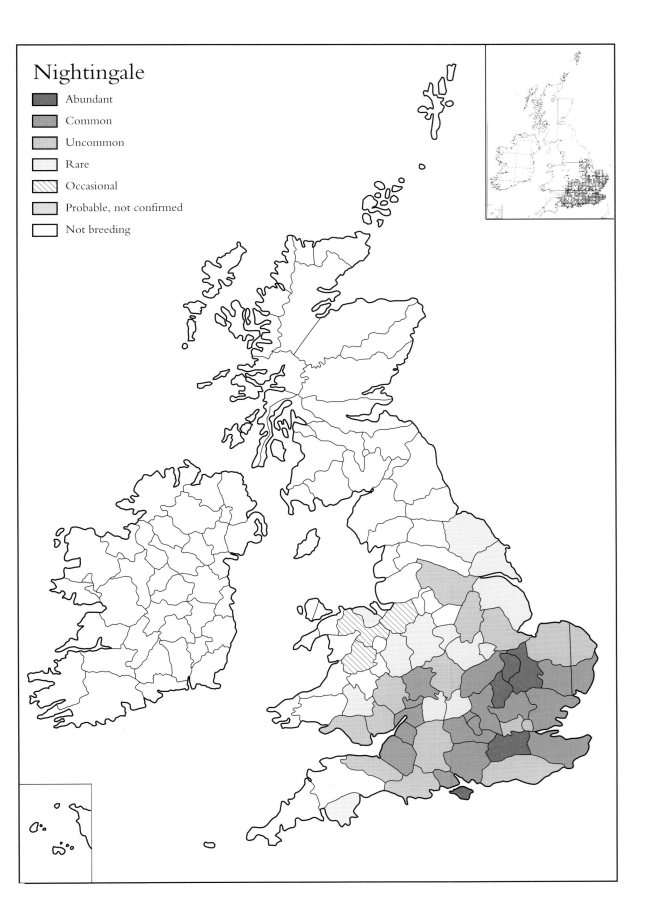

Nightingale

- Abundant
- Common
- Uncommon
- Rare
- Occasional
- Probable, not confirmed
- Not breeding

Redstart

Phoenicurus phoenicurus

The Redstart bred in every county of mainland Britain at the end of the 19th century. It was absent only from the Isles of Scilly and most Scottish islands. Its heartland appears to have been Wales and some of the bordering English counties.

The Redstart's status during the 19th century was evidently undergoing some change. Yarrell (1837–43) suggests that it was not well known in Wales in the early years of the century, but he considered that it had recently increased but was still rare. By the 1860s it was breeding regularly throughout Wales but was considered to breed sparsely in Scotland, especially north of the Great Glen (More 1865). During the last quarter of the century more detail is available of these, and other, changes. Throughout lowland England it was decreasing. In counties from Wiltshire through the Midlands to Bedfordshire and Leicestershire it was noted as less common during the last 20 years of the 19th century than during the 1860s and 1870s. The decrease here was largely unexplained but some evidence suggests that it may have been related in small part to the removal of dead and dying trees, which deprived the Redstart of nesting holes (Prentis 1894; Ticehurst 1909).

In contrast, the Redstart was increasing in Scotland, particularly in the west and north. The increase in Argyll had been especially apparent from the 1870s and had evidently been rapid and extensive. It seemed clear to Harvie-Brown and Buckley (1892) that the increase had been made possible by an increase in nesting holes, particularly in the high stone walls lining the new roads being built through the area. This was not suggested as a possibility further north but the increase was similarly extensive. Many areas of West Ross and NW Sutherland that had never recorded Redstarts before the 1880s held considerable breeding groups by 1900. Eighteen ninety-one was noted as the year in which an unprecedented number of Redstarts returned to Scotland in spring and from which the main thrust of the increase began, although the increase in this year in the Spey, Findhorn and Avon valleys was followed, in 1892, by a notable absence (Harvie-Brown and Buckley 1895). These conflicting statements suggest that the increase noted widely and the subsequent local decreases may have been a manifestation of the fluctuations characteristic of Redstart populations (Parslow 1973). There is little 20th century evidence of an increase in Scotland, and Alexander and Lack (1944) were even able to discern a slight decrease. Their confirmation of a very marked decrease throughout SE and central England was accepted with some reservation by Parslow (1973) who felt that an increase could also be claimed locally during the first half of the 20th century, and that no significant or widespread changes in abundance or distribution have been indicated—the changes noted were natural fluctuations.

Prior to 1885 the Redstart was only recorded as an occasional visitor to Ireland. In that year the first breeding attempts were recorded in Ireland—two pairs were discovered breeding at Powerscourt in Wicklow and nesting occurred there at least until 1895. During the 1890s the Redstart was recorded breeding or suspected of doing so in other parts of Wicklow. In 1888 breeding was suspected in Tyrone and finally proven at Baronscourt, Tyrone, in 1894. These breeding records did not lead to sustained colonisation, however. Throughout the 20th century breeding has been erratic and, apart from the instances mentioned above and a period between 1955 and 1960, there have been very few breeding records.

Later 20th century research confirmed the pattern of a population that fluctuates naturally throughout its range. The *88–91 Atlas* survey and CBC data show that, since the *68–72 Atlas* survey, the Redstart has probably increased in those areas where it is most common but has decreased on the fringes of its range.

Number of counties in which recorded:

Period	Probable breeding		Confirmed breeding		Combined		
	Br	Ir	Br	Ir	Br	Ir	Both
1875–1900	0	0	101	2	101	2	103
1968–1972	1	1	103	4	104	5	109
			change		3	3	6
					3%	150%	6%

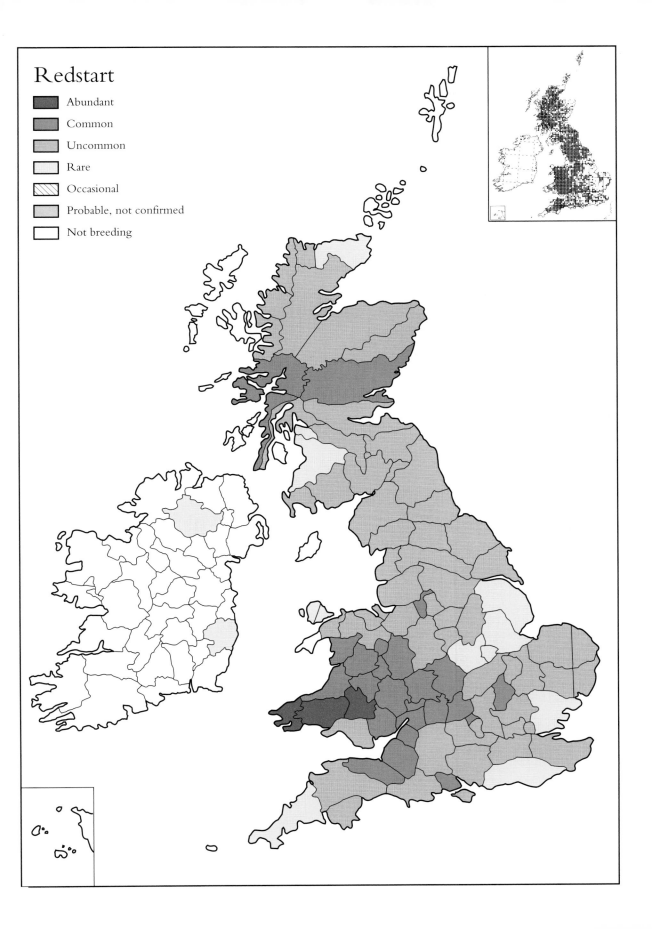

Redstart

- Abundant
- Common
- Uncommon
- Rare
- Occasional
- Probable, not confirmed
- Not breeding

Whinchat
(Furzechat)

Saxicola rubetra

During the last quarter of the 19th century the Whinchat was recorded breeding in all areas of the British mainland, being especially common on some of the southeastern downlands, through the English midlands, N England, Borders and parts of the Highlands. It did not breed in the Isles of Scilly, Isle of Man or Shetland, and was recorded there only on passage. In Ireland it bred, in the main, in the counties of the north and northwest. Some counties in S Ireland were host to breeding season pairs, but proof of breeding was lacking.

Little indication was given of any decline throughout the 19th century so the impression gained is of a stable population at that time. Yarrell (1837–43) described a distribution similar to that described here. This is somewhat surprising as other species utilising similar habitat were recorded as having decreased following reclamation and changes in agriculture during this period. It is possible, therefore, that the traditional nest sites in rough grassland and heath were replaced to some extent by new sites in roadside verges, railway cuttings and embankments. Witherby *et al.* (1938–41) noted that the Whinchat was 'somewhat local, but widely distributed and in many parts very

numerous', noting also that 'railway cuttings and embankments are much frequented'. This latter comment is interesting as none of the earlier, and very few of the later, 19th century writers mentioned breeding in this, or any other, artificial habitat. It is also likely that, as the Whinchat prefers bracken as nesting cover, the introduction of sheep on to open fellsides during the 19th century would have helped the species consolidate, as sheep eat all else but bracken (J. Callion in litt). The species will nest in heather if this is not occupied by the more dominant Stonechat, and Whinchats may also benefit in years of lower Stonechat numbers (J.Callion in litt).

In 1909 breeding was first proved in the Isle of Man, (Cullen and Jennings 1986). Otherwise, little widespread distributional change can be discerned during the first quarter of the 20th century. The breeding distribution described by Witherby *et al.* matches very closely that recorded by the 19th century authors and, so, the population and distribution of Whinchats appears to have changed very little up to the 1930s or 1940s. This view was confirmed by Alexander and Lack (1944) who discerned no evidence of widespread change.

The picture starts to change, however, at about this point. Parslow (1973) noted a 'general decline this century in parts of England, especially in the Midlands and southeast'. He goes on to describe the species in western and northern mainland Britain as 'fairly numerous; widely distributed'. This is probably no different to that descibed earlier in this account. By the 1960s the Whinchat appears to have undergone a considerable decline in the Midlands and SE England. It was entirely absent from some south and southeastern counties, thinly distributed in others and far more local in the rest. In Ireland overall numbers may not have changed very much but losses from Connaught have probably been balanced by an expansion of range into the central and eastern counties—hinted at by the 19th century accounts. Little further change can be discerned in the *68–72 Atlas* apart from the confirmation of the British losses and the marked Irish distributional change.

The *88–91 Atlas* confirms graphically the continuing decline in the area south and east of a line drawn from the Humber to the Severn but also shows losses in the N Midlands, N England and Ireland. Changes in farming methods and practices continue to destroy the Whinchat's breeding habitat. This on its own did not appear to affect Whinchat numbers in the 19th century as other changes in land use apparently added almost as much suitable ground as was destroyed. In the 20th century, however, roadside verges are themselves subject to the same sanitisation as farmland, and railway lines have fallen into disuse and become overgrown, rendering both unsuitable for use by Whinchats.

Number of counties in which recorded:

Period	Probable breeding		Confirmed breeding		Combined		
	Br	Ir	Br	Ir	Br	Ir	Both
1875–1900	0	7	106	15	106	22	128
1968–1972	4	1	101	26	105	27	132
			change		−1	5	4
					−1%	23%	3%

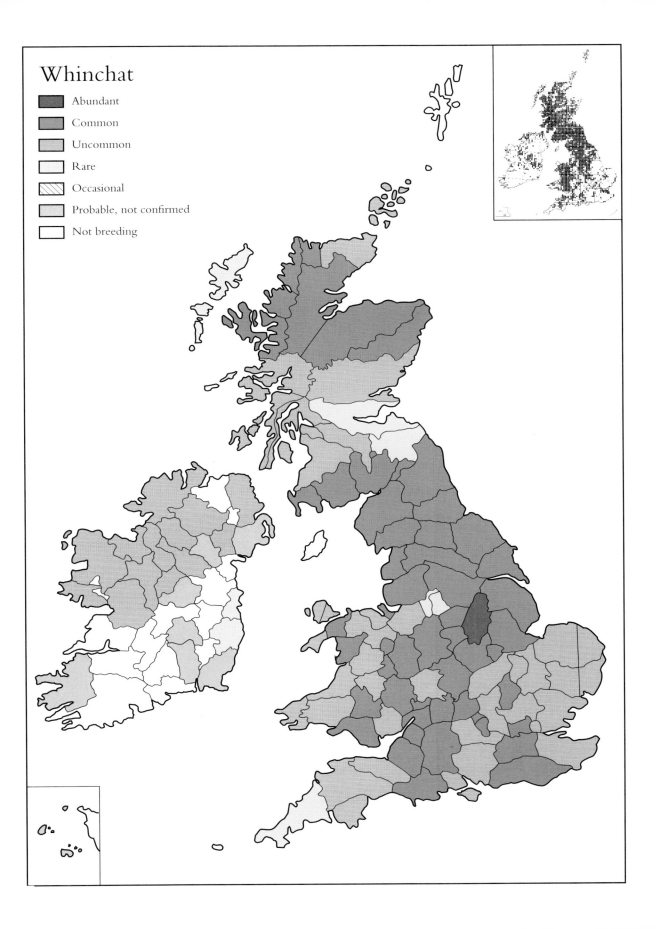

Whinchat

- Abundant
- Common
- Uncommon
- Rare
- Occasional
- Probable, not confirmed
- Not breeding

Stonechat

Saxicola torquata

The Stonechat was absent as a breeding bird only from the islands at the extremes of Britain (Shetland and the Isles of Scilly), at the end of the 19th century. In Orkney and the Outer Hebrides it evidently bred in very few numbers and may not have done so in the early decades of the century. It bred locally in all counties in rough field corners, commons, downs, the tops of sea-cliffs, warrens and chases, and anywhere that gorse grew (although there are indications that stonechats nested in a wider variety of plant species early in the 19th century than in the late 19th and 20th centuries; Morris (1851–57) noted broom in this context and the Stonechat's old specific name *rubicola* was derived from 'inhabitant of bramble-bushes'). The Stonechat was generally considered more common in the south and west and along the coast than elsewhere. In a few, widely separated, counties a decrease in numbers had been noted in the 19th century. Accelerating agricultural changes may have been responsible for this decline, as the enclosure of wastelands and the wholesale clearance and burning of gorse destroyed the Stonechat's breeding habitat (Whitlock 1893). In general, however, the Stonechat population was widespread and stable throughout the 19th century.

Away from its strongholds in Ireland, parts of Scotland, W Wales, SW England, the Hampshire New Forest and much of the south and west coasts, local reports indicated that Stonechat numbers began a decline during the first 30 years or so of the 20th century, although it is apparent that the decline may have begun during the closing years of the 19th century. This slow decline took place in the counties that had experienced the greatest agricultural changes and may have been the result of widespread habitat destruction. The effect of agricultural changes is not clear, however, as the decline in Stonechat numbers occurred during the agricultural depression. Locally, leisure use of the coast resulted in increasing disturbance and broke up some breeding groups. As the population thinned, breeding groups were isolated in the little suitable habitat that remained and were wiped out during years of high winter mortality. In optimal habitat they recovered fairly quickly; however, as the population became more fragmented then large areas were not subsequently re-populated (Parslow 1973). This was especially true following the very severe winters of the early 1940s. This period of harsh weather coincided with the end of the agricultural recession and the drive to plough up more marginal land to support the 1939–45 war effort. Since that time the decline has continued and the widespread withdrawal of the Stonechat from E Britain and inland Ireland is demonstrated clearly by the *68–72* and *88–91 Atlas* surveys. Interestingly, the *Atlases* also reveal the extent to which the Stonechat has increased in W Scotland, both on the mainland and in the Western Isles. No increase in this area had been noted prior to this time, although the Stonechat was apparently more common prior to the winters of the 1940s than during the closing years of the 19th century. This suggests that factors other than destructive human intervention may have acted upon the fluctuating Stonechat population in Britain and that losses in the east may have been partially compensated for by increases in the north and west.

Recent research has revealed that the Stonechat is a partial migrant throughout its range in Britain and Ireland. Mid winter Mediterranean recoveries include individuals bred in S England, N Scotland and many points in between. This strategy clearly improves the survival chances of a species where the bulk of the population has evolved to 'rough it out in the winter' even in the most severe years. Nevertheless, the size of the resident portion of the population varies depending on the severity of the winter and, although it is likely that habitat destruction is likely to have played a large role in range reduction, other 'hidden' factors may have influenced the conclusions of the writers of the 19th and early 20th century (J. Callion in litt).

Number of counties in which recorded:

Period	Probable breeding		Confirmed breeding		Combined		
	Br	Ir	Br	Ir	Br	Ir	Both
1875–1900	0	0	106	34	106	34	140
1968–1972	1	0	86	34	87	34	121
			change		19	0	19
					18%		14%

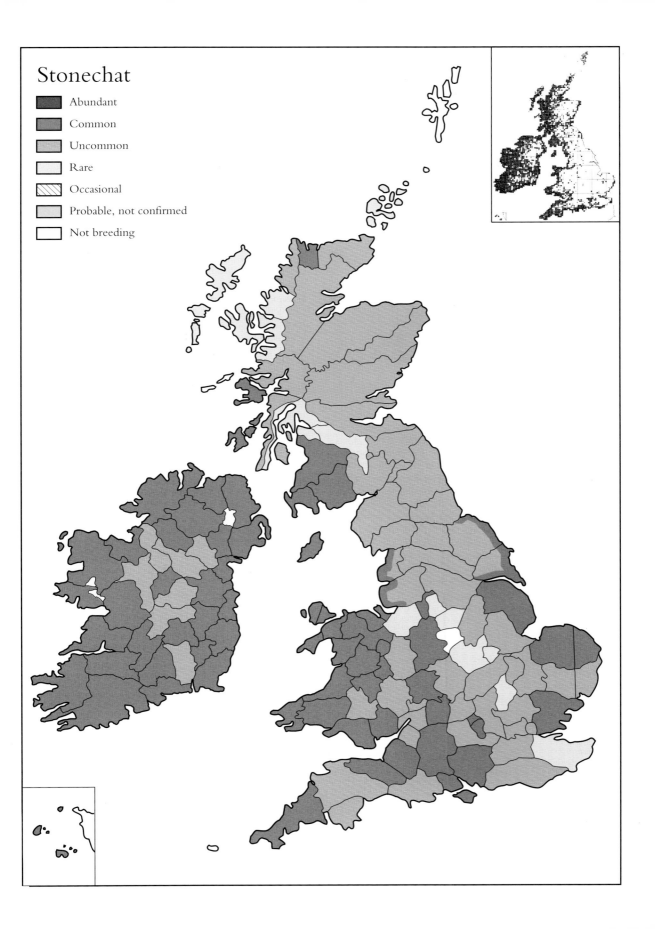

Stonechat

- Abundant
- Common
- Uncommon
- Rare
- Occasional
- Probable, not confirmed
- Not breeding

Wheatear

Oenanthe oenanthe

Throughout much of Britain and Ireland the Wheatear bred commonly in the 19th century, albeit locally over much of England. In Wales, SW England, the Borders, Scotland and along much of the Irish coast it was particularly common. The Wheatear bred in most uncultivated areas of many different habitat types. Its distribution in Ireland was almost universal, except in wooded, cultivated or marshy land, and extended even to the rugged coastal islands. In the English Midlands the Wheatear was absent from some counties and rare in most of the others. It was found breeding not uncommonly in much of S and E England. In some counties rabbit warrens were particularly noted as providing breeding cavities, and were frequently an important nesting resource where natural cavities were scarce; this was apparently particularly true of Norfolk and Suffolk. In other counties, other artificial sites such as cavities in walls, quarries and pits from which stone, gravel or sand had been dug and slag heaps in industrial areas of the midlands (McAldowie 1893) were used, allowing Wheatears to breed in otherwise unsuitable areas. During the period of widespread construction of roads, railways, and canals and of rapid urbanisation, these pits and quarries became more widespread and probably contributed to some local population expansions. The trapping of Wheatears for the table, however, clearly had a negative effect on numbers. A great many were taken in various areas of the country. It was recorded, for example, that a shepherd on the South Downs had caught up to a 1000 in one day, using a horsehair noose, and that about 22,000 were taken annually around Eastbourne at the end of the 18th century (Borrer 1891). By the second half of the 19th century, however, many shepherds on the Downs had ceased to set traps as the yield was not worth the trouble and the numbers of Wheatears seen during the northward migration had decreased dramatically. Nevertheless, the population of Wheatears in Britain and Ireland appears to have been reasonably stable up to the end of the 19th century.

Until the 1930s no significant change in either distribution or population of the Wheatear appears to have taken place although this statement is made on scant evidence (Witherby *et al.* 1938–41). By the 1940s, however, decreases had been noticed in parts of England, S Scotland and Orkney, and a significant decrease had begun to take place in the southern half of England. The Wheatear was becoming extinct or rare in counties where, formerly, it had been considered common. This decrease may have started in the 1930s from Lancashire and Yorkshire southwards. The decrease accelerated after the 1939–45 war following further agricultural changes and afforestation of marginal land. Ploughing of the southern downlands, especially in Wiltshire, Hampshire and Sussex, led to the virtual extinction of the species there. These pressures were compounded in the mid 1950s with the outbreak of myxomatosis and the severe decline of the rabbit. The rabbit warrens afforded almost the only possible breeding sites in many lowland areas and rabbits maintained the short turf that the Wheatear requires to feed on. On one E Suffolk heath, for example, 40 pairs bred prior to the myxomatosis outbreak in 1954, but none nested after 1957.

Since the initial myxomatosis outbreak numbers of rabbits may have recovered a little and the *68–72 Atlas* does not reveal any further, serious losses in Britain. The *88–91 Atlas*, however, reveals further losses on the Sussex coast. A return to regular breeding in the S Pennines is indicated in both *Atlases*. The picture in Ireland, however, was looking less hopeful, with distinct thinning in the midland counties continuing a trend through both *Atlas* periods.

Number of counties in which recorded:

Period	Probable breeding		Confirmed breeding		Combined		
	Br	Ir	Br	Ir	Br	Ir	Both
1875–1900	0	3	105	27	105	30	135
1968–1972	2	1	97	30	99	31	130
			change		−6	1	−5
					−6%	3%	−4%

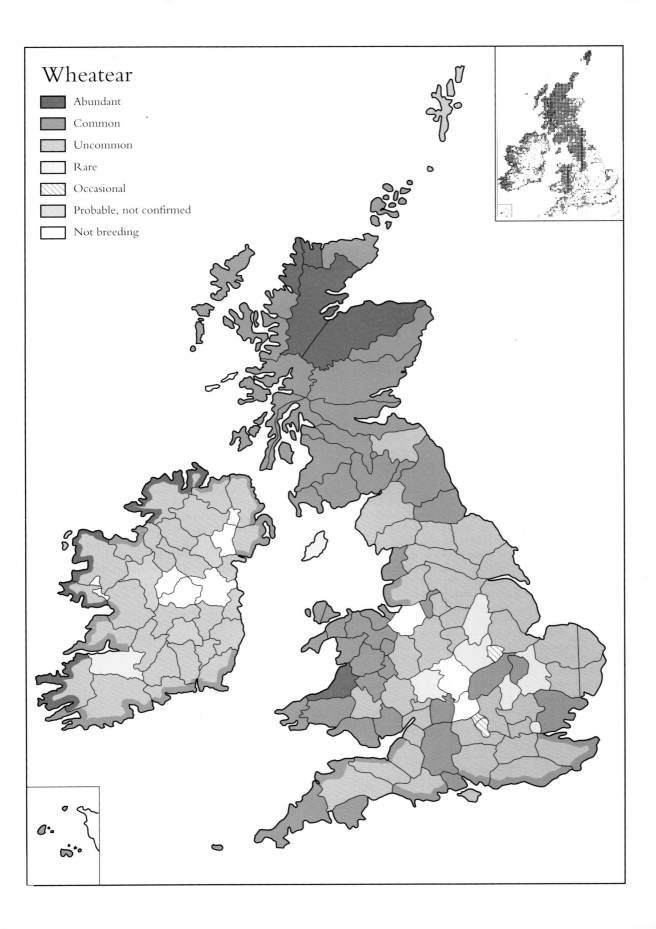

Wheatear

- ■ Abundant
- ▨ Common
- ▨ Uncommon
- □ Rare
- ▨ Occasional
- ▨ Probable, not confirmed
- □ Not breeding

Ring Ouzel

Turdus torquatus

The Ring Ouzel population in Britain and Ireland appears to have been stable during the 19th century. It bred in its highest numbers in the uplands of SW England, N and mid Wales and the Pennines, Lakeland and the Scottish hills, particularly in those of the west. It bred in many of the Inner Hebrides and on Orkney and in most counties of Ireland.

A great many were said to breed on the moors of the SW peninsula, particularly Bodmin in Cornwall, Dartmoor in Devonshire, and Exmoor on the Devonshire/Somerset border, although it was also recorded from some of the smaller hills. Ring Ouzels bred throughout the moors and mountains of N Wales, nowhere more abundantly than the Berwyns range in Denbighshire, and in fewer numbers south to the Black Mountains in Radnorshire and into the west of the adjacent English counties (especially Herefordshire and Shropshire, although a nest was found as far east as the Malvern Hills, Worcestershire in 1877). Elsewhere in Wales it bred very locally. From the Roaches of N Staffordshire and the lower Pennines of N Derbyshire and E Cheshire it bred commonly through into Scotland.

Outside these areas the Ring Ouzel had bred occasionally. More (1865) asserted that it occasionally bred in Kent before *ca* 1860 and there were also records from that county in 1875 (in the Stockbury Valley), in 1879 near Sit-

tingbourne and in a holly tree near Thanet in 1887. Yarrell (1837–43) believed that Ring Ouzels may have bred near Saffron Walden in Essex in 1836 and a nest and four eggs were found in Wickham in that county in 1879. In Surrey, they were said to breed regularly on Hindhead probably before 1827. In Suffolk, there were three records of nests, the last in 1849, and in Norfolk nests had been recorded before the 1860s. In Warwickshire a nest was reported from Coventry in 1848, and in Leicestershire Ring Ouzels were said to breed regularly in Charnwood Forest before 1850. The Ring Ouzel was a frequent breeding species on the western edge of the Cotswolds in Gloucestershire up to about 1885. Collectors shot many birds here, however, and by the turn of the century few remained to breed. The evidence for nests on the Isle of Man was scant. Assertions that a few had been found in the east of the island were accompanied by little supporting information.

There were a number of early 19th century records from English counties well away from the main breeding areas. In some of these, for instance Surrey, Ring Ouzels were apparently banished from the hills when they were either ploughed up or built upon. It is possible that Ring Ouzels may have bred regularly in some of these S England downs and hills when they were less influenced by human activities.

The Ring Ouzel started a long and steady decline early in the 20th century. In Scotland there is much evidence documenting this decline, as there is in S Wales. The progress of the decline in Ireland has not been documented although, by the 1970s and 1980s, it had a far more limited distribution than formerly.

It has been suggested that climatic changes have favoured the Blackbird allowing that species to compete with the Ring Ouzel in the latter species' favoured upland habitat although the evidence for this is circumstantial (Marchant *et al.* 1990). Anecdotal evidence from the 19th century suggests that the Ring Ouzel may be intolerant of human disturbance; this may have affected local populations, probably leading to the widespread contraction in range at core parts of the population (Gibbons *et al.* 1993). The dramatic increase in public access to the remotest and most isolated parts of moorland in recent times is probably accelerating the decline of this species (Marchant *et al.* 1990).

Number of counties in which recorded:

Period	Probable breeding		Confirmed breeding		Combined		
	Br	Ir	Br	Ir	Br	Ir	Both
1875–1900	1	2	66	28	67	30	97
1968-1972	2	4	57	5	59	9	68
			change		−8	−21	−29
					−12%	−70%	−30%

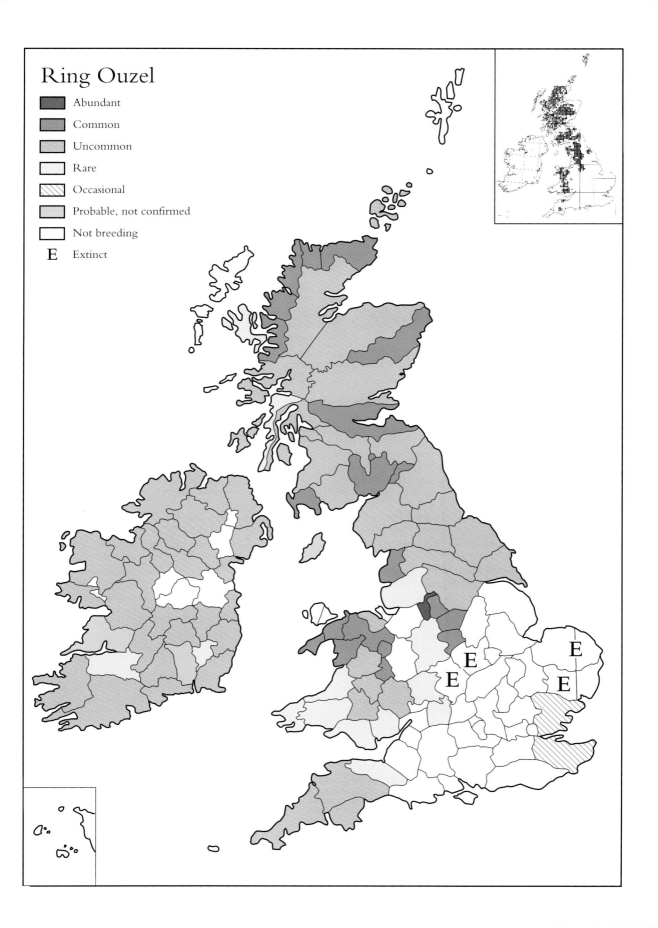

Ring Ouzel

- Abundant
- Common
- Uncommon
- Rare
- Occasional
- Probable, not confirmed
- Not breeding
- E Extinct

Blackbird

Turdus merula

Although the evidence is meagre, the Blackbird population probably underwent an expansion into N Scotland during the late 18th century. The old Statistical Account of Scotland (1791–99) indicated that it appeared to have been a regular and common winter visitor in the past but the population gradually settled and began to breed in many areas. The New Statistical Account (1834–45) included the Blackbird as a breeding species in lists from all over Scotland and contained many notes of its recent increase. Other accounts from the late 18th and early 19th centuries spoke in similar terms. Some attributed the increase to the recent establishment of plantations and others thought that the Blackbird bred in its largest numbers in the lowland cultivated districts (it appears to have adapted quickly to the development of hedgerows and managed coppices in Scotland as well as the rest of Britain)—overall it seems that the Blackbird followed the increase of the human population in the Highlands and Islands. During the 19th century it increased substantially in Orkney, in the 1890s colonised Shetland, and subsequently rapidly increased there, whilst in the Outer Hebrides it was commonest around the Stornoway woods; it also bred, in very small numbers, on Harris and North Uist (Baxter and Rintoul 1953). By the final quarter of the 19th century the Blackbird bred almost as uniformly and commonl y throughout Scotland as it did in the rest of Britain.

From about the middle of the 19th century, throughout Britain, the Blackbird began to spread out of its original typical woodland habitat into the suburban gardens of the expanding towns and cities and into the larger town parks. It has been said that it was unknown as a breeding bird in the neighbourhood of houses before the mid 19th century (Parslow 1973) but this is clearly not the case (Mudie 1834), although it probably only bred in large country gardens well supplied with suitable food crops such as fruit. Its solitary and shy nature was often commented on at this time but the growth of suburbia and the change in nature of the associated gardens from the cultivation of food produce, and the attendant persecution of anything that fed on those plants, to the planting of ornamental plants and shrubs, which provided better nesting sites and little persecution, led to an increase of Blackbirds in those habitats and probably allowed them to become much tamer. In areas of extensive soft-fruit culture (for instance in SE England) the Blackbird was an important pest and organised persecution took place. Systematic 'thinning' was organised in the form of 'Blackbird drives'. Several guns were placed under the cover of hedges on the field margins and the Blackbirds beaten towards them. As many as 400–600 birds were sometimes thus shot in a day, although how many of these were of the resident population is impossible to determine (Ticehurst 1909).

In Ireland, by the end of the 19th century, the Blackbird was the commonest thrush and bred in every county. It was still rare in some treeless districts of the west but was apparently increasing; several notes of its first breeding were made in Connaught during the 1890s.

The increase in numbers of Blackbirds in the centres of cities, where a spread into the smaller parks and city centre gardens was apparent by the 1930s, and further colonisations of, and increases in, the smaller Scottish and Irish marine islands which continued to the 1950s, have both presumably helped numbers of Blackbirds to outstrip those of the Song Thrush (the Blackbird probably became the dominant species during the 1939–45 war), although the decline of the latter species is probably the main cause of this change (Parslow 1973). The Blackbird has also spread into upland habitats during the 20th century where these have been made suitable by the extensive planting of conifers.

Number of counties in which recorded:

Period	Probable breeding		Confirmed breeding		Combined		
	Br	Ir	Br	Ir	Br	Ir	Both
1875–1900	0	0	108	34	108	34	142
1968-1972	0	0	108	34	108	34	142
			change		0	0	0

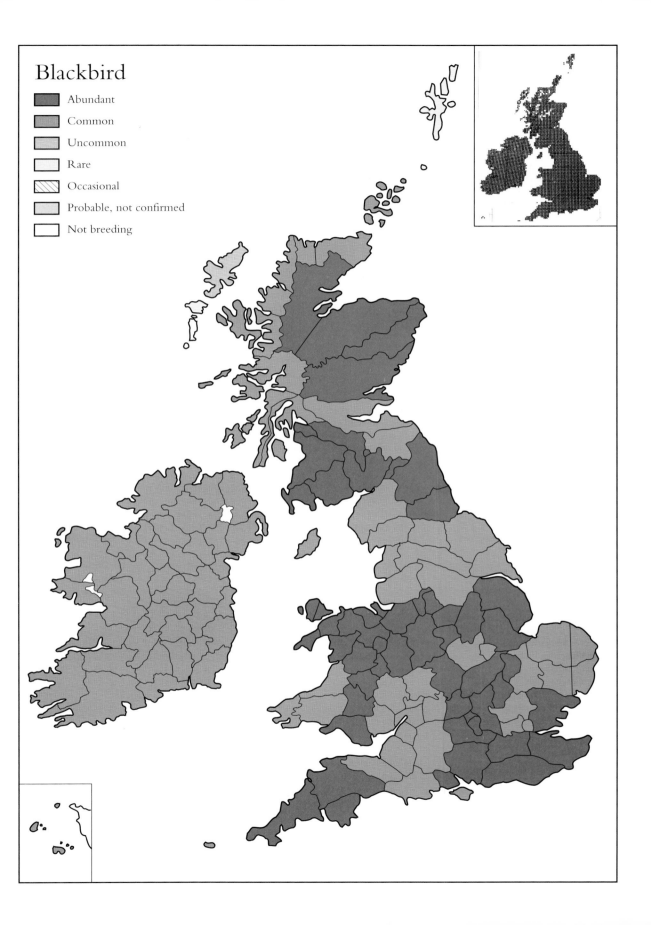

Blackbird

- Abundant
- Common
- Uncommon
- Rare
- Occasional
- Probable, not confirmed
- Not breeding

Song Thrush

Turdus philomelos

The Song Thrush was a familiar and popular bird during the 19th century. It bred throughout Britain, Ireland and their islands during 1875–1900, the only significant exception being Shetland, where breeding records were never proven.

In Ireland it was described as breeding commonly and widely distributed. Although normally nesting in trees, bushes and hedgerows, in some of the upland, moorland or island habitats of Ireland the Song Thrush was recorded breeding in gorse and even ferns. It was recorded breeding on the islands of Valentia, Lambay, Rathlin and Achill, but some very exposed coastal areas such as Dunglow in Donegal, Belmullet in Mayo and Carna in Galway did not sustain breeding pairs.

That the Song Thrush is particularly affected by hard winters is indicated by the 19th century accounts. In Scotland it was claimed that, by the end of the 19th century, numbers had still not recovered fully in the extreme north and parts of the east from the series of severe winters of 1878/79, 1880/81 and 1890/91. The evidence for this slow recovery must, however, be treated with great caution as, without counts, it is very difficult to measure changes in the numbers of common species reliably. In addition, the Song Thrush recovered after only about five years in S Britain after the very severe winter of 1962/63. If the late 19th century recovery was really as slow as was suggested then some other factor may have been involved (S. Baillie in litt). Comments were made of large losses following the 1880/81 and 1890/91 winters in parts of England but

numbers here, however, apparently recovered quicker than they did in Scotland. No other widespread change in distribution or range appears to have taken place through the 19th century.

As the 20th century opened breeding was proven in Shetland for the first time. Pairs were first located about 1900 and the population gradually rose to just over 20 pairs by 1946. No major change appears to have occurred in Britain up to the 1940s. Considerable losses were recorded in Ireland after the severe winter of 1916/17, but numbers were rapidly restored during the following breeding seasons. This recovery may, in fact, explain the assertion that colonisation of some of the smaller Irish west coast islands occurred early in the 20th century. They were more likely to have been recolonisations following extinctions during the 1916/17 winter.

Unsupported accounts assert that a decline in the numbers of Song Thrushes started from the 1920s in Britain, others that it began around 1940. This assertion was usually expressed as a change in the numbers breeding in comparison with the Blackbird (although the extent to which this change reflects an increase in Blackbirds or a decline in Song Thrushes is unclear (S. Baillie in lit). Quantitive evidence from ringing returns, however, noted that after the hard winters of the 1940s Song Thrush numbers declined for some time (Ginn 1969). The winter of 1947/48 took the population to a very low level, and wiped out the few Song Thrushes on Shetland. A slow recovery in the British population was set back during the severe 1962/63 winter at which time around 40% of the population was wiped out. The species' capacity to recover, however, was demonstrated by the CBC which recorded that the numbers encountered had returned to normal levels within two breeding seasons. The population then remained stable until the mid 1970s, after which it declined. The increase in the number of freezing days in January and February from this time through the early 1980s probably accounted for some loss on farmland in S Britain but is not enough to explain the full extent of the losses (Baillie 1990). Other factors such as land-use changes and pesticides are probably also responsible.

The pattern of relative abundance shown on the accompanying map is similar to the abundance map in the *88–91 Atlas*, and to the pattern shown in the Winter Atlas (Lack 1986) and by the CBC data for S Britain (O'Connor and Shrubb 1986). It should be pointed out, however, that for an abundant species such as the Song Thrush large changes in numbers could take place without any corresponding changes in range (S. Baillie in litt). The point is well illustrated by the large decline that took place between the *68–72* and *88–91 Atlases* without any significant distributional change.

Number of counties in which recorded:

Period	Probable breeding		Confirmed breeding		Combined		
	Br	Ir	Br	Ir	Br	Ir	Both
1875–1900	0	0	107	34	107	34	141
1968–1972	0	0	107	34	107	34	141
			change		0	0	0

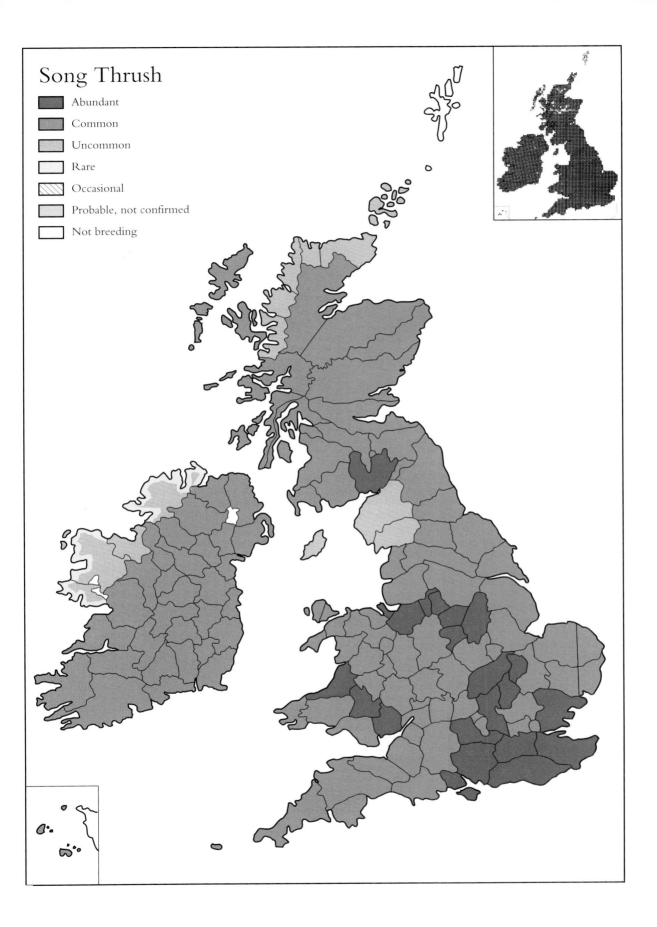

Song Thrush

- Abundant
- Common
- Uncommon
- Rare
- Occasional
- Probable, not confirmed
- Not breeding

Mistle Thrush (Missel Thrush)

Turdus viscivorus

The Mistle Thrush apparently underwent a significant expansion of range at the end of the 18th century that continued through the 19th. By the late 1800s it was common throughout almost all of Britain and Ireland. The evidence for the species' former scarcity in Scotland and Ireland is fairly clear. In Scotland, in areas north of the Tweed, it was probably rare up to the early 1800s. There were few notes about its presence there in the old Statistical Account of Scotland compiled between 1791 and 1799, suggesting that it was relatively unknown at that time. A fairly rapid increase in Mistle Thrush numbers then seems to have taken place. Few details exist of the range expansion but the Mistle Thrush was certainly breeding as far north as Sutherland by 1834. The consolidation of this range expansion is rather better documented. By the 1840s the species was already being described as common as far north as Moray and, as the century progressed, it continued to increase until, in the 1890s, it was considered abundant in some areas.

The old Statistical Account also recorded the Mistle Thrush as rare in areas around the Tweed and Borders. In 1817 Sir William Jardine noted that it was rarely seen. By 1832 it was described as frequent, however, and in 1864 it was common and multiplying yearly. Evidence to support the supposed increase in N England is less clear. Hancock (1874) supposed that Bewick's note of his difficulty in obtaining a specimen from Newcastle around 1844 was evidence of its scarcity in the north. Hancock, however, knew that the species regularly bred in the area at least as early as 1835. Bolam (1912) too was sceptical of the evidence of an increase but quoted Selby's comments that it was very rare in Northumberland around 1820, but very common by 1832 and 1840. In Cumberland a breeding record exists for 1782, but Mistle Thrushes were considered by Macpherson and Duckworth (1886) as scarce around 1800. In the rest of England and Wales little information exists to determine early 19th century distribution. Mudie (1834) felt that the Mistle Thrush was more common in Wales and S and W England than in the east at this time.

Though common and widely distributed by the end of the 19th century the Mistle Thrush was apparently unknown in Ireland before the century began. A bird, shot early in 1808 in Antrim, was the first Irish bird that Thompson (1849–56) had note of. There is also a record of a nest in Louth in 1807. During the first half of the 19th century the Mistle Thrush spread rapidly throughout Ireland, the western coast being the last area to be colonised. Before the middle of the century the Mistle Thrush bred in every Irish county and within the next 10–15 years its colonisation of the off-shore islands was complete.

The reasons for the increase during the early years of the 19th century are not clear. Contemporary writers had their own ideas. On the one hand the early plantations in Scotland may have provided nesting trees where there were previously none. In other parts of Britain the drainage of wet areas and the increasing uniformity and extent of agriculture with their attendant hedgerows were believed to have increased potential nesting sites. In the expanding towns and cities, parks and gardens also provided suitable habitat. The only suppression of this increase appeared to have been caused by severe winters, for example those of 1878/79 and 1880/81—the Mistle Thrush is particularly susceptible to hard weather (Elkins 1983).

The population and distribution of the Mistle Thrush appear to have settled by the end of the 19th century, and few further changes in either appear to have occurred during the 20th century. The Scottish islands remain largely uncolonised.

Number of counties in which recorded:

Period	Probable breeding		Confirmed breeding		Combined		
	Br	Ir	Br	Ir	Br	Ir	Both
1875–1900	0	0	106	34	106	34	140
1968-1972	0	0	105	34	105	34	139
			change		−1	0	−1
					−1%		−1%

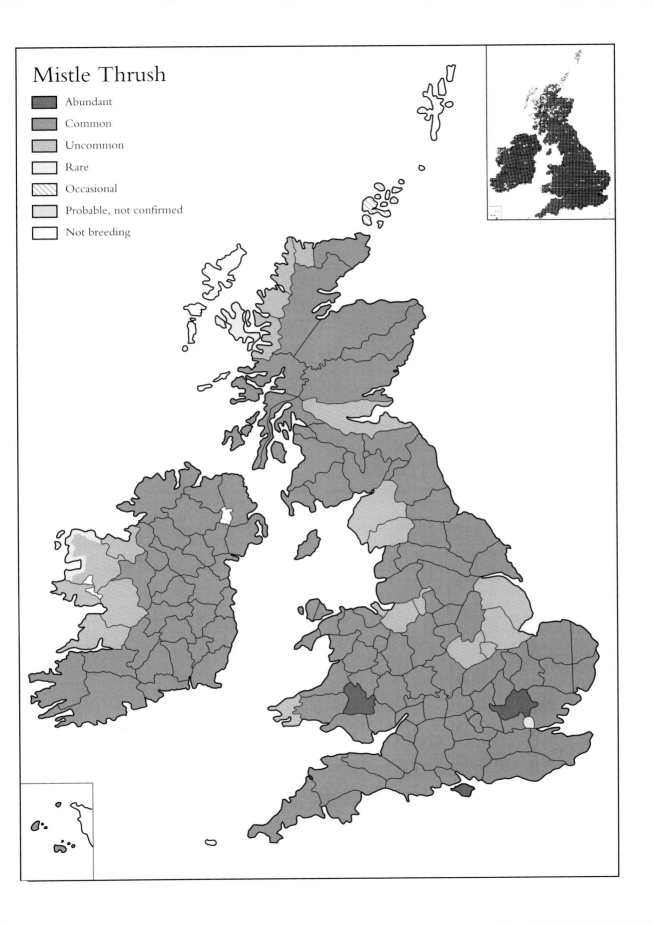

Mistle Thrush

- ■ Abundant
- ■ Common
- ▨ Uncommon
- ▢ Rare
- ▨ Occasional
- ▨ Probable, not confirmed
- ▢ Not breeding

Grasshopper Warbler

Locustella naevia

The song of the Grasshopper Warbler was well known during the 19th century, but evidence of breeding was not easy to ascertain, although the presence of singing males indicated that breeding may have taken place. The nest is normally well hidden in tussocks of grass or sedge and very difficult to find but the distinctly marked eggs were a frequent target of collectors. Counties in which nests were found were restricted to those south of a line drawn from the Severn estuary to the Wash, N England and some in N Wales. The Grasshopper Warbler was also included in some lists of the birds of Ireland. It is unlikely that other English and Welsh counties were colonised during the 19th century or that Ireland accommodated a significant increase, as the literature suggests, but rather that the species was overlooked; there is evidence, however, that it increased substantially in W Wales and spread north from the English counties to breed regularly in the Scottish Borders and, sporadically, a little further north.

Breeding may have occurred in the Solway region throughout the 19th century and the Grasshopper Warbler had been a familiar species in Ayrshire since the 1850s, but it was little known in Dumfriesshire prior to the 1880s. Clearly, however, by the 1860s, throughout SW Scotland, numbers were increasing in the newly planted conifer plantations. This increase may have fuelled an expansion of range up the west mainland coast. In the 1890s the Grasshopper Warbler was considered to be spreading in Argyll. It first nested in N Argyll in 1868 on Ardnamurchan, and a nest found near Arisaig in 1891 marked the northern breeding limit on the western Scottish mainland, up to the end of the century. Further north it bred very irregularly on Skye and probably colonised the island of Bute at the turn of the century. In E Scotland it had been recorded breeding in the Forth region since 1835 but may not have bred further south in the Tweed region until the middle of the century. In Fife it was first mentioned in 1870 with the first nesting report near St Andrews in 1895. The most northern breeding records occurred between 1896 and 1898 alongside the R Lossie near Elgin.

The Grasshopper Warbler was believed to have colonised W Cardiganshire and Merioneth in about the 1880s and, by inference, it may not have bred in other parts of W Wales prior to that time.

The difficulty in proving breeding was illustrated in the Irish records. It was described as common in many places, too widespread to be called local but liable to be overlooked, and probably did not breed on the marine islands or along the western seaboard. Proven breeding records were erratic and have created an impression of a patchy distribution, although in Ireland, as in the rest of its range, the Grasshopper Warbler's biology is characterised by short-term fluctuations in numbers (Marchant *et al.* 1990).

The increase in forestry in the 20th century has certainly benefited the Grasshopper Warbler. It uses the new forests soon after planting. They remain suitable for around ten years and have become one of the species' most important breeding habitats, particularly in W Britain, but also in southern counties such as Berkshire and Buckinghamshire. Loss of other suitable habitats in Britain, including osier beds, as a result of the clearance of scrub and wasteland and drainage of wetlands, for instance, has been largely compensated for, up to recent decades of the 20th century, by tree planting (Parslow 1973, Sharrock 1976). In Scotland the Grasshopper Warbler continued to spread north through this century and nesting occurred throughout the mainland as far north as the Caithness coast, spreading to some of the maritime islands. Most of the breeding attempts were sporadic but there are some regular sites. Since the 1939–45 war conifer plantings will have contributed in part to the surge in numbers that took place up to the 1960s but since then a substantial, although fluctuating, decline has taken place as shown by the *88–91 Atlas*. There have been large habitat losses as a result of scrub clearance, the development of conifer plantations beyond the shrubby stage and changing farming practices in the 1970s and 1980s. The decline has taken place in parallel with those of other migrants, such as the Whitethroat, and may be linked to the drought that occurred in Sahealian Africa (Marchant *et al.* 1990).

Number of counties in which recorded:

Period	Probable breeding		Confirmed breeding		Combined		
	Br	Ir	Br	Ir	Br	Ir	Both
1875–1900	0	11	91	20	91	31	122
1968–1972	8	1	98	33	106	34	140
	change				15	3	18
					10%	10%	15%

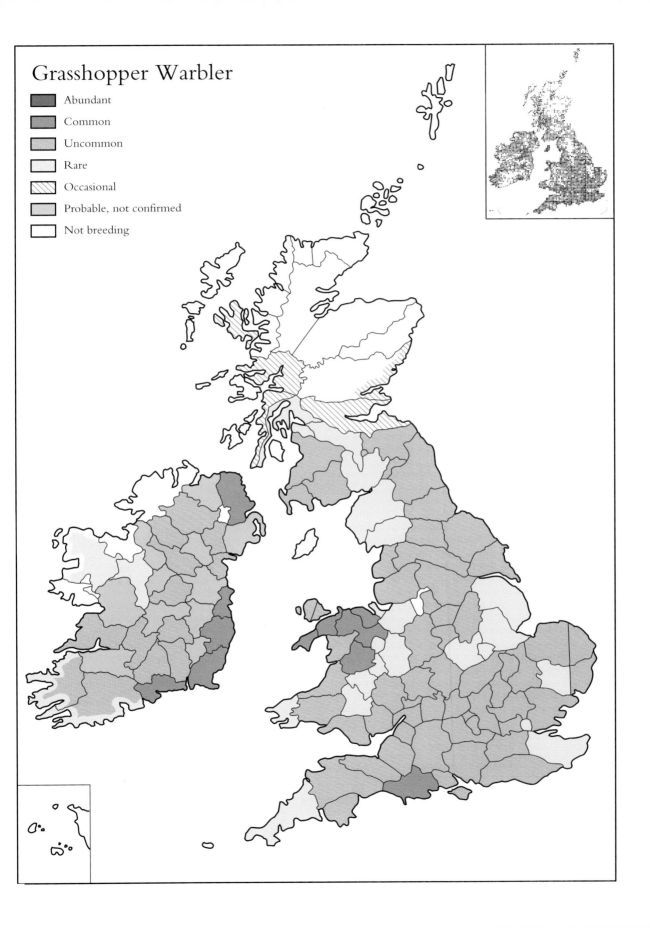

Grasshopper Warbler

- Abundant
- Common
- Uncommon
- Rare
- Occasional
- Probable, not confirmed
- Not breeding

Sedge Warbler

Acrocephalus schoenobaenus

The Sedge Warbler was a very familiar bird in Britain and Ireland during the 19th century. Throughout England, especially, it was described breeding along the banks of all streams and rivers, drainage ditches with emergent or bankside vegetation, along hedgerows of both damp meadows and drier fields, and in crops, especially bean fields. Its association with reeds was celebrated for a short time by its systematic binomial of *Acrocephalus phragmitis*. Elevated sites in England contained smaller populations of the Sedge Warbler, and in higher land in Scotland only the most sheltered valleys provided suitable breeding habitat. In Orkney the first record of the Sedge Warbler was in 1857; although sightings of this species occurred with increasing frequency, breeding was not recorded there until 1884 but then increased throughout the rest of the century. This led to suggestions that a population expansion was in process in the extreme N of Scotland. The Sedge Warbler did not breed in the Outer Hebrides or Shetland but did breed in the Inner Hebrides, sometimes commonly in the southern islands of the group. In Ireland it was common in most counties although surprisingly uncommon in some areas where apparently suitable habitat existed, and it was scarce in the valley of the Shannon, around the loughs of the Irish Midlands and in the more exposed west of the country.

Little change ensued into the 20th century. The Sedge Warbler remained scarce in the extreme north of Scotland, but breeding was proven for the first time in North Uist in 1937 and was suspected in Benbecula and South Uist in 1938. At the same time the population in Orkney declined somewhat, but through the 1950s and 1960s the Sedge Warbler's numbers increased to a greater extent than those of any other Orcadian passerine. This increase was shared in other Scottish islands; for instance it spread into the northern Outer Hebrides in the 1950s and Lewis in 1963 after which it then increased rapidly. There was some evidence of a redistribution of the population, especially in some areas of England. Local losses caused by drainage of breeding areas have been offset by the increase in the number of gravel pits and reservoirs with vegetated banks created, particularly, since the end of the 1939–45 war.

The Sedge Warbler population appeared very stable, probably at least from the beginning of the 19th century up to 1968. In 1968 the CBC recorded a marked peak in its population in common with other summer migrants. This peak was followed by a conspicuous decline in the number breeding in the 1969 season. This decline was followed by a more severe deterioration of numbers in the mid 1980s. The overall decline of the Sedge Warbler since the late 1960s has been linked to conditions on the W African wintering grounds. In years of drought the survival of the Sedge Warbler can be very low; the overall distribution in Britain and Ireland has probably changed little during this period of decline. The *88–91 Atlas* recorded obvious gaps extending in S Ireland, central and SW England. The maps in both *68–72* and *88–91 Atlases* show the thin distribution in the upland areas of Wales, N England and Scotland that the resolution of the 19th century map cannot.

Number of counties in which recorded:

Period	Probable breeding		Confirmed breeding		Combined		
	Br	Ir	Br	Ir	Br	Ir	Both
1875–1900	0	0	105	34	105	34	139
1968–1972	0	0	107	34	107	34	141
			change		2	0	2
					2%		1%

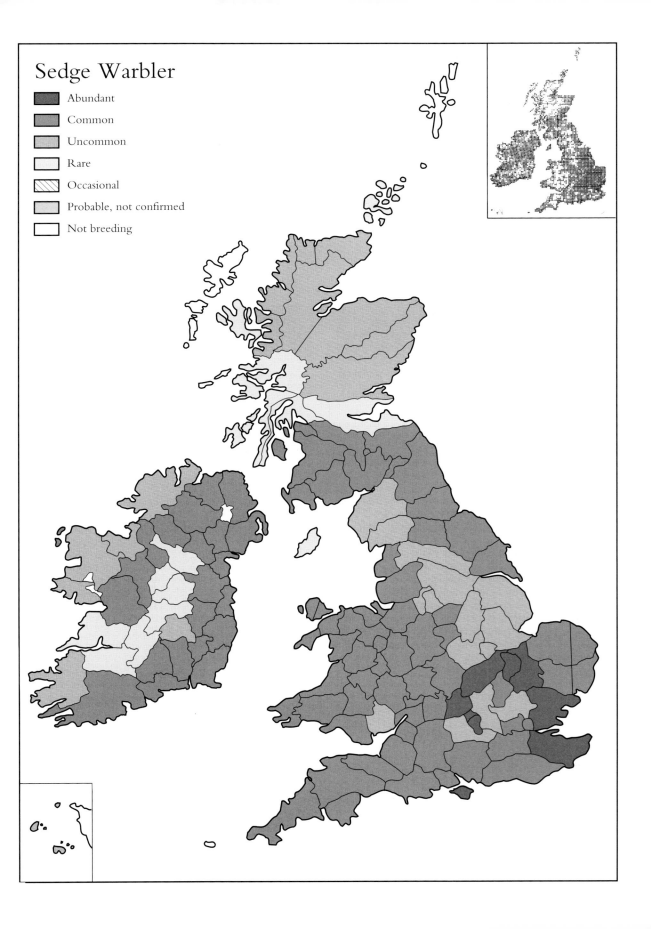

Sedge Warbler

- Abundant
- Common
- Uncommon
- Rare
- Occasional
- Probable, not confirmed
- Not breeding

Marsh Warbler

Acrocephalus palustris

The Marsh Warbler was first recognised as a separate species in 1803. The first breeding records appear to be from Alresford Great Pond in Hampshire in 1863, Christchurch, Dorset, at the end of the 1860s, the Thames–Severn canal at Siddington, near Cirencester in 1886 and in Worcestershire in 1887 (Tomes 1901). Both Tomes and Bund (1891) indicate, however, that the Marsh Warbler had bred in the Avon Valley at least from the late 1870s. The 1890s then produced a number of further records. Meinertzhagen noted that one or two pairs bred regularly at this time at Mottisfont near Southampton, Hampshire, a few were discovered breeding in a stone quarry near Littleton, Worcestershire in 1892, and Witherby *et al.* (1938–41) mentioned a breeding record in Warwickshire in about 1890. Glegg (1929) mentioned a Marsh Warbler clutch said to have been taken at Tillingham, Essex in 1892. However, the record was ignored by Wetherby *et al.* (1938–43). The final dated report from the 1875–1900 period came from Wiltshire in 1900. By the end of the century, the Marsh Warbler was recorded breeding in three locations with up to ten pairs each along the Severn in Gloucestershire. The chief area was in the Vale region of the county near Gloucester, with other sites near Bristol and 'in the north of the county'. In Worcestershire it was regarded as not uncommon in the Avon valley and one breeding site was extant on the Teme. No other breeding records were mentioned in Hampshire at this time but later records suggested that it bred rarely but regularly there (Cohen and Tavener 1972).

As the 20th century opened records from other counties began to appear. By around 1910 the Marsh Warbler was recorded breeding irregularly in Kent, Surrey, Sussex, Buck-inghamshire, Berkshire, Hampshire, Dorset and Cambridgeshire. The majority, however, appear to have bred in Oxfordshire, Somerset, Gloucestershire and Worcestershire, the Severn valley remaining the chief stronghold. Howard (1907–14) considered that the species was gradually extending its range northwards, first breeding occurring on the northern boundary of Worcestershire around 1905. Marsh Warblers were described as fairly common along the Avon Valley in Worcestershire (Harthan 1946) and more common than Sedge Warblers along the R Severn from Upton to Worcester although none was present on that stretch in 1970 (Harrison 1982). Other evidence of a possible increase comes from Gloucestershire where, up to the 1930s or so, breeding took place in 8–10 localities from Purton to Tewkesbury.

Witherby *et al.* (1938–41) noted regular breeding at this time in Sussex (since 1920) and Kent (since 1926). Sporadic breeding was said to have occurred in Devonshire (1928), Surrey (1907), Berkshire (1918, 1920–23, 1936), Herefordshire (1938) (a small population became established from 1938 where 4–5 pairs bred until the mid 1950s (Gilbert and Walker 1954)), Warwickshire (1917), Staffordshire (1914, 1916, 1918), Cheshire (1910), Huntingdonshire (1917) and Middlesex (1903) although the evidence for most of these claims is now lost. Breeding had declined in Oxfordshire by this point—small populations were known between 1893–1904 (Warde-Fowler 1906) and 1941–47 (Radford 1966). This pattern, of regular breeding in Gloucestershire and adjacent counties and sporadic breeding elsewhere, appears to have continued for the next 10–20 years or so. Between 1920 and 1950 data are scanty, but by 1950 a decline in Gloucestershire was evident. Throughout the 1960s the Marsh Warbler totals in this county fluctuated between one and 12 pairs annually but breeding was sporadic by the end of the 1970s. Throughout this period regular breeding continued in S Worcestershire.

During the *68–72 Atlas* survey around 75% of the breeding population of 50–80 pairs in Britain were in Worcestershire. Pairs bred sporadically in Somerset, Dorset, Monmouth, Surrey, Kent and Nottinghamshire. By the time of the *88–91 Atlas* survey, however, the Worcestershire breeding group had declined to just a few pairs. The average breeding population at this time was fewer than 12 pairs most of which occurred in a recently established colony in SE England.

Reasons for the apparent rise in population (the increase may have been merely an artefact of increased familiarity and observer effort) of the Marsh Warbler from about 1880 to a peak in about the 1930s and 1940s to its subsequent decline are complex. It is clearly on the edge of its geographical range. Although habitat destruction in some areas may have exacerbated the recent decline, the Marsh Warbler may only ever have gained a tenuous hold in Britain and long-term, permanent colonisation may not be feasible.

Number of counties in which recorded:

Period	Probable breeding		Confirmed breeding		Combined		
	Br	Ir	Br	Ir	Br	Ir	Both
1875–1900	1	0	7	0	8	0	8
1968–1972	0	0	10	0	10	0	10
			change		2	0	2
					25%		25%

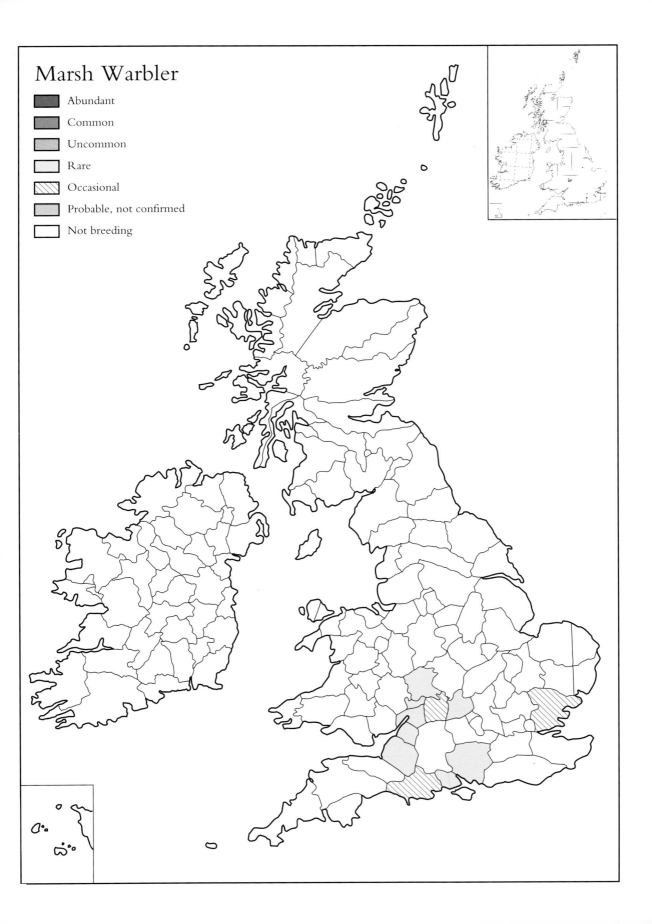

Marsh Warbler

- Abundant
- Common
- Uncommon
- Rare
- Occasional
- Probable, not confirmed
- Not breeding

Reed Warbler

Acrocephalus scirpaceus

At the end of the 19th century the Reed Warbler bred in most English and Welsh counties south from, and including, Lancashire and Yorkshire. It did not breed in Anglesey, Denbighshire or the counties of SW Wales. Then, as now, it was closely associated with *Phragmites* and hence the vicinity of wet areas. In the West Riding of Yorkshire the Reed Warbler was regarded as not very numerous but bred throughout the area from Sheffield to Leeds, where a small colony was discovered near that city in 1880. It bred more numerously in the East Riding where reed beds were more widespread, for instance, along the Humber and the Driffield trout streams. It was rarer in the north of the county but did breed right up to the border with Durham (it was found not far from Redcar, which was probably the Reed Warbler's most northerly proven breeding record at that time) and east as far as Bedale. In Lancashire it bred as far north as Morecambe and east almost to the boundary with Yorkshire. The Reed Warbler's western boundary was marked, in Wales, by regular breeding just into the detached part of Flintshire near Ellesmere and probably in a marsh near Abersoch, Caernarvonshire. It bred rarely in Cornwall. Earlier in the century it had not been identified any further north than Northamptonshire up to about 1820 and then the counties of Staffordshire, Derbyshire and Lincolnshire by around 1840. The later records from Yorkshire and Lancashire may demonstrate an expansion northwards

during the first half of the 19th century. Care must be taken, however, not to discount the difficulties experienced at that time in identifying the species in the field.

By the 1930s the Reed Warbler had been lost from those boundary areas frequented at the end of the 19th century (Witherby *et al.* 1938–41). The figure included here demonstrates these losses, especially in N England. The breeding distribution during the period of the *68–72 Atlas* corresponds very closely to that in the 1930s—little change appears to have occurred in the intervening period. Expansion, however, has occurred westwards to the Welsh coast and northwards along the Cumbrian and northeastern coasts during the 1970s and 1980s. The *88–91 Atlas* also demonstrates the expansion in N England that has taken place since the *68–72 Atlas*. Breeding was recorded in Scotland (perhaps by individuals overshooting from the expanding Scandinavian population) and, by that time, was regular at a number of sites in E and SE Ireland. The series of four maps now available showing the Reed Warbler's distribution over about a 100-year period reveals an interesting cycle of extinction and recolonisation over that period.

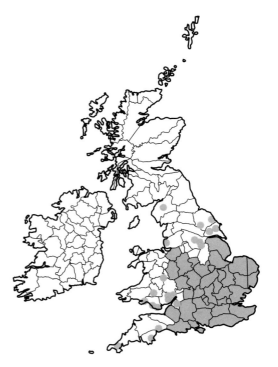

Source: Witherby *et al.* 1938–41.

Number of counties in which recorded:

Period	Probable breeding		Confirmed breeding		Combined		
	Br	Ir	Br	Ir	Br	Ir	Both
1875–1900	1	0	67	0	68	0	68
1968–1972	5	0	59	0	64	0	64
	change				−4	0	−4
					−6%		−6%

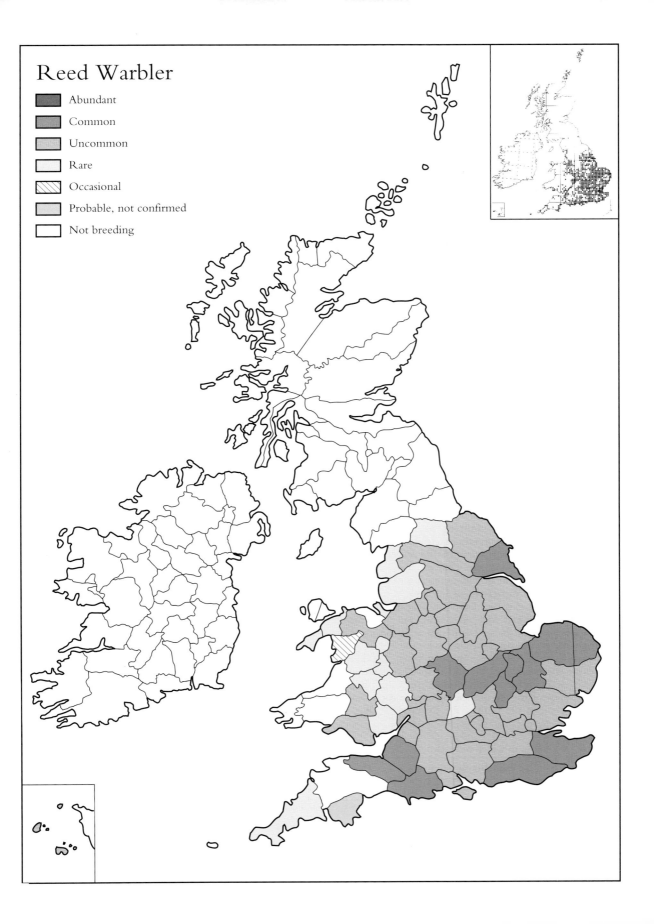

Reed Warbler

- **Abundant**
- **Common**
- **Uncommon**
- **Rare**
- **Occasional**
- **Probable, not confirmed**
- **Not breeding**

Dartford Warbler

Sylvia undata

The Dartford Warbler was first recognised as a British bird by John Latham from a pair that was shot in 1773 on Bexley Heath near Dartford in Kent, but it was not until 1806 that a nest was found (by Montagu near Kingsbridge, Devonshire). Pennant published a description of the Kent pair in the 4th edition of his *Zoology* in 1776. At this time the Dartford Warbler was common in SW England, but became extinct in Devonshire soon after and probably lingered on into the last quarter of the 19th century in Cornwall. By then proven breeding records came only from SE England, with a probable breeding record as far north as Staffordshire. The main populations towards the end of the century were those in Hampshire and Surrey; other counties within the main range were the Isle of Wight, Dorset, Sussex, Berkshire and Wiltshire. Difficulty was expressed by many writers of the time in finding the nest of the Dartford Warbler, owing to the extent of the gorse scrub in existence at the time and the secretive nature of the birds whilst breeding. This led to a high price being put on authentic British specimens of the nest and eggs at auction and the resulting interest was blamed by some for the decline of the species in some counties (e.g. Bucknill 1900). In addition, the severe winters of 1880/81 and 1886/87 certainly did a great deal of damage to the population, particularly because the proximity of the events left little time for recovery. Before the end of the century the Dartford Warbler had probably become extinct in Cornwall, Dorset, Oxfordshire, Middlesex and London, Kent, Gloucestershire, Hertfordshire and Staffordshire. One or two pairs bred in Shropshire in 1903. It is likely that destruction of heathlands, particularly prior to the agricultural depression, by the development of arable agriculture and the decline of grazing was at least partly responsible for these extinctions.

A further severe winter in 1917 reduced the population to, probably, its lowest level since ornithological records began. However, a period of mild winters followed so that, by the 1930s, the Dartford Warbler was, once again, plentiful in its main breeding habitats. The 20th century continued with the same pattern—population crashes during severe winters followed by gradual recovery. Underlying this, however, the continual and gradual reduction of the gorse-rich heathlands throughout S England fragmented suitable breeding habitat so that recovery and expansion became more difficult and, in fact, counties such as Hertfordshire, Oxfordshire and Gloucestershire now have no suitable breeding habitat at all. Tubbs (1963, 1967) calculated that a peak of 450 pairs in Dorset, Hampshire and some adjacent counties in 1961 fell to just ten pairs in the 1963 breeding season after two successive hard winters. By 1966 22 pairs bred of which all but six were on the Dorset heaths. During the *68–72 Atlas* survey breeding took place mainly in Dorset and the Hampshire New Forest with a few pairs breeding west to Devon and east to Sussex. The first complete formal survey of this species in 1974 recorded that 560 pairs bred that year.

Since about 1970 a series of mild winters and the development of conservation and management strategies of heathland habitats have seen the population of the Dartford Warbler rise. A substantial population has developed in Surrey since 1974 in addition to the main Dorset and Hampshire groups (Batten *et al.* 1990). Pressures on the heathland habitats from afforestation and agricultural changes have now totally gone but housing and road building pressures still exist and we may yet see the loss of further breeding sites. Dereliction of sites following the cessation of grazing is a more difficult threat to combat. The *88–91 Atlas* recorded a population maximum of 950 pairs, a number that had probably not occurred since the first half of the 20th century.

Number of counties in which recorded:

Period	Probable breeding		Confirmed breeding		Combined		
	Br	Ir	Br	Ir	Br	Ir	Both
1875–1900	3	0	15	0	18	0	18
1968–1972	0	0	5	0	5	0	5
			change		−13	0	−13
					−72%		−72%

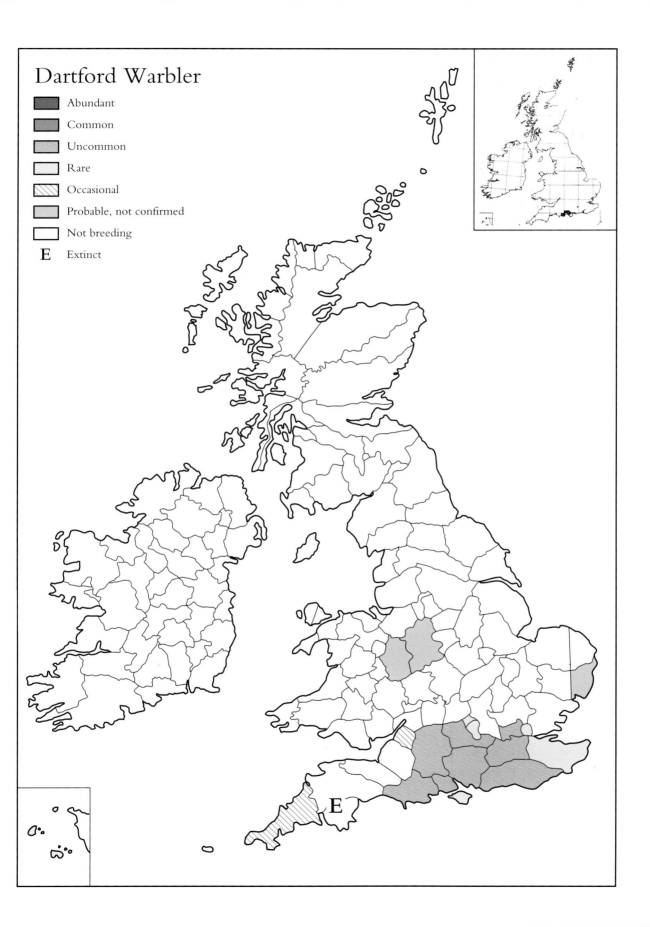

Dartford Warbler

- Abundant
- Common
- Uncommon
- Rare
- Occasional
- Probable, not confirmed
- Not breeding
- E   Extinct

E

Lesser Whitethroat

Sylvia curruca

The first specimen of the Lesser Whitethroat in Britain was collected near Bulstrode in Buckinghamshire by the Rev. John Lightfoot, and a figure and description of it was first published in the 1787 supplement of Latham's *A General Synopsis of Birds*. From that point naturalists attempted to elucidate the breeding distribution and status of the species. Up to the 1830s it was not known to breed any further north than the N Midlands. Even when More (1865) wrote his account he did not know of any nests having been found in N Wales but surmised that it bred rarely there. Gradually, during the rest of the 19th century, naturalists began to understand the status of the Lesser Whitethroat more clearly and the general conclusion reached was that it bred widely, but uncommonly, over much of England, being absent from Devonshire and Cornwall, but particularly common in the milder counties of the southeast. In Wales it had only been recorded in counties to the east of the Cambrian hills and, although recorded in Merioneth, it only bred as far west as Llanuwchllyn near Bala in the foothills of Snowdonia. Even in these counties it was regarded as rare or uncommon. In Scotland it was recorded breeding only in the most southern counties and seen in summer as far north as mid Argyll by Gray (1871), but, only the breeding records from Dumfriesshire and

Berwickshire appeared to be credible and were accepted by later writers. Only one record existed of the Lesser Whitethroat in Ireland, that of a bird on autumn passage shot on the 1st October 1890 on the Tearaght, Co. Kerry, the most western island in Europe.

During the early years of the 20th century the Lesser Whitethroat spread west to Devonshire (there is an unconfirmed record of breeding near Tiverton in 1886) where it nested sporadically until the 1930s when breeding appears to have become more regular. Very occasional breeding has taken place in Cornwall since 1906. Breeding remained very local in Wales and nests have been found as far west as Pembrokeshire and Anglesey, but breeding remains occasional in the west. Similarly, Baxter and Rintoul (1953) cited occasional nesting as far north as Ross and Inverness in Scotland but regular breeding in Scotland does not appear to have been established.

The distribution of the Lesser Whitethroat documented in the *68–72 Atlas* appears to have changed little since that recorded at the end of the 19th century. The *68–72 Atlas* map clearly shows the thin breeding distribution of the northern fringe but may also show a very slowly retreating boundary when compared with the map here. The *88–91 Atlas*, on the other hand, revealed a stronger westerly and northerly edge to the distribution that is probably a function of the fluctuating nature of populations of this species (Marchant *et al.* 1990). Breeding had been proven as far north as Orkney and, for the first time, in Ireland, but sporadic breeding records are not unusual for this species. It will remain to be seen whether a more widespread expansion will now occur.

Number of counties in which recorded:

Period	Probable breeding		Confirmed breeding		Combined		
	Br	Ir	Br	Ir	Br	Ir	Both
1875–1900	0	0	73	0	73	0	73
1968–1972	4	0	75	0	79	0	79
change					6	0	6
					8%		8%

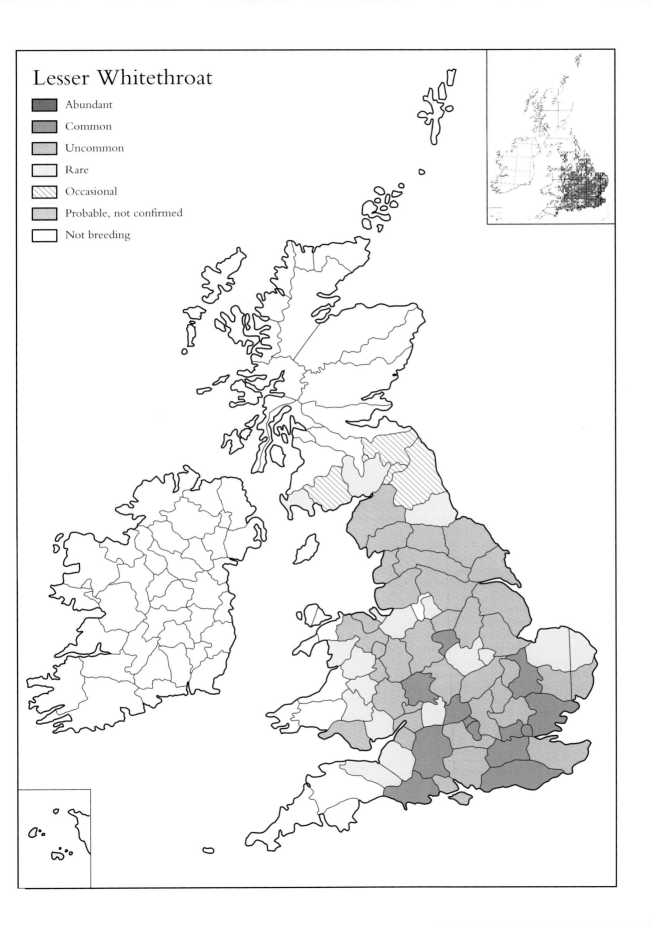

Lesser Whitethroat

- Abundant
- Common
- Uncommon
- Rare
- Occasional
- Probable, not confirmed
- Not breeding

Whitethroat (Common Whitethroat)

Sylvia communis

Throughout Britain and Ireland in the 19th century the Whitethroat was considered the commonest of the warblers and, often, the commonest of the summer migrants. It had readily taken to the hedges of the recent, and continuing, process of enclosure and found nesting sites in field corners, rough land, bramble patches and nettle beds—areas unchanged by the agricultural process. These habitats abounded in the 19th century but will have declined as enclosure continued, fields got larger and the agricultural process was sanitised (Grigg 1989).

In general, writers in the earlier years of the 19th century gave the impression that the Whitethroat was less common in Scotland and the extreme N of England than in the rest of its British range. Few confirmed records of Scottish breeding were published and those that exist were only of very local breeding in a few of the most sheltered valleys. Evidence of a northern expansion of the Whitethroat is implied by some of the authors of the accounts at the end of the 19th century. By that time there was no longer any doubt that the species was extremely common throughout N England, the Borders and Central Scotland. In Argyll, for instance, the species was recorded breeding on only one occasion prior to about 1850, yet Harvie-Brown and Buckley (1892) noted that it was common. In more northern parts of Scotland, however, it appeared to have recently become more common. This was especially clear in Sutherland where Selby (1835) considered it rare and More (1865) considered that it nested only occasionally. By the 1880s it was breeding regularly in a few localities in the east of the county and was adjudged common in some (Harvie-Brown and Buckley 1887). By 1904 it had been recorded breeding commonly in a number of localities in W Sutherland. In the Outer Hebrides too some evidence of colonisation survives. Gray (1871) wrote it was wholly unknown in the Outer Hebrides but Harvie-Brown (1888) was able to record it as 'far from uncommon' around Stornoway. At this time it had not been recorded breeding in Caithness or Orkney.

In Ireland it was said in the 19th century that few birds were more widespread than the Whitethroat although in some very bare mountain and moorland regions it did not occur (such as at Erris in W Mayo). Evidently some colonisation of islands had taken place during the 19th century, for instance Achill, but the species did not breed on the most exposed islands such as Aran.

Few further changes then appear to have occurred through the 20th century. The increase in numbers in N Scotland continued and during the 1950s numbers in some of the Inner Hebrides may have increased. Breeding was first recorded on the Isles of Scilly in 1965. Ruttledge (1966) recorded that a general decrease had occurred recently in Ireland. This relatively stable picture was altered dramatically in the breeding season of 1969. The CBC revealed that 77% of the 1968 breeding stock failed to return to Britain and Ireland in 1969. This catastrophic decrease was attributed to failure of the rains in the Whitethroat's wintering quarters in the Sahel area of W Africa causing heavy mortality there. Following this decline numbers gradually increased to between 35% and 50% of the pre-1968 level. During the winter of 1983/84 mortality occurred that resulted in a further crash to around 20% of the 1960s level. The population gradually increased until the sharp decline of 1991 reduced numbers again. The present distribution of the Whitethroat described in the *88–91 Atlas* shows areas of absence in N and central Scotland, the Scottish Borders, the Pennines, parts of central Wales and NE and SW Ireland.

Number of counties in which recorded:

Period	Probable breeding		Confirmed breeding		Combined		
	Br	Ir	Br	Ir	Br	Ir	Both
1875–1900	0	0	104	34	104	34	138
1968–1972	1	0	104	34	105	34	139
			change		1	0	1
					1%		1%

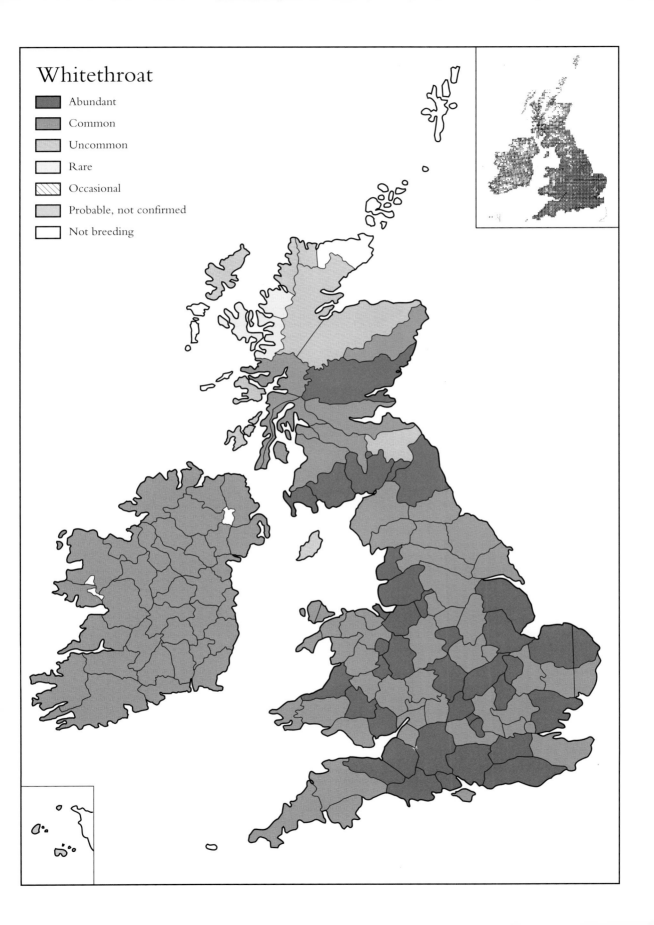

Whitethroat

- Abundant
- Common
- Uncommon
- Rare
- Occasional
- Probable, not confirmed
- Not breeding

Garden Warbler

Sylvia borin

The Garden Warbler was not formally recognised as a British breeding species until the closing years of the 18th century. As naturalists gradually assembled records the true distribution began to become clear, but Yarrell (1837–43) was apparently not aware that it bred in Cornwall, Wales or much of central and W England. In contrast, it had been observed throughout most of Scotland although Yarrell apparently knew of no breeding records. Records during the first half of the 19th century give an impression that the Garden Warbler was increasing in both range and numbers; however, it is likely that the increase reflected an improving understanding of the species and not a real expansion. At the end of the 19th century the Garden Warbler was recorded breeding very generally throughout England and Wales and as far north as Perth in Scotland. Numbers of Garden Warblers fluctuate quite significantly from year to year, however, and the timing of the 19th century accounts may have recorded the population at different stages of its cycle.

In Ireland, only one nest had been found up to about the middle of the century and the species was considered a great rarity at that time. During the rest of the century it was found to breed throughout Ireland albeit extremely locally. The main breeding areas appeared to be around the Shannon valley and the loughs of the midlands. It is likely that the apparent increase post-1850 was, in fact, only a measure of increasing familiarity with the species by local observers.

Few quantitive data are available for the 20th century but it is likely that the population throughout its British and Irish range changed very little during the first half. Anecdotal evidence suggests some local fluctuations, and most of these recorded small increases. As Parslow (1973) declared, the only thing that can be inferred from this period is that it is unlikely that there was any decrease. From around 1960 or so singing males were observed further north into Scotland than their normal breeding range. Few, if any, of these records concerned nests, however, until a pair was proven breeding in Orkney in 1960. More records followed throughout N Scotland so that, at the point of the *68–72 Atlas* survey period, a number of confirmed breeding records existed and regular breeding was taking place, especially around the Cromarty Firth. During recent decades breeding has remained very local in Ireland, where the species is puzzlingly patchily distributed, and is absent from many apparently suitable areas. The favoured localities appear still to be the lowland country around the midland loughs but the Garden Warbler is slowly decreasing in numbers in Ireland.

The *88–91 Atlas* recorded the consolidation of breeding in N Scotland, particularly the spread along the Great Glen. Otherwise little widespread difference of distribution can be discerned between the 19th century and that recorded during the two *Atlases*. CBC indices, however, documented the decline and recovery in the intervening period coincident with the Sahel drought. The Garden Warbler appears to have been affected less severely than other species as its winter quarters lie elsewhere in Africa and it was perhaps influenced only during passage through the area (Marchant *et al*. 1990).

Number of counties in which recorded:

Period	Probable breeding		Confirmed breeding		Combined		
	Br	Ir	Br	Ir	Br	Ir	Both
1875–1900	0	0	91	12	91	12	103
1968–1972	6	6	93	7	99	13	112
			change		8	1	9
					9%	8%	9%

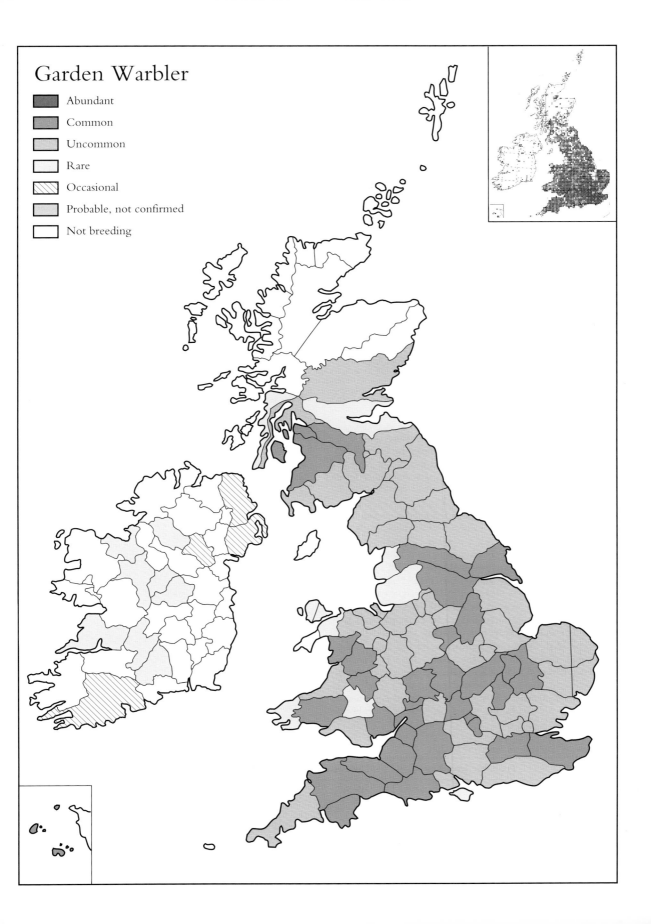

Garden Warbler

- **Abundant**
- **Common**
- **Uncommon**
- **Rare**
- **Occasional**
- **Probable, not confirmed**
- **Not breeding**

Blackcap

Sylvia atricapilla

During the last quarter of the 19th century the Blackcap was generally distributed throughout England and Wales although absent from the Lleyn peninsula in Caernarvonshire, Anglesey, the Isles of Scilly and the Isle of Man and rare in Pembrokeshire. It bred in its greatest numbers south of a line drawn from the Mersey estuary and the Wash. North of this line it bred more locally.

By 1900 the Blackcap had been recorded breeding in ten Irish counties but regularly in only five of these. In six others it had been observed on a number of occasions in the summer and may have bred. Ussher and Warren (1900) believed that it had increased in Waterford and Dublin and probably in some others but that its main breeding site in Ireland was Wicklow where it had been known through most of the 19th century. Parslow (1973) was doubtful about the accuracy of the statement by Alexander and Lack (1944) that the Blackcap had generally increased through the second half of the 19th century in Ireland and, perhaps, continued doing so into the 20th century. Parslow's impression was, in fact, of an erratically fluctuating population rather than one that showed a long-term tendency to change. The literature, however, has recorded a population that apparently withdrew from its patchy distribution

around the country at the end of the 19th century to its Wicklow stronghold by the 1960s. Although the *68–72 Atlas* survey recorded breeding in every county but Mayo, it was apparent that by then the Blackcap bred more commonly in the east of the country. This may confirm Parslow's suggestion that poor observer coverage underrecorded the species and that, over much of Ireland, the Blackcap was an erratic breeder.

In Scotland it bred frequently as far as S Perthshire but was sporadic north of this at the end of the century, but there was an indication that it was extending northwards then. More (1865) considered the Blackcap a very occasional breeding species beyond the Forth but Harvie-Brown's (1906) records steadily increased from about the 1880s to as far north as Dunkeld, Perthshire. It was seen irregularly in the Spey valley and as far north as the Great Glen but no nest was found during the last quarter of the 19th century.

During much of the 20th century there was little indication of any change in geographical range in Britain although it became apparent that the population fluctuated from year to year at its northern fringe. The Blackcap's northern regular breeding limit was shown to be around Inverness during the first half of the century although it was recorded breeding in Shetland in 1948 and Orkney in 1949. By the time of the *68–72 Atlas* survey Blackcaps had colonised the Isles of Scilly, Anglesey and the Isle of Man. That survey also hinted at increased numbers breeding in N England; breeding had evidently become less local in Lancashire and Yorkshire since the end of the 19th century. The *88–91 Atlas* confirmed the northward spread. The increase had become apparent in Scotland, especially in the south, and a discrete population is developing along the valley of the Great Glen. In addition there was a westward expansion in Ireland. The increase has been largely unexplained although it seems possible that improved winter survival is responsible (Gibbons *et al.* 1993).

Number of counties in which recorded:

Period	Probable breeding		Confirmed breeding		Combined		
	Br	Ir	Br	Ir	Br	Ir	Both
1875–1900	0	6	87	11	87	17	104
1968–1972	6	2	94	31	100	33	133
			change		13	16	29
					15%	94%	28%

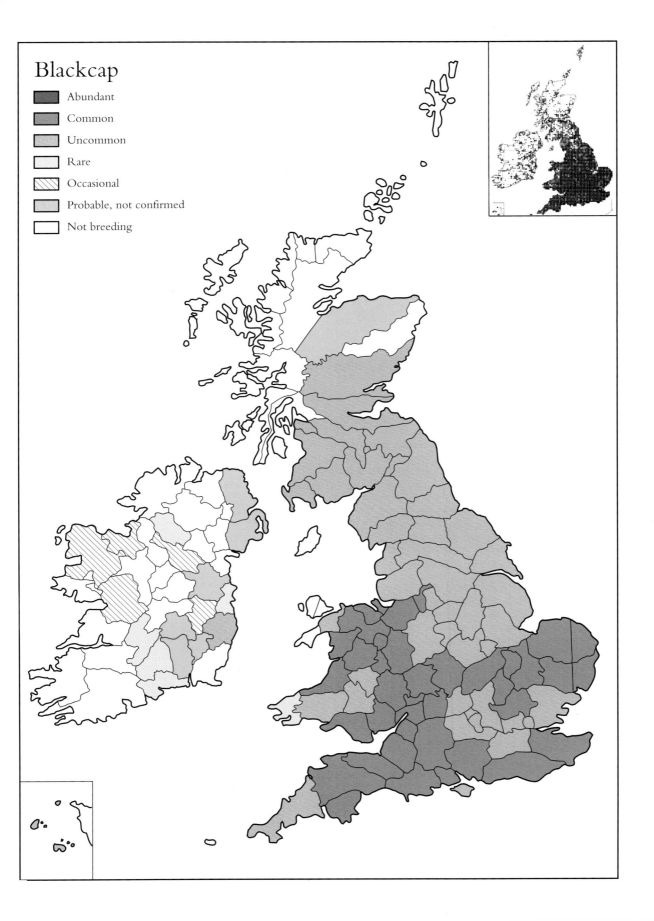

Blackcap

- **Abundant**
- **Common**
- **Uncommon**
- **Rare**
- **Occasional**
- **Probable, not confirmed**
- **Not breeding**

Wood Warbler (Wood Wren)

Phylloscopus sibilatrix

The Wood Warbler underwent an expansion of range during the 19th century. Yarrell (1837–43) had no record of its occurrence in Scotland at all although records furnished by Gladstone (1910) and others suggest that it did breed in Solway in the 1820s and 1830s and probably bred sparsely through the Borders and even as far north as the Forth/Clyde valley. Up to the 1860s its range expanded to the foothills of the Grampian Mountains and thereafter spread slowly further north. The Wood Warbler's spread northwards in the 19th century evidently took place along the west coast and thereafter it populated the valleys eastwards into the middle uplands confirmed, for example, by the first record in 1894 in the vicinity of Aviemore and apparently a number were recorded in the same area in 1895 (Dennis 1984). It remained very scarce in E Scotland, and especially on the east coast, throughout the 19th century. By 1900 the limit of its northerly breeding was probably Altnaharra, Sutherland although, on the west coast, it bred only very occasionally north of West Ross.

The Wood Warbler generally occurred in its highest numbers along the English south coastal counties, in the counties of the W Midlands and in N Wales. It was distinctly scarce or very local in some counties of the E Mid-

lands; it was confined to those woods that had sparse undergrowth and, in Bedfordshire for instance, conifer plantations were more frequently used by Wood Warblers than deciduous woods. In Cambridgeshire no nest had been found but birds had been recorded singing on a few occasions.

In Ireland the Wood Warbler was a very scarce, occasional summer visitor and, although a few records exist of singing males, only one (or possibly two) nests had ever been found. The records were distributed throughout the country but they appeared to become less frequent as the century progressed. A cluster of records from some Wicklow woods (especially near Powerscourt) suggested that they may have been annual visitors there.

In 1901 the first Wood Warbler was heard singing in the Isle of Man. In 1905 several were heard singing in the Elfin Glen and subsequently in Lhergy Frissel where the first Isle of Man nest was found in 1924. During the 20th century the increase in N Scotland continued slowly, and N Sutherland was finally colonised after the 1940s. In contrast, however, the species has decreased in England, particularly south of Humberside (Cramp 1977–94). It remains in its highest numbers in woods with a high canopy layer but a thin understorey and groundcover. In Britain this combination is most frequent where heavy grazing by herbivores has occurred over many years; where stock has been fenced out the woods become unsuitable for Wood Warblers. In some S English woods on poor soils, for instance sand or chalk, growth of the shrub layer may similarly be inhibited and these woods are particularly preferred by Wood Warblers. This preference for woods on poor soils had been noted in the 19th century, for instance in Sussex (Borrer 1891).

Since the *68–72 Atlas* it is apparent that losses are still occurring throughout much of S England but the species is consolidating its distribution in Scotland and, interestingly, it may be increasing in SW Wales, an area where it has always been scarce. Its main, and probably longest established, breeding centre in Ireland remains mid Wicklow and, at the present time, it is increasing here.

Number of counties in which recorded:

Period	Probable breeding		Confirmed breeding		Combined		
	Br	Ir	Br	Ir	Br	Ir	Both
1875–1900	0	3	96	3	96	6	102
1968–1972	9	2	91	1	100	3	103
	change				4	−3	1
					4%	−50%	1%

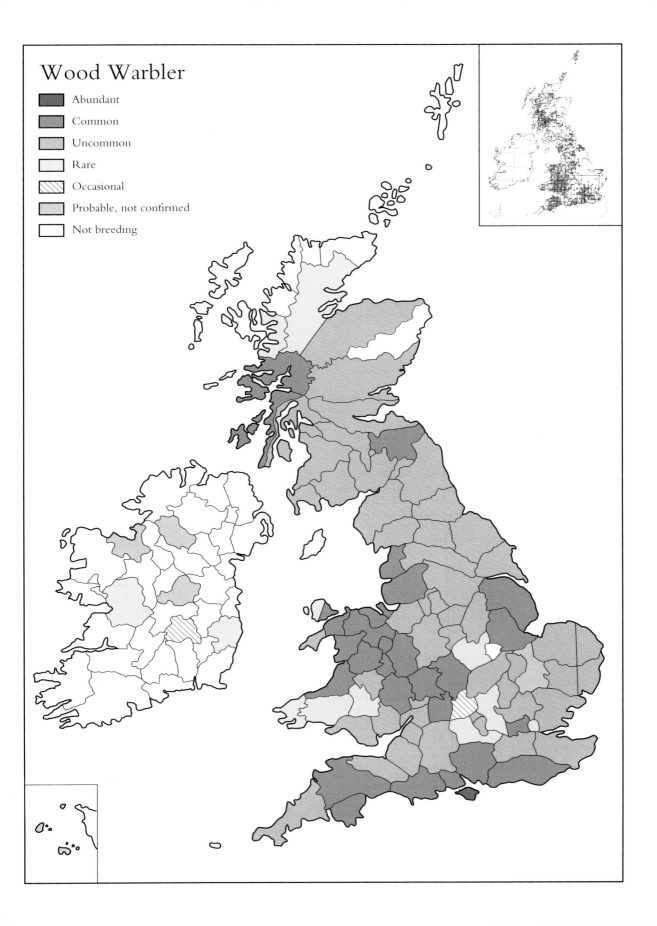

Wood Warbler

- ███ Abundant
- ███ Common
- ███ Uncommon
- ░░░ Rare
- ▨▨▨ Occasional
- ▒▒▒ Probable, not confirmed
- ☐ Not breeding

Chiffchaff

Phylloscopus collybita

The Chiffchaff underwent an expansion of range in the 19th century on two fronts. During the first half of the century only a few bred in S and SW England, and records from Wales were scant (Yarrell 1837–43, Morris 1851–57). In the Isle of Man it appears not to have been noticed before the 1880s. In these areas it apparently increased somewhat as the 19th century progressed, but the largest expansion of range was in Ireland. Before 1850 it was only known to have occurred in seven counties. In Down and Antrim in the northeast, small numbers were recorded around Belfast and other localities. It had been recorded regularly near Dublin and a small population frequented the south coast and coastal hills from Waterford to Cork. Other than this, two records existed in isolated areas, one of which was from near Tralee in Kerry. In 1864, it was recorded from only two areas. The expansion, when it occurred, must have been rapid for, although locally distributed and absent from, or rare in, exposed country, it was very generally distributed throughout Ireland by the end of the century. Even by the 1880s it was dismissed as 'frequent' in a list of Irish birds (More 1890).

In Britain Yarrell (1837–43) was unable to find any reference to the species further north than Northumberland and Westmoreland and, he believed that it did not breed in Scotland. In this he may have been mistaken: Morris (1851–57) noted that it had been observed in the Lothians,

albeit rarely, and in the neighbourhood of Edinburgh, although, once again, it was very rare. Significantly, there were no records of breeding—these early records may well have been of passage birds. Clearly, if it did breed in Scotland during the first half of the 19th century it was very rare indeed. From the first record of occurrence in Dumfriesshire in 1832 it may have increased slightly, as by the first decade of the 20th century it was breeding regularly, if locally, but was confined particularly to the coastal parishes. In the Tweed region it was regarded as rare in the 1830s (in Berwickshire) but then it evidently increased, as it was found distributed over most suitable localities by the end of the century. The first nest was not found in Tweed until that at Paxton in 1879. Several records existed of breeding in the Tay region but all of the eggs claimed as those of the Chiffchaff were dismissed as those of the Marsh Tit (Harvie-Brown 1906). Outside Scotland the Chiffchaff was a well-known species although much notice was made of the difficulty in separating it from other *Phylloscopus* species. The distinctive call was recognised as the primary distinguishing feature in the field and the first description of a wing formula to aid the discrimination of cabinet specimens of the Chiffchaff, Willow and Wood Warblers was published by Harting (1901).

The spread continued in Scotland very slowly during the 20th century and was especially noticeable from the 1950s (although care must be taken to allow for an increase in observer frequency and cover during recent decades). From this time numbers seemed to have increased in SW Scotland whilst singing birds, and occasionally nests, were recorded as far north as Caithness and in the Western Isles particularly where rhododendrons provide early spring cover (Parslow 1973, Sharrock 1976).

Number of counties in which recorded:

Period	Probable breeding		Confirmed breeding		Combined		
	Br	Ir	Br	Ir	Br	Ir	Both
1875–1900	0	0	92	34	92	34	126
1968–1972	7	0	100	34	107	34	141
			change		15	0	15
					16%		12%

344

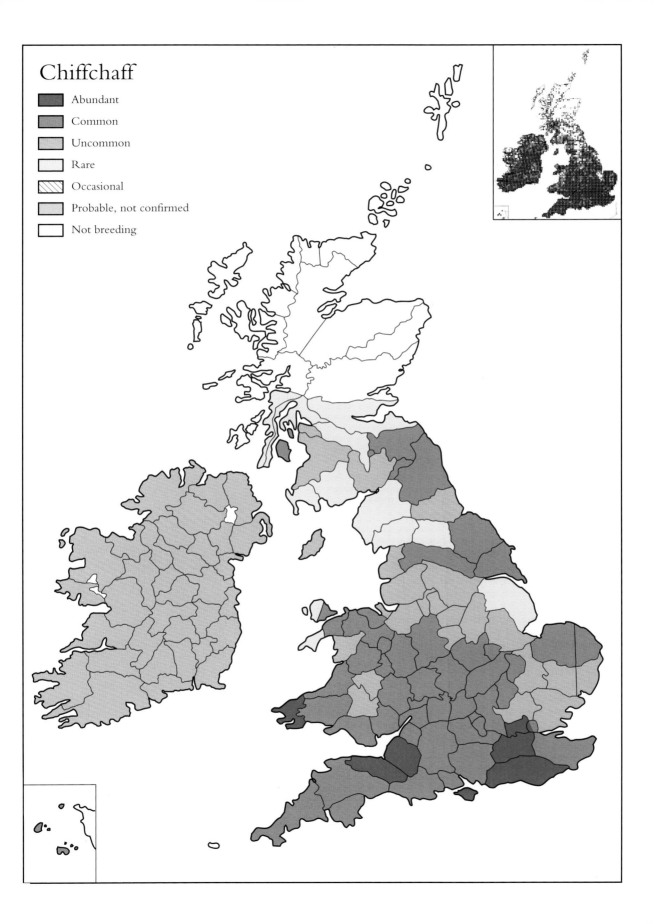

Chiffchaff

- ■ Abundant
- ■ Common
- ■ Uncommon
- □ Rare
- ▨ Occasional
- ▨ Probable, not confirmed
- □ Not breeding

Willow Warbler (Willow Wren)

Phylloscopus trochilus

The Willow Warbler was one of the commonest summer migrants in Britain and Ireland at the end of the 19th century. As far as the warblers are concerned, it was certainly the commonest in N England and Scotland, but elsewhere it was generally regarded as second in terms of abundance to the Whitethroat. It was absent, at this time, from the Isles of Scilly and Shetland, and breeding in Orkney and the Outer Hebrides was only a possibility. Willow Warblers were first observed singing in Orkney at the end of the 1880s and in the Outer Hebrides from 1876, but they probably bred in Harris in 1879. An increasing number of Willow Warblers were reported singing throughout the Outer Hebrides from 1879 until by about 1890 they appeared every year, and were widely distributed and common. The Fen district of parts of Norfolk, Lincolnshire, Cambridgeshire and Huntingdonshire held fewer numbers than other parts of the country probably reflecting a lack of suitable breeding habitat. Thinner numbers also frequented SW Wales. There is some evidence that the Willow Warbler was undergoing a western expansion of range at this time. Colonel Montagu at the beginning of the 19th cen-

tury believed that it did not frequent Devonshire and Cornwall and, by inference, Yarrell (1837–43) suggested that it was absent from Wales. In Ireland it was very numerous and widespread throughout the country except for parts of Donegal, W Connaught and the extreme south-west, notably along the western edge of the country.

Up to the 1930s the Willow Warbler was recorded breeding commonly everywhere except for the extreme N of Scotland and Skye (Witherby *et al.* 1938–41). Colonisation of the Isles of Scilly occurred around this time and it had nested occasionally in Shetland. As the 20th century progressed no widespread population changes occurred but there were records of some local increases and decreases. The Willow Warbler took advantage of the emerging conifer plantations (Parslow 1973). It breeds readily in plantations that are less than 15 years old, and this has enabled it to colonise areas of upland and moorland where previously breeding sites did not exist (Sharrock 1976).

The *68–72* and *88–91 Atlases* revealed no widespread change prior to 1968 and almost none during the intervening period. Further consolidation of the Outer Hebrides population by 1991 was the only apparent change. The 20th century distribution and population of the Willow Warbler, then, was more or less stable. This stability followed the consolidation of the population in Cornwall, W Wales and W Ireland in the late 19th and early 20th centuries. This consolidation itself may have been preceded by an expansion of range into those western areas although the evidence for this is slight. Major population fluctuations of this species in W Europe have not been recognised during the last 100 years.

Number of counties in which recorded:

Period	Probable breeding		Confirmed breeding		Combined		
	Br	Ir	Br	Ir	Br	Ir	Both
1875–1900	2	0	104	34	106	34	140
1968–1972	0	0	107	34	107	34	141
			change		1	0	1
					1%		1%

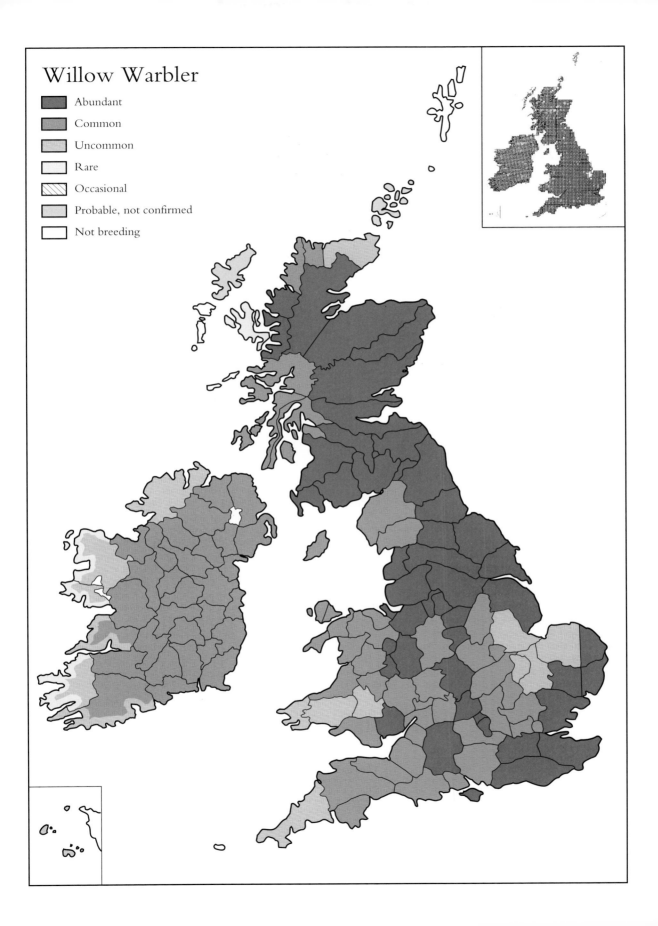

Willow Warbler

- Abundant
- Common
- Uncommon
- Rare
- Occasional
- Probable, not confirmed
- Not breeding

Goldcrest (Golden-crested Wren, Golden-crested Regulus, Golden-crested Kinglet)

Regulus regulus

The status of the Goldcrest in Britain before the middle of the 19th century is difficult to determine. Yarrell (1837–43) gave few examples of breeding records although he noted that it was generally distributed in S England and Wales, was common in Ireland and that it had been observed throughout the rest of England and Scotland as far north as Orkney and Shetland. He did not, however, distinguish between summer and winter birds and so it is difficult to determine the Goldcrest's breeding range at this time. More (1865) was more positive. He wrote that it bred as far north as Sutherland and Caithness but not in the Scottish Isles. It is interesting to speculate on the species, Scottish distribution prior to the felling of the native pine forests—perhaps it had been common there up to the end of the 18th century (S. da Prato in litt.).

Gray (1871) appears to have been the first to note an increase in Goldcrest numbers up to the 1870s. He drew attention to the records of Scottish ornithology that attested to its rarity during the first decade of the century: 'Nor can this be wondered at when it is considered that the numerous fir plantations now beautifying the borders of our lakes and covering our hills with their tall green spires could hardly then have been in existence'. As conifer plantations increased in extent so the Goldcrest increased in numbers and distribution. Its spread through Scotland was dependent on these new plantations but it remained infrequent and very local in the west and in the bare uplands.

Baxter and Rintoul (1953) were able to trace the expansion of the Goldcrest's range in Scotland to an earlier period. The records of birds in the old Statistical Account suggest that the Goldcrest had recently colonised parts of S and mid Scotland in the 1780s and 1790s although it had bred at Strichen, Aberdeenshire in conifer plantations since at least the middle of the 18th century. By the time that the New Statistical Account (1834–45) was written it had apparently increased and regular breeding was taking place as far north as Banff and Moray.

The avifaunas of the last quarter of the 19th century were able to add several of the smaller Western Isles and Orkney to the list of breeding sites. A nest was found on Eigg in 1882 and young birds were seen in 1885. The Goldcrest was considered not uncommon in the 1880s in the young larch plantations on Mull, Jura and Islay and a little later on Bute. On Skye it bred 'in the larger woodlands, but [was] not very numerous'. In Orkney, however, the breeding records were old and it had not been proven to breed after the middle of the century.

In Ireland it was considered more common than in England and bred in every county. This is true today (both in conifer and deciduous woods) and is likely to be due to a higher winter survival rate in the more equable Irish climate (Gibbons *et al.* 1993). Its colonisation of the bleak west (mainly in Connaught) may have occurred during the second half of the 19th century and was achieved only following the maturation of plantations there. For instance, by 1900 it bred regularly in plantations in Achill Sound, Mayo but was only known as a winter visitor there in 1875 and prior to that was unknown.

The Goldcrest population continued to increase through the 20th century. From about the 1930s the maturation of the conifers planted following the 1914–18 war began a new wave of increases in Goldcrest numbers. Several marine islands, for example in the Hebrides, the Northern Isles and the Isles of Scilly, have been colonised as plantations there have matured and numbers have increased. This is particularly true of the Outer Hebrides and Orkney. The CBC returns have demonstrated the extent to which the Goldcrest is affected by the recent series of cold winters and cool summers from the high population levels of the early 1970s.

Number of counties in which recorded:

Period	Probable breeding		Confirmed breeding		Combined		
	Br	Ir	Br	Ir	Br	Ir	Both
1875–1900	0	0	102	34	102	34	136
1968–1972	0	0	108	34	108	34	142
			change		6	0	6
					6%		4%

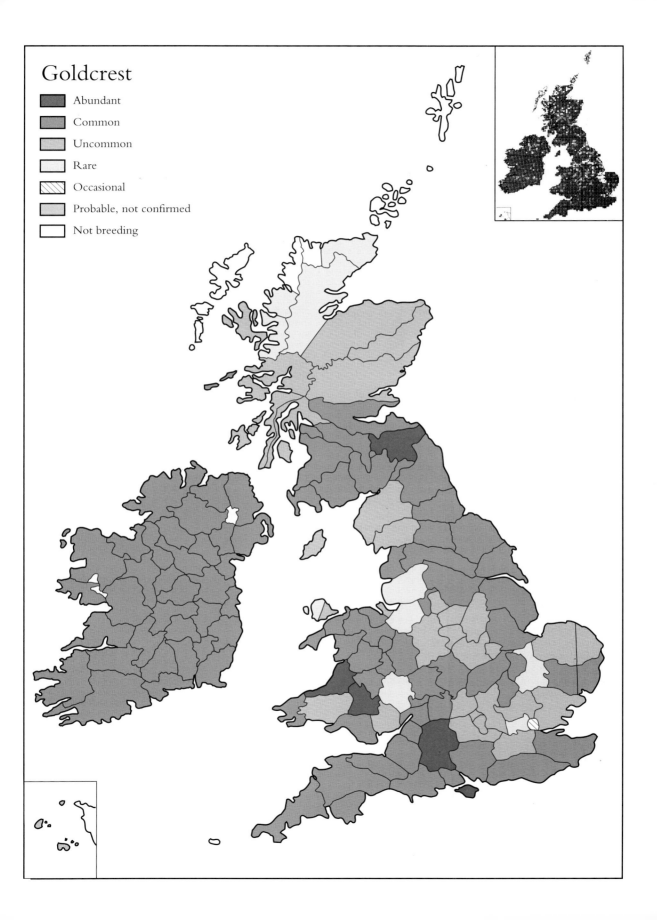

Goldcrest

- Abundant
- Common
- Uncommon
- Rare
- Occasional
- Probable, not confirmed
- Not breeding

Spotted Flycatcher

Muscicapa striata

By the end of the 19th century the Spotted Flycatcher was distributed almost universally throughout Britain and Ireland. It was absent only from the Outer Hebrides, Orkney (although it colonised the islands briefly in 1867 at Melsetter) and Shetland, and bred less commonly in N and NW Scotland and in W Ireland. In these latter two regions it may have been increasing. In Ireland, in the 1830s, Thompson (in Yarrell 1837–43) noted it as occurring only in Ulster. By 1900 it was recorded in every Irish county but it was believed to have increased in the west during the last couple of decades of the century. In Assynt, in West Ross, it was not recorded prior to 1878 but by 1902 several pairs were breeding around Inchnadamph and in Caithness, Harvie-Brown and Buckley (1887) believed that breeding began there sometime during the 1860s. Graham (1890) had not recorded the Spotted Flycatcher in Mull up to about 1871, but Harvie-Brown and Buckley (1892) recorded it breeding commonly there by that year. Elsewhere in Scotland it penetrated into the hills as far as trees grew and was commonly found in the gardens of the hill cottages, but it avoided bare mountainside. Note was often made throughout Britain of fluctuations year to year in the numbers returning to breed but the Spotted Flycatcher was generally considered one of the commonest of the summer migrants.

Little widespread change appears to have occurred in distribution through the 20th century. Locally, however, some changes are recorded. Breeding became established during the 1940s in the Outer Hebrides and has continued in small numbers since. Similarly, breeding recommenced in Orkney during the late 1950s and two or three pairs breed annually there. Nesting was first recorded on Lundy, off the N Devonshire coast, in 1956 and has occurred irregularly since. However, regular breeding ceased in the extreme SW of Pembrokeshire in 1939, although a pair bred in 1948.

The *68–72 Atlas* showed that the distribution of the Spotted Flycatcher in Britain and Ireland during the study period was similar to that of the 19th century. The *68–72 Atlas* map, however, does not reveal the 50% decline in the CBC index that had occurred from 1965 to 1976. Similarly, the *88–91 Atlas* recorded little further distributional change in Britain but CBC figures had fallen further to a point about a quarter of that in the early 1960s. In Ireland, the oft declared decline, from Kennedy *et al.* (1954) onwards, was confirmed by absences recorded, especially, in the west and southwest.

No single factor has caused this decline. Certainly, the number of Spotted Flycatchers returning from their winter quarters fell dramatically in the springs of 1983 and 1984 and the species has subsequently disappeared from known breeding areas where there has been no obvious change (D. Summers-Smith in litt.). This decline coincided with the failure of the rains in the Sahel region used on passage to and from the wintering grounds in southern Africa. A series of cooler, wetter and later springs in Britain and Ireland of recent years will have adversely affected the breeding success of the species: more pairs breed earlier and lay larger clutches when temperatures in May are higher and the species' insect prey are likely to be more abundant (Gibbons *et al.* 1993).

Number of counties in which recorded:

Period	Probable breeding		Confirmed breeding		Combined		
	Br	Ir	Br	Ir	Br	Ir	Both
1875–1900	0	0	104	34	104	34	138
1968–1972	0	0	107	34	107	34	141
			change		3	0	3
					3%		2%

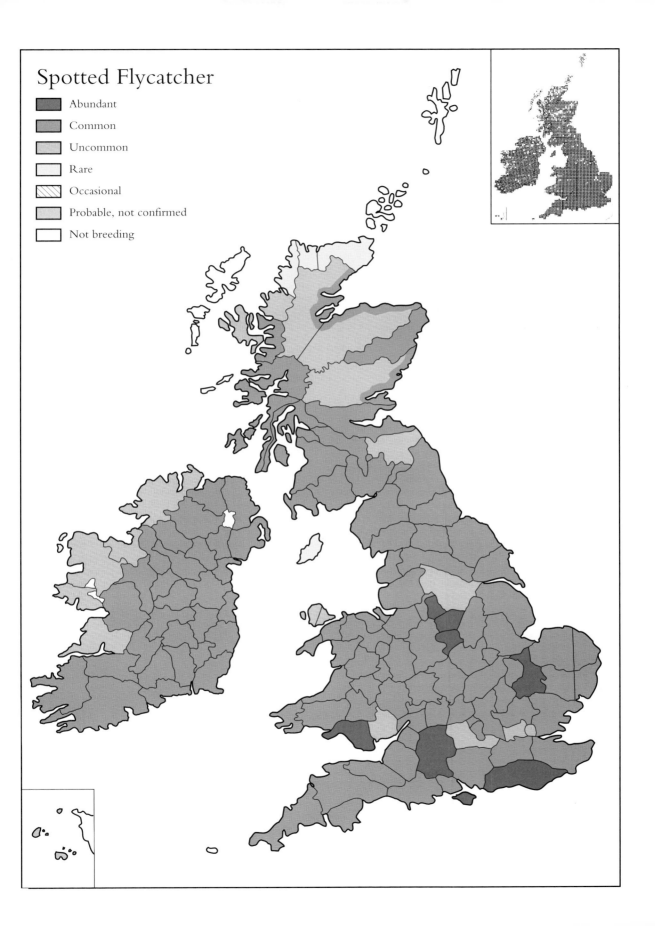

Spotted Flycatcher

- ■ Abundant
- ■ Common
- ■ Uncommon
- □ Rare
- ▨ Occasional
- ▨ Probable, not confirmed
- □ Not breeding

Pied Flycatcher

Ficedula hypoleuca

The scarcity of the Pied Flycatcher in Britain in the first half of the 19th century is demonstrated by the Rev. F. O. Morris' (1851–57) comment, 'With us it is very local [compared with parts of continental Europe]; and like the majority of ornithologists, I have never seen it alive'. Up to the middle of the 19th century it had been recorded breeding from London to the Scottish border and very occasionally in Wales, but, by the last quarter of the 19th century, the main population appears to have been centred around the lakes of Cumberland and Westmorland with sparse numbers breeding regularly in Northumberland, Durham and N Yorkshire. It probably also bred regularly in NE Wales; it may have been confined to Denbighshire and Flintshire, but there are few records.

As the century progressed the true status of the Pied Flycatcher became clear. In N Wales, a survey by E. A. Swainson organised via *The Field* in 1893 and Forrest (1907) ascertained that it bred regularly, and commonly, through all of the mainland N Wales counties. Records from S Wales indicate that, if at all, it bred only irregularly and rarely prior to the 1880s. It was considered far from uncommon in Brecon by 1899, but had appeared in unusually high numbers in 1897 and in Glamorgan only one 19th

century breeding record exists, of a nest in the castle grounds at Cardiff sometime before 1891 (Drane and Proger 1891), although this was later questioned (Cardiff Naturalists' Society 1925). It was said to have been abundant in the upper Towy valley in Carmarthenshire (Barker 1905). These, and other, records perhaps indicate that there had been an expansion of range southwards from the N Wales core population during the closing years of the 19th century. It is evident that the same was happening in an easterly direction into the English border counties. The Pied Flycatcher bred in small numbers near Ludlow, Shropshire and in W Herefordshire by the 1890s. A single record exists of a nest found in 1882 in Sutton Park, Warwickshire. Although now regarded with some suspicion (Cohen 1963), there were several breeding records from the New Forest giving the impression that, if identified correctly, there was a small group breeding regularly there. Extraordinary early records from Surrey, at Peckham in 1812 and two nests near Tooting, undated but published in 1834, were apparently considered acceptable by respected contemporary ornithologists

Pied Flycatchers seen on passage were apparently more common in the early 1800s but a decline was noted in SE England up to the 1880s. At this time, however, an increase in passage birds was noted, most notably in Kent (Ticehurst 1909) which provides complementary evidence of the increase in Pied Flycatcher breeding numbers that probably occurred in Britain at the end of the 19th century. In May 1884 the first nest was found in N Northumberland and in the same year the Pied Flycatcher was found breeding for the first time in Dumfries-shire. Clearly it bred through the Borders in small numbers prior to this year (Evans 1911), but in the spring of 1885 a considerable influx took place and a number of breeding attempts were noted. Little more was recorded until very large numbers were reported during the passage of 1898 and 1899.

From this point numbers increased slowly in Wales and the Borders but no widespread expansion of range was noted until the 1940s when it colonised 5 new counties (Sharrock 1976). Breeding has since consolidated further in the species' main breeding range and it now breeds regularly throughout W England, Wales and Scotland to the Great Glen, sporadically elsewhere in Britain and, very occasionally, in Ireland.

Number of counties in which recorded:

Period	Probable breeding		Confirmed breeding		Combined		
	Br	Ir	Br	Ir	Br	Ir	Both
1875–1900	0	0	31	0	31	0	31
1968–1972	4	0	49	0	53	0	53
			change		22	0	22
					71%		71%

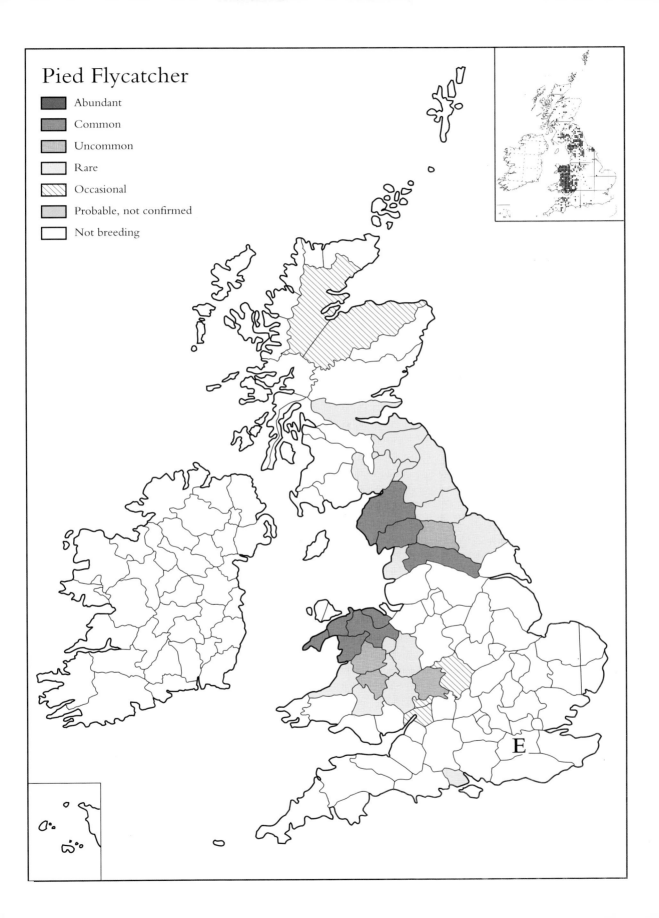

Pied Flycatcher

- Abundant
- Common
- Uncommon
- Rare
- Occasional
- Probable, not confirmed
- Not breeding

E

Bearded Tit
(Bearded Titmouse)

Panurus biarmicus

Drainage and the resulting conversion of land to agricultural use had so reduced the extent of suitable reed beds by the 1860s that even then it was clear that the Bearded Tit was fast disappearing. It was still breeding in E Suffolk, Norfolk and, possibly, Lincolnshire and along the banks of the Thames in Surrey and, probably, Essex (More 1865). It was already extinct in Sussex, Cambridgeshire and Huntingdonshire and had bred occasionally, in the past, in Kent, Gloucestershire and W Yorkshire. In Surrey, it did not breed after 1850, and in Kent and Essex the last nests were found in the 1870s, and 1868, respectively.

By the last quarter of the 19th century it had become extinct everywhere but Norfolk and, although said to have been extinct in Suffolk in 1874, it probably hung on in very small numbers throughout this period, but may have ceased breeding for a short period during the 1870s. Numbers in Norfolk, however, had been decreasing for some years. As Bearded Tits became rarer, the demand for skins led to their wholesale slaughter during the winter and the value of their eggs caused many to be taken. Following the

mild 1862/63 winter when numbers were relatively high, 'about five dozen eggs' and several birds were taken at Hickling by a dealer. This persecution was still taking place in the 1890s—in 1890 eight birds slaughtered by a shooting party were offered for sale but were so badly mutilated by the duck shot used to kill them that they would have made poor stuffed specimens (Stevenson 1866–90). They sold, however, such was their rarity. The decline in the Broads was caused by a combination of severe persecution and loss of habitat following the extensive drainage that had taken place since the 18th century. Gurney (1899) estimated the numbers of nests in the Broads from accounts of fensmen and others; his figures graphically illustrated the decline: 1848, 160 nests; 1858, 140 nests; 1868, 125 nests; 1878, 90 nests; 1888, 45 nests; 1898, 33 nests (the 1848 estimate was revised in 1900 to 170 nests).

In Suffolk during the 19th century, the Bearded Tit had been recorded breeding in many reed beds and along the banks of a number of rivers. Most of these sites were destroyed which led to the belief that the Bearded Tit was extinct in the county (Yarrell 1871–85). Newton wrote, in 1874, that he had no proof that it nested at that time. Babington (1884–86) asserted in his main account that it was probably extinct; he had no breeding records later than the 1860s, but in his appendix he noted that in 1886 it had been found in some numbers on Oulton Broad. It had bred on and off here before this date and probably bred for a few years afterwards. In 1883 a dealer named Smith attempted to exterminate the species on the R. Waveney (thereby increasing the value of specimens), along which almost all the Suffolk nests were built, and evidently almost succeeded. In 1900, Gurney stated that he believed that the Bearded Tit was almost extinct in Suffolk again.

After 1900 the Bearded Tit tended to increase in both Suffolk and Norfolk but the severe winters of 1917, 1940 and 1947 reduced numbers substantially—following the 1947 winter the known population was reduced to 2–4 pairs in Suffolk and a single male in Norfolk. After each of these set-backs, however, numbers recovered quickly. Since about 1960 immigration from the massive populations in the newly created Netherlands polders caused a rapid rise in British numbers (Mead and Pearson 1974). Small numbers began to breed regularly in Essex and Kent and over the next few years the Bearded Tit bred sporadically in at least three other counties. Since that time the species has spread along the coast, both north and west, and now breeds regularly from the Humber to Dorset.

Number of counties in which recorded:

Period	Probable breeding		Confirmed breeding		Combined		
	Br	Ir	Br	Ir	Br	Ir	Both
1875–1900	0	0	2	0	2	0	2
1968–1972	0	0	11	0	11	0	11
			change		9	0	9
					450%		450%

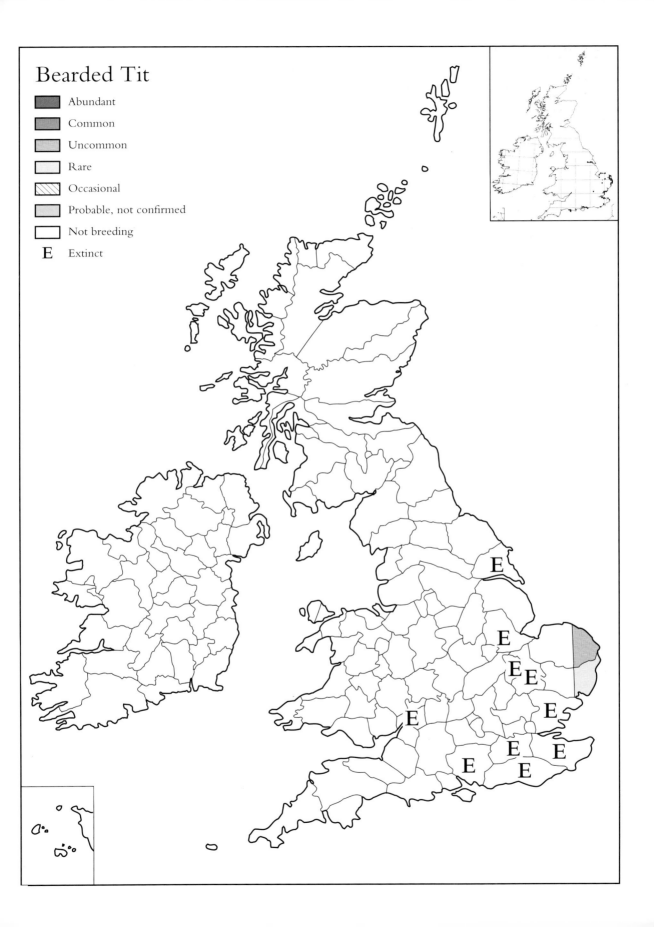

Bearded Tit

- Abundant
- Common
- Uncommon
- Rare
- Occasional
- Probable, not confirmed
- Not breeding
- E Extinct

Long-tailed Tit

Aegithalos caudatus

The Long-tailed Tit was distributed more or less commonly throughout Britain and Ireland during the 19th century but, as with many other small passerines, was largely absent from most of the islands. It occurred in its largest numbers south of a line drawn from the Dee estuary to the Humber and gradually became less frequent further north, although it was notably frequent in some parts of the Highlands of Scotland at this time. It was considered abundant in some parts of West Ross in the 1880s and 1890s when it also occurred frequently on Speyside. In the northern parts of the Moray region it occurred locally round the SE coast of Sutherland, and up the adjacent straths (broad, Highland valleys). In the Highlands it frequented the birch woods where it bred regularly, but locally, as far north as Tongue in Sutherland but had not been recorded from the west of that county. It was not common in the tree-less areas of Fenland or the uplands of N England. Locally, particularly in areas surrounding the largest cities but also elsewhere, it had been almost exterminated through the collection of nests as curios; these were fashionable items for display in numerous Victorian parlours (Tomes 1901).

In Ireland there was evidence of an increase during the 19th century. Before the middle of the century Thompson considered that it was distributed throughout the north but

in only a few numbers; if it occurred further south it did so very sporadically (Yarrell 1837–43, Ussher and Warren 1900). By the end of the century it was common throughout the woods over the greater part of Ireland but became scarcer as the trees thinned in the extreme west.

Little note was made of the effect of severe winters on Long-tailed Tits during the 19th century, but those of the 1880s and 1890s would probably have reduced numbers. The great mortality caused by such winters in the 20th century (Parslow 1973), especially those with prolonged frost, has been noted and following the worst of these (for instance a severe frost in early 1917) Long-tailed Tits remained scarce for a number of years. During the 20th century the Long-tailed Tit was recorded breeding in the Outer Hebrides (a family party was seen by a party of visiting ornithologists in the Stornoway woods in 1939), W Sutherland (first breeding record in 1960), in Caithness and in some of the Inner Hebrides. Most of these colonisations proved to be transient and the species remains scarce in the N and W Scottish mainland and islands. Elsewhere local changes have been noted, particularly in combination with habitat loss, for instance when widescale hedgerow grubbing has occurred; but overall no widespread changes in status have taken place in Britain since, at least, the early years of the 19th century and, in Ireland since the closing years of that century.

Number of counties in which recorded:

Period	Probable breeding		Confirmed breeding		Combined		
	Br	Ir	Br	Ir	Br	Ir	Both
1875–1900	0	0	101	34	101	34	135
1968–1972	0	0	104	34	104	34	138
			change		3	0	3
					3%		2%

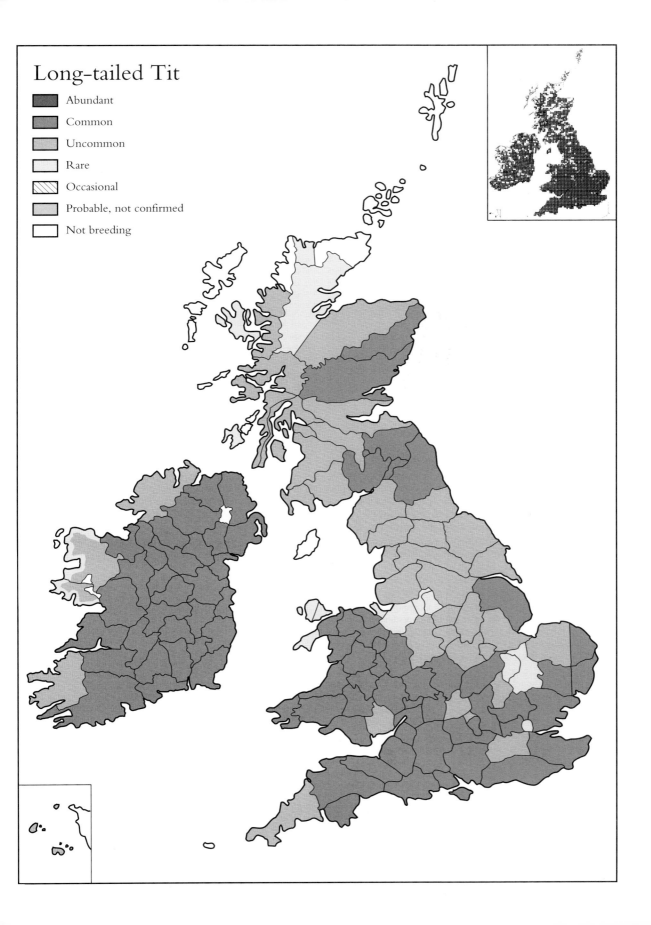

Long-tailed Tit

- Abundant
- Common
- Uncommon
- Rare
- Occasional
- Probable, not confirmed
- Not breeding

Marsh and Willow Tit

Parus palustris and P. montanus

The Willow Tit was first distinguished from the Marsh Tit in Britain from a specimen collected in Coalfall Wood near Finchley in Middlesex in 1897 and described by Hellmayr in 1900. Lord Rothschild published the first full description in *British Birds*, in 1907. It is clear, then, that all 19th century records of black-capped tits attributed to the Marsh Tit include records of Willow Tit and the consequent distribution map is a composite of the distribution of both species. In practice, as has become evident from 20th century research, it is likely that the majority of 19th century Scottish records were of the Willow Tit. The 1893 Aviemore breeding record (see below), attributed at the time to the Marsh Tit, was, on subsequent examination of specimens collected, found to have been of Willow Tits. When this discovery was made no other Willow Tit breeding site was known further north than Middlesex (Harvie-Brown 1906). As all 19th century records were considered to have been of the Marsh Tit, that name is used for those records.

In the 19th century the Marsh Tit bred commonly throughout most of England and Wales, although locally in most counties. In Cornwall it was found breeding regularly in the east but was rare in the west and was regarded as sparingly distributed in Leicestershire and Rutland. No authenticated records exist for Anglesey (Forrest 1907), the Isles of Scilly or the Isle of Man.

In Scotland the Marsh Tit was distributed mainly along the eastern counties as far north as Speyside. In the Tweed and Forth regions it was a familiar bird and was met with commonly but locally. It was recorded rarely in Dumfriesshire but earlier accounts suggest that it may have been more common in the first quarter of the 19th century and, although observed on a very few occasions, it had not been proven breeding anywhere else in the Solway region. In Ayrshire, Lanarkshire and Dunbartonshire it was recorded very occasionally but had not

been recorded from Argyll. The Marsh Tit was recorded breeding very sporadically through the Tay region, but, although observed on a few occasions, no breeding records exist from Dee. The first fully authenticated record in Moray was an observation of a Marsh Tit in Strathspey in 1889 and then, in 1893, two nests were found near Aviemore. These nests remained the most northerly breeding records of the species in the 19th century.

It took a number of years following the recognition of the Willow Tit to work out the relative distribution of the two species and so, until that became clear, it is difficult to judge early trends. The Marsh Tit's English and Welsh distribution in the 20th century has probably changed little since the 19th but a small expansion of range into SE Scotland has occurred. It was observed in Berwickshire in the 1920s but the first nest was not found until 1945 (Baxter and Rintoul 1953). This population has since consolidated and Marsh Tits now breed regularly and have spread into some of the neighbouring Border counties. Since at least the late 1960s a slow decline has been taking place and at the present time the Marsh Tit has an all-time low CBC index. In addition, the *88–91 Atlas* records a 17% decline in its distribution since the *68–72 Atlas*. The causes of the decline may include inter-specific competition with other tit species for food (Marchant *et al.* make the point that all other tit species have apparently become more common since CBC records began) and for nesting sites, and a lack of suitable nest holes in managed woods (Marchant *et al.* 1990).

The first reasonably comprehensive outline of Willow Tit distribution in Britain was completed in 1937; later, more detailed, local surveys have filled in the gaps. It is not possible to quantify any population trends of this species prior to the *68–72 Atlas* survey, but it does appear to have been withdrawing from Scotland since the 1930s or 1940s. At that time it bred as far north as Ross-shire but during the *88-91 Atlas* survey only one record of breeding was collected. It has also decreased in parts of S Scotland but overall the *88–91 Atlas* recorded a contraction of range of about 10% since the *68–72 Atlas* survey. There has been no other significant change in either numbers or distribution.

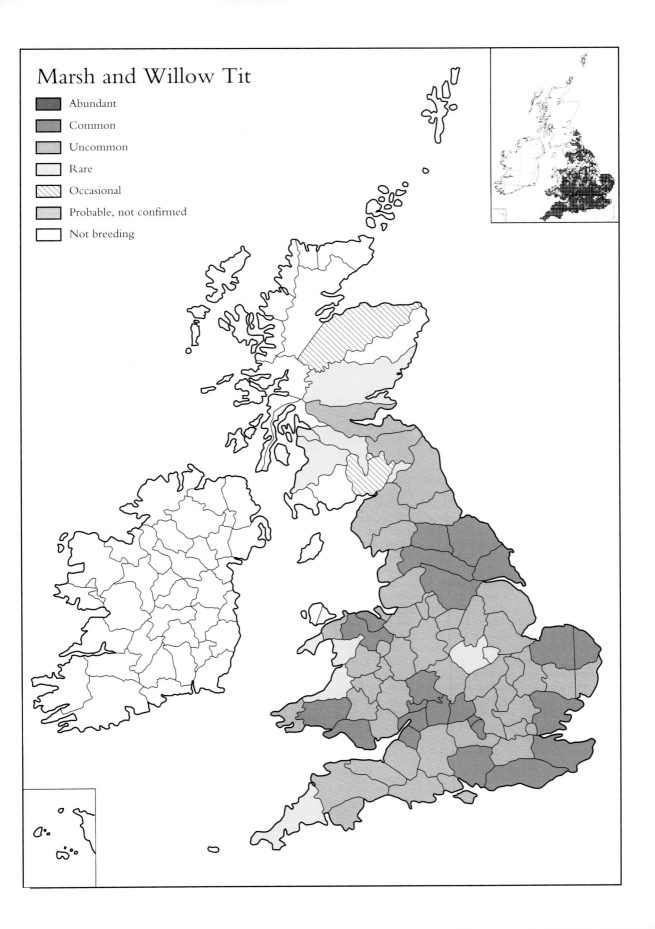

Marsh and Willow Tit

- Abundant
- Common
- Uncommon
- Rare
- Occasional
- Probable, not confirmed
- Not breeding

Crested Tit

Parus cristatus

In the 18th century the Crested Tit was not known to breed in Scotland. It was first observed in 1789 and Bewick (1797–1804) considered it a very rare visitor. As the 19th century progressed it became clear to the contemporary naturalists that it did indeed breed and that it was confined to the woods of the Spey Valley. Harvie-Brown and Buckley (1895) described the known distribution of the Crested Tit at that time as follows.'The Crested Tit is resident, and seldom seen outside the pine woods, or where pine woods are mingled with hardwoods, or at any great distance from these. It occurs over an extent of country about thirty miles in length, and varying in width from three miles to ten miles, here and there, over the whole area of the pine tracts of Spey valley, in Abernethy, and Rothiemurchus, and Dulnan (Dulnain), up to the base of the Cairngorms, above Loch Morlich and the Larig Ghru; and down the valley of Spey nearly to Ballindalloch, where … it breeds in one locality. Perhaps nowhere is it more abundant than along the banks of the Upper Nethy from Forest Lodge, up as far as the old pine reaches, and from that through the Sluggan Pass of Abernethy into and along Glen More and Loch Morlich side, continuing at intervals down as far as Aviemore, wherever suitable ground and shelter is afforded.

They stretch across the Spey to the west bank, and over into the old wood of Crannach near Dulnan.' Although aware of a recent record from the woods near Cawdor Castle, Harvie-Brown and Buckley had not been able to confirm any records in the valleys connecting Cawdor with the main breeding range (it took a further 10–15 years to fill in the gaps along the Findhorn Valley). Confirmation that the Crested Tit was expanding its range along the Spey Valley occurred in 1899 when two nests were found in a wood just outside Fochabers. It seems probable that the Crested Tit bred more widely when the Caledonian Forest was more extensive but most of the old forest was destroyed prior to the 19th century and the species' former distribution can only be guessed at.

If the apparent extension of range noted at the end of the century was not just a function of increased familiarity it was facilitated by the maturation of the Scots pines planted in the area since the end of the 18th century. Further plantings in the 19th and 20th centuries have allowed the Crested Tit to expand its range into other areas of the Moray Basin. The stronghold of the species has remained centred on the Spey Valley but it has spread towards, and east along, the coast as far as Banff. Local breeding also now takes place around the Cromarty Firth, SE Sutherland and W Inverness-shire.

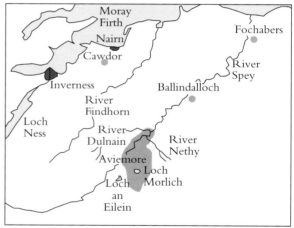

The breeding range of the Crested Tit.
From Harvie-Brown and Buckley (1895)

Number of counties in which recorded:

Period	Probable breeding		Confirmed breeding		Combined		
	Br	Ir	Br	Ir	Br	Ir	Both
1875–1900	0	0	1	0	1	0	1
1968–1972	0	0	2	0	2	0	2
			change		1	0	1
					100%		100%

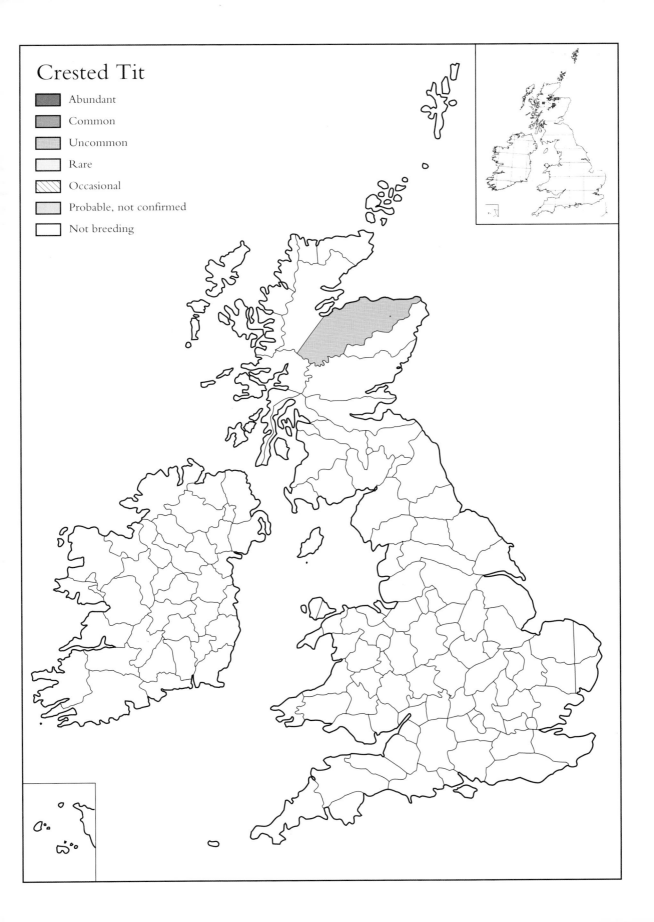

Crested Tit

- ▨ Abundant
- ▨ Common
- ▨ Uncommon
- ▢ Rare
- ▨ Occasional
- ▨ Probable, not confirmed
- ▢ Not breeding

Coal Tit (Cole Tit)

Parus ater

In the fir, oak and birch woods of Britain and Ireland in the 19th century the Coat Tit was generally considered the most common of the tits; elsewhere it was said to have occurred in fewer numbers than the Great and Blue Tits. Throughout Scotland it was considered more common than others of its family; it bred in the mountains as far as the treeline, especially in the stream valleys, and on occasions into areas devoid of trees. One nest, for example, was discovered in a dried peat mound near Loch Shin in Sutherland, in 1878. The Coal Tit was a common bird of the remnant pine forests of Scotland and, in a number of areas where plantations of conifers on some of the estates had matured, Coal Tit numbers increased substantially throughout the century (first noticed in 1839 by Jardine) as conifer plantations extended. Afforestation accelerated through the 19th century not only in Scotland, but also elsewhere in Britain, and led to local increases of Coal Tits (for instance Stevenson 1866–90, Ussher and Warren 1900). In other areas, particularly in the E Midland counties of Leicestershire, Rutland, Northamptonshire and Huntingdonshire, it was also increasing but the reasons for the increase were not clear (Browne 1889, Lilford 1895).

Following the 1914–18 war, and the establishment of the Forestry Commission, plantations of conifers increased substantially and planting accelerated after the 1939–45 war. Coal Tits begin to invade these new woods at the thicket stage and numbers may reach very high densities (Gibbons *et al.* 1993). Wherever conifers were planted numbers of Coal Tits increased and plantations were responsible for the colonisation of Caithness from about 1900. The Coal Tit first bred in the Outer Hebrides in 1966 (near Stornoway) and since then has maintained a tenuous hold. Elsewhere there has been no evidence of any widespread changes. Small local decreases following severe winters in some parts of Britain have been noted through CBC statistics but the Coal Tit is apparently able to survive cold periods better than other small passerines as the declines noted have not been as great as in populations of other species.

Number of counties in which recorded:

Period	Probable breeding		Confirmed breeding		Combined		
	Br	Ir	Br	Ir	Br	Ir	Both
1875–1900	0	0	103	34	103	34	137
1968–19720	0	0	107	34	107	34	141
			change		4	0	4
					4%		3%

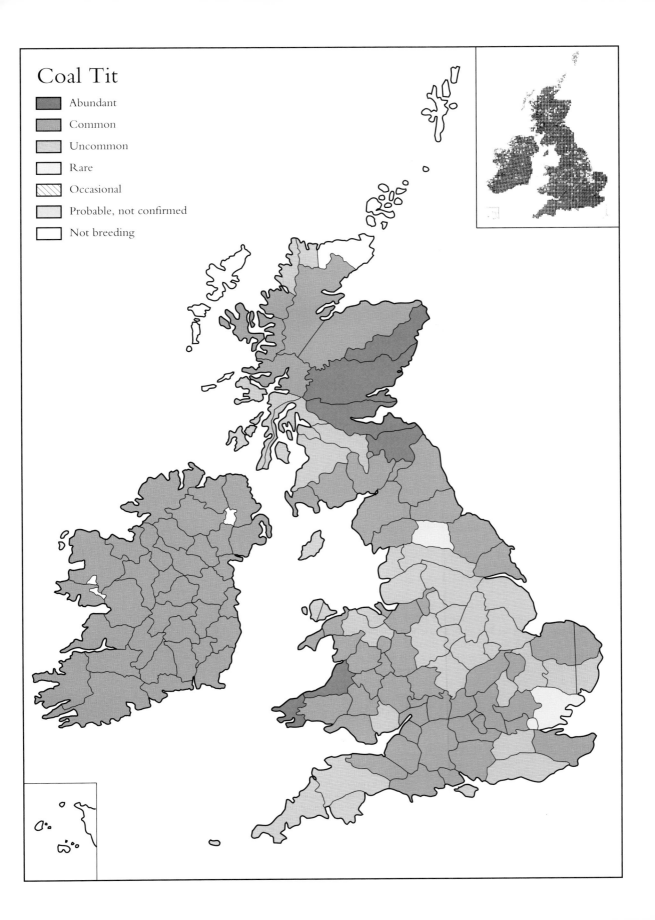

Coal Tit

- ■ Abundant
- ■ Common
- ■ Uncommon
- □ Rare
- ▨ Occasional
- ▦ Probable, not confirmed
- □ Not breeding

Blue Tit

Parus caeruleus

In the 19th century the Blue Tit was considered the commonest of its family over much of its British range. It bred everywhere where there were trees or bushes. Its short and squat beak particularly adapts it to feed in broadleaved trees; consequently, where conifers predominated, for instance in the old woods in Scotland or the new plantations over Penrith Beacon in Cumberland, the better adapted Coal Tit, generally, and the Crested Tit locally, occurred in greater numbers. In Ireland it was thought that in many heavily, and densely, wooded areas the Coal Tit occurred in greater numbers and that the Blue Tit preferred more open woodland (Ussher and Warren 1900).

In Scotland the Blue Tit did not breed in the Northern Isles or the Outer Hebrides and bred only on those islands of the Inner Hebrides that afforded suitable habitat such as Raasay, Mull and Jura. In the extreme north of the mainland it was rare or absent. In Caithness only a few had been collected, none had been proven breeding, and in Sutherland it was regularly found only in the southeast of the county; in W Sutherland it bred very rarely and locally. Over the rest of the Highlands it was confined to the stream valleys as far up as the birch trees grew.

The Blue Tit was not an inhabitant of the Isle of Man in the early 19th century. It is not clear when it colonised the island, but it was seen occasionally near Onchan in the 1870s and regularly since 1894. The first nest found was in the garden of Sulby parsonage in 1896; by 1905, the Blue Tit was distributed all over the island and increasing rapidly. It is not clear from the Manx literature what facilitated the colonisation and subsequent expansion but Alexander and Lack (1944) considered that it was made possible by increased tree planting.

It is not clear exactly when the Blue Tit spread into Caithness. It had not been recorded breeding prior to the 1880s (Harvie-Brown and Buckley 1887) but was doing so in 1907, and it bred in many woods in the county in 1931 (Baxter and Rintoul 1953). At the same time it was increasing in numbers in N and W Sutherland. The Outer Hebrides were colonised in 1963 when breeding was proven in the woods around Stornoway Castle from which point Blue Tits increased in numbers and are now firmly established there. Breeding has recently been recorded on Eigg and Canna and on other islands in the Inner Hebrides it occurs sporadically, as on Rum and, possibly, Coll. There is little evidence to explain the Blue Tit's recent expansion into new parts of Scotland and on to the islands. Perhaps the same conifer plantings that encouraged the spread of the Coal Tit also allowed this species to cross areas that were otherwise unsuitable for them (e.g. moorland and fell) so enabling them to reach otherwise isolated broadleaved woodlands such as those on some of the inner Hebridean islands (A. Gosler in litt). Breeding first took place in the Isles of Scilly in the late 1940s.

Number of counties in which recorded:

Period	Probable breeding		Confirmed breeding		Combined		
	Br	Ir	Br	Ir	Br	Ir	Both
1875–1900	0	0	103	34	103	34	137
1968–1972	0	0	105	34	105	34	139
			change		2	0	2
					2%		1%

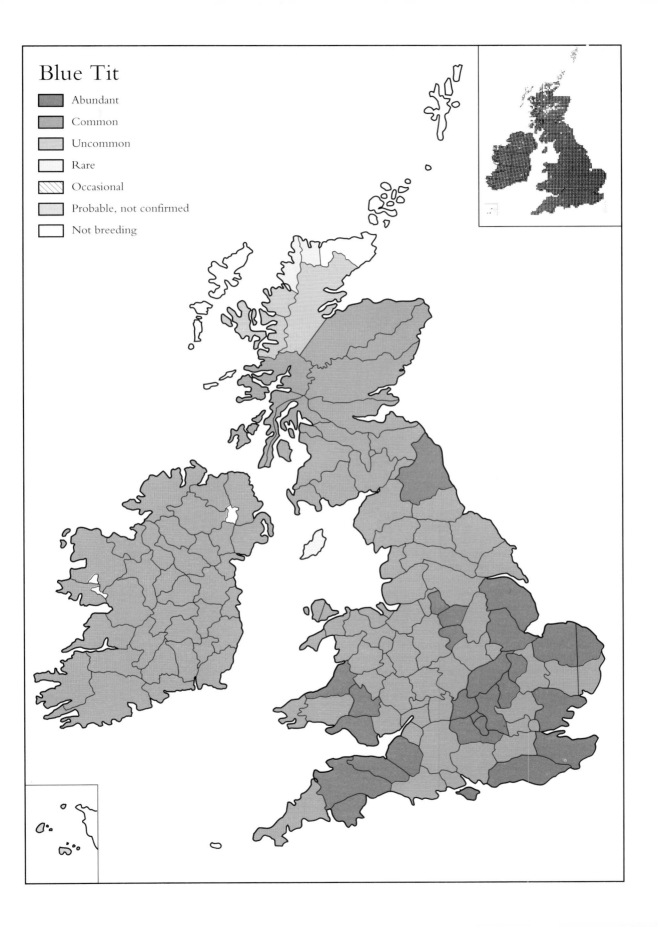

Blue Tit

- Abundant
- Common
- Uncommon
- Rare
- Occasional
- Probable, not confirmed
- Not breeding

Great Tit

Parus major

Over England, Wales and Ireland in the 19th century the Great Tit was a common and familiar species. In Scotland it bred commonly up to the foothills of the Highlands but further north it was rare. The Great Tit is a bird of deciduous woods and occurs in its highest numbers there. It was regarded, in the 19th century, as occurring in equal numbers to the Blue Tit in these woods. Outside of this habitat, in farmland and conifer forests, it occurred in far fewer numbers. In farmland it was apparently less common than the Blue Tit and in conifer forests, especially in Scotland, it was believed to be far less common than either the Blue or Coal Tits. In Ireland, however, it was believed that it bred commonly in areas with few trees (Ussher and Warren 1900). Its northernmost breeding record up to the 1890s came from Muir of Ord, Inverness-shire, elsewhere north of the Great Glen it did not breed beyond the Inverness-shire boundary. It was becoming apparent at this time that a slow expansion northwards was underway. Evidence of colonisation of new areas was scant (breeding was suspected to have taken place for the first time in Skye in 1890) but local increases in numbers in N Argyll and Inverness-shire were noted (Harvie-Brown and Buckley 1895, Harvie-Brown and Macpherson 1904).

The progress of the northwards expansion during the first quarter of the 20th century is difficult to trace. Afforestation in Caithness was believed to have allowed the expansion of the range of the Great Tit into that county. The first sight record was near Wick in 1903; in 1904 and 1905 it was seen in the breeding season in the woods around Castletown. Little is recorded of its consolidation in Caithness until, in 1931, it was recorded breeding in the woods at Langwell. The Caithness colonisation probably came about as an extension of breeding from Inverness-shire through SE Sutherland. Breeding had been suspected around the Dornoch Firth at the beginning of the 20th century and, by 1928, the Great Tit's range was expanding there, but no information exists of the colonisation of the intervening area between the Dornoch Firth and the Caithness breeding groups. In NW Scotland the Great Tit remained scarce and into the 1950s it still did not breed in W Sutherland. It had increased by this time in a number of the wooded Inner Hebrides. The next 15 years saw the completion of the colonisation of Sutherland and in 1966 the first pair bred in the woods around Stornoway Castle. As in the case of Blue and Coal Tits it is likely that the extensive planting of conifer forests in Scotland in the 20th century has enabled the Great Tit to cross unsuitable moorland and fells to reach suitable, but otherwise isolated, broadleaved woodlands. The *68–72 Atlas* recorded the extent to which it had spread. Noticeable gaps in the Great Tit's northern distribution represent unwooded and elevated areas that remain unsuitable for breeding. Other than fluctuations in numbers evident around severe winters no other widespread changes in the Great Tit's status have occurred (Gibbons *et al.* 1993).

Number of counties in which recorded:

Period	Probable breeding		Confirmed breeding		Combined		
	Br	Ir	Br	Ir	Br	Ir	Both
1875–1900	1	0	98	34	99	34	133
1968–1972	0	0	105	34	105	34	139
			change		6	0	6
					6%		5%

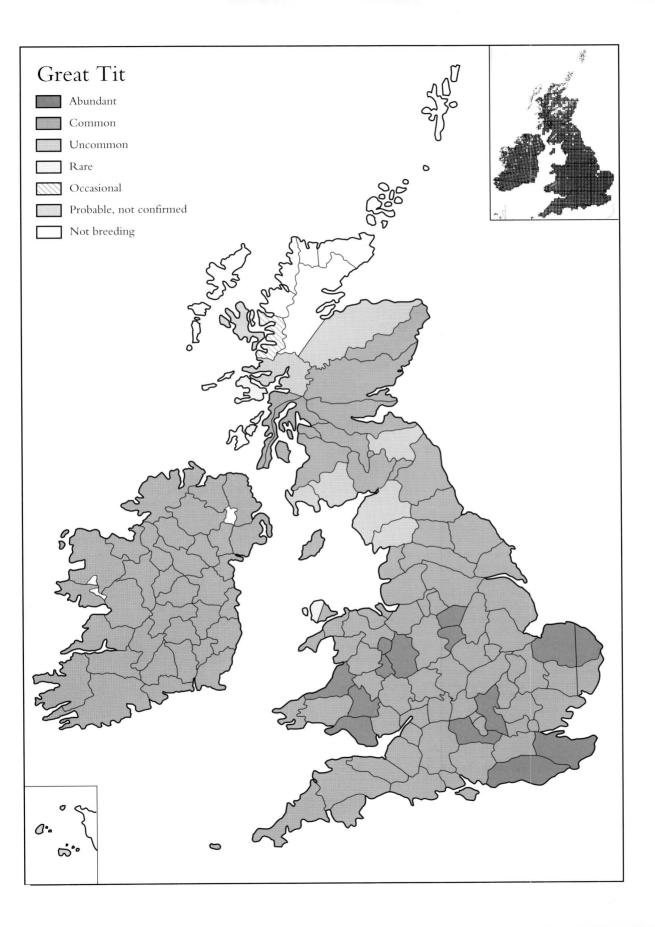

Great Tit

- Abundant
- Common
- Uncommon
- Rare
- Occasional
- Probable, not confirmed
- Not breeding

Nuthatch

Sitta europaea

The Nuthatch was an irregularly and locally distributed species at the end of the 19th century. It was common in many well wooded counties of England and Wales but was rarer in counties most affected by recent agricultural changes, especially in parts of E England and the Midlands, and it was absent from some of the coastal counties of Wales. Regular breeding did not occur any further north than Harrogate, but occasional breeding did take place in parts of Yorkshire a little further north. It was absent from Ireland and most of the off-shore islands of England and Wales. Apart from sporadic breeding that took place in Durham up to about 1845 the map represents the distribution of the Nuthatch at any time during the 19th century. Overall its distribution appears to have been stable, possibly a little more irregular locally as felling took place in some areas and plantations matured in others. There was an interesting, but unlikely, published account of breeding in Roxburghshire about 1850 and the Duke of Argyll introduced some in an apparently suitable wood in Inveraray in Argyll but there were no resulting records of breeding.

The first years of the 20th century saw small, local colonisations, especially in the Welsh counties of Pembrokeshire, Caernarvonshire and Anglesey, more wide-spread breeding in Cheshire with colonisation of new areas in Wirral and the northeast hills and, perhaps, some thinning in, especially, E England and the E Midlands, as the stock of mature trees continued to decline. The Nuthatch was suspected of breeding for the first time in Anglesey in 1910 and in Caernarvonshire in 1908. The recolonisation of Durham occurred around the turn of the century. The first 20th century nest in Durham was discovered near Wynyard but the Nuthatch did not breed there regularly until about 1927, spreading to the north of the county by the 1940s. Around this period the Nuthatch probably bred on the Northumberland side of the Tyne, but by 1935 had almost certainly ceased to do so. Losses from most of Lincolnshire (it was only breeding in the southwest corner in 1950) may have been regained by around the mid 1960s. Another recolonisation of S Northumberland had expanded by this time to include the north of the county.

During the *68–72 Atlas* survey the consolidation of the Yorkshire, Durham and Northumberland breeding population became very clear and encouraging. Clearly the losses in Lincolnshire, SE Yorkshire and parts of Fenland have been substantial and are probably due to the paucity of mature trees in those areas. The outlying record in the Lake District at this time was materially increased upon during the period up to the *88–91 Atlas* survey, apparently as a result of the spread of the species through Lancashire. The first modern Scottish breeding record occurred in 1989. The present northerly breeding extremity is further than the species has been regularly recorded since at least the end of the 18th century. The recent Scottish records give rise to the expectation that colonisation of further new areas will occur.

The Nuthatch has not (within written ornithological history) been an inhabitant of Ireland; despite an apparently adequate flight capability and apparently suitable habitat it is among those species resolutely not even attempting colonisation (J. Flegg in litt).

Number of counties in which recorded:

Period	Probable breeding		Confirmed breeding		Combined		
	Br	Ir	Br	Ir	Br	Ir	Both
1875–1900	0	65	0	65	0	65	
1968–1972	3	0	77	0	80	0	80
			change		15	0	15
					23%		23%

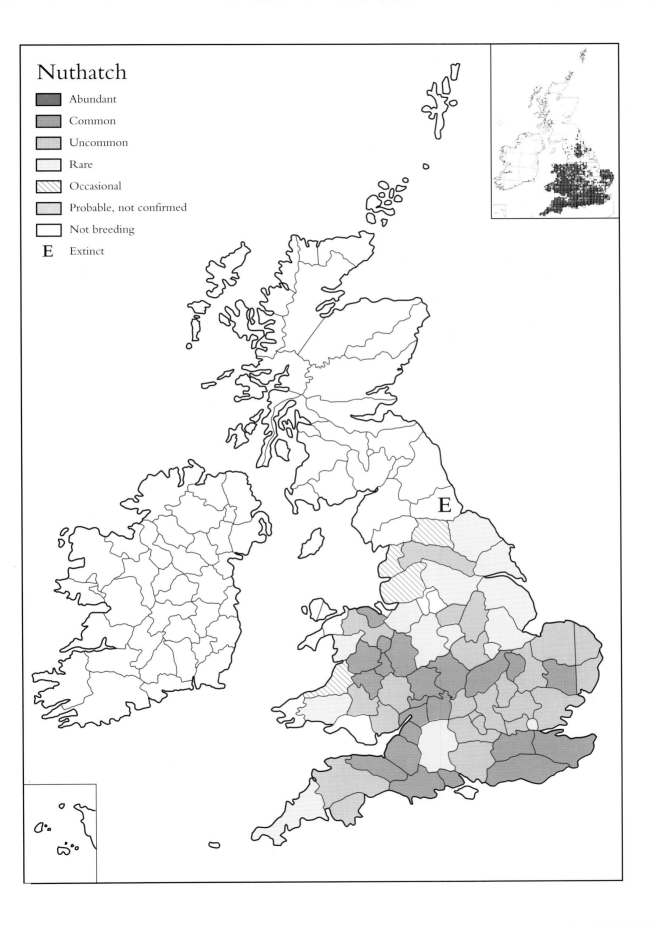

Nuthatch

- Abundant
- Common
- Uncommon
- Rare
- Occasional
- Probable, not confirmed
- Not breeding

E Extinct

Treecreeper (Common Creeper, Creeper)

Certhia familiaris

It seems probable that afforestation allowed the expansion of the Treecreeper's range through Scotland in the early years of the 19th century. At the time of the old Statistical Account of Scotland, assembled at the end of the 18th century, it was known only in S Scotland with records from Midlothian, Peeblesshire, Dunbartonshire and Dumfriesshire. Before 1837 it had been noted from Edinburgh but by the 1840s it was recorded widely throughout Scotland and, around the middle of the century, it was regarded as occurring in all woods as far north as Sutherland, but nowhere was it common. It had not, by the 1860s, been recorded from any of the maritime islands and colonisation here took place slowly.

By the end of the 19th century, Treecreepers were breeding regularly in all parts of mainland Scotland apart from W Sutherland and appear to have been more common (or less local) in areas of Moray, Dee and parts of Argyll than previously in central Scotland. By the end of the century, there were records from the wooded isles of W Scotland and breeding occurred, or probably did so, in Skye and Raasay, Mull, Jura, Bute and Arran.

Elsewhere in Britain and Ireland Treecreepers were ubiquitous. In well-wooded counties they bred generally and commonly; in those with fewer and smaller woods they also bred commonly but necessarily more locally. This was demonstrated most clearly in Ireland, a country more sparsely wooded than most of Britain. Ralfe (1906) was cautious in accepting that the Treecreeper had recently colonised the Isle of Man and considered that it may have been overlooked in the past; nevertheless, the first specimen was procured on the island in the winter of 1882 and a nest was not found until 1890. In view of Ralfe's comments whilst discussing the colonisation of the island by other woodland species following the maturation of recently planted woods, it is possible that the Treecreeper colonised the Isle of Man during the 1870s or 1880s.

The Treecreeper's sensitivity to severe winters was recorded throughout Britain; those of the 1880s reduced numbers considerably but, evidently, recovery was quick (Mitchell 1892, Harvie-Brown and Buckley 1892).

The spread in N Scotland continued in the 20th century, and W Sutherland was soon colonised. As the century progressed the Treecreeper was recorded from further maritime islands; it bred not uncommonly in Islay by 1937 and was noted on Eigg in the 1940s and, in those islands where it had bred for some years, it was breeding in larger numbers (Parslow 1973). Breeding was first proven in the woods around Stornoway Castle on Lewis in 1962 (Parslow 1973) but the Treecreeper withdrew from there sometime between 1972 and 1988 (Gibbons *et al.* 1993). The population has, otherwise, remained very stable. Fluctuations in numbers have been apparent following hard winters, decreases being most severe in the north and west. In the intervening periods re-establishment has been rapid as Treecreepers spread out from the comparative security of the woods to occupy more isolated groups of trees such as those in churchyards and farmland spinneys (Marchant *et al.* 1990).

Number of counties in which recorded:

Period	Probable breeding		Confirmed breeding		Combined		
	Br	Ir	Br	Ir	Br	Ir	Both
1875–1900	0	0	103	34	103	34	137
1968–1972	0	0	104	34	104	34	138
			change		1	0	1
					1%		1%

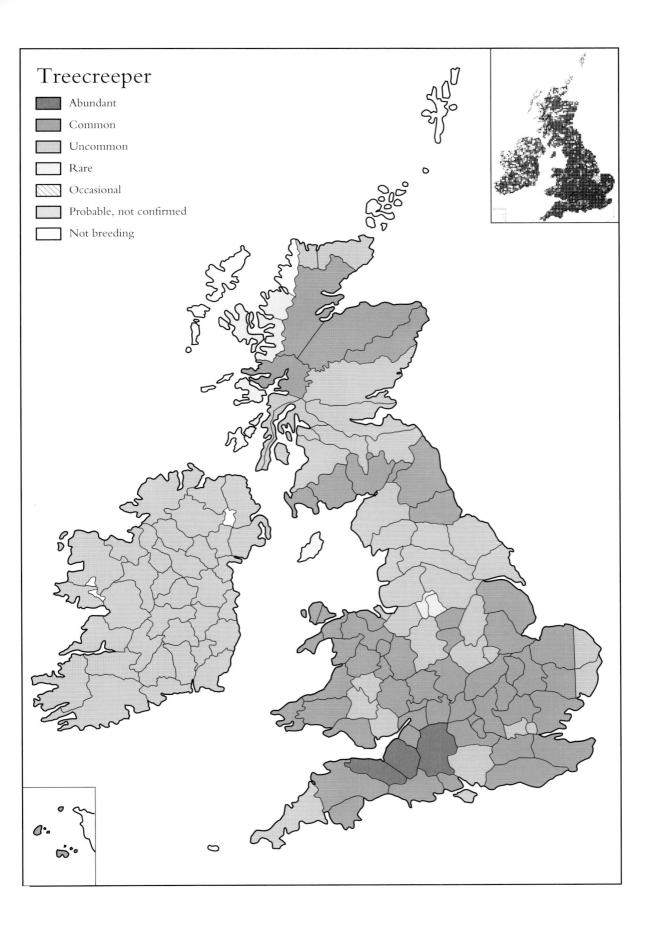

Treecreeper

- Abundant
- Common
- Uncommon
- Rare
- Occasional
- Probable, not confirmed
- Not breeding

Golden Oriole

Oriolus oriolus

Nests and eggs of the Golden Oriole had been occasionally recorded since about 1840 in England. Many writers of county avifaunas wrote that they believed that if specimens of this striking and unusual species were not shot as soon as they arrived in spring many more breeding attempts would have been made. Indeed, the numbers arriving in spring were, at times, substantial, as the undated (and unsubstantiated) record of 14 seen together in a bush on Henfield Common in Sussex may attest. The records came, in the main, from East Anglia and the southeast counties although there may have been a small, regular, population in N Devonshire and Dorset around the middle of the century. Breeding was proven to have taken place during the 19th century in Devonshire, Surrey, Kent, Essex, Hertfordshire, Suffolk, Norfolk and Northamptonshire and was suspected in Dorset, Sussex and Lincolnshire. During 1875–1900 breeding records that were regarded acceptable by contemporary naturalists were published for five counties and less satisfactory records were published for Lincolnshire.

Kent held the only well-recorded regular population. Most of the records came from the east of the county (a series of records from Dumpton Park is an example) and by the end of the century there was a regular site in parkland somewhere in the south. Breeding did appear to have been annual, or almost so, from at least the 1870s. It is interesting to note the habitats in which the birds were recorded. One regular site was in groves of 'evergreen oak' in S Kent: a nest was found suspended from the extreme end of the top branch of an oak tree whilst singing males were noted in a holly grove there. One nest was found in an ash plantation (possibly coppiced) and another at the top of an elm tree. Elsewhere (for instance in Devonshire and Lincolnshire) nests were found in garden shrubbery.

One well-authenticated record was published from Hertfordshire where a nest containing three eggs was found near Amwell near Ware in June 1881. A pair probably bred at Haileybury in 1876 and there is a record of a breeding pair shot before they were able to rear young near Welwyn in 1886.

A nest was found at West Raventhorpe near Scunthorpe, Lincolnshire in 1871 but, extraordinarily, Blathwayt (in Smith and Cornwallis 1955) recorded that the Golden Oriole bred, or had attempted to do so, in NW Lincolnshire for the previous 40 years. His assertion was, unfortunately, not supported by any evidence and must remain as no more than an intriguing possibility.

Of the many spring records in Essex one or two suggest that Golden Orioles had bred, and Clarke Kennedy in 1880 (in Ticehurst 1932) wrote that 'I ... know that it has nested' in Suffolk. A record from an unknown source stated that it bred at Ormesby, Norfolk in the early 1880s (Stevenson 1866–90). The E Kent population probably ceased breeding around the end of the century (Ticehurst 1909). Very few further records of breeding in England were published through the first half of the 20th century but, from 1949, an increase seems to have taken place. Since that time summering or breeding birds have been recorded from over 20 counties and, from about 1965, a regular breeding group has become established in maturing poplar plantations in Norfolk, Suffolk and Cambridgeshire (*68–72 Atlas*). Up to 30 pairs breed or attempt to breed there now, and sporadic breeding continues to be recorded throughout Britain (Gibbons *et al.* 1993).

Number of counties in which recorded:

Period	Probable breeding		Confirmed breeding		Combined		
	Br	Ir	Br	Ir	Br	Ir	Both
1875–1900	0	0	2	0	6	0	6
1968–1972	1	0	4	0	5	0	5
			change		−1	0	−1
					−17%		−17%

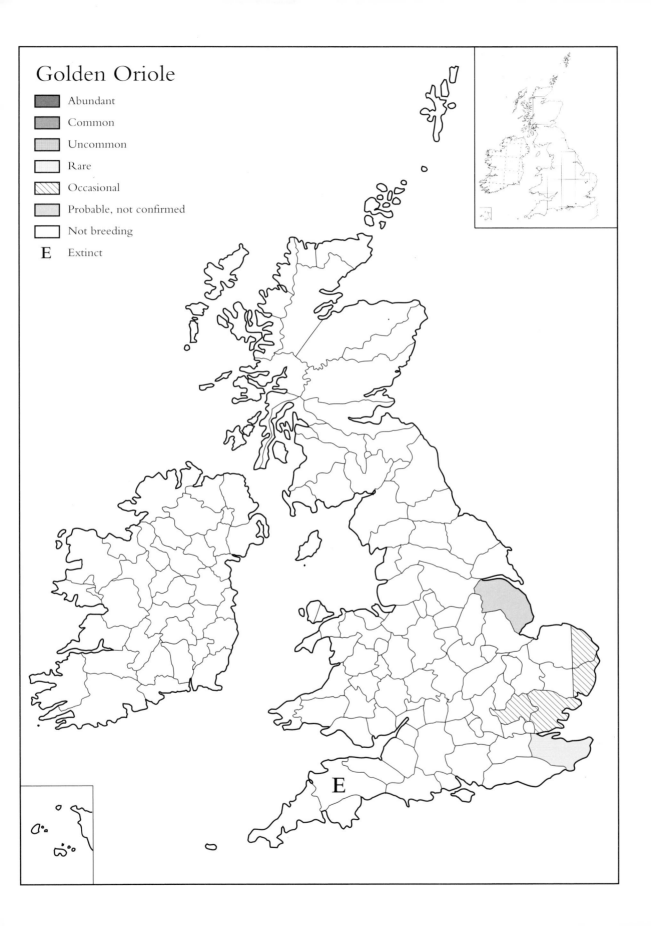

Golden Oriole

- Abundant
- Common
- Uncommon
- Rare
- Occasional
- Probable, not confirmed
- Not breeding
- **E** Extinct

Red-backed Shrike

Lanius collurio

The Red-backed Shrike bred more or less regularly, if uncommonly and locally in places, in the majority of Welsh counties and England S of Yorkshire and Lancashire at the end of the 19th century. In N England it bred occasionally up to the Scottish border and was suspected of doing so in Scotland, for instance in Berwickshire, Roxburghshire, East Lothian and Lanarkshire. Saxby (1874) recorded breeding in Shetland in 1870, a record that was not considered acceptable by Witherby *et al.* (1938–41) but that seems less surprising now in light of recent breeding there. It had never been known to breed in Ireland.

It was evident that the Red-backed Shrike was declining rapidly during the later decades of the 19th century. In the north of its British range it had clearly been more common earlier in the century (in Lakeland, and especially Westmorland, it was considered to have bred not uncommonly up to around the 1850s) but this slow decline was not noted by the early 19th century writers and only recognised in retrospect by the writers at the end of the century. The same was true of Northumberland and Durham, whilst breeding records from Scotland were more frequent during that earlier period. Looking at more southerly records there were also indications of a decrease. In N Wales particularly,

Eyton (1838) considered that the Red-backed Shrike was, at the very least, a common species throughout, but also very common in parts. This was clearly not true when Forrest (1907) carried out his enquiries. The decreases in some southern counties were attributed to various causes. In Norfolk, for instance, the intensification of agriculture had resulted in the removal of hedgerows and this was blamed for a parallel decrease in the number of breeding Red-backed Shrikes. In other counties gamekeepers shot any bird with a hooked beak, including the Red-backed Shrike, and some were seen on gamekeepers' gibbets.

A widespread decline, which probably began around the middle of the 19th century, was well underway by the end of the century. By 1920 breeding had ceased, or become very irregular, in Cornwall, Anglesey, the counties of the northwest and the eastern coast north from the Wash. Populations in the Pennines, S Wales and the Isle of Wight had withdrawn from those areas by 1940. Little of the Welsh population remained in the 1950s, breeding occurring scantily in Merioneth, Montgomeryshire and Glamorgan. Elsewhere, by this time, breeding had more or less ceased anywhere north of a line drawn from the Wash to the Severn estuary. By 1971, the Red-backed Shrike bred in only eight counties. These were Hampshire, Surrey, Buckinghamshire, Bedfordshire, Essex, Suffolk, Norfolk and Cambridgeshire. Just 81 breeding pairs were located then, 43 of them in Suffolk. The accumulation of records during the *68-72 Atlas* survey recorded breeding in other counties, but these exaggerate the true picture of a single season's performance. The *88-91 Atlas* apparently caught the species at the point of extinction as a breeding bird in England— 1989 was the first year in recorded ornithological history when it did not breed here. Interesting records of birds seen during the breeding season in Scotland and breeding records from Orkney and Shetland have been seen by some to give hope of expansion from the Scandinavian populations.

The reasons for the decline are still unclear. The most frequently suggested reasons include climatic change, loss of breeding habitat and the use of pesticides and subsequent loss of large insects, but the *88-91 Atlas* dismisses these as primary causes. The decline has been of long duration and widespread in extent and some wider cause than the above must be to blame.

Number of counties in which recorded:

Period	Probable breeding		Confirmed breeding		Combined		
	Br	Ir	Br	Ir	Br	Ir	Both
1875–1900	0	0	73	0	73	0	73
1968-1972	3	0	18	0	21	0	21
			change		−52	0	−52
					−71%		−71%

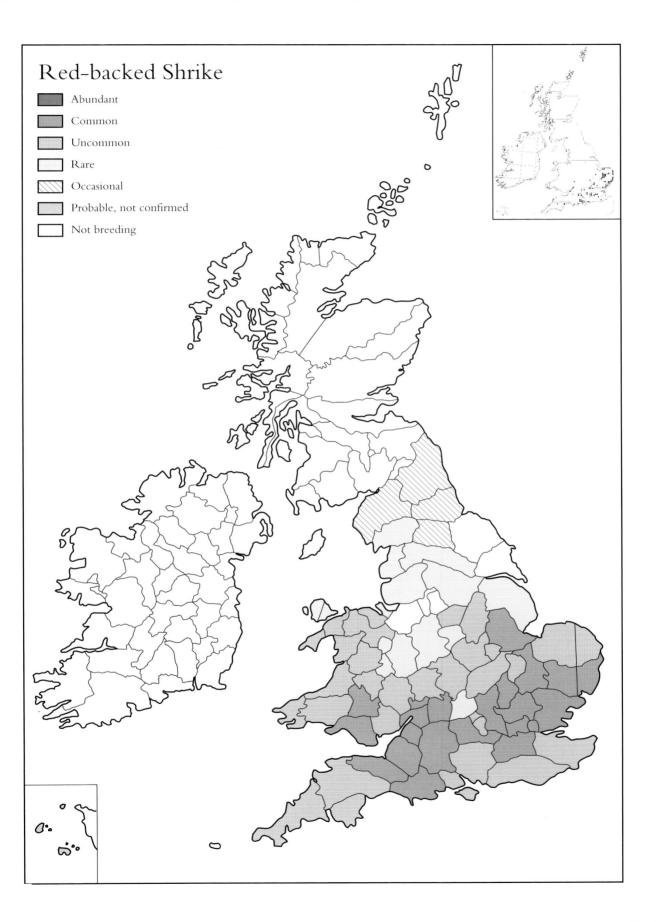

Red-backed Shrike

- Abundant
- Common
- Uncommon
- Rare
- Occasional
- Probable, not confirmed
- Not breeding

Jay

Garrulus glandarius

A decline in numbers of Jays during the 19th century was recorded by most of the ornithological writers, particularly towards the end of that century. This decrease was mentioned by writers from Devonshire in SW England and Surrey in the southeast, through England to the Jay's northern breeding limit in the woods in the foothills of the Scottish Highlands. Its overall distribution may not have changed very much by the end of the century, but it was probably a little more widespread in S and mid Ireland in the first half, and had been persecuted to extinction in some parts of S Scotland. The primary cause of the large decrease in numbers was persecution at the hands of sportsmen, gamekeepers and farmers. All writers, without exception, noted the unceasing persecution suffered by the Jay, but as many writers felt that it was holding its own against the onslaught as those that had noted a decline. The Jay's nest-robbing habits caused it relentless persecution along with other corvids, raptors and mammals. However, being more secretive than the Magpie, it was not so successfully eradicated as that species. It was shot for its feathers too. The blue feathers of the wing coverts, especially, were valued for use for fishing flies and many were killed to supply this trade. These plumes were also in demand for the adorn-

ment of Victorian ladies—the Duchess of Edinburgh was castigated by many naturalists when, in February 1880, she was described touring Cannes sporting a muff made entirely from the blue, 'borrowed', feathers of the Jay.

There is some evidence that the persecution-induced decline followed an earlier expansion of range in Scotland as the old Statistical Account of Scotland at the end of the 18th century made no mention of the Jay north of the Forth/Clyde valleys but it was present there in the 19th. This early expansion may have been facilitated by the conifer plantings that began in the first half of the 19th century.

Several influences in the first few years of the 20th century served to assist an increase in the Jay population in Britain. The fashion for bird plumage as a style accessory passed, but more significantly, the 1914–18 war removed gamekeepers from the woods and persecution lessened dramatically. The creation of the forerunner of the Forestry Commission took place in 1918 and as the planting of conifer forests progressed so habitats suitable for the Jay were created. The further reduction of persecution and the maturing of the early 20th century conifer plantations around the time of the 1939–45 war served to ensure that the increase in numbers accelerated. The increase in numbers of the Jay in Ireland was complemented by an expansion of range: the Jay recolonised Meath in 1909 and Cork about 1915. It gradually spread through the country until, after 1936, much of Ulster to the north and Mayo in the west had been colonised. Interestingly, Deane (1954) attributed the increase in Northern Ireland in part to the prohibition of the ownership of firearms at the beginning of the 'troubles'.

The Jay's distribution in Britain during the *68–72 Atlas* survey was similar to that at the end of the 19th century but the increase of the Irish range was very apparent. The *88–91 Atlas* recorded some interesting changes in the period since the *68–72 Atlas* survey. The breeding limit in Scotland appears to be pushing northwards, particularly in the Great Glen, probably because of conifer plantings, whilst in Ireland dramatic decreases have been noted throughout the Jay's range there with the exception of expansion of the range in the southwest and north of the country. Interestingly, the 1875–1900 map bears a close similarity to the *88–91 Atlas* abundance map with higher populations in S Britain than elsewhere.

Number of counties in which recorded:

Period	Probable breeding		Confirmed breeding		Combined		
	Br	Ir	Br	Ir	Br	Ir	Both
1875–1900	0	1	89	9	89	10	99
1968–1972	0	0	92	32	92	32	124
			change		3	22	25
					3%	220%	25%

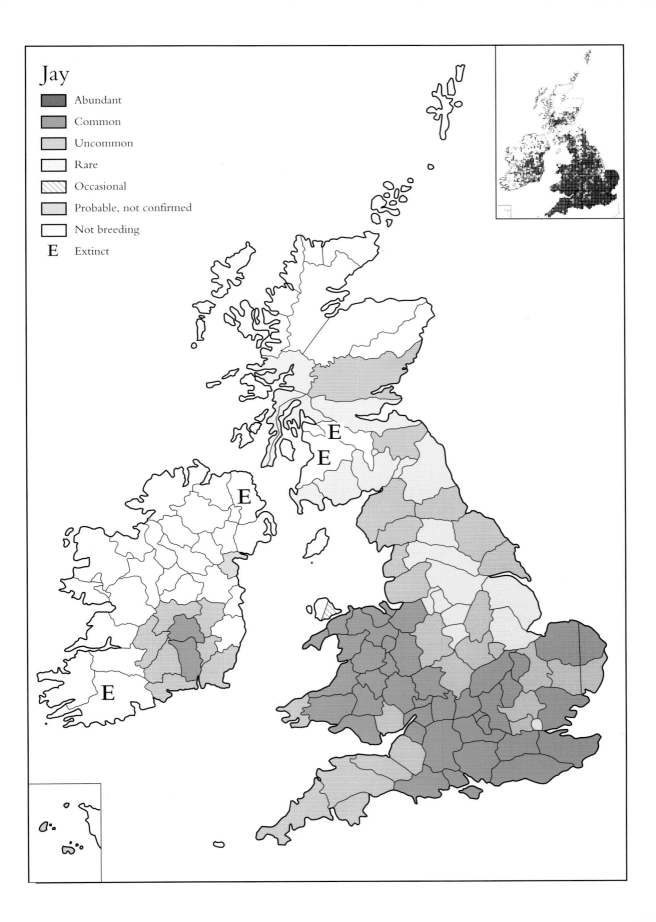

Jay

- Abundant
- Common
- Uncommon
- Rare
- Occasional
- Probable, not confirmed
- Not breeding
- E Extinct

Magpie

Pica pica

For many reasons the Magpie suffered far more than other corvids at the hands of game preservers, farmers and gardeners in the 19th century. It was near to the top of the gamekeepers' list of avian vermin and was shot, trapped and poisoned to protect the eggs and young of gamebirds. It is clear, however, that the more confiding nature of the Magpie brought it more commonly into the range of the shotgun than, for instance, the Jay. The bulky hedgerow nests of the Magpie were also far easier to locate and destroy than those of Crows and Jays and bounties were collected by many country dwellers in this way. Superstitious fear caused its destruction in some areas whilst in others the young were taken and reared as pets, their amusing antics and ability to imitate speech making them popular. All in all the Magpie endured systematic and concerted persecution at the hands of many people that resulted in a dramatic reduction of the population in Britain and, especially, Scotland. Only in Wales and parts of W England, where game rearing was not so widespread, was it still considered common. The reduction in numbers in Britain was so severe that late 19th century writers were contemplating its extinction in some areas. Interestingly, there was some condemnation of this abuse by contemporary naturalists who recognised that the few eggs and young gamebirds that the Magpie took were far outweighed by the volume of invertebrate pests that constituted the main proportion of their diet (e.g. Smith 1869). Recent research confirms this view. Tatner (1983) found that the Magpie's diet comprised mainly invertebrates in summer and plant material in winter, with only a minority of individuals taking any birds or eggs.

In Ireland, many writers testified to the absence of Magpies until the early years of the 17th century. A small flight of 'under a dozen' Magpies was noted arriving from the east in Wexford about 1676 and, by 1684, Magpies were breeding there. Belief that destruction of their nests or eggs would bring divine retribution upon the local human population caused the Magpie to be preserved in Ireland, and neither was there any persecution by game preservers. Perhaps as a consequence, the population has continued to increase, and the entire island had been colonised by the 1850s.

The 20th century, particularly during the 1914–18 war, saw an almost universal recovery in numbers in Britain commensurate with the lapse in gamekeeping and, perhaps, a 1911 Act of Parliament that banned the use of non-specific poisoned bait. Local increases at this time may also be attributed to afforestation as the Magpie is one of the few birds able to thrive in conifer forests (Prestt 1965, Parslow 1973). This increase did not begin until the 1930s in E and S England, but accelerated during and following the 1939–45 war. The increase in the 1940s was considerable and saw an expansion from the countryside into suburbia with breeding birds establishing themselves in the bushes and trees of gardens. The recolonisation of Scotland never took place to the same extent as it did in England and Wales, the main changes being the movement into conifer plantations and the vicinity of the largest cities.

During the *68–72 Atlas* survey the Magpie bred in all counties of England, Wales and Ireland but remained absent from the uplands and islands of Scotland. The low population densities in E England noted from the late 1950s on were probably caused by the removal of hedgerows and increased use of pesticides (Prestt 1965, Cooke 1979) and are clearly evident in the *68–72 Atlas* distribution map, although this area had not been densely populated at the end of the 19th century. Few changes occurred between the *68–72* and *88–91 Atlases*. The distribution in E England now appears to be more continuous but the Scottish population shows little sign of recolonising the areas it inhabited during the 19th century. Why this is so is still not fully understood but continuing persecution may play a part.

Number of counties in which recorded:

Period	Probable breeding		Confirmed breeding		Combined		
	Br	Ir	Br	Ir	Br	Ir	Both
1875–1900	0	0	99	34	99	34	133
1968-1972	0	0	94	34	94	34	128
			change		−5	0	−5
					−5%		−4%

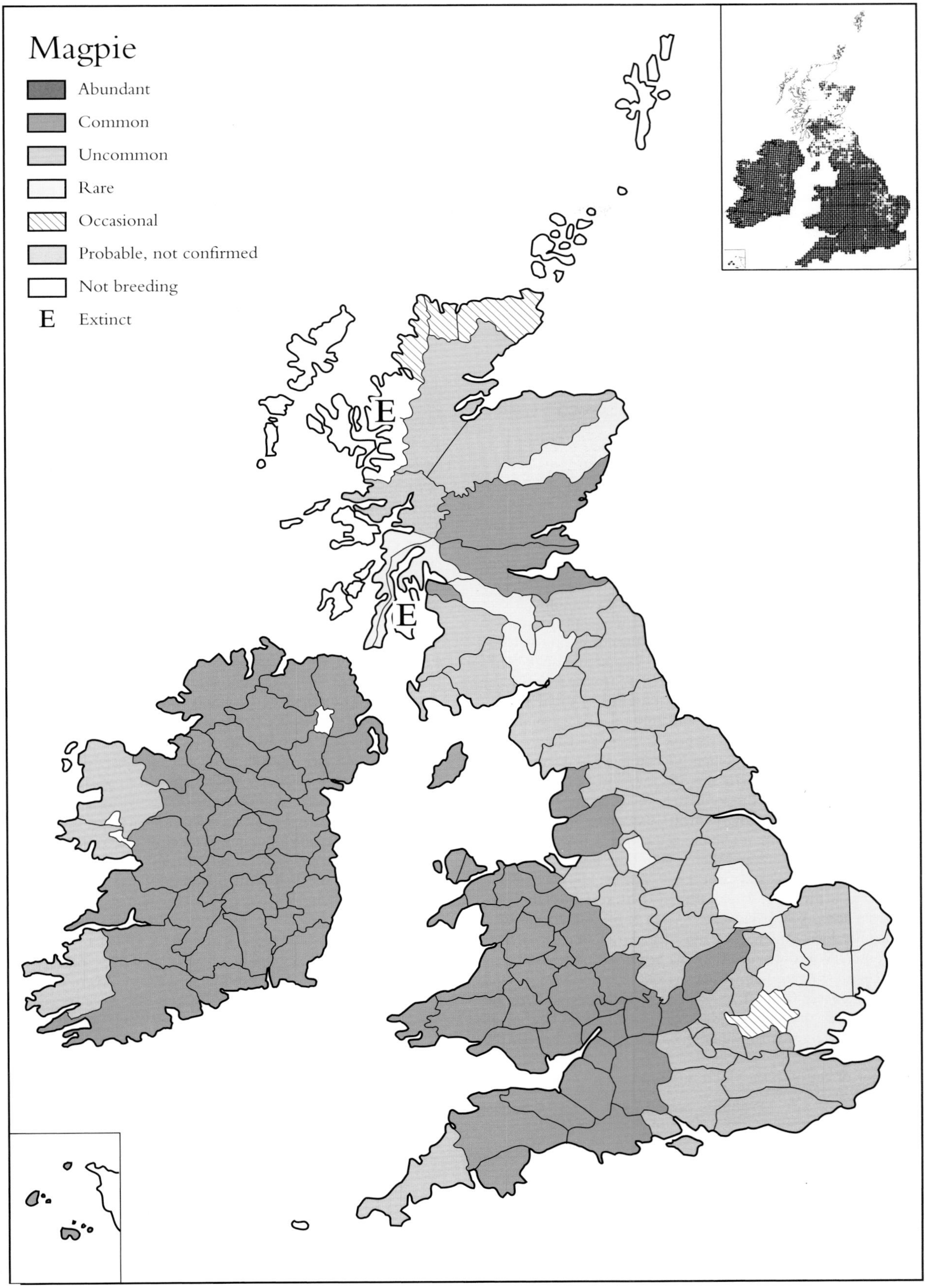
Magpie
Abundant
Common
Uncommon
Rare
Occasional
Probable, not confirmed
Not breeding
E Extinct
E
E

Chough
(Cornish Chough)

Pyrrhocorax pyrrhocorax

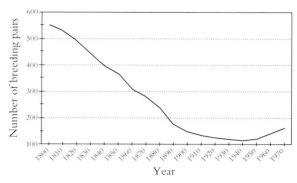

Estimated number of Chough pairs England and Wales 1800–1970. Source: Owen (1988).

The Chough was already beginning to lose ground during the late 19th century. The *68–72 Atlas* saw a coincidence between the Chough's decline and the long run of cold winters in the 19th century, and although this was not recognised formally by the contemporary naturalists it had been noted locally by some. Other causes of the decline were guessed at. One speculation related reductions in Chough numbers to Peregrine predation where the Peregrine was common but this is now considered unlikely (E. Bignal in litt). Although postulated or referred to occasionally, the Jackdaw was not generally considered a cause of the Chough's decline, evidence for its defence mainly revolving around the Jackdaw's concurrent decline in some areas and recognition of its differing ecological requirements. Certainly, in some areas, collection by egg and specimen collectors accelerated extinctions and reductions and, overall, this seems to have had an important effect on Chough numbers (E. Bignal in litt). Extinctions occurred during the 19th century in counties along the English south coast during the 1830s to 1850s and then a little later along the English northeast and Scottish southeast coasts. The last known breeding dates were, in the Isle of Wight, around 1840, in Hampshire 1858, in Sussex around 1830, in Kent 1845, in Northumberland 1851. Some anecdotal evidence suggests that the Chough may have bred on the Yorkshire coast until the beginning of the 19th century. Later extinctions in Anglesey (1890), Cumberland (around 1865), Scotland (around 1870), Outer Hebrides and Ireland demonstrated thinning in the core areas. Witherby *et al.* (1938–41) perceived that, although numbers had decreased in the past, the British population had stabilised; abandoned sites were balanced by re-occupation and new occupation.

In estimating the number of breeding pairs in England and Wales at ten-year intervals from 1800 to 1970, Owen (1988) demonstrated a long-term decline that was at its most rapid during the second half of the 19th century, slowed up to about 1940 and reversed from that point. A dramatic decrease became apparent in S Scotland in 1963 during the severe winter of that year. This may give a clue to the Chough's long-term decline. Little further change appears to have occurred in Wales up to the *68–72 Atlas* survey except for the loss of breeding birds from the Glamorgan Gower coast area; the same is true of Ireland and the Isle of Man, but the species has almost completely abandoned the Scottish west coast, northwest coast and western islands such as Mull and Skye.

The *88–91 Atlas* shows a misleading picture. An increasing population in inland Wales, Anglesey and Islay and Jura and the re-colonisation of Gower is welcome but may have reflected a slight recovery from low numbers during the *68–72 Atlas* that peaked around 1986. Certainly, the Chough population was greater in 1992 than 1982 but since 1986 it has been steadily decreasing. The population continues to contract to fewer and fewer core areas where conditions remain suitable—numbers have decreased every year on Islay since 1986 (E. Bignal in litt). With care and some luck, including suitable land-use management, protection from persecution and favourable weather conditions for a number of years, although a notoriously slow coloniser, the Chough may return to a more widespread distribution.

An interesting development in breeding habits seems to have occurred during the 20th century. Inland breeding sites were unrecorded on the British mainland during the 19th century although in Scotland it was recorded breeding inland during the 18th century. Clearly, the Welsh mines that are now used as breeding sites were still worked during the 19th century and so were unavailable to Choughs. In Ireland, however, Choughs bred regularly in the inland mountain cliffs in Down, Donegal and Sligo and the Connemara Hills; this may have reflected a change in agricultural land management and, perhaps, the numbers of sheep and cattle in the hills (E. Bignal in litt).

Number of counties in which recorded:

Period	Probable breeding		Confirmed breeding		Combined		
	Br	Ir	Br	Ir	Br	Ir	Both
1875–1900	0	0	19	11	19	11	30
1968–1972	2	0	10	9	12	9	21
			change		−7	−2	−9
					−37%	−18%	−30%

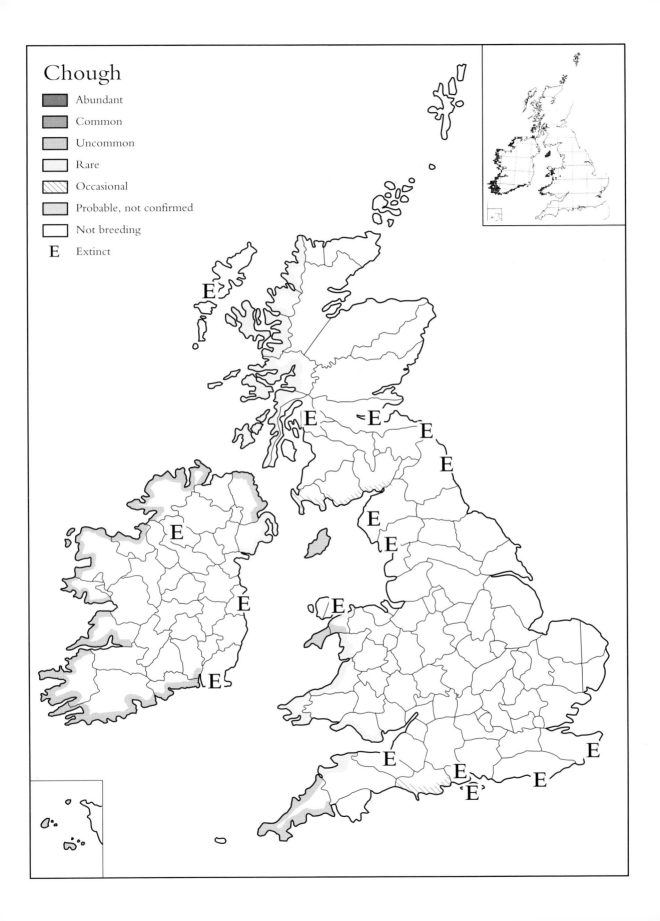

Chough

- ▓ Abundant
- ▓ Common
- ░ Uncommon
- ☐ Rare
- ▨ Occasional
- ░ Probable, not confirmed
- ☐ Not breeding
- **E** Extinct

Jackdaw

Corvus monedula

The Jackdaw was widespread throughout Britain and Ireland during the last quarter of the 19th century, and was only absent as a breeding species from some of the more exposed Inner Hebridean islands, North and South Uist and Shetland. In the W and NW of Scotland and on Lewis it bred in very small numbers but elsewhere in Britain and Ireland it was very common. Indeed, in N England and E Scotland it increased in numbers, particularly after about 1890.

Lewis was colonised in the autumn of 1893 when Jackdaws arrived with a large influx of Rooks. A few stayed about Stornoway and in 1895 breeding was first noted on the castle. It continued breeding at this site but there were never more than one or two nests noted in any one year. In other western isles the Jackdaw bred in varying numbers. It bred for many years on Iona Cathedral and, in 1888, about 40 pairs bred there. On Gigha Jackdaws bred in great numbers and on the adjacent small island of Cara colonies occupied a deep gully that cuts across the island. It was very common on Islay and Mull and increased greatly on both islands from the 1880s. On Skye there were two small colonies—one was in an old building near Dunvegan, the other at Corry—and a few pairs bred on nearby Raasay. Jackdaws occurred occasionally in Shetland throughout the century, but were never known to breed.

On the NW coast of Scotland the Jackdaw bred regularly, but locally, up to Loch Torridon but only a single colony was known further north—on the cliffs of Leckmelm near Ullapool in West Ross. From the N Sutherland coast round to Inverness it bred more commonly and was similarly common along the Caledonian Canal. North of the Great Glen it bred only occasionally away from the coast although its range increased inland from about the mid 1880s and extended into the more wild and rugged valleys north of Loch Ness such as Glen Affric and Strath Glass.

Throughout the rest of Britain and in Ireland it was a common and widespread species and in some areas was said to be increasing (for instance in Kent, Lancashire, Northumberland and Tweed) particularly in the vicinity of the expanding towns and, especially on the northeast coast, on sea cliffs. It did not appear to suffer at the hands of gamekeepers to the same degree as other corvids, despite accusations that it ate the eggs of other birds. Only in Cheshire was persecution considered significant enough to have limited numbers of breeding birds.

As the 20th century progressed the increase first noted in Scotland at the end of the 19th century continued. Shetland was colonised in 1943 and even in the 1960s increases were still being noted in Ayrshire, Eigg, in the Inner Hebrides, and in Sutherland, although the species still remained scarce in the west. Jackdaws evidently increased in numbers in Ireland during the same period and this trend continued into the 1960s. Most of the local literature suggests that the Jackdaw increased in Britain after the 1939–45 war (Parslow 1973), and although none of the mainland increase was quantified, a study carried out on Skomer Island, Pembrokeshire, recorded an increase from about 20 pairs in 1946 to 200–250 pairs in 1961 (Saunders 1962). CBC data suggest that this growth has continued to the present day throughout Britain (Marchant *et al.* 1990) and probably so in Ireland too (Hutchinson 1989), although no significant range change has occurred in recent decades (Gibbons *et al.* 1993).

Number of counties in which recorded:

Period	Probable breeding		Confirmed breeding		Combined		
	Br	Ir	Br	Ir	Br	Ir	Both
1875–1900	0	0	105	34	105	34	139
1968–1972	0	0	105	34	105	34	139
			change		0	0	0

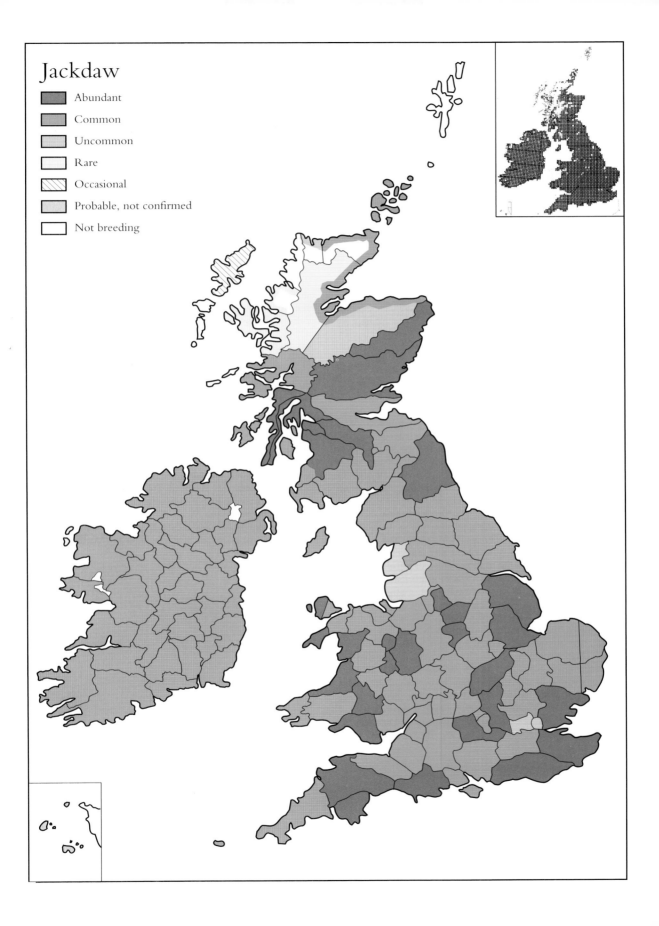

Jackdaw

- **Abundant**
- **Common**
- **Uncommon**
- **Rare**
- **Occasional**
- **Probable, not confirmed**
- **Not breeding**

Rook

Corvus frugilegus

The Rook bred commonly throughout Britain and Ireland and was even increasing in some places at the end of the 19th century. The extraordinary colonisation of Lewis in the Outer Hebrides left only Shetland, some of the small, treeless islands off W Scotland and Ireland and the Isles of Scilly without nesting Rooks. The bulk of the records of an increase came from marine islands, especially the Isle of Wight, the Isle of Man and Skye. Otherwise the Rook was recorded increasing in some S English counties (for instance Devonshire, Kent and Norfolk) and in N Scotland.

The Rook probably underwent the bulk of its range expansion during the 18th and, perhaps, the early 19th centuries (Yarrell 1837–43). This expansion probably began in England at the time of enclosures and the maturing of the newly planted trees. As these changes in the landscape spread north and west so the Rook followed. Yet the Rook never really became common in NW Scotland, mirroring the limited agricultural changes there (J. Reid in litt). It bred thinly in areas devoid of trees and with concentrated agriculture. This was especially true over most of Scotland north of the Great Glen; however, it was common here in the coastal lowlands of the east. Orkney was colonised in the autumn of 1846 when a small party of Rooks found their way to a small plantation at Papdale near Kirkwall, stayed and bred successfully. By 1891, they were breeding plentifully. A great westerly movement of Rooks occurred in Scotland in October 1893 and many landed on the W coast of Lewis. Around 4,000 birds found their way to the small, stunted trees of the only wood on the island at the time, in the grounds of Stornoway Castle, and spent the winter there. Around 200 remained through the following summer but did not breed. In 1895 they bred for the first time and the colony subsequently grew; in 1902 there were over 100 nests.

In Ireland Rooks were considered to breed in every district that was not lacking trees and bushes and to be increasing their range 'unchecked', especially westwards. In the treeless west they nested in many low bushes such as the stunted hawthorns on lake islands or around remote houses. The largest Rookery recorded during the last quarter of the 19th century was in Rash Wood, Tyrone and was estimated to contain 10,000 nests.

Despite being blamed for ruining root crops in some areas, the Rook's general usefulness in consuming great quantities of agricultural pests was widely recognised and meant that it was not persecuted to the same extent that other corvids were (Yarrell 1837–43, Coward and Oldham 1900). Indeed stories circulated of landowners, who, after eliminating the Rook from their lands, found it necessary to re-establish the species after finding that their crops failed in the absence of this natural form of pest control (D'Urban and Mathew 1892). Rooks were, however, subject to some sport shooting at their colonies, and young Rooks were collected for food.

The Rook continued to increase generally into the 20th century and Shetland was colonised in 1952. A widespread decline in Rook numbers occurred during the 1950s and 1960s that was presumed to have been caused by the use of organochlorine pesticides but numbers have recovered somewhat since (J. Reid in litt). The decline was least extensive in the least intensively farmed parts of Britain (particularly in N and W Scotland) but numbers remained low into the 1970s. Since then there has been evidence of some redistribution of the population (Marchant et al. 1990).

Number of counties in which recorded:

Period	Probable breeding		Confirmed breeding		Combined		
	Br	Ir	Br	Ir	Br	Ir	Both
1875–1900	0	0	106	34	106	34	140
1968–1972	0	0	106	34	106	34	140
			change		0	0	0

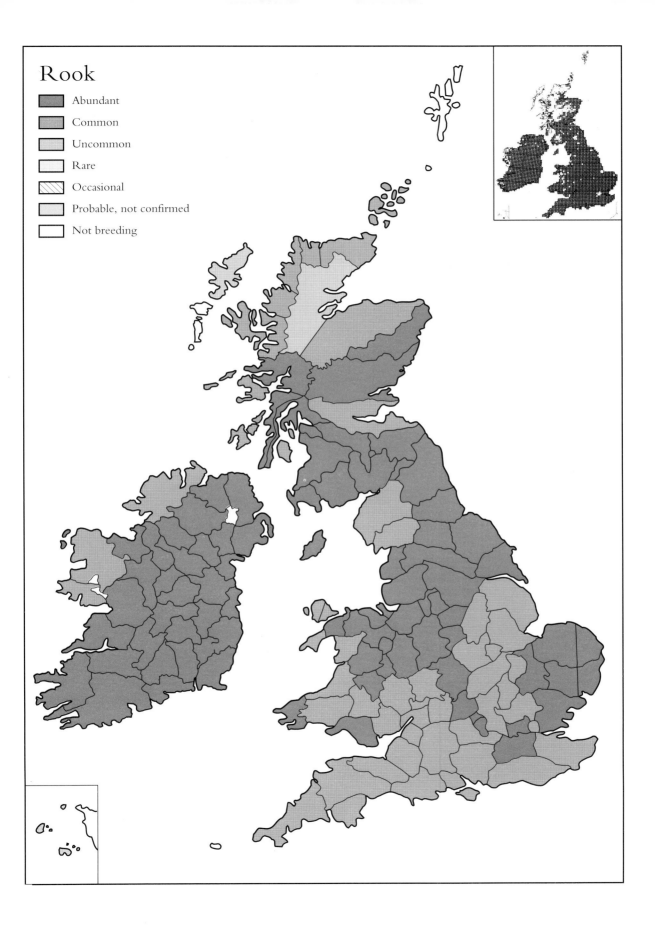

Rook

- Abundant
- Common
- Uncommon
- Rare
- Occasional
- Probable, not confirmed
- Not breeding

Carrion and Hooded Crow

Corvus corone corone and *C. c. cornix*

No bird was more hated and persecuted by gamekeepers and land owners in the 19th century than the Crow. It was a ubiquitous species, breeding in its two forms over the whole of Britain and Ireland and throughout its range it was systematically poisoned, shot and trapped, and the young and eggs destroyed. These efforts to exterminate it met with varying degrees of success. At the end of the 19th century the Carrion Crow's distribution was patchy, espe-cially in England, and followed closely the distribution of gamekeepers. Over much of England the Carrion Crow was recorded as having decreased during the 19th century, substantially so in the Midlands and southeastern counties—the density of gamekeepers was at its highest here. In other areas gamekeepers had remarkably little success in affecting the population size. This was clearly true of Wales; no counties there had recorded a decline in numbers despite numerous accounts of large numbers killed. In Scotland too numbers were little affected. On an estate near Invergarry during the 1880s, for example, the Carrion Crow had 'increased enormously' despite heavy persecution: 53 were killed on just one day of shooting by two keepers in the spring of 1887. The futility of the operation was demonstrated in the following year when the landowner complained of the abundance of Crows on his estate. The northern limit of regular breeding of the Carrion Crow did not extend further than the Great Glen although single birds mated with grey (i.e. Hooded) Crows bred occasionally as far north as SE Sutherland. In Ireland a handful of

Number of counties in which recorded:

Period	Probable breeding		Confirmed breeding		Combined		
	Br	Ir	Br	Ir	Br	Ir	Both
1875–1900 Carrion Crow	0	0	97	1	97	1	98
Hooded Crow	0	0	33	34	33	34	67
Hybrid Crow	0	0	10	0	10	0	10
1968–1972 Carrion Crow	0	1	99	2	99	3	102
Hooded Crow	0	0	23	34	23	34	57
Hybrid Crow	0	0	17	2	17	2	19
			change	Carrion Crow	2	2	4
					2%	200%	4%
				Hooded Crow	−10	0	−10
					−30%		−15%
				Hybrid Crow	7	2	9
					70%		90%

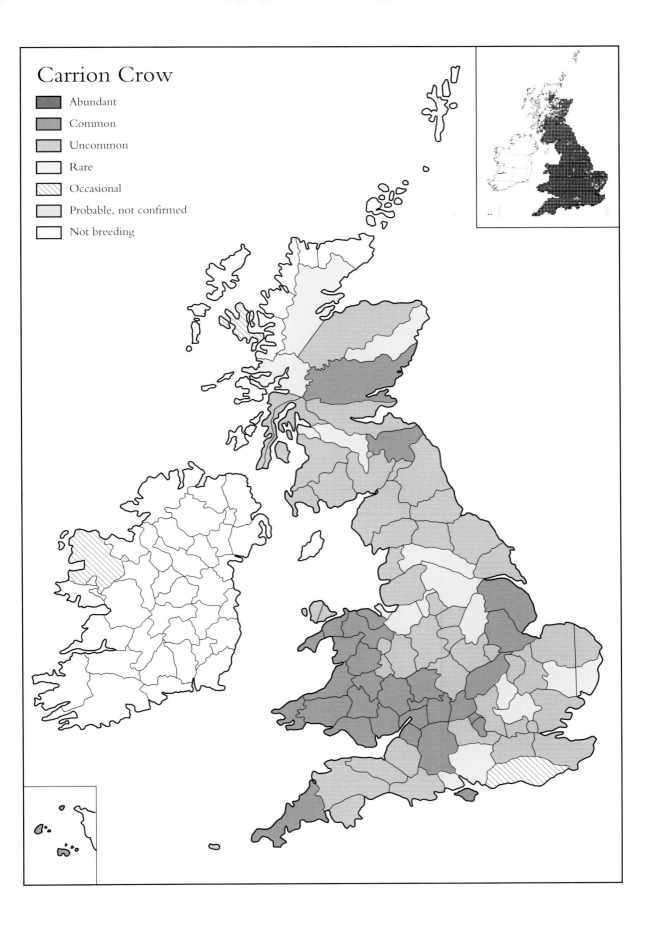

Carrion Crow

- **Abundant**
- **Common**
- **Uncommon**
- **Rare**
- **Occasional**
- **Probable, not confirmed**
- **Not breeding**

records of breeding black (i.e. Carrion) Crows were reported during the 19th century, although many of these were of uncertain provenance, the last being a brood in Mayo in 1890.

During the 19th century naturalists debated whether the black and grey forms belonged to the same species. By the end of the century, most, however, were quite prepared to accept Newton's argument that they did (Yarrell 1871-85).

The Hooded Crow bred commonly throughout Ireland and the Isle of Man (the Carrion Crow had not been recorded even as a vagrant on the latter island during the 19th century) and in Scotland north of the Forth/Clyde valley. Beyond this area it bred rarely through S Scotland, occasionally in the Borders and into NE England, breeding in coastal areas as far south as Flamborough Head, Yorkshire.

The Carrion Crow increased substantially in numbers during the 20th century. This was first noted during the 1914–18 war with the reduction in game preservation and numbers of gamekeepers that occurred at that time. With the subsequent decline of sporting estates the increase in

Carrion Crow numbers continued through the 1920s and 1930s. The 1939–45 war saw a dramatic rise in the rate of increase with the further decrease in persecution that the war brought. Numbers continued to rise after the war and it has become apparent that the Carrion Crow has adapted very well to the modern agricultural environment. Its opportunistic nature has also allowed it to move into urban habitats such as parks and large gardens.

The zone of hybridisation between Carrion and Hooded Crows has moved northwards in Britain, particularly during the first half of the 20th century, with the amelioration of the climate that occurred then (Cook 1975); this movement has continued since 1974. Comparison of the centre of black and grey form hybridisation in 1928, calculated by Cook, with the hybridisation range of the late 19th century indicates that the mean hybrid line was moving prior to 1928 and in fact may have started with the period of warmer winters that began around the middle of the 19th century.

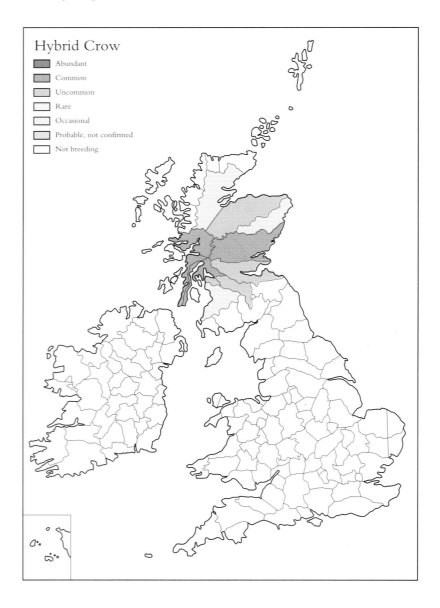

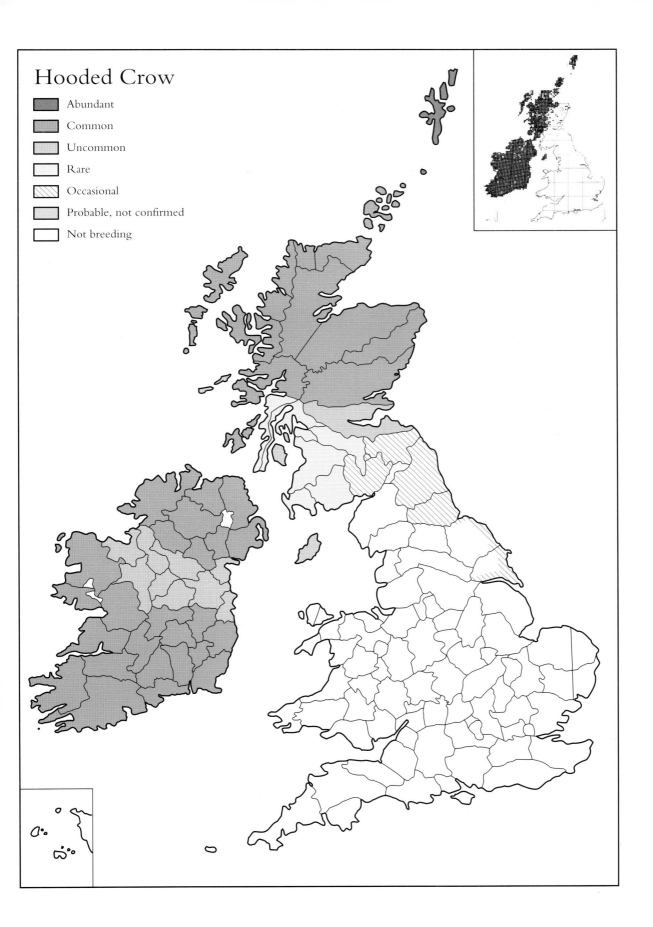

Hooded Crow

- ■ Abundant
- ■ Common
- ■ Uncommon
- □ Rare
- ▨ Occasional
- ▨ Probable, not confirmed
- □ Not breeding

Raven

Corvus corax

At the beginning of the 19th century the Raven bred in almost every county of Britain, and it probably bred in the four counties for which there are no records. As the century progressed, however, the Raven withdrew from lowland haunts in E and mid England. The breeding range boundary moved gradually towards the north, west and southwest, i.e. to the rugged coasts and mountain districts. Tree nesting declined greatly and most breeding took place on cliffs and crags. Persecution by gamekeepers and farmers took its toll, and collectors of skins, eggs and the young, for pets, exterminated the bird in many areas. At the end of the 19th century the Raven still managed to hang on in parts of the north, along the south and southwest coasts and parts of the S Midlands of England, and over much of Wales and upland Scotland.

In Ireland the Raven appears to have been, on the whole, a coastal species during much of the 19th century, there being evidence of limited usage of inland crags in the northwest of the country, areas that Ravens subsequently abandoned. Inland Kerry, Cork and Mayo were not mentioned as being inhabited by breeding Ravens by Ussher and Warren (1900), yet the species must have been present in these wild and little trodden districts, as well as on their coasts (D. Ratcliffe in litt).

Up to around the beginning of the 1939–45 war the Raven appears to have increased slightly in both numbers and range. It had been lost from SE England but was considered to have been breeding in considerable numbers throughout the southwest and it had returned to Gloucestershire. The Raven had greatly increased in Wales but still bred sparsely in the Pennines and was comparatively rare or absent in E Scotland. The apparent recovery during the 1914–18 war and the following stability has been attributed to the reduction of persecution coincident with gamekeepers and others leaving the land to help the war effort. For the same reasons the Raven increased further during the 1939–45 war, continuing to do so locally until the 1950s, and, in a few places, later. Tree nesting increased in Wales, the Welsh borders and SW England, and the Irish population increased away from its coastal strongholds.

In the next 20 years or so this recovery continued; the main British stronghold was in Wales and the west country, and Ravens were especially common in Ireland. The *88–91 Atlas* recorded the continuing recovery in Ireland, but also recorded thinning in Scotland and the almost complete loss of breeding Ravens in Northumberland and some areas of S Scotland. The species remains virtually absent from much of the grouse moor country of E Scotland from the Borders to Inverness as further evidence of the lingering effects of persecution by gamekeepers (D. Ratcliffe in litt). Raven populations are currently threatened by such influences as afforestation, improved sheep husbandry, removal of stock from the hills in winter and conversion of pasture to arable land, whilst persecution is still carried out especially on game preserves. It is likely that disturbance from increased leisure activities in some of the remote areas in which the Raven breeds also has an adverse effect on its success. Thom (1986) considered that the Raven may yet disappear from further inland regions in Scotland if the present trends continue.

Where known the dates of last 19th century breeding follow. **Hampshire**—last bred in the New Forest in 1858. **Kent**—bred up to *ca* 1890. **Surrey**—last bred in 1850. **Essex**—last bred in 1890. **London**—last bred in 1830. **Middlesex**—bred to about 1850 in Hyde Park. **Oxfordshire**—last bred in 1834. **Suffolk**—last bred inland in 1867 in the east and 1878 in the west and to 1895 on the coast. **Norfolk**—last certain nest 1859. **Bedfordshire**—last bred about 1850. **Northamptonshire**—last bred about 1850. **Gloucestershire**—last bred in the north-west in 1873 and the Cotswolds in 1875. **Worcestershire**—last bred in 1859. **Warwickshire**—last bred at the turn of the century. **Staffordshire**—last bred in 1844. **Shropshire**—last bred in 1884. **Lincolnshire**—last bred about 1860. **Leicestershire**—last bred about 1840. **Derbyshire**—last bred around 1860 in the northern hills.

Number of counties in which recorded:

Period	Probable breeding		Confirmed breeding		Combined		
	Br	Ir	Br	Ir	Br	Ir	Both
1875–1900	0	0	66	12	66	12	78
1968–1972	3	2	61	28	64	30	94
			change		−2	18	16
					−3%	150%	21%

390

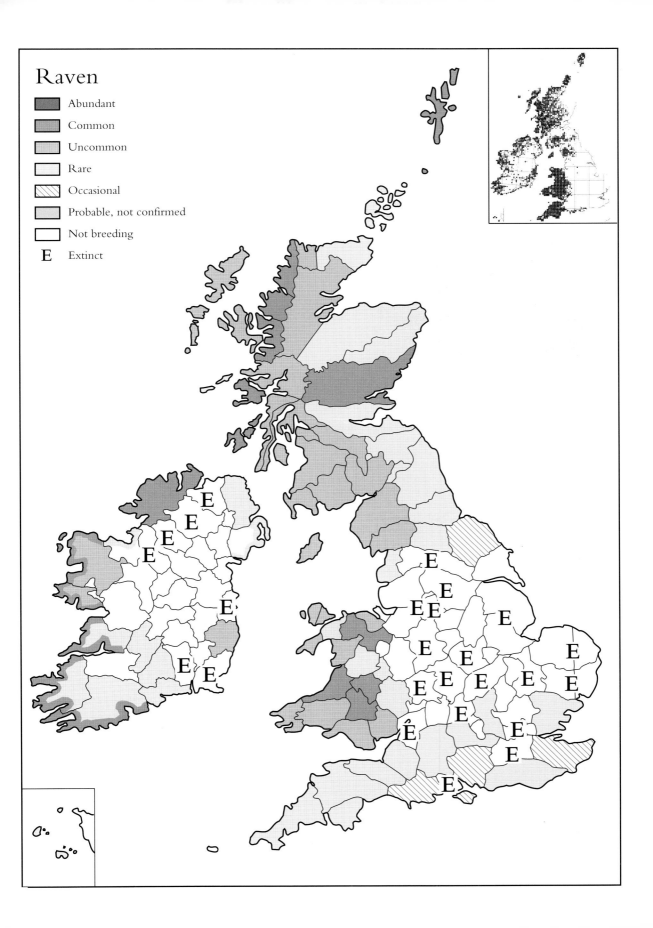

Raven

- **Abundant**
- **Common**
- **Uncommon**
- **Rare**
- **Occasional**
- **Probable, not confirmed**
- **Not breeding**
- **E** Extinct

Starling

Sturnus vulgaris

At the end of the 19th century the Starling was an abundant species everywhere but the Highlands of Scotland and on the western side of Ireland. It was not always so, however. In the first half of the century it was absent from much of SW England, W Wales, the mainland of Scotland north of the Forth/Clyde valley and W Ireland. It was rare, too, at this time in N England. In Cornwall it first bred in the east in 1855 and five pairs were breeding there in 1864, but it did not breed in W Cornwall until 1878. It did not breed in Devonshire until around 1800; colonisation of the southeast corner occurred sometime prior to 1844 and after this it gradually spread north and west. Up to the 1880s it was almost unknown in W Wales but increased there subsequently, especially in Caernarvonshire, Merioneth and Pembrokeshire, whilst in Cardiganshire it only colonised the vicinity of the larger towns. Although known from Cumberland since at least 1621 the Starling remained a rare bird there up to the first half of the 19th century. A large increase was noted over Lakeland from the 1860s onwards, until by the end of the century it was regarded as common in all areas except the most exposed upland areas.

The expansion of range in Scotland was well documented by Harvie-Brown (1895). Starlings had bred commonly in the Outer Hebrides, Orkney, Shetland and the NE coast of Caithness since time immemorial. From around the turn of the 19th century an expansion had, in retrospect, become apparent from these centres and from

the south. By 1900 the Starling had reached deep into the Highlands, nesting far up the valleys in shepherds' huts and hunting lodges. An increase in Ireland mirrored that in Scotland with the expansion moving from northeast to southwest. Here, as in Britain, the increase in numbers in the summer was more than matched by increases in the winter, due, most likely, to increases in the number of immigrants from the continent, suggesting a widespread increase in numbers at this time (C. Feare in litt). Many reasons were postulated at the time for the widespread increase. The persecution of raptors, especially the Sparrowhawk, agricultural changes that provided more feeding areas, an amelioration of the climate and urbanisation that provided more nesting sites and food may well have played their part. The increase continued, albeit at a slower pace, to the 1960s but declines have occurred since then, especially in the south and east, which may have been due to agricultural intensification (Feare 1994).

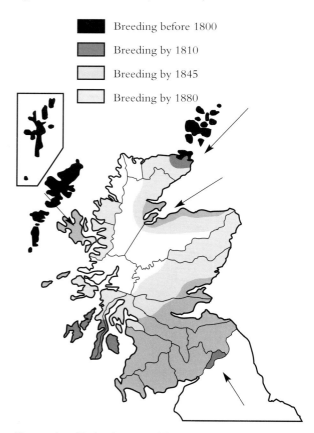

The extension of the breeding range of the Starling in Scotland during the 19th century (adapted from Harvie-Brown 1895).

Number of counties in which recorded:

Period	Probable breeding		Confirmed breeding		Combined		
	Br	Ir	Br	Ir	Br	Ir	Both
1875–1900	0	0	108	34	108	34	142
1968–1972	0	0	108	34	108	34	142
			change		0	0	0

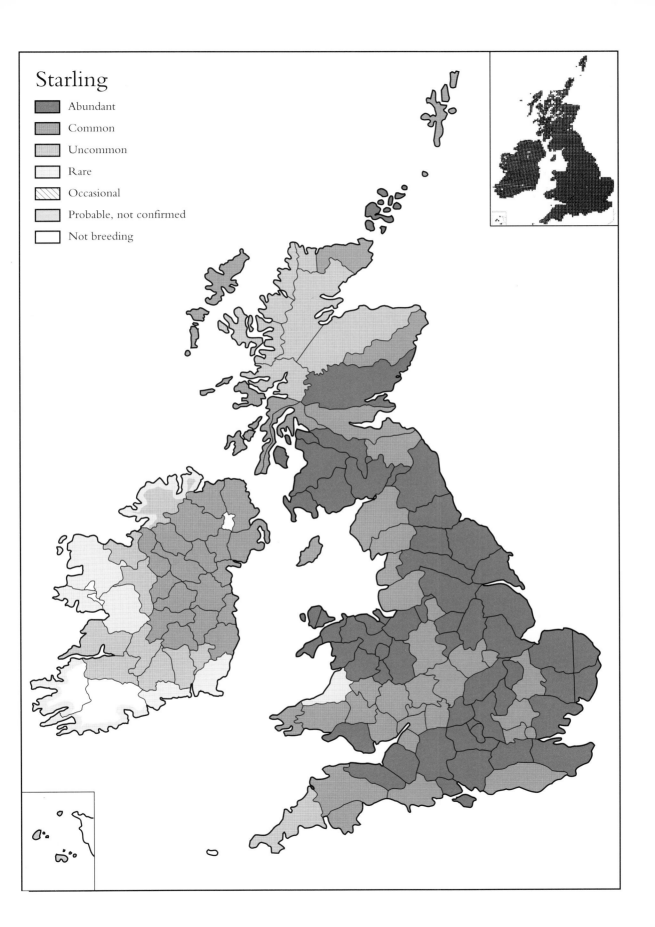

Starling

- Abundant
- Common
- Uncommon
- Rare
- Occasional
- Probable, not confirmed
- Not breeding

House Sparrow
(Common Sparrow)

Passer domesticus

The House Sparrow population of Britain had increased substantially, together with that of the human population, in the 19th century. In England the bulk of the increase had taken place before the 19th century but, locally, it was still occurring. Numbers were evidently still increasing in Oxfordshire during the 1880s but at the same time the House Sparrow had yet to colonise SW Wales away from the coast in any numbers. In the north and west of the Scottish Highlands it was still spreading, even to the end of the century, firstly along the coast and then up the valleys into the uplands. A spread eastwards evidently followed the spread of people and agricultural crops into those areas. The House Sparrow had long been recorded from E Scotland and around the north coast as far as Sutherland but was probably absent from much of the central Highlands and West Ross prior to the 1880s. After about 1880 it became common in Rannoch, Perthshire, and then it spread just a few years later to the west coast. It remained scarce in some of the smaller Western Isles throughout the 19th century and the colonisation of the Outer Hebrides was apparently recent. It was very scarce or absent there to around 1840 although the first record of a nest was that from Stornoway in 1833. In 1865 it was still regarded as uncommon in the Outer Hebrides but by 1871 it had become very abundant and a pest to farmers.

Its tremendous increase and the amount of damage that it did to crops brought the House Sparrow a lot of attention. Sparrow Clubs of the early 19th century were set up with the aim of eradicating it from every parish and the House Sparrow was the subject of much research and investigation. Books were published to spread the belief that it was the duty of every country dweller to kill the House Sparrow at every opportunity, whilst others drew attention to the caterpillars, beetles and other insects fed to the young in the nest. Under the weight of all the evidence the House Sparrow was almost universally disliked; even Aplin believed that their destruction was desirable and gave some instruction on the best ways of doing so (Aplin 1889).

In Ireland the House Sparrow was distributed throughout, even to the remotest coasts and islands off the north and west coasts where there were thatched cottages in which to nest. Only in areas thinly peopled was it scarce or local. There seems little evidence that the status of the House Sparrow had changed during the 19th century.

Numbers continued to increase generally into the 20th century in W Scotland and coastal and upland areas of W Wales, and by 1940 the House Sparrow had reached most of the remote areas of Britain in which it is now found. In other areas, however, the density of House Sparrows decreased with the disappearance of the horse from towns and cities from the 1920s. In general, increasing urbanisation through the 20th century must have been beneficial to the House Sparrow, and numbers probably increased overall as a result; however, the species has followed the human withdrawal from some of the remotest parts of Britain and Ireland (Parslow 1973). Also in Ireland, in areas with few alternative nest sites, the replacement of thatched roofs by tiles has led to a decrease (Kennedy *et al.* 1954). Since the 1970s, however, although the evidence is not completely clear, it is apparent that a decrease is underway, particularly in urban areas. This may be because modern farming practices have reduced the amount of food (both insects and seeds) available. However, Tawny Owls, Sparrowhawks and domestic cats are all significant predators of the House Sparrow and their increase in suburban areas may be sufficient to reduce the House Sparrow's population levels in these habitats (Gibbons *et al.* 1993).

Number of counties in which recorded:

Period	Probable breeding		Confirmed breeding		Combined		
	Br	Ir	Br	Ir	Br	Ir	Both
1875–1900	0	0	108	34	108	34	142
1968–1972	0	0	108	34	108	34	142
			change		0	0	0

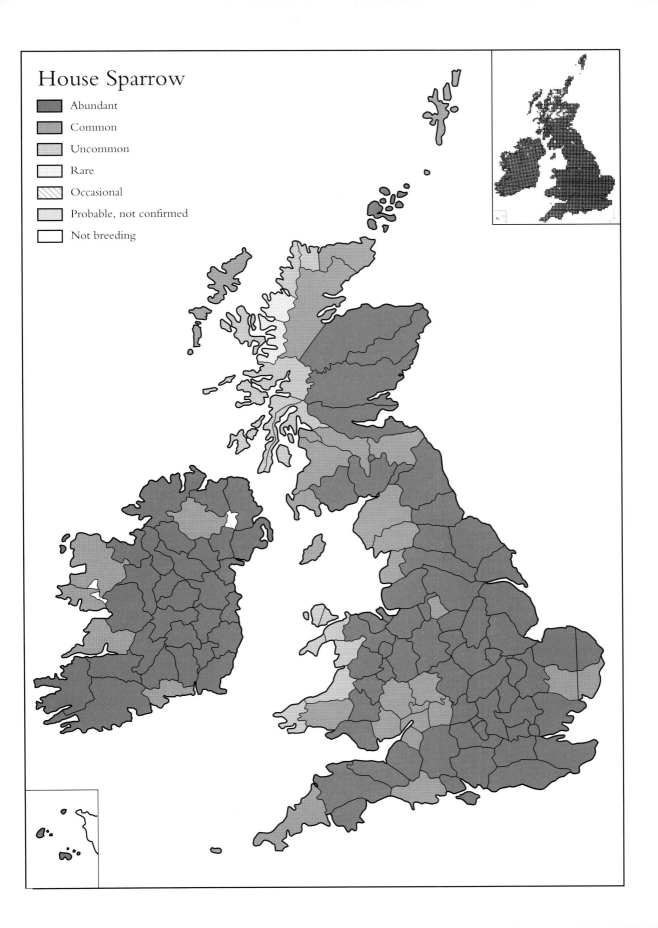

House Sparrow

- Abundant
- Common
- Uncommon
- Rare
- Occasional
- Probable, not confirmed
- Not breeding

Tree Sparrow

Passer montanus

The Tree Sparrow was widely distributed throughout Britain by the end of the 19th century, being absent only from SW England, W Wales and much of Scotland. In Scotland it bred in very small numbers only in coastal regions and the islands off the west coast, apart from some inland groups in the Lothians. In Ireland it was resident in one district only. The first Irish specimen was taken from a small area north of Dublin Bay in 1852; by the end of the century the population had increased there but had not spread elsewhere. There is a record of a pair found breeding on Aranmore Island, Co. Donegal in 1886, but the species did not breed there again during the 19th century.

The Tree Sparrow's apparently patchy distribution at the end of the 19th century may be explained in one of three ways (or a permutation of the three). 1. The Tree Sparrow is not easy to identify and its nests are difficult to find. This is particularly true of isolated pairs. In addition, the data for the map were taken from accounts published throughout 1875–1900; for two reasons this may lead to an impression of uneven distribution. 2. Observer familiarity and frequency may have increased during the period leading to an increased frequency of recording. 3. There is some evidence that the Tree Sparrow population was increasing rapidly during this period and the county accounts may have recorded the increase at different points in its progress. For these reasons, this map is less reliable as a record of

Tree Sparrow frequency than others; the species' distribution, however, is recorded with no less accuracy.

The Tree Sparrow's range was apparently expanding in the late 19th century. Yarrell (1837–43) had regarded it as rare in the southern and northern counties, more common in the eastern and midland counties and absent from the southwestern counties of England. The impression is given that it was not a well-known species anywhere in its English range in the early 1800s. Yarrell was not aware of it ever having bred in Wales, Scotland or Ireland, yet by the end of the century it bred in all three countries. Summers-Smith (1989) suggested that the species is eruptive from Continental Europe and a number of accounts around the turn of the 19th century noted increases in winter populations in E England (Cordeaux 1866–82 and Cordeaux 1879–89, Clarke and Roebuck 1881, Christy 1890, Prentis 1894, Ticehurst 1909). The reasons for large-scale movements of European Tree Sparrows to Britain are not clear. Certainly, these movements follow population increases on the Continent; they may indicate a period of drier weather, the Tree Sparrow being an inhabitant of dry areas throughout its range. These immigrations may have fuelled an increase in breeding numbers in Britain but recent research suggests that this may be unlikely (Summers-Smith in litt). Sparrowhawks may have a more important effect on Tree Sparrow numbers: the Tree Sparrow population increased when Sparrowhawk numbers were decreasing in 1946–65, and decreased during the Sparrowhawk's recovery in 1966–92 (Summers-Smith in litt).

The Tree Sparrow population remained stable from the end of the 19th century until about 1930. Sporadic breeding took place in some areas, notably Ireland, but no widespread change occurred until a slow decline started in 1930 that continued until about 1955. During this period the species was lost from many areas of Scotland and Wales and by its end had ceased to breed in Ireland. In about 1958 a massive increase in numbers and range began. Many areas of Britain and Ireland were recolonised through the early 1960s and, some areas were colonised for the first time. By 1979, the population was six times that of the period from the mid 1940s to the mid 1950s. The *68–72 Atlas* estimated the population at around 250,000. The Scottish and English distribution at this time was little different to that recorded during 1875–1900 but in Ireland several new coastal localities were populated. Thinning of the population appears to have taken place in Britain during the intervening period between the *68–72* and *88–91 Atlases*, but in E Ireland the species continued to increase.

Number of counties in which recorded:

Period	Probable breeding		Confirmed breeding		Combined		
	Br	Ir	Br	Ir	Br	Ir	Both
1875–1900	0	0	90	1	90	1	91
1968-1972	0	0	96	23	96	23	119
change					6	22	28
					7%	2200%	31%

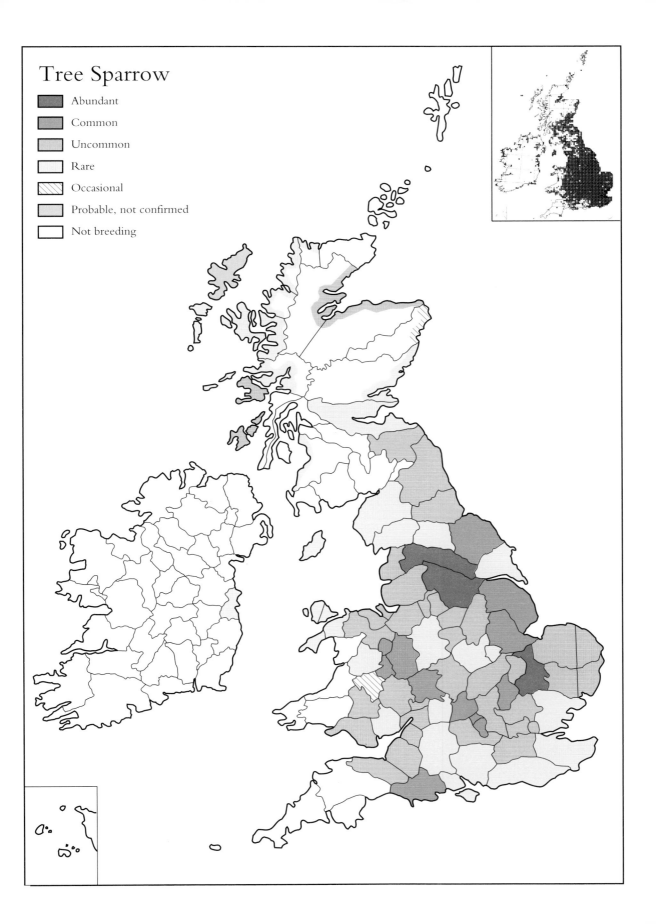

Tree Sparrow

- **Abundant**
- **Common**
- **Uncommon**
- **Rare**
- **Occasional**
- **Probable, not confirmed**
- **Not breeding**

Chaffinch

Fringilla coelebs

The Chaffinch was abundant and widespread throughout most of Britain and Ireland during the 19th century. In only a few areas was it scarce. The lack of trees and bushes in the Isles of Scilly was probably the reason for its absence there, and their planting may have facilitated the colonisation of some of the minor Western Isles in the 20th century (Parslow 1973). There may have been other reasons, however, for the increase in numbers of Chaffinches that occurred on the NW Scottish mainland after the middle of the 19th century. Prior to the 1870s the Chaffinch probably did not breed in that area but in 1877 a nest was found in an ash tree near Inchnadamph in SW Sutherland. From this point it increased rapidly in NW Ross and W Sutherland and by 1901 was regarded as common at Kylestrome in the latter county, but further north it was still rare. It had also increased in numbers in Caithness after about 1850. In the Outer Hebrides it was confined to the Glen of Rodel in Harris in 1841. Gray (1871) later described it as occurring in several sheltered localities in Harris and Lewis and indicated that it occurred elsewhere but, by the 1880s, the Chaffinch was considered abundant in suitable localities in the islands. Records of breeding in Orkney were rare; several anecdotal accounts existed, some from the 1850s, but the general impression was that it bred, perhaps regularly, in very few numbers. It did not breed on some of the Inner Hebridean Islands or Shetland.

Outwith these areas the Chaffinch was ubiquitous. Its abundance during the breeding season is clear from almost all ornithological accounts of the 19th century and the large flocks that collected during autumn and winter were also commonly remarked upon. It is likely that the Chaffinch was able to profit from the growth of arable farming that took place through much of the 18th and 19th centuries and arable weed seeds and spilt grain were an important food resource for the species. The spread of agriculture was perhaps responsible for the increase in the range of the Chaffinch that took place in NW Scotland.

The increase in numbers in Scotland continued into the 20th century. A number of Hebridean Islands and the Isles of Scilly were colonised around the turn of the century whilst numbers increased slowly in Orkney through the century. In upland areas particularly, over the last 50 years or so, an increase in Chaffinch numbers has been associated with afforestation, which has provided huge areas of breeding habitat. In other areas, however, a population decline was reported from a number of counties beginning in the late 1950s (Parslow, 1973). The reason for the decline was likely to have been poisoning by newly introduced organochlorine pesticides. Quantitive data from 1962 have described a steady increase in Chaffinch numbers up to the present day, especially from the early to mid 1970s. This increase may have been a recovery from the decline in the 1950s, following action to reduce the use of organochlorine pesticides, but was clearly a return from the very low numbers that followed the winters of the early 1960s (Marchant *et al.* 1990) which were both severe and coincided with a peak in the use of organochlorine pesticides (I. Newton in litt).

Number of counties in which recorded:

Period	Probable breeding		Confirmed breeding		Combined		
	Br	Ir	Br	Ir	Br	Ir	Both
1875–1900	0	0	107	34	107	34	141
1968–1972	1	0	107	34	108	34	142
			change		1	0	1
					1%		1%

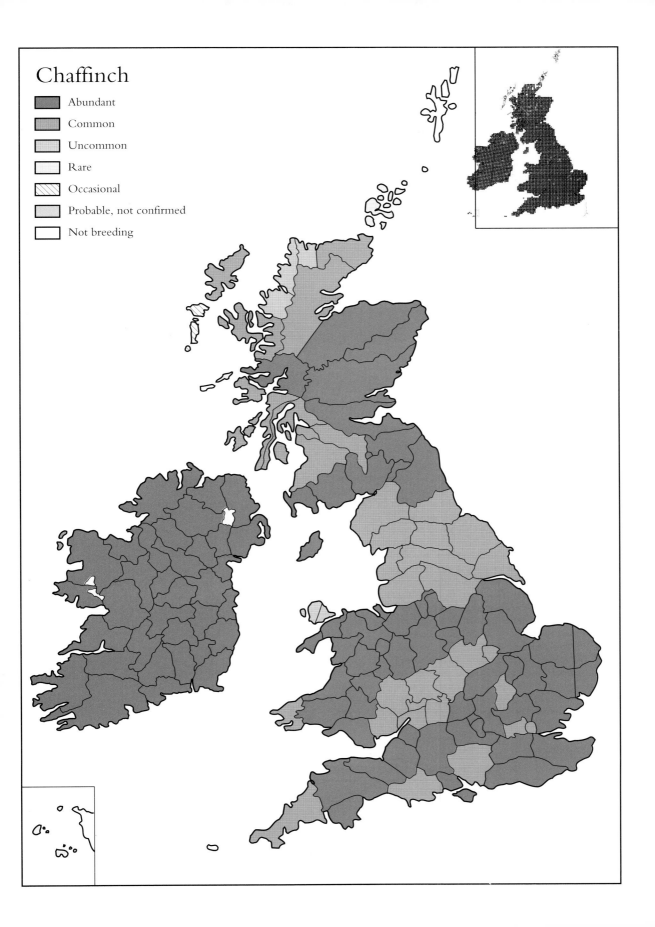

Chaffinch

- Abundant
- Common
- Uncommon
- Rare
- Occasional
- Probable, not confirmed
- Not breeding

Greenfinch (Green Linnet)

Carduelis chloris

The Greenfinch bred commonly throughout most of Britain and Ireland during the 19th century. Large winter flocks were often recorded on stubble and wasteland, and when snow lay they were often found in the farm and stack yards. The enclosure activities of the early part of the century, and gradual intensification of agriculture up to the 1870s, may have contributed to an improved winter survival, especially in combination with the milder climate that predominated around the end of the century. By the last quarter of the 19th century many of the authors of the county avifaunas wrote about the large numbers of Greenfinch that they had encountered. In Kent it was considered to occur in numbers 'only surpassed by those of the Sparrow' and farmers claimed that they caused great damage to small-seed crops (such as turnip, rape, mustard, etc.) and in fruit orchards and hop gardens. That these large numbers were a reasonably recent phenomenon is suggested by the fact that there was little indication that they were controlled or widely considered a pest in the same way that the House Sparrow was.

The Greenfinch bred sparsely in the uplands of N England and, indeed, was absent from the eastern fells of Lakeland. In S and E Scotland it bred commonly through the agricultural districts but, again, was scarce in the uplands although numbers increased locally north of the Great Glen. It was absent from most of NW Scotland and most of the islands. Of the Inner Hebrides it bred on the larger wooded islands, such as Mull and Jura, Iona and Raasay, but did not breed on Skye, the Outer Hebrides or Shetland.

Baikie and Heddle (1848) were able to record the Greenfinch only as a winter visitor to Orkney. It seems unlikely that it did not breed there at all before the late 1870s, but by at least 1890 it was breeding commonly throughout Mainland. It bred on a few of the other islands but only on those that had any woodland cover. The colonisation of Orkney and subsequent rapid increase was considered to have been the result of an increase in the planting of, mainly, sycamore woods grown to provide shelter.

During the first half of the 20th century the Greenfinch increased and extended its range in N Scotland into new conifer plantations; this was probably a continuation of the general expansion into Scottish plantations that began with the maturing, by the middle of the 19th century, of the trees planted in the late 18th century. The woods at Stornoway, Lewis were colonised in about 1906 and other Hebridean islands were colonised as the century progressed.

The Greenfinch was common in Ireland and bred widely at the end of the 19th century. It was absent only from the bare coastal districts of W Galway, Mayo, NW Donegal and Rathlin Island, off the coast of Antrim, although it had been recorded breeding on Achill Island. After the 1939–45 war a spread into parts of W Mayo and Donegal had become apparent although a general decline in Ireland has been noted since the 1960s.

In general, through the 19th and 20th centuries, Greenfinch numbers, before the days of widespread garden feeding, depended on the amount of stubble grain and weed seeds available in the fields. It is likely that the Greenfinch increased in numbers as the area of arable land increased and, as the species also needs shrubs for nesting, it would have moved into previously open areas following tree planting (I. Newton in litt). The greatest change in the Greenfinch's status during the 20th century has been the spread into urban and suburban areas, both in the breeding season and in winter, and the considerable increase noted in gardens. This is due, at least partly, to the provision of supplementary foods now put out for birds in gardens, an apparently successful replacement for the spilt seed and grain and weed seeds that are scarce on modern farms.

Number of counties in which recorded:

Period	Probable breeding		Confirmed breeding		Combined		
	Br	Ir	Br	Ir	Br	Ir	Both
1875–1900	0	0	101	34	101	34	135
1968–1972	0	0	107	34	107	34	141
			change		6	0	6
					6%		4%

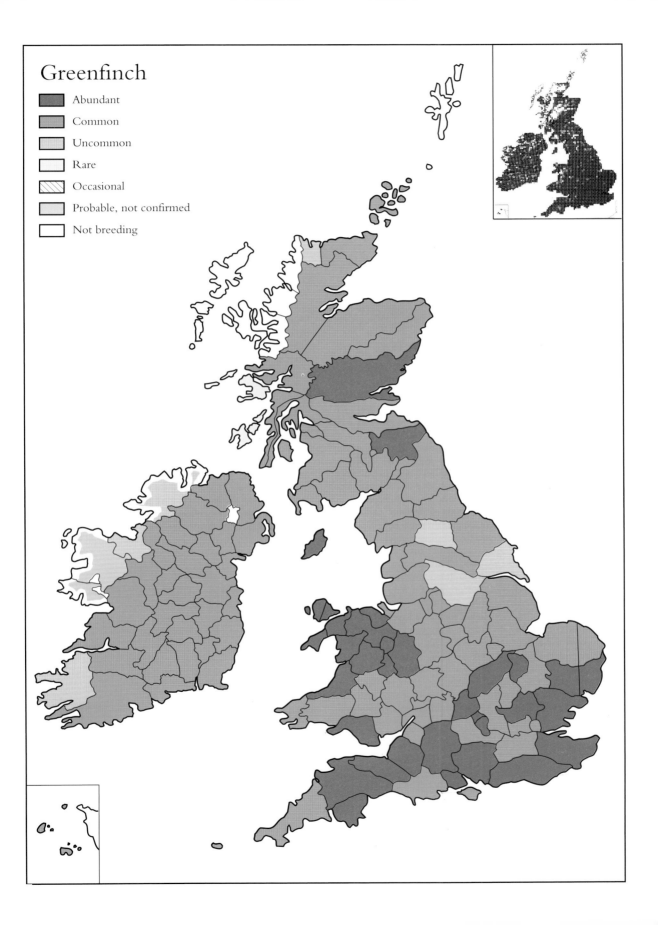

Greenfinch

- **Abundant**
- **Common**
- **Uncommon**
- **Rare**
- **Occasional**
- **Probable, not confirmed**
- **Not breeding**

Goldfinch

Carduelis carduelis

The Goldfinch was a very popular cage bird in the 19th century. Its bright plumage and the ease with which it could be attracted by decoys, and hence caught, put it at the top of the birdcatcher's list. From the early years of the 19th century many were caught to supply the insatiable demand, especially in the larger cities, and populations decreased, particularly in England and Scotland. The Goldfinches of Wales were apparently little troubled as few catchers were resident there, and in Ireland noticeable decreases occurred only in the vicinity of the largest towns. Agricultural changes, including ongoing enclosure and ploughing of marginal lands, eradicated many of the weed species in the Goldfinch's diet. This process may have helped to compound the birdcatchers' activities, although its effect on an already reduced population may have been slight.

Populations of Goldfinches fell to such a low level by the 1870s (it was probably extinct, or very nearly so, in many N England and S Scotland counties) that it was included in the Wild Birds Protection Acts of 1880 and 1881. In general, however, local authorities failed to enforce the law and it was not until the Amendment Act of 1894, which conferred upon the local authorities extra powers of enforcement, that the collection of Goldfinches began to lessen.

Coincident with the Act, and probably as a result of it, the fashion for captive birds in the parlour began to wane. By the turn of the century, noticeable and, apparently, in places, large increases in the Goldfinch population were recorded. These increases were aided by further protection Acts, although it was not until 1930 and 1931 that similar Acts were passed in the Irish parliament.

The gradual withdrawal of Goldfinches from N Scotland (north of the Great Glen) was probably complete by the end of the 1870s. Goldfinches had always been rare there and could not sustain the birdcatchers' depredations; agricultural changes may have played a part in the extinctions too. By the 1920s, the species was no longer breeding in Tayside, Forth or the Borders.

In England and S Scotland, however, Goldfinch numbers increased slowly through the 20th century, partially as a result of the reduction in trapping, but it is likely that the primary cause was the agricultural depression of the late 19th and early 20th century, which allowed thistles, one of the Goldfinch's most important foods, to increase. N Scotland was never repopulated by regular breeders but, through the 1940s to the 1960s the Goldfinch gradually returned to SE Scotland, the Forth region and, finally, S Tay, and breeding took place locally in the Grampian region and around Inverness. In general, from a peak in 1961, the population fell to a low point during the mid 1960s (partially the result of the severe winter of 1964) but recovered quickly and rose again into the 1970s (Parslow 1973). From around 1980, with the widespread use of new, very effective herbicides, the population has fallen dramatically, although recently has apparently recovered in farmland areas (Marchant *et al.* 1990).

The patchy distribution shown in the map is due to the rapid decline during the last part of the 19th century. Accounts made at different times have recorded different points of the decline and subsequent recovery. In general, the population throughout Britain declined up to about 1880 and began to grow from the 1890s.

Number of counties in which recorded:

Period	Probable breeding		Confirmed breeding		Combined		
	Br	Ir	Br	Ir	Br	Ir	Both
1875–1900	0	0	93	34	93	34	127
1968–1972	3	0	95	34	98	34	132
			change		5	0	5
					5%		4%

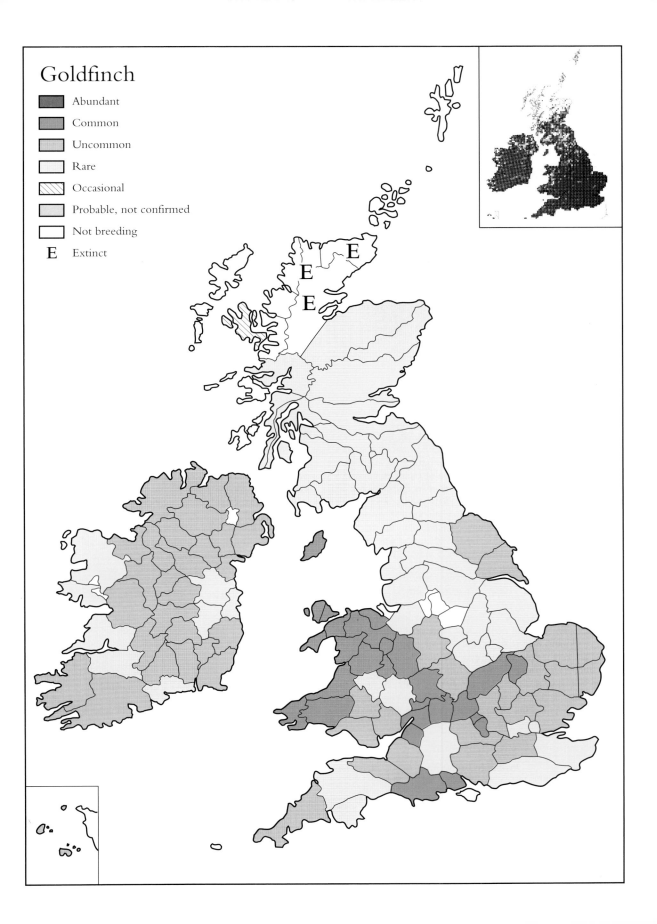

Goldfinch

- ■ Abundant
- ■ Common
- ■ Uncommon
- □ Rare
- ▨ Occasional
- ▨ Probable, not confirmed
- □ Not breeding
- **E** Extinct

E
E
E
E

Siskin

Carduelis spinus

The Siskin was only a localised breeder in England and Wales during the 19th century. It bred regularly in Surrey from 1836 but this, and other records from S England, probably resulted from escaped cage birds (Bucknill 1900). Pairs were noted in plantations around Longtown, Cumberland during the 1870s and 1880s and, in N Wales, it had been suspected of breeding for some years. A flock of 20, almost all young of the year, was seen in Denbighshire in August 1872, suggesting that they had been reared locally, although by this date they may also have moved from more distant breeding grounds. Singing males were located in N Wales in the springs of 1882 and 1902, but it was not until June 1899, when an unfledged bird was picked up dead near Colwyn Bay, that breeding was confirmed (Forrest 1907).

Scotland held the main British population during the 19th century. The earliest recorded Siskin's nest in Scotland was taken near Inverness in 1850 but since that time breeding had been reported from many parts of E Scotland. The old Caledonian forests were the Siskin's stronghold; it bred from Wick, Caithness (where it was only rarely recorded) and, more commonly, Golspie in SE Sutherland, to the Forth. South of this river it was more local, but some of the plantations in Dumfriesshire held well-known, regularly breeding populations. The distribution of the Siskin in Scotland was coincident with mature cone-bearing forest and the accompanying map should be considered with this in mind.

In Ireland, Thompson (1849–56) was not aware that the Siskin bred at all. The first Irish nest was found in 1857 at Cappagh, Waterford. That season, however, the woods abounded with singing Siskins and so it is unlikely that 1857 was the first year that the species bred in Ireland. Whatever the date of colonisation, by the end of the 19th century the growth of plantations had facilitated breeding in most Irish counties; pairs or juveniles were seen or males heard singing during the breeding season in six others where breeding was not proven.

A nadir in the population of Siskins in Britain was likely to have been reached after the 1914–18 war when large areas of mature forest had been felled. The new plantations took time to mature but led to first breeding by 1930 in Cumberland, Durham, Yorkshire and Shropshire. By the 1950s counties as far south as Hampshire and Devonshire and as far east as Kent and Suffolk held breeding pairs and, by the time of the *68–72 Atlas* survey, W and S Scotland were firmly populated and breeding was taking place regularly in parts of N England, East Anglia and N and mid Wales. In Ireland, a decline had been suggested in the 1960s but the extent was not clearly apparent.

As conifers planted since the 1939–45 war matured to seed bearing age so the population of the Siskin has increased. The *88–91 Atlas* recorded very large increases in S Scotland, N, S and SW England and throughout, but especially S and mid, Wales. Similar increases occurred in Ireland, especially in Mayo in the west.

Siskins in the 20th century have probably benefited from the increased planting of spruce, which would have been relatively rare in the 19th century, as they breed at higher densities in spruce than in pine forests (Avery and Leslie 1990). The species' future will depend on the rate of new planting of conifers and also the effects and scale of restructuring of the post-war plantations. If age-class distributions are evened out then the Siskin population should stabilise and annual oscillations will occur in response to the fruiting of trees. New planting of conifers is currently greater in Ireland than in Britain so it is possible to predict a greater increase there (D. Jardine in litt).

Number of counties in which recorded:

Period	Probable breeding		Confirmed breeding		Combined		
	Br	Ir	Br	Ir	Br	Ir	Both
1875–1900	2	7	9	18	11	25	36
1968–1972	5	3	46	28	51	31	82
			change		40	6	46
					364%	24%	128%

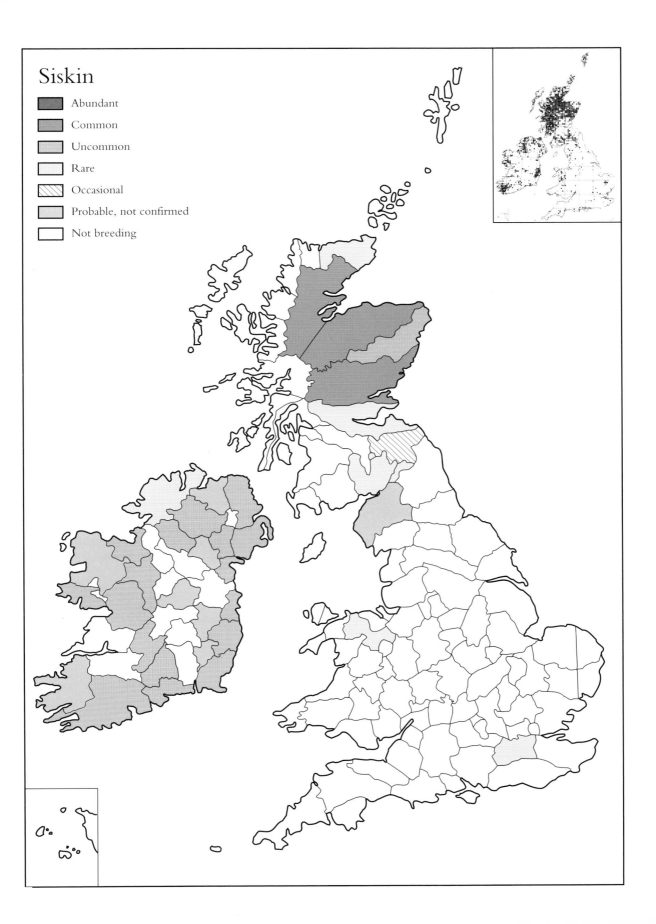

Siskin

- ▨ Abundant
- ▨ Common
- ▨ Uncommon
- ▨ Rare
- ▨ Occasional
- ▨ Probable, not confirmed
- ☐ Not breeding

Linnet (Common or Brown Linnet)

Carduelis cannabina

During the 19th century the Linnet was distributed throughout Britain and Ireland, although locally in the Inner Hebrides, and was absent, in the breeding season, only from the Outer Hebrides and Shetland. Over most of its range it was a common and familiar species often breeding in 'furze' bushes as well as scrub patches and hedgerows. The agricultural changes of the first 70 years or so of the 19th century would have had a mixed effect on the fortunes of the Linnet. At first the ploughing up and enclosure of rough, bushy areas would have destroyed much nesting habitat but Linnets were heavily dependent upon arable weeds for food and so the growth of arable agriculture would have balanced, to some extent, the loss of breeding habitat. The decline in agriculture from the 1870s, however, caused a decline in the numbers of the Linnet that became apparent during the last quarter of the 19th century. During this time the losses in nesting habitat that had taken place throughout the century were compounded by a reduction in available food as the amount of arable crops grown declined; recent research has suggested that unploughed land does not feed Linnets for many years (I. Newton in litt).

The Linnet was particularly valued as a cage bird in the 19th century and the activities of the birdcatchers almost certainly had a widespread effect on its decline. A direct effect was noted near the larger cities (London and Glasgow/Edinburgh particularly) where entire breeding groups were wiped out. Extensive catching of migrants in counties surrounding London, for instance, would have affected populations in much of E Britain (I. Newton in litt). In addition, British migrants were taken in large numbers in Belgium, France and Spain. This pressure was relieved somewhat by the 1890s as a succession of Acts of Parliament reduced the activities of birdcatchers and made caged birds less desirable, but the catching and confinement of British songbirds was not made illegal until 1953.

The population of Linnets in Britain appears to have stabilised as the 20th century opened and during the first half of the century only local fluctuations were apparent. As the century progressed new nesting sites were created by the extensive planting of conifer forests and the appearance of scrubby verges alongside roads, motorways and railways. Some note was made of an increase in parts of S England and the Midlands in the early decades of the century, as the Linnet recovered from the depredations of the birdcatchers, although decreases in NW Scotland and the Inner Hebrides were also noted during this time. The Outer Hebrides were colonised around the turn of the century but breeding has remained irregular there. Shetland was colonised briefly from around 1934, but by the 1960s the species had disappeared again.

The *68–72 Atlas* revealed the gaps that had become manifest in central, western and northern areas of the Scottish Highlands in which the Linnet was common in the 19th century. Further losses from this area were evident during the *88–91 Atlas* survey and large reductions in the numbers of breeding Linnets were recorded throughout Ireland. CBC data indicate that the Linnet is in sharp decline throughout Britain. Continued loss of breeding habitat has taken place, although many apparently suitable nesting areas remain unpopulated by Linnets. The maturation of conifer plantations and other agricultural changes have all combined to reduce numbers. It has become clear, however, that the increased sterilisation of farming and its unprecedentedly successful eradication of weeds through the increased use of herbicides has had the most widespread effect on numbers of Linnets during the last few decades (I. Newton in litt).

Number of counties in which recorded:

Period	Probable breeding		Confirmed breeding		Combined		
	Br	Ir	Br	Ir	Br	Ir	Both
1875–1900	0	0	105	34	105	34	139
1968–1972	0	0	104	34	104	34	138
			change		−1	0	−1
					−1%		−1%

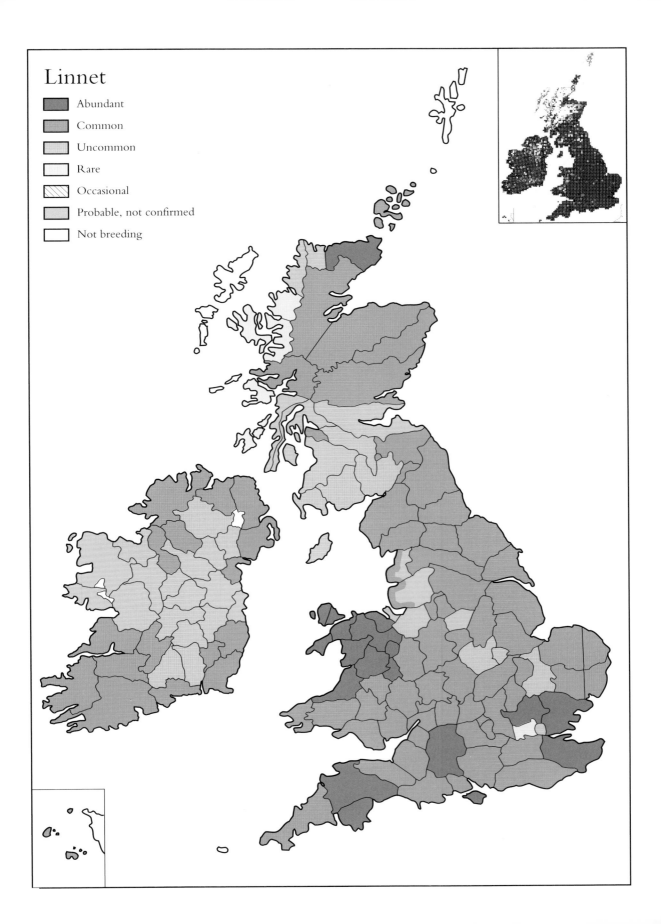

Linnet

- Abundant
- Common
- Uncommon
- Rare
- Occasional
- Probable, not confirmed
- Not breeding

Twite
(Mountain Linnet)

Carduelis flavirostris

Apart from outlying records in Herefordshire (Hutchinson 1900) and Shropshire (Forrest 1899), the distribution of the Twite at the end of the 19th century covered N England from Mansfield Forest in Nottinghamshire and the extreme N Staffordshire, through the Peak District and Pennines, to Scotland. In Scotland it was particularly common in the Outer Hebrides and on the northeast coast and bred as far north as Shetland. Ireland was another stronghold of the Twite, it being commonly, if in places locally, distributed throughout the country, absent only from the central plain. It was considered here particularly common near the rocky west coasts and bred on the exposed rocky islands of Kerry, Inishturk, Achill and Rathlin. Earlier 19th century accounts described the distribution of the Twite in a similar way to that presented here and so it is assumed that the distribution and population of the Twite were reasonably stable during the 19th century.

A small colony of Twites was reported nesting in 1904 in N Devonshire by Pearson (1904) but by the 1930s they had ceased to breed there. Similarly, nesting was recorded in Merioneth in 1905, but this appears to have been an isolated record and up to about the 1930s was the only one (Witherby *et al.* 1938–41). In Scotland, by around 1940, the Twite was considered a scarce bird on lower ground on the southeast side and to have, apparently, deserted the Pentland Hills there.

From this point the Twite has suffered a steady decline in breeding distribution, halted only by a few recolonisations of former breeding areas. Throughout the 20th century the range in Scotland has decreased towards the north and west so that, by the *68–72 Atlas* survey the Twite had disappeared from many counties of S Scotland. In the Borders, the Twite was recorded as having disappeared from the Cheviots sometime prior to 1944, although the last breeding record occurred here in 1953 on the Northumberland side. A parallel contraction of range occurred in England and during the first half of the 20th century or so it gradually disappeared from the Lakeland, Yorkshire and Lancashire mosses. Extinction from the extreme southern tip of the Pennines and the Peak District occurred sometime during this period, but during 1964–67 the Twite apparently recolonised its old southern breeding limit in E Cheshire, N Derbyshire and N Staffordshire. In 1967 a nest was found in an area of saltmarsh in Flint in N Wales—only the second Welsh record. In Ireland the Twite's old stronghold of the coasts of Kerry, Connemara, Mayo and Donegal maintained their populations. The western islands also held on to their colonies. Elsewhere, however, a similar contraction of range had occurred in Ireland as in Britain so that outside of the stronghold areas by the 1960s thin populations remained only in inland Connemara, Mayo and Antrim.

The *68–72 Atlas* appears to have recorded one further area of loss with the almost complete disappearance of the Lakeland population. It also may have recorded the continuing extension northwards of Twite in the Pennines. Otherwise the distribution recorded appears very similar to that described by Parslow (1973). The *88–91 Atlas* recorded the continuing decline in the Scottish and Irish populations and also the continuing increase throughout the Pennines. An interesting development was the N Wales breeding records—practically the first since at least the beginning of the 19th century.

Number of counties in which recorded:

Period	Probable breeding		Confirmed breeding		Combined		
	Br	Ir	Br	Ir	Br	Ir	Both
1875–1900	0	3	45	24	45	27	72
1968–1972	3	2	32	9	35	11	46
			change		−10	−16	−26
					−22%	−59%	−36%

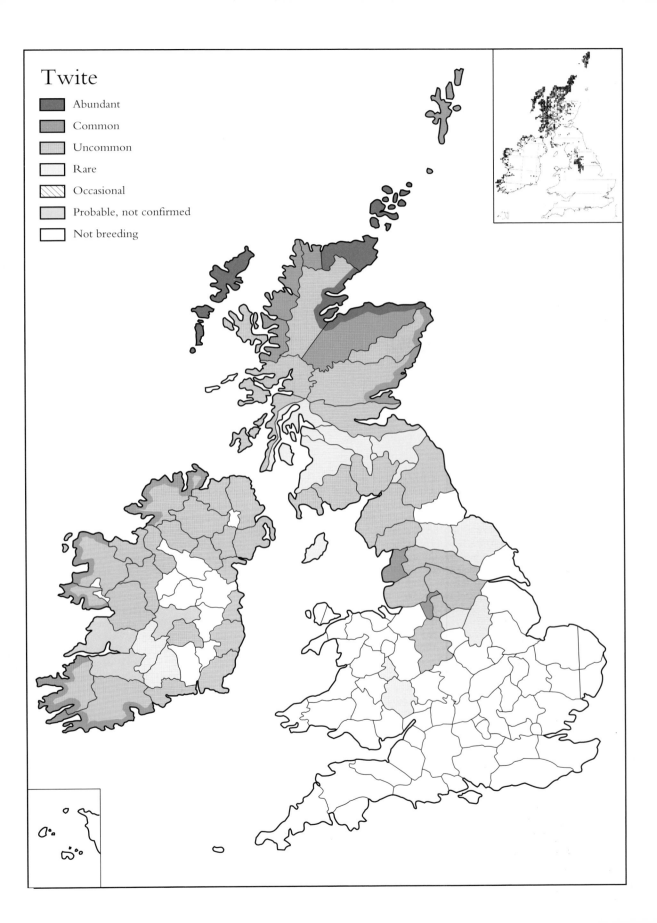

Twite

- **Abundant**
- **Common**
- **Uncommon**
- **Rare**
- **Occasional**
- **Probable, not confirmed**
- **Not breeding**

Redpoll
(Lesser Redpoll, Lesser Redpole)

Carduelis flammea

The Redpoll was widely distributed in Britain and Ireland at the end of the 19th century. It had not been recorded breeding in Cornwall, Devonshire (an adult was recorded feeding a fledgling in 1879 by Macpherson, but this was not noted by later writers and is not included on the map), Somerset, Dorset, some of the Inner Hebrides, the Outer Hebrides and Shetland. In those English and Welsh counties where breeding was recorded it was very local, and in most counties south of a line from the Wash to the Wirral breeding was rare. The exception to this was the counties that included the Welsh mountains where breeding was more extensive. Although often uncommon, the Redpoll bred more widely north of this line and the uplands and moorlands N England held good breeding populations. In Ireland the species was considered to have increased in numbers and to be completing (by 1900) a westward expansion. Kerry was the only county in which breeding was not known at this time and the Redpoll was still increasing in Connemara.

There is evidence, albeit scant, of a southerly expansion in England and Wales during the 19th century. Yarrell (1837–43) noted that the nests that he received from Halifax in 1835 and 1836 represented the most southerly known breeding of the species at the time. The Redpoll was not recorded from Wales by Yarrell at that time and More (1865) could only record it as probably breeding in N Wales, a few pairs having been seen in the summer. Later, Lilford (1895) recorded that breeding took place rarely in Northamptonshire following the first breeding attempt that had been reported in 1881. The species was probably continuing to undergo an expansion of range as the 19th century closed.

Witherby *et al.* (1938–41) seems to have described a continuing range expansion of the species in the first 10–15 years of the 20th century. By the 1930s it was breeding in most counties of Britain, albeit locally in Wales and S England, apparently into E Devonshire (Moore 1969, however, does not record proven breeding in Devonshire until 1954). It was probably absent from Cornwall. The Redpoll bred sparingly in the Inner Hebrides and had nested on Barra in the Outer Hebrides. Thence, a decline in central and Southern England during the 1920s was followed, from around 1950, by a further expansion of numbers recolonising those areas gained up to 1910. This recovery was aided by the afforestation being carried out in post-war Britain and the proliferation of weeds on industrial wasteland, both of which enabled the species to occupy areas not hitherto populated. The expansion in Devonshire, for instance, followed new conifer plantings, and Lovegrove *et al.* (1994) confirmed that from the 1920s conifer plantations in Wales probably facilitated the largest increase in numbers.

In the few years before the *68–72 Atlas* survey, Cornwall and Caithness were colonised and Pembrokeshire, Orkney and the Outer Hebrides recolonised. The obvious gap in central and S England was clear at this time. The *88–91 Atlas*, once again, revealed changes in the Redpoll's distribution. Consolidation of breeding in the Isle of Man probably returns the species to its 19th century status. Gains were also apparent in Lewis, Caithness, Dyfed and around the New Forest. Conversely losses were apparent throughout other areas of Britain and Ireland, particularly in the Grampian area of Scotland, throughout England, especially in the Midlands, and in S and E Ireland.

Redpolls fluctuate markedly in abundance, both from year to year and, as the present study reveals, in a longer-term cycle, over periods of decades (I. Newton in litt), possibly linked to cycles in the abundance of birch and alder seed crops. Clearly, afforestation has allowed colonisation of some areas against what is probably a tendency to retreat from its former breeding areas.

Number of counties in which recorded:

Period	Probable breeding		Confirmed breeding		Combined		
	Br	Ir	Br	Ir	Br	Ir	Both
1875–1900	4	1	91	32	95	33	128
1968–1972	6	0	100	34	106	34	140
change					11	1	12
					12%	3%	9%

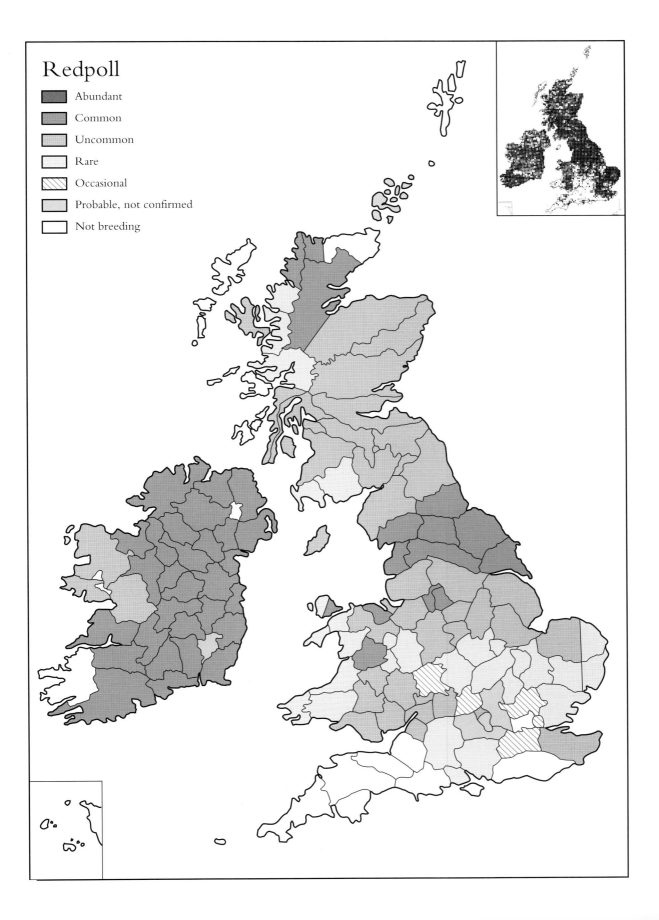

Redpoll

- Abundant
- Common
- Uncommon
- Rare
- Occasional
- Probable, not confirmed
- Not breeding

Common Crossbill and Scottish Crossbill

Loxia curvirostra and *L. scotica*

The Scottish and Common Crossbills were not recognised as separate forms until 1904 so almost all 19th century records of breeding Crossbills refer to *L. curvirostra*. Hence, the accompanying map has been produced with no attempt to identify the breeding range of the Scottish Crossbill. However, Knox (1990) argued that, as the habitat requirements of the Scottish Crossbill (the ancient Caledonian pinewoods) are unlikely to have changed over at least the past 200 years or so and that this habitat has existed in the Highlands and NE Scotland (the area in which the species is now known to be more or less confined) over that period then the Scottish Crossbill is likely to have been present in the old pinewoods in this area continuously since at least the late 18th century.

Irruptions of the Common Crossbill into Britain have been recorded since the Middle Ages (Newton and Gadow 1893–96) and the 19th century saw many such irruptions recorded. Apparently the largest, that in 1838/39 led to records of breeding in at least ten English counties and during that decade there were seven irruptions in as many years (Knox 1990). Breeding was recorded in many subse-

quent years during the 19th century but records became more frequent from the end of the 1880s. This may have been the result of improving observer competency and, possibly, increasing effort but equally may have resulted from the development of new, suitable feeding and breeding habitat. Overall, the 19th century saw a nadir in the amount of woodland in Britain but also saw an increase in the amount of new woodland planted. Much of this new woodland was pine on which Crossbills are dependent.

The accumulation of records over the 1875–1900 period exaggerates the probable status of the Crossbill in any one year. Regular breeding probably took place in very few areas of NW and SW England and in Wales, but in E England and in Scotland breeding was probably regular, if not annual. Certainly, the plantations on the great sporting estates of the Brecklands of E England were some of the most extensive in Britain at that time and may have contributed to the establishment of regular breeding populations of Crossbills there.

The establishment of a resident population of Crossbills in Ireland may have followed an irruption into the country in 1838. In this year breeding was recorded for the first time in Tipperary and continued throughout the 19th century. Supported by further irruptions (most notably in 1867/68, the early 1880s and mid 1890s) the small conifer plantations, particularly of the southeast and midland counties of Ireland, gradually supported an increasing resident population of Crossbills.

Breeding of the Common Crossbill has increased in the 20th century in Britain particularly from the invasion of 1909/10. As the conifer plantings following the 1914–18 war matured, so breeding increased and Britain now has substantially more suitable breeding habitat than existed during the 19th century. The population in Ireland has, however, declined to the point where the *68–72 Atlas* recorded no proven breeding. Breeding was restored following irruptions, most notably that of 1990. The history of the species in Ireland has differed from that of Britain because extensive conifer plantings began later than in Britain and the recent return of the Crossbill as a breeding species in Ireland has followed the maturation of large areas of forest.

Number of counties in which recorded:

Period	Probable breeding		Confirmed breeding		Combined		
	Br	Ir	Br	Ir	Br	Ir	Both
1875–1900	3	1	31	17	34	18	52
1968–1972	3	0	40	0	43	0	43
			change		9	−18	−9
					26%	−100%	−17%

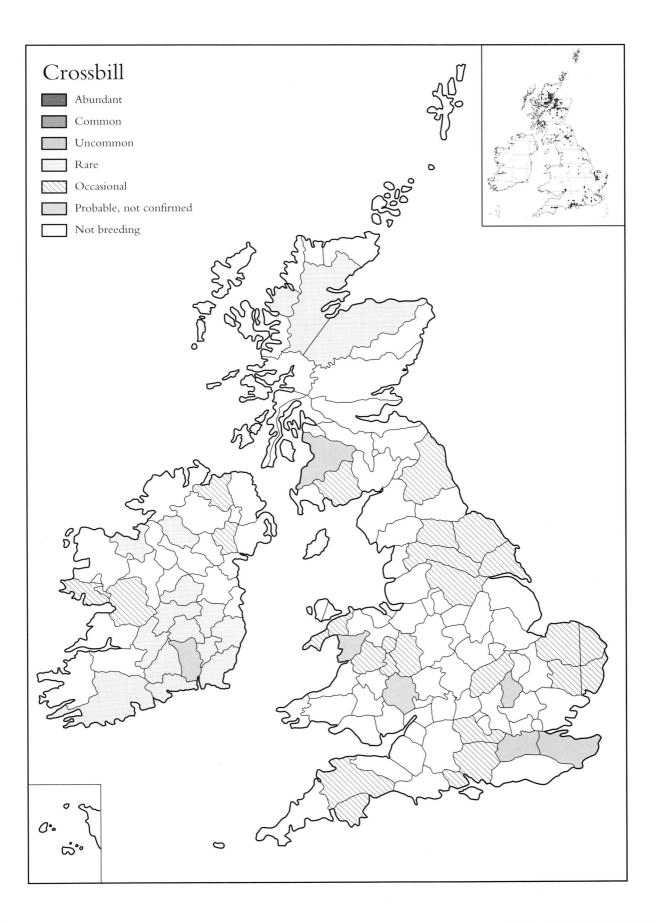

Crossbill

- Abundant
- Common
- Uncommon
- Rare
- Occasional
- Probable, not confirmed
- Not breeding

Bullfinch

Pyrrhula pyrrhula

At the end of the 19th century the Bullfinch was thinly dispersed as a breeding resident throughout Britain and Ireland, absent only from many islands and was not known to breed in Caithness (Harvie-Brown 1887). It may have undergone an expansion in Scotland at the end of the 18th century. Several accounts of birds in the old Statistical Account, particularly from S Scotland, remarked on its recent arrival and rapid increase. Nevertheless it bred frequently throughout Scotland by the middle of the 19th century.

Several influences throughout the 19th century conspired against the Bullfinch such that, by 1880, it had decreased in numbers appreciably. It was a very popular cage bird throughout the century, not only because of its plumage but also, surprisingly, for its song. Bullfinches are good mimics and were generally trained to imitate tunes produced with a bird-flute or flageolet. The best birds fetched very high prices. The numbers caught for this trade, although probably never as large as the numbers of Goldfinches taken, might nevertheless have been one of the primary causes of the widespread decline noted from Devonshire to central Scotland.

In addition, the Bullfinch gained a reputation as a destroyer of fruit tree buds during the 19th century. War was waged upon it by both professional and domestic gardeners and many were trapped or shot. Most rural homes of the period grew much of their own fruit and vegetables and the garden was an important source of these foods. Hence there was a far greater proliferation of food sources for the Bullfinch during the 19th century than in more recent times, and it was probably seen far more frequently in the garden at that time. Householders hated anything that destroyed their garden produce, however, and, so, there was little sympathy for the Bullfinch at this time. Locally (for instance in Middlesex) the increasing practice of laying hedges was also causing declines in Bullfinch numbers as they preferred high, tangled hedgerows in which to breed and feed.

In Ireland the Bullfinch had increased markedly within the living memory of the late 19th century naturalists. It was virtually unknown from the south and southwestern counties before the middle of the century but had increased there rapidly so that by 1855 it was considered common throughout that region. The newly planted conifer and larch plantations apparently aided this increase but it remained scarce in those areas thinly wooded—for instance some of the counties in the north, especially Londonderry, parts of Donegal and W Connaught. It did not breed on the islands of the west.

It is evident that the Wild Birds Protection Acts of the 1880s and 1890s stopped the decline of the Bullfinch. During the early 20th century numbers were clearly increasing steadily throughout Britain in the light of reduced persecution, and in Scotland and Ireland the Bullfinch was increasing in the new forests. This increase accelerated rapidly from the mid 1950s. Increasing numbers in widely scattered parts of England and Wales were reported from the 1940s, and from 1957 it was becoming clear that the Bullfinch population was expanding into more open areas than it had previously inhabited. These new habitats included, commonly, parks and town gardens. Newton (1967) suggested that lower numbers of Sparrowhawks were allowing the Bullfinch to feed farther from cover, making much more food available to it, and it is possible that changing gardening habits provided new food plants in abundance. Recent CBC data, however, shows that the Bullfinch's increase of the 1950s and 1960s has reversed and the population is now in decline, perhaps associated with the recovery of the Sparrowhawk (Newton 1993).

Number of counties in which recorded:

Period	Probable breeding		Confirmed breeding		Combined		
	Br	Ir	Br	Ir	Br	Ir	Both
1875–1900	0	0	101	34	101	34	135
1968–1972	1	0	103	34	104	34	138
			change		3	0	3
					3%		2%

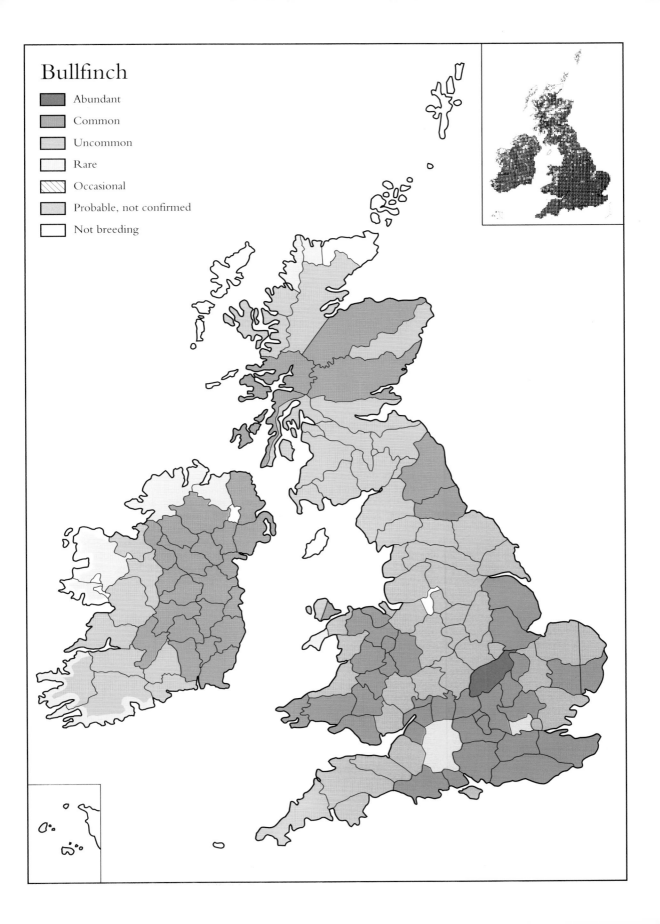

Bullfinch

- Abundant
- Common
- Uncommon
- Rare
- Occasional
- Probable, not confirmed
- Not breeding

Hawfinch

Coccothraustes coccothraustes

The naturalists of the 18th century were unaware that the Hawfinch bred in Britain. It was believed at that time that it was only a winter visitor as none were known to have been collected during spring or summer. It has been supposed that the secretive nature of the Hawfinch may have caused the early naturalists to overlook it during the breeding season but, in fact, it may not have bred, or bred in only very small numbers, prior to the 19th century. Firstly, although it is easier to observe in the leafless branches of winter than in summer it seems unlikely that it should have been well known as a winter bird in Britain but almost wholly unknown in summer. Secondly, the early naturalists were certainly able to find the nests of other secretive species, even those that bred sporadically in very small numbers, such as the Crossbill. Thirdly, as can be seen later, there was good evidence that the species underwent a large expansion of range and numbers throughout England and Wales beginning before the middle of the 19th century.

The Hawfinch was first recorded breeding in Britain in the early 19th century; by the 1830s, when a detailed account of a colony in Epping Forest, Essex, was published, it was clearly breeding locally in some numbers. The population was centred, at that time, in the counties to the east and south of London. Breeding was suspected in Berkshire and Oxfordshire but records further west and north cannot be distinguished as summer occurrences. A rapid expansion of breeding range then took place from about 1835 and continued through to the early 20th century, culminating in the colonisation of almost all counties of England and Wales and occasional breeding in Scotland. The start of the increase in the southeastern counties may have been linked to the abundant food supply provided by extensive cherry orchards, as stones from the fallen fruit were eaten into the winter (I. Newton in litt). The increase in fruit tree cultivation may also have provided nesting sites and in some areas the Hawfinch became more evident following caterpillar plagues of the oak moth (Ticehurst 1909). Urbanisation of farmland provided new habitat with the increase in the number of suburban gardens and their attendant nesting sites (Bucknill 1900). In addition, the persecution suffered by the Hawfinch at the hands of fruit growers and gardeners in the south lessened following the species' legal protection in the 1880s. All these factors may have aided the expansion northwards (Nelson *et al.* 1907). The Hawfinch only really thrives in well-wooded areas of broadleaved trees and so the species would be expected to have been scarcest when Britain was least wooded (as was the case during the 19th century) but to have expanded its range with the planting of extensive orchards, wooded gardens and other woods (I. Newton in litt).

As the 19th century progressed, new counties reported breeding—in Nottinghamshire it had probably not bred before 1869 or 1870 and in Lancashire the first breeding record was of two unfledged birds in a garden in 1878. In Yorkshire it was very rare in the extreme south in the 1860s, was recorded breeding for the first time near Wakefield in 1878, in Nidderdale in 1886, in E Yorkshire in the 1890s and on the northern border with Durham in 1897. In N Wales it was practically unknown prior to 1880; the increase from the east had not reached the coast by 1900, but at that time it bred in all N Wales counties apart from Anglesey. The expansion into S Scotland did not begin until 1900 although a number of summer records in Dumfriesshire in the 1890s indicated that it may have begun breeding there at that time and a young male found in a strawberry net in Midlothian in 1894 may represent the first proven case of breeding in Scotland. The expansion into SE Scotland was complete by the 1920s, and that into SW England and W Wales in the 1950s and 1960s.

Number of counties in which recorded:

Period	Probable breeding		Confirmed breeding		Combined		
	Br	Ir	Br	Ir	Br	Ir	Both
1875–1900	3	0	71	0	74	0	74
1968–1972	6	0	63	0	69	0	69
			change		−5	0	−5
					−7%		−7%

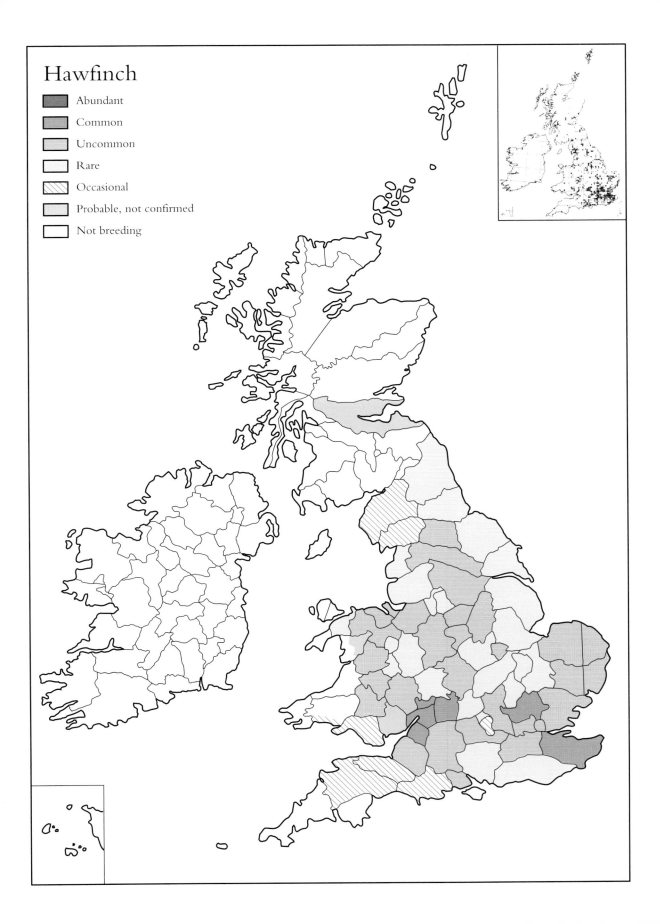

Hawfinch

- Abundant
- Common
- Uncommon
- Rare
- Occasional
- Probable, not confirmed
- Not breeding

Snow Bunting (Snowflake)

Plectrophenax nivalis

The Snow Bunting was highly valued for the table in the 19th century and many wintering birds were killed to satisfy the demand in the 18th and 19th centuries. Its primary value to the hunter later in the 19th century, however, shifted to its nest and eggs. Breeding had been believed to have taken place in Scotland since at least the end of the 18th century. Many assertions of this kind were made in the old Statistical Account of Scotland and Gray (1871) detailed several records from the 19th century of pairs in breeding plumage and fledged young throughout the Highlands in summer. The first claim of breeding came via Saxby (1874). He had seen Snow Buntings in breeding plumage on and around Saxavord, Shetland for many years prior to being given eggs from that locality in 1861. In 1867 he saw eggs in a dealer's collection and in 1871 was given another nest and eggs said to have been taken from the same locality. Incidental evidence, however, caused Nethersole-Thompson (1966) to dismiss these records. A more likely record from Shetland occurred in 1887 when a report was received by Buckley and Evans and Buckley (1899) of a nest and two eggs taken from near Mid Yell in 1881. The female was also captured on the nest. This has

been regarded by later writers as the first proven instance of breeding in Britain.

The first mainland nest was found in 1886. Several pairs with fledged young had been seen around a corrie on Ben More Assynt, Sutherland, in 1885. In the following July a nest was finally found in the same locality with five young in pin feathers. Another nest was found here, and a clutch of five eggs was taken in June 1888 by John Young, and recorded in *Ootheca Woolleyana, part II* (1902). Although no details were given, Harvie-Brown and Buckley (1895) noted that several pairs were breeding in the Sutherland hills by 1893. Evidence for breeding further west was not forthcoming, but some records did exist of summer birds and fledged young. Only one irrefutable record exists for the Cairngorms, that from Ben Avon of five eggs taken in June 1893 from an altitude of *ca* 1100m. The records thus described include all those proven during 1875–1900 and these are specifically marked on the accompanying map. Between 1864 and 1913 there were nine definite breeding records, seven unconfirmed breeding records and ten occurrences of Snow Buntings seen during the breeding season (Nethersole-Thompson 1966).

The breeding distribution throughout the 20th century is not apparently different to that in the 19th century, although, perhaps, in the 19th century most of the tiny population bred further north. The Scottish Snow Bunting population has fluctuated to some extent from only a few apparently unmated males being located in the hills in some seasons to up to five or six broods being raised up to the 1960s. Between 1970 and 1987, however, up to 11 breeding pairs were located in the central Cairngorms and up to 14 males held other territories (Watson and Smith 1991). This increase in records may have resulted from special efforts made to locate summering Snow Buntings but from 1988 an increase in breeding records (both confirmed and suspected) has taken place. In the four breeding seasons to 1991 up to 40 breeding pairs and up to 47 territorial males were located (Smith 1993). The Snow Bunting is essentially an Arctic species nesting on the tundra, rocky coasts, mountain tops and, even, nunataks inside the Arctic Circle and the changing size of the species' population in Scotland appears to fit climatic oscillations (Nethersole-Thompson 1966). Subsequent analysis of the available data, however, suggests that this is far too simple an explanation and a number of other possibilities have been discussed to explain the fluctuating Snow Bunting population and, especially, its clear increase in recent years. The increase may be due to relaxed pressure from egg collectors, increased winter survival of adults and juveniles and an increase in the proportion of immigrant birds staying to breed in Scotland, whether induced to do so by an external agent or purely by chance (Smith *et al*. in press).

Number of counties in which recorded:

Period	Probable breeding		Confirmed breeding		Combined		
	Br	Ir	Br	Ir	Br	Ir	Both
1875–1900	4	0	3	0	7	0	7
1968–1972	1	0	4	0	5	0	5
			change		−2	0	−2
					−29%		−29%

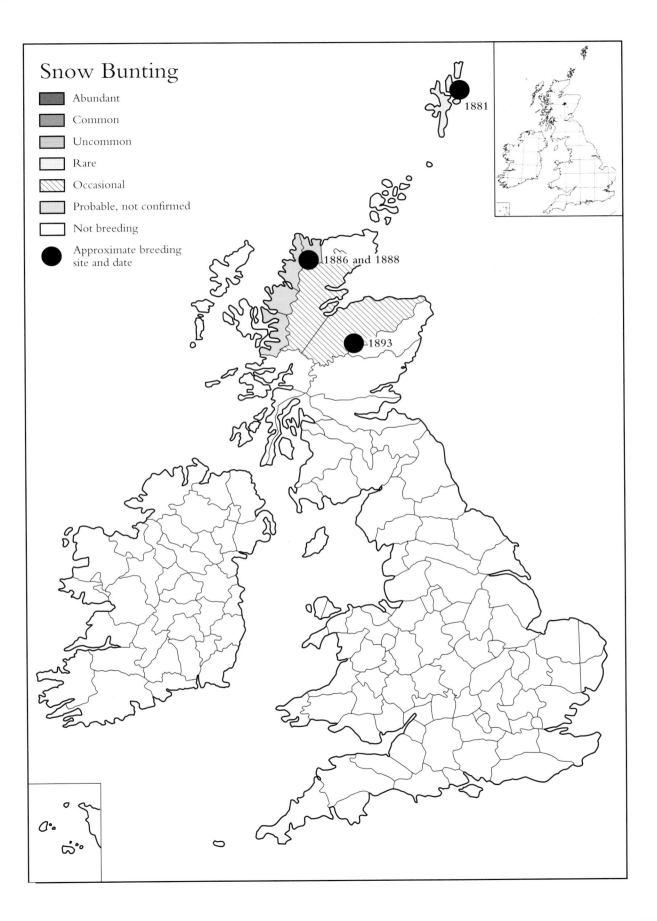

Snow Bunting

- **Abundant**
- **Common**
- **Uncommon**
- **Rare**
- **Occasional**
- **Probable, not confirmed**
- **Not breeding**
- ● **Approximate breeding site and date**

1881

1886 and 1888

1893

Yellowhammer (Yellow Bunting)

Emberiza citrinella

The Yellowhammer was one of the most common birds throughout Britain and Ireland during the 19th century. It was recorded breeding in the rough corners of meadows, hedgerows, road verges and gardens. Its habit of sometimes nesting in areas of the country devoid of trees and bushes meant that it was abundant even in the most desolate moorlands and mountainous regions of some areas (Macpherson 1892). It was absent only from Shetland and bred only irregularly in the Outer Hebrides and on some of the Inner Hebridean islands. The colonisation of Orkney appears to have taken place fairly recently. Low (1813) made no record at all of the Yellowhammer in Orkney; Dunn (1837) noted that it occurred as a winter visitor only during his travels there but, by 1855, it was breeding regularly. Said to be aided by the planting of whin hedges and plantations from the 1860s, it increased to the point where it was considered common, and was resident throughout the year by the end of the 19th century. It seems likely that the colonisation and subsequent expansion of the Yellowhammer on Orkney was aided by a sudden increase in the amount of cultivation, particularly of cereals, that took place in the islands from about 1832 when kelp-burning became uneconomic. When steam communication with the south began, reclamation of new land to increase the acreage of cereals occurred at least into the 1890s (Buckley and Harvie-Brown 1891), providing the Yellowhammer with new food sources.

During the first half of the 20th century the range and distribution of the Yellowhammer remained at the same level as that of the 19th century. Increasingly, however, smaller numbers were noted in some parts of its British and Irish range as the second half of the century began. In Ireland, it had withdrawn from Tory and Rathlin Islands by 1954 and from other western islands by 1966. Breeding density may also have become less over the last hundred years or so: Ussher and Warren (1900) described the Yellowhammer as very common and widespread, and Kennedy *et al.* (1954) described it as generally distributed, but Hutchinson (1989) regarded it as rather thinly distributed. Over much of its British range there have been reports of decreasing numbers. The extent to which this has happened is difficult to measure, but numbers in E England clearly fell dramatically in the late 1950s and early 1960s. Numbers recovered somewhat subsequently, as indicated by the increase that followed the severe 1962/63 winter recorded by the CBC and, so, the *68–72 Atlas* revealed no significant new absences. Breeding was proven for the first time in the Outer Hebrides in 1970 and 1971 when young were discovered on North Uist and Lewis, respectively.

The decreases apparent in the 1950s and 1960s may have been caused by hedgerow losses, urbanisation and increased use of pesticides but this is certainly not true of major losses apparent from the surveys published in the *88–91 Atlas*. The bulk of the most recent losses have occurred in coastal and upland areas in W Britain, from Cornwall, through Wales and the Pennines to the W and Highlands of Scotland. Losses in Ireland between the *68–72* and *88–91 Atlases* have been much more concentrated and dramatic— over a third of 10-km squares had lost all their breeding Yellowhammers during this period. It is probable that other agricultural changes, such as the switch from spring to autumn sowing of wheat, will have had a severe impact on winter survival through the loss of winter stubble.

Number of counties in which recorded:

Period	Probable breeding		Confirmed breeding		Combined		
	Br	Ir	Br	Ir	Br	Ir	Both
1875–1900	2	0	105	34	107	34	141
1968–1972	0	0	107	34	107	34	141
			change		0	0	0

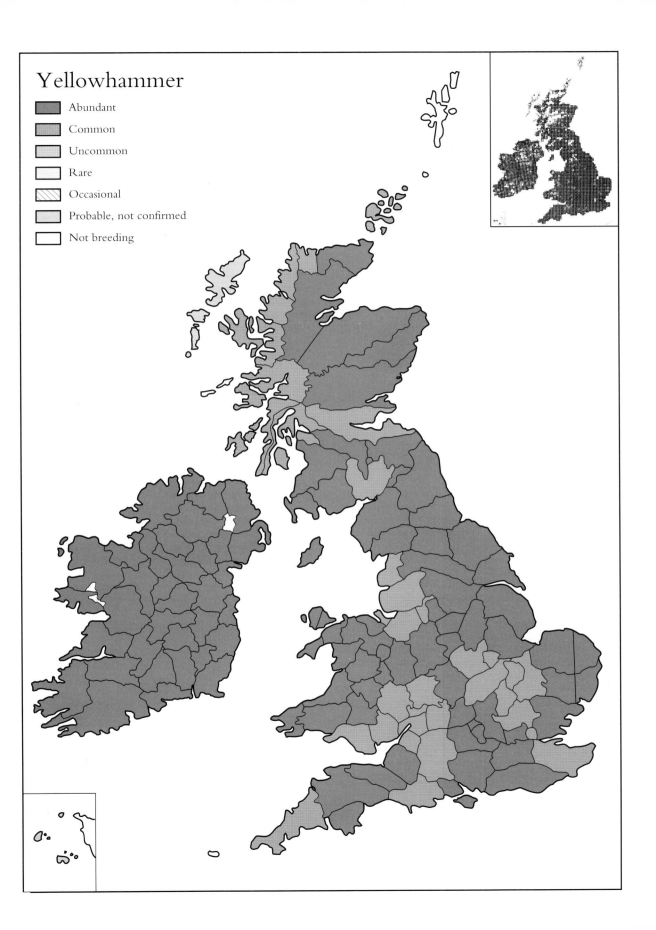

Yellowhammer

- Abundant
- Common
- Uncommon
- Rare
- Occasional
- Probable, not confirmed
- Not breeding

Cirl Bunting

Emberiza cirlus

The distribution of the Cirl Bunting was the subject of a special investigation by Aplin (1892) and this map is based largely upon his work. Records published between the time of his investigation and the end of the 19th century have been added.

Montagu was the first to discover that the Cirl Bunting was a British bird when in the winter of 1800 he noticed it feeding amongst flocks of Yellowhammers and Chaffinches. He subsequently collected specimens from near Kingsbridge in Devonshire. During the rest of the century naturalists (for instance Yarrell 1937–43, Morris 1851–57) attempted to discover the full distribution of the species. Its main, and most regular, breeding areas included the counties of S and SW England, along the Severn and Wye valleys and in Denbighshire where a colony existed in the Ceiriog Valley and it was subsequently discovered breeding in the neighbouring counties of Flintshire and the Conway coast of Caernarvonshire. From these areas nesting was reported rarely and locally in adjacent counties. North of the main English range it had been recorded breeding in London on at least four occasions including on Wimbledon Common in 1890. The Cirl Bunting was considered very rare in Cambridgeshire during the late 19th century (Evans 1904) although was apparently considered to breed in the county (Aplin 1892). The first dated record of a nest, however, was not made until 1904 (Lack 1934). The Brecon and Glamorgan records came, in the main, from the Usk valley and the adjacent Glamorgan coast, whilst in Cardiganshire a small number of birds frequented the coast and narrow valleys around Aberystwyth. Records in outlying counties existed. In Yorkshire breeding was accepted as having taken place at Lofthouse and near Ossett in 1882 and 1889 respectively, but these records should be treated with suspicion as Cirl Buntings were introduced into Yorkshire on at least one occasion. A record exists for Lancashire of a nest taken in a warren at Formby but this has not been considered acceptable by later writers.

The contraction of the Cirl Bunting's breeding range towards the south began during the early decades of the 20th century. There are different views concerning the timing of the beginning of the decline but Sitters' (1982) account suggests that it began in the 1930s. If so, then the decline coincided with farming changes that are likely to have had an effect from the mid 1930s onwards (A. Evans in litt). During the 1930s breeding all but ceased in the Midlands and Wales outside the northern colony. Elsewhere sporadic breeding still occurred but, even in the main breeding area, numbers were apparently decreasing. The Cirl Bunting was not described anywhere as common. As the century progressed the decline continued. At some point after the 1930s breeding ceased in N Wales. In the mid 1950s up to 50 pairs were recorded in Sussex, but only about 20 could be located in the early 1970s. The decline continued steadily until the late 1950s/early 1960s and then the population collapsed (Sitters 1982). By the time of the *68–72 Atlas* survey, the Cirl Bunting was a coastal species, inland breeding being sporadic except in Somerset and on the Hertfordshire/Buckinghamshire border. Northernmost breeding took place on the Malverns, and Kent had lost its population. Further losses occurred up to the *88–91 Atlas* survey period with the result that breeding was mainly taking place along the S Devonshire coast between Plymouth and Exeter by that time with a few breeding pairs in Somerset and Cornwall (Evans 1992). By 1989 only 118–132 pairs remained, 97% of which were in S Devonshire (Evans 1992). A number of theories have been put forward to explain the decline. The primary cause is likely to be habitat losses, particularly the reduction in winter weed-rich stubble fields following the change to autumn sown cereals (Evans and Smith 1994).

Number of counties in which recorded:

Period	Probable breeding		Confirmed breeding		Combined		
	Br	Ir	Br	Ir	Br	Ir	Both
1875–1900	1	0	38	0	39	0	39
1968–1972	3	0	16	0	19	0	19
			change		−20	0	−20
					−51%		−51%

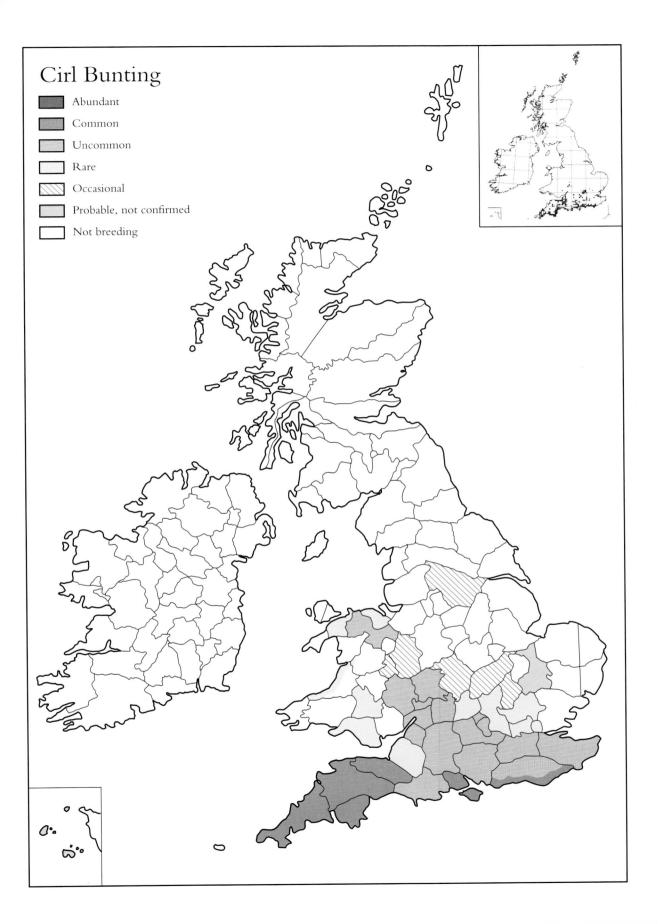

Cirl Bunting

- ◼ Abundant
- ◼ Common
- ◼ Uncommon
- ☐ Rare
- ▨ Occasional
- ▦ Probable, not confirmed
- ☐ Not breeding

Reed Bunting (Black-headed Bunting)

Emberiza schoeniclus

The Reed Bunting bred throughout Britain and Ireland at the end of the 19th century. Its preference during the breeding season for wet areas, such as marshy edges of lakes and ponds, river and canal banks, water meadows and osier beds, meant that it was distributed locally throughout its range. It was absent only from Shetland and the most exposed, dry upland areas of its range. It was also absent from, or occurred only rarely in, most of the Western Isles. In the early years of the 19th century it was recorded very irregularly in Orkney and probably did not begin breeding there until the late 1840s. It subsequently increased until, by the end of the century, it was breeding regularly but not commonly. Local population fluctuations were recorded throughout its range such as the Peaks, Lakeland and much of upland Scotland but especially in England. The destruction of natural breeding habitat, such as the drainage of wet meadows and marshes and continuing enclosure activities, was balanced to a large extent by the provision of artificial sites. The expanding network of canals created new waterside habitats, as did the flooded clay and gravel pits and the large, new reservoirs. Overall, then, throughout much of the 19th century, the population of the Reed Bunting,

although suffering local fluctuations, remained broadly stable.

Indeed, this stability continued through much of the first half of the 20th century although Baxter and Rintoul (1953) indicated that there was a belief that the Reed Bunting had increased over much of Scotland. In the Inner Hebrides some islands were colonised and numbers increased on others. Numbers also increased on Orkney and the Reed Bunting eventually spread into Shetland where breeding first occurred around 1949 and regular breeding took place subsequently. From around the middle of the 20th century increasing numbers were noted in many areas of Britain and Ireland. This coincided with further evidence that the ecological range of the species was expanding in counties as far apart as those in S and N England and SW Scotland. Reed Bunting nests were being located in dry habitats such as uncultivated fields, young conifer plantations, bracken slopes and heather-covered sand dunes. In retrospect this change began much earlier in the 20th century (Sharrock 1976) but by the 1960s the Reed Bunting could no longer be considered a wholly wetland species in years and areas of high abundance. It seems likely that the use of drier habitats is linked to the species' population level; other than a weather-induced crash of the early 1960s the Reed Bunting's population level appears to have been high from the mid 20th century until the 1970s. References to 'ecological expansion' are, in fact, the best evidence prior to the CBC that population levels were high (R. Prys-Jones in litt).

The *68–72 Atlas* demonstrated a breeding range very similar to that of the 19th century. This is despite further widespread losses during the 20th century of wet habitats and indicates that, although probably affecting abundance within the range, this has had little effect on overall distribution.

Factors that have reduced numbers of other small seed eating passerines, for instance the Linnet and Tree Sparrow, have probably caused the decline of the Reed Bunting recorded in the *88–91 Atlas*. The species has probably declined over much of its range, and, in areas with initially low populations (such as SW and N England, Wales, much of Scotland and its islands and, particularly, S Ireland) some gaps have opened up in its distribution. The increased effectiveness of agricultural herbicides from the 1970s onwards has reduced the amount of weed seeds available during the winter and has been blamed for some of the decline (O'Connor and Shrubb 1986). It seems probable that Reed Bunting numbers are limited in winter, when they are using non-wetland habitat to a considerable extent (R. Prys-Jones in litt).

Number of counties in which recorded:

Period	Probable breeding		Confirmed breeding		Combined		
	Br	Ir	Br	Ir	Br	Ir	Both
1875–1900	0	0	107	34	107	34	141
1968–1972	0	0	108	34	108	34	142
			change		1	0	1
					1%		1%

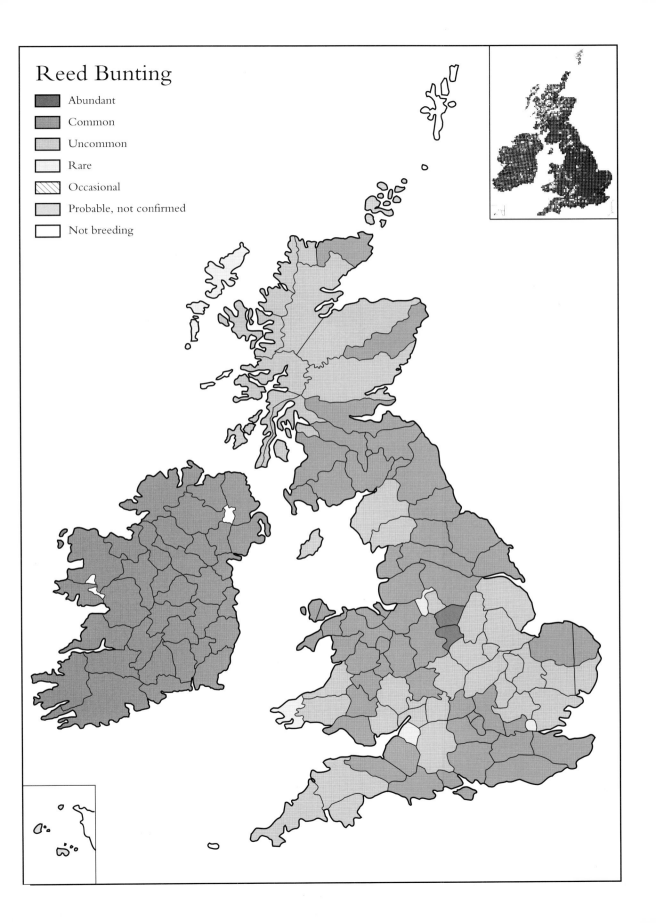

Reed Bunting

- Abundant
- Common
- Uncommon
- Rare
- Occasional
- Probable, not confirmed
- Not breeding

Corn Bunting
(Common Bunting)

Miliaria calandra

Historical trends in the numbers and distribution of Corn Buntings and the possible causes of changes have been discussed in detail by Donald *et al.* (1994). The expansion of the Corn Bunting's range into Britain and Ireland probably followed the forest clearances that opened up the countryside to allow the development of permanent cultivation. Most of these clearances were complete by the time of the Roman Conquest but the range of many bird species of open landscapes may have further increased with the huge increase in the area of arable land following agricultural changes from the late 18th century onwards. Although there is little direct evidence, it seems likely that the population and range of the Corn Bunting was at its height during the last half of the 19th century. It was distributed throughout Britain and Ireland but avoided upland areas in SW England, Wales, N England, S Scotland and the Scottish Highlands. During this period densities on the Scottish islands were probably higher than anywhere else in Britain, and in the Outer Hebrides the Corn Bunting was still increasing in numbers during the 1880s as peatland was being converted to farmland. On the mainland coast, especially in the west, it was often considered abundant but did not reach very far up the straths and valleys into the interior in the Highlands north of the Great Glen; further south in

Scotland it bred more frequently inland but was very local. It was local in the Lakeland hills and much of the Pennines, its stronghold in Cumberland being along the Solway coast. An early record of decline was recorded in Cumberland from about the 1880s. It did not venture very far into the Welsh uplands from the coast and, on the east of the Cambrian Mountains in the border counties, it bred in very low numbers.

In Ireland it was commonly met with on the small holdings near the coasts and, in a few areas, was common further inland. In general, however, it was decidedly less common and more local, and frequently absent, in inland areas.

The agricultural depression from the 1870s to the 1930s led to a substantial decline in the total area of cereals in Britain. This may have caused the Corn Bunting population to begin a decline that has largely continued to the present day. The decline became pronounced during the 1920s and 1930s and the breeding range began to contract. Populations in western regions of Britain and Ireland were particularly badly affected, although declines were noted in many counties throughout the species' range in Britain. The population stabilised during the 1940s, and during the 1950s and 1960s a general recovery became apparent, particularly in eastern areas. During the late 1970s and throughout the 1980s, however, the British population again declined. Numbers fell by at least 60% and the range contracted by 35% between the early 1970s and the early 1990s. These declines have again been particularly apparent in northern and western regions of Britain and the species is on the verge of extinction as a breeding bird in Ireland, Wales, W Scotland and SW England. The reasons behind the decline of this species are unclear, but a number of changes in farming practice are implicated. Reductions in the cultivated area of barley, a switch towards autumn sowing of cereals, replacement of hay by silage and a decline in traditional rotations and mixed farming practices may all have played a part in the changes in numbers and range noted during the 1970s and 1980s. The increased use of pesticides and the removal of hedgerows may also have reduced the food supply of Corn Buntings. Climatic factors may also be involved.

Number of counties in which recorded:

Period	Probable breeding		Confirmed breeding		Combined		
	Br	Ir	Br	Ir	Br	Ir	Both
1875–1900	0	0	100	32	100	32	132
1968–1972	5	0	80	9	85	9	94
			change		−15	−23	−38
					−15%	−72%	−29%

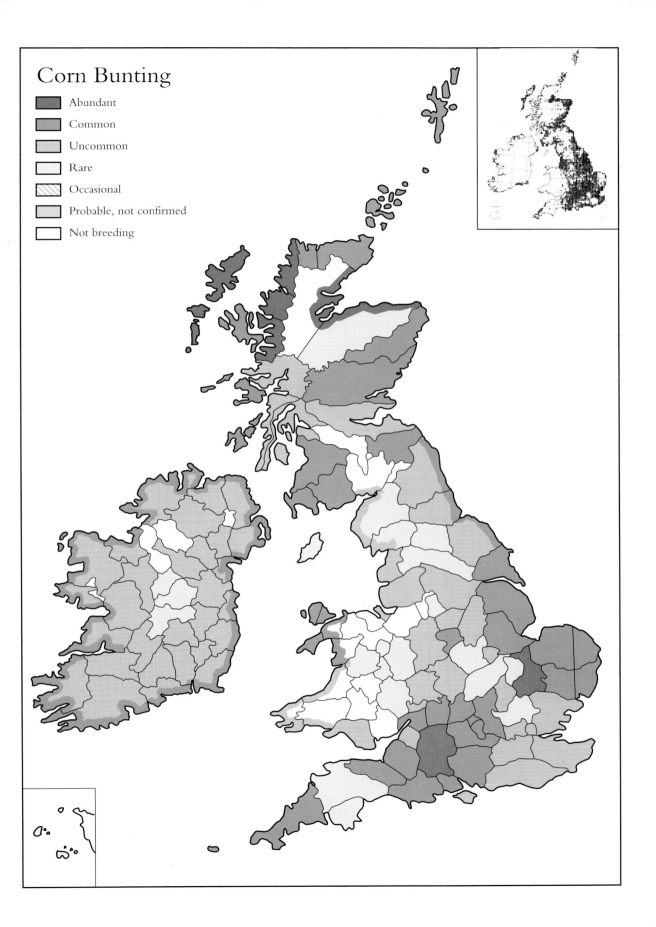

Corn Bunting

- Abundant
- Common
- Uncommon
- Rare
- Occasional
- Probable, not confirmed
- Not breeding

Great Northern Diver

Gavia immer

Evans and Buckley (1899) considered all of the claims of Great Northern Divers breeding in Shetland up to 1898. It was apparent that none provided reliable evidence that breeding had taken place but some famous accounts have been repeated as evidence of possible breeding—these are recounted here along with Harvie-Brown's objections.

The first assertion that the Great Northern Diver bred in Shetland was made by Low during his tour of the Northern Isles in 1774 when he shot a young bird in July that had been accompanied by parents he had identified as this species. This account must be treated with the greatest caution as all of the diver species were regularly confounded throughout Scotland and a sight identification on sea water from this time (without the aid of optics) must be considered valueless.

Saxby's (1874) account was the most famous of the period. In about 1858 he was sent a number of eggs collected by a friend from Yell and was struck by the large size of what was obviously a diver's egg. Shortly afterwards, on visiting the locality from which the egg was said to have been collected, he saw a Great Northern Diver on the loch in summer plumage. He searched the area the following year but found neither nest nor birds. However, in about 1860 he was sent two further eggs from an adjacent loch together with a description of a bird that Saxby considered to be this one. One of these eggs was subsequently examined by two noted ornithologists, A. H. Evans and Professor Newton, who considered that the egg was that of a Black-throated Diver.

Three further records were considered by Harvie-Brown but were of even more slender evidence than the preceding and similarly dismissed by him.

Breeding has been suspected on many occasions in Scotland during the 20th century in consequence of the few Great Northern Divers that spend the summer there. Adults and two young were seen on a loch with wooded islands in West Ross in June 1970 (Hunter 1970) and, in the following year, a Great Northern X Black-throated Diver hybrid paired with a Black-throated Diver and reared a single young bird on the same loch (Hunter and Dennis 1972). Since that time no further records of breeding have been made although individuals in full summer plumage are frequently seen in summer around Scottish and Irish coasts and on inland waters, particularly in N and W Scotland and Ireland.

Red-necked Grebe

Podiceps grisegena

There was no suggestion that the Red-necked Grebe bred in Britain or Ireland during the 19th century, when this species was considered to be solely a winter visitor.It occurred chiefly on the E coast of Britain, occasionally on the S coast of England and rarely on the west side. Only a handful had been obtained in Ireland.

Despite suggestions that the Red-necked Grebe has declined around the edges of its breeding range (Cramp 1977–94) the records of the RBBP have shown an increase in the number summering in Britain from the 1970s. Breeding was suspected in 1987 when a pair was seen with a very young juvenile and then, in 1988, the first confirmed breeding attempts in Britain, in both Scotland and England, were recorded (Gibbons et al. 1993). During the *88–91 Atlas* survey two or three summering pairs were noted.

Slavonian Grebe (Horned Grebe)

Podiceps auritus

The Slavonian Grebe had been noted in pairs in summer on inland waters periodically throughout the 19th century. An example was a pair shot in breeding plumage in June 1860 on Loch Killisport, Argyll (Gray 1871) but birds in breeding dress were also taken in Arisaig, West Ross, Barra and Orkney. Breeding was suspected, but not proven, in Benbecula in the Outer Hebrides in 1893.

The first confirmed breeding attempt took place on Loch Ruthven, Inverness-shire in 1908. During the 20th century this loch became the centre of a small breeding group and by 1937 breeding had occurred on the surrounding lochs. This group of lochs remains the stronghold of the species in Scotland. In 1929 Slavonian Grebes were discovered breeding in Sutherland, four pairs inhabiting two lochs there, and in 1932 the first nest was found in Caithness. By the 1960s Slavonian Grebes had been recorded breeding in Moray and Aberdeenshire and the population numbered 'probably less than 50 pairs' (Parslow 1973). The population steadily rose to a peak of 80 pairs in 1978–80 but has since levelled out at about 60 pairs (Gibbons et al. 1993). Recent survey work has demonstrated that several factors may be adversely affecting breeding productivity (Crooke et al. in Andrews and Carter 1993).

The colonisation of Scotland has been paralleled by an increase in Sweden and a southward expansion in Norway and it is likely that these are linked by the same influence (Parslow 1973).

Black-necked Grebe (Eared Grebe)

Podiceps nigricollis

The discovery in Anglesey, by Oldham and Cummings, of at least five pairs of Black-necked Grebes with young and one other pair on Llyn Llywenan in June 1904 was the first time that breeding had been confirmed in Britain. It has often been added that the species probably bred here before this record (Witherby et al. 1938–41, Lovegrove et al. 1994). Other evidence that breeding took place on Anglesey before 1904 is contained in Forrest's (1907) records. Coward shot a specimen on Llyn Maelog in 1892 and one of Forrest's correspondents stated that the 'Eared Grebe was formerly found on Llyn Maelog, but has disappeared for many years, having been shot down'. In a paper in *The Zoologist* in 1892 Banks also stated that the Eared Grebe bred in Anglesey. Forrest, seemingly unaware of Coward's 1904 breeding records, was unwilling to accept that the Black-necked Grebe bred in Anglesey. He added the cautionary note that the term Eared Grebe was also used to describe the Great Crested Grebe (which bred in Anglesey until about 1900 but was shot out) and the Slavonian Grebe. Interestingly, however, in his account of the Great Crested Grebe he did not mention any breeding records from Llyn Maelog. An early record of possible breeding in Oxfordshire was recounted by Aplin (1889) and concerned an adult in full summer plumage shot on the Isis in June 1847. Stevenson (1866–90) wrote of many records of Black-necked Grebes taken in Norfolk up to the 1860s in spring and summer, and some females, on dissection, contained partially formed eggs. Since the end of the 19th century there have been a number of breeding records throughout Britain and Ireland.

The species continued to breed in Anglesey to 1923 and, probably in 1927. It was first proven breeding on the Tring reservoirs in Hertfordshire and Buckinghamshire in 1918 and bred, or was suspected of doing so, until 1930. Three nests were found in central Yorkshire in 1928 and a pair with young was reported in Norfolk in 1931. A pair was present in 1931 and breeding occurred in 1932 in E Somerset, in 1935 in Westmorland, in 1937 in Cambridgeshire and in 1939 in Cheshire. Three to four pairs bred at a site in Midlothian from 1930 (and 1934 at a second site). At one site in Fife two pairs bred from 1931 and numbers increased there from 1937. Two pairs bred that year at a second locality in Fife. Breeding was suspected in other areas of Scotland in 1903, 1931 and 1935. The earliest evidence of an Irish breeding attempt was in June 1906 when Walpole-Bond saw several adults in breeding plumage and two empty nests on Keel Loch in Achill and a bird was seen there in June 1909 (Kennedy et al. 1954). In 1915 a partially fledged bird was shot on a lough in the west and, in 1918, a pair in breeding plumage and three downy young were presented to the National Museum of Ireland. These birds were shot on a lake in the W Midlands but the donor died without disclosing the exact locality. After many years of searching a very large colony was discovered in 1929 on Lough Funshinagh in Roscommon and was estimated at 250 pairs in 1930. In 1932 155 nests were examined but in 1934 (and the following two years) the lake all but dried up and the site was deserted. In 1937, when conditions improved, the Black-necked Grebes returned and bred in small numbers for many years following (Kennedy et al. 1954).

This period, from the turn of the century to about 1940, saw a rapid growth in the incidence of breeding Black-necked Grebes in W and NW Europe resulting from massive invasions during periods of desiccation of the steppe lakes in the Caspian region (Kalela 1949). Thereafter, without further recruitment, breeding was not sustained in Britain and Ireland particularly where suitable breeding lakes were drained. The Black-necked Grebe bred in a few other parts of Ireland during this period but gradually died out by the 1950s (Parslow 1973). Scotland then became the main breeding area in Britain until the 1970s. An increase in N and W mainland Europe, evident from at least 1980, seems to be encouraging a more stable British population to exist and this is increasing slowly at the present time (Gibbons et al. 1993).

Little Bittern

Ixobrychus minutus

Throughout the 19th century the Little Bittern was suspected of having bred in England. The evidence was based on individuals or pairs seen or shot in suitable habitat during the spring or summer, females shot and found, on dissection, to contain well developed ovaries and, in one case, the capture of downy young. No nests, however, were ever found. Early examples of possible breeding attempts included a pair shot in July 1839 near South Walsham, Norfolk and a female shot near the R Credey in Devonshire in May 1808. It was seen in the company of a male and was found to have well-developed ovaries. In Suffolk there were a number of possible records. The earliest was of a female containing a well developed egg shot on Oulton Broad in June 1830. Breeding was suspected at Benacre Broad when birds were seen in July 1854 and May 1863. The most interesting record was of a young bird in down caught in a gorse bush by a dog at Mutford near Oulton Broad in September 1885. A similar series of records exists for Norfolk and the latest interesting 19th century records were those from Rollesby of males in full breeding plumage in July 1893 and October 1896.

Into the 20th century similar records were made at various locations. There was an interesting series of records from two locations in Kent in the 1930s and 1940s (Harrison 1953) and of males heard 'singing' for some weeks in a southwestern county in Britain during the 1970s and early 1980s. It is extremely difficult to prove breeding of this species particularly as its rarity and reed bed habitat require that neither must be disturbed (although this was clearly not an issue amongst 19th century sportsmen). The Little Bittern is all but silent except during the breeding season when the advertising call of the male (often described as croaking, frog-like or resembling the muffled, deep bark of a dog) is often the only indication of the species' presence. The only confirmed breeding attempt that has taken place was in Yorkshire in 1984, when a pair raised four young. Little Bitterns were seen at the same site in 1985, but breeding was not proven (Batten *et al*. 1990).

Whooper Swan (Hooper, Wild Swan)

Cygnus cygnus

Fea, writing in 1775 of Orkney, said 'Here also are several small holms [in Loch Stenness on Mainland] where Swans were formerly in use to build ...' Subsequent writers have asserted that these were Whoopers. Fea complained that their extinction was caused by the local people who collected the eggs for sale to southern gentlemen who hatched them and introduced them to their ornamental lakes. Shirreff (1814) recorded the breeding of the Whooper Swan down to a later date saying that several pairs used to nest on the islands in the Loch of Harray 'until about twenty years ago, but being much annoyed about that time deserted the lake'. Evidently the Whooper Swan became extinct in Orkney by the 1800s.

Clearly, pinioned birds bred in captivity and a number of breeding records during the 19th century were of this origin (for instance in the London Zoological Gardens in 1839, 1840 and other years and at Petworth, Sussex) but there were no records of unassisted breeding until those of three consecutive years around 1919 in W Perthshire. A pair of injured birds bred in Sutherland from 1910 until they were shot in 1918 and another, possibly feral, pair bred in the W Highlands between 1912 and 1921. A pair bred at Benbecula in the Outer Hebrides in 1947 but then there were no records of breeding during 1948–77. In 1978 a pair in Scotland raised three young. Since that time it seems likely that between two and five pairs of Whooper Swans breed each year in Britain although the provenance of some records is unclear. In 1992 the first Whooper pair bred in Donegal, Ireland.

Barnacle Goose

Branta leucopsis

The Barnacle Goose is a winter visitor to Britain and Ireland, particularly to the north and west coasts, in fairly large numbers. There is evidence that numbers declined substan-tially during the last quarter of the 19th century, perhaps owing to the numbers shot by sportsmen, since numbers recovered when shooting was controlled. There is little evidence that wild Barnacle Geese have ever bred in Britain under natural conditions although individuals suspected of having been injured by shot and incapable of flight have been recorded breeding in the Inner Hebrides. During the *68–72 Atlas* survey breeding outwith wildfowl collections was recorded in only two 10-km squares: on Strangford Lough in Down, Northern Ireland. From the end of the 1980s it became clear that Barnacle Geese that had escaped from captivity were breeding widely in Britain and on Strangford Lough. The *88–91 Atlas* recorded (or suspected) feral breeding pairs in 45 10-km squares. The scattered nature of the breeding records suggests that the present population is not sustainable without further recruitment from captive flocks; however, it seems likely that such a population could become established (Gibbons *et al*. 1993). A survey of introduced and escaped geese in the summer of 1991 counted 925 Barnacle Geese at 89 sites throughout Britain (Delaney 1993). The population thus seems on the point of becoming self supporting (Vinicombe *et al*. 1993).

Egyptian Goose

Alopochen aegyptiacus

The Egyptian Goose is native to Egypt, where it is now rare, and to Africa south of the Sahara, the source of most of the early importations to Britain. From as early as the 17th century (when it was included in the King's wildfowl collection in St James's Park) and more generally from the 18th century, this species' attractive appearance caused it to be in great demand for the ornamental wildfowl collections of great houses throughout Britain and Ireland. It was commonly seen on those lakes by 1785 and, by the 19th century, there were unpinioned breeding groups on the private estates of Holkham, Gunton, Blickling and Kimberley in Norfolk, Bicton and Crediton in Devonshire, Woburn in Bedfordshire and Gosford in East Lothian. Many accounts were given in the 19th century literature of the appearance of birds outwith these collections apparently not showing signs of confinement. Most of these sightings were during the winter and indicated that a substantial amount of movement took place at that time of the year. These birds were most often recorded in Devonshire, Dorset and Hampshire (where, in the last county, about 80 appeared near Longparish in 1824 after a strong westerly gale) presumably from the Bicton collection and regular winter records from the N Northumberland coast (for instance on the Tweed and the Farne Islands) were probably from Gosford (Yarrell 1837–43, Morris 1855, Sharrock 1976).

The present day feral population in Norfolk is the only one that has become well established (Sharrock 1976). Stevenson (1866–90) and Patterson (1905) gave numerous examples of unpinioned birds seen in Norfolk outside the wildfowl collections, but only after the commencement of the 19th century were there records of apparently wild–living birds. The occurrence of Egyptian Geese on the

Norfolk coast after strong easterly winds led Lubbock (1845) to suppose that they may have been stragglers from the large collections in Holland (this may also have been the source of the NE coastal birds).

It was not until the Egyptian Goose was admitted to the British list in 1971 that detailed documentation of its status took place. The *68–72 Atlas* survey was the first indication of the summer distribution of this species. The population, mainly in Norfolk, may then have been of about 300–400 birds, whilst the Winter Atlas (Lack 1986) recorded 504, 429 of which were found in Norfolk. It is evident that the British population is expanding. The *88–91 Atlas* demonstrated a spread into N Suffolk and estimated the population to have reached 750–800 individuals, although Delaney (1993) put the figure at 906.

Wood Duck (Summer and Carolina Duck)

Aix sponsa

The Wood Duck was kept on many ornamental waters in England during the 19th century and was apparently easy to encourage to breed in confinement. Few records remain of the sites to which it was introduced but, from the records of birds seen and shot outwith wildfowl collections, it seems that the largest and most successful breeding groups during the 19th century were in Devonshire (especially at Bicton House near Exeter), the Duke of Bedford's Woburn Abbey estate and especially in Surrey. In Devonshire it was said to be kept frequently, bred freely and 'roams about the country at will', so much so that D'Urban and Mathew (1892) considered it as much a part of the British avifauna as other introduced species, such as the Pheasant. Early records of birds shot included two males and a female near Dorking, Surrey in the early 1830s in an apparently wild state, two in Kent in 1848 and one in Worcestershire in the same year From the evidence, therefore, it seems that the Wood Duck may have bred outside confinement sporadically since the first half of the 19th century. Despite this long history a naturalised population has taken many years to become established and, today, is still very small; it is unlikely that the population of Wood Ducks in Britain would persist for many years without annual recruitment from captivity (whether by escapes or releases, C. Lever in litt.). The breeding group around the Surrey/E Berkshire border is probably the largest at present.

Mandarin

Aix galericulata

The Mandarin Duck was known in captivity in Britain in 1747 but did not breed in confinement until two pairs were procured for the London Zoo in 1834. Even after that time breeding was sporadic and there was a suggestion that the Chinese exporters caponised the males to protect their trade. The first concerted attempt to establish free-living Mandarin Ducks was made by the Duke of Bedford at Woburn Park, Bedfordshire around 1900. By 1914 there were over 300 there but the 1914–18 and 1939–45 wars showed that these birds were sustained by artificial feeding because, as this feeding ceased during the two wars, numbers halved each time. Since that introduction several others have been made, throughout England particularly, the most important of which have been those at Foxwarren Park, Surrey and in the London Parks around 1930. These have evidently led to the establishment of the main British feral population in Surrey and E Berkshire. Between 300 and 400 pairs probably nested in Britain in 1972 (Fitter 1959, Sharrock 1976) although this has since been considered an underestimate (Gibbons *et al.* 1993). Since the *68–72 Atlas* survey it is apparent that the population of the Mandarin Duck has increased substantially and, by 1991, may have exceeded 7,000 individuals (Gibbons *et al.* 1993). The breeding range has similarly increased, particularly in S England; it has spread successfully into the Midlands and is in the process of doing so into Wales, N England and Scotland. Interestingly, the population of wild Mandarins in Britain now almost certainly exceeds that of the Far East outside Japan and probably equals that of the latter country (Gibbons *et al.* 1993). The decline in its natural range due to deforestation (Marchant *et al.* 1990) means that the British population is now of international significance.

Red-crested Pochard

Netta rufina

The Red-crested Pochard was known only as a very rare winter vagrant during the 19th century. Since it was first identified in Britain in 1818 no more than about 50 examples had been obtained or seen up to the 1890s mainly between the mouths of the rivers Thames and Humber (Dixon 1895). There do not appear to have been any attempts to raise the species in wildfowl collections.

During the 1930s and 1940s Red-crested Pochards were reared at Woburn, Bedfordshire. Eggs were hatched in incubators and the chicks raised by chickens and allowed to fly free. Young Red-crested Pochards were also let free on the waters of some London parks in 1933, 1936 and from 1950. There were numerous records of this species in the neighbourhood of the releases but an early record of a pair, in 1937, which bred on the NE Lincolnshire coast may have concerned wild stock as the Red-crested Pochard had been spreading northwestwards in Europe for some years and had recently established breeding populations in N Germany and, perhaps, in Holland. The presence of four birds earlier in the year in Lincolnshire and one in Westmorland indicates that there may have been a small influx from the continent in 1937. The first record of feral breeding was that of a pair in Essex in 1958 (Fitter 1959, Pyman 1959).

The bulk of the present population is centred about the Cotswold Water Park on the Gloucestershire/Wiltshire border where sightings outwith the collection began to increase during the 1960s. Others breed in the London Parks and sites in E England (Gibbons *et al.* 1993).

Long-tailed Duck

Clangula hyemalis

Throughout much of the 19th century eggs were taken in Shetland that were attributed to this species. Evans and Buckley (1899) recorded most of these but the identification of the species rested solely on the description of the eggs. In Orkney Long-tailed Ducks were recorded throughout the summer on a number of occasions during the first quarter of the 20th century and this led to the belief that they stayed to breed. In 1911 Aplin received a clutch of eggs and down from a nest said to have been of this species; this remains the most well-attested claim of the Long-tailed Duck breeding in Britain. It was said to have probably bred again in 1912 and 1926 (Groundwater 1974) and was recorded during the *68–72 Atlas* survey in the Western Isles (in 1969) and Shetland (in 1971). Breeding was strongly suspected at the 1969 site (Sharrock 1976).

Goldeneye

Bucephala clangula

The Goldeneye was generally distributed around the coasts and estuaries of Britain in the winter during the 19th century and was less often seen inland on lakes and rivers. It was sometimes seen inland in summer in Scotland and numerous accounts were published of breeding attempts made there, but all were subsequently dismissed. Harvie-Brown dealt with most of them in his Fauna of Scotland series. One of the last was his dismissal of the account of a nest in a hollow tree in S Perthshire in 1879 as probably that of a Goosander He was not, however, dismissive of the possibility of breeding taking place in Scotland and thought that the forest-fringed lakes and rivers of, for instance, Speyside provided suitable habitat and, if so many were not shot during the spring, more might stay into the summer

(evidently a few did so into June).

Single pairs, thought to have been injured by gunners, were reported to have nested in rabbit burrows near to salt-marsh at Burton, Cheshire, on the Dee estuary in 1931 and 1932. A clutch and down were taken and identified as from this species despite the improbable site (Bell 1967). The erection in parts of Scotland, of nest boxes, which take the place of the Black Woodpecker nest holes that are used on the Continent, has appeared to have assisted the rapid increase in the number of breeding pairs that has occurred since breeding was first reported in Strathspey in 1970 (Dennis 1987). Most of the nesting attempts have taken place in the same part of Scotland. In 1990, 95 nesting attempts were made in Britain almost all of which were in one extensive nest-box scheme in Scotland although some breeding attempts in natural sites may have been missed (*88–91 Atlas*).

Ruddy Duck

Oxyura jamaicensis

The Wildfowl Trust imported three pairs of Ruddy Ducks from their native North America in 1948. The following year they began breeding in the Slimbridge, Gloucestershire, collection but the ducklings proved difficult to rear with the artificial techniques in use then. It was found that better results were obtained by allowing parents to rear their own young but this meant that some young escaped being pinioned. It has been estimated that about 70 juveniles flew away from Slimbridge during 1956–63 and led to the feral breeding attempts in Somerset in 1960 and 1961 and Staffordshire in the latter year. By 1975 the number of breeding pairs, mainly along the R Severn and neighbouring counties, was about 50–62 and the winter population numbered about 350 individuals. In 1974 a pair nested successfully on Lough Neagh in Northern Ireland (Sharrock 1976). The numbers and breeding range of the Ruddy Duck continued to increase at a meteoric rate. By 1991 the total British population, from the E coast of Scotland through much of England, E Wales and Anglesey, numbered about 3,400, which represents a breeding population of about 570 pairs. In Ireland about 15–20 pairs bred (Gibbons *et al.* 1993).

Ruddy Ducks, probably originating from Britain, had, by 1992, been recorded in 15 European countries, Morocco and the Ukraine. This species has recently been the subject of much controversy following allegations that it poses a threat, through competition and, especially, hybridisation, to populations of the threatened and closely related White-headed Duck of which only 19,000 are believed to survive (Vinicombe *et al.* 1993).

Bobwhite Quail (Virginian Colin)

Colinus virginianus

Some of the numerous attempts to introduce the Bobwhite Quail to Britain and Ireland (from the first probably sometime before 1813 in Ireland) led to temporarily sustained breeding. The majority of Bobwhites normally survived for no more than two or three years after being turned down; a few lived for up to 10 years. The only 19th century attempt that suggested that Bobwhites could be naturalised was at Holkham, Norfolk in 1820; there were still some seen in the locality in 1846 but they died out a few years afterwards. From 1898 until the 1950s there were no dated occurrences of this species but substantial introductions in Dunwich, Suffolk in 1956 and Tresco in the Isles of Scilly in 1964 and 1965 led to the records of breeding groups during the *68–72 Atlas* survey. These groups have, however, now apparently died out as there was only a single bird seen during the *88–91 Atlas* survey (coincidentally, just a few miles east along the coast from Holkham, the site of the 1820 introduction).

Reeves's Pheasant

Syrmaticus reevesii

Reeves's Pheasant, a strikingly coloured species with a gigantic tail, seems to be one of the foreign species of gamebird most suited to British conditions (Fitter 1959) but feral populations do not appear to be able to sustain themselves indefinitely. Fitter suggested that this may have been because of its proneness to interbreed with the Pheasant or that its huge territories and tendency to fly long distances took it away from the protection of its home estate. It is possible that this wandering habit, coupled with its quiet call, took males out of contact with others of its species (Sharrock 1976). During the last 30 years of the 19th century it was introduced to a number of estates in England, Scotland and Ireland. The first introduction was by Lord Tweedmouth at Guisachaen in W Inverness and the species was said to be thoroughly acclimatised in 1895. The apparent success encouraged others to introduce Reeves's Pheasant but all eventually failed. Records of, apparently, free-living birds were included in the *68–72 Atlas* from Woburn, Bedfordshire (they were introduced here during the 19th century), in Breckland (a few were introduced at Elvedon, Suffolk in 1950) and in Kinveachy Forest (amongst others) in Inverness-shire. The species has been introduced into a number of continental European countries and, during the 1970s, existed in the wild in Germany (where it was released in 1910–12 but had declined to the

point where few were left) and had been recently released in at least 15 areas of France (Cramp 1977–94).

Crane

Grus grus

An Act of Parliament of 1533 demanded that a fine of 20 pence (about 8p now but a fortune at the time) be imposed on anyone who took the eggs of the Crane and five entries in the 'Household Book' of the L'Estranges' of Hunstanton Norfolk between 1519 and 1533 (just one of these entries, however, was made during the spring) mentioned the supply of this species to their larder (Stevenson 1866–90). It has been inferred from the above evidence (and one or two items more) that the Crane bred in parts of East Anglia but died out there prior to the end of the 16th century probably because of persecution. It must be borne in mind, however, that the Grey Heron is known in some parts of rural East Anglia as 'crane' even to this day and the possibility of confusion in the old records is evident (J. Sharrock in litt). The Crane remained an uncommon winter visitor to Britain until 1981. A single pair has bred or attempted to breed in East Anglia in every year since 1981, a total of four young were raised up to 1988, and two pairs bred unsuccessfully in 1989

Great Bustard

Otis tarda

The Great Bustard was of such interest, because of its rarity and striking appearance, that almost every occurrence, whether shot or just seen, was recorded. For many years, at least as far back as the 16th century, it commanded the highest price of all gamebirds. Some have suggested that this indicated great rarity and that it was never a common species in England, it is plausible, however, that many aspects of its biology, habits and physique made it a very difficult bird to procure or that it was so prized for the table that it was in great demand. The relatively weak firearms of the period often made little impression on it, horses could not outrun it and the open habitals in which it resided made a furtive approach very difficult. At the end of the 18th century it bred widely from Devoshire through S England, East Anglia and further up the east coast as far as Yorkshire. However, during the first few years of the 19th century, although it still bred in a few of these counties, the Great Bustard very quickly became extinct.

Wiltshire was always considered the main stronghold of the Great Bustard in Britain. It bred on the wide, open downs in the north of the county and on Salisbury Plain. In recognition of the declining numbers in 1775 an Act was passed banning hunting during the breeding season. Notwithstanding this effort it continued to decline, partially due to the numbers killed, but primarily due to the ploughing up of the downlands. The last nest was found in 1801 with one, abandoned egg. In Hampshire the last indication of breeding occurred in July 1806 when an unidentified harrier species was flushed from the body of a young Bustard. In Sussex it bred in some numbers on the Downs in the 18th century but the last nest was taken from near Patcham around 1810. East Anglia held breeding bustards for longer than anywhere else. Three principal breeding areas were apparent. One was around Swaffham, especially at Westacre, in Norfolk. The last eggs were taken at Ash Breck, Westacre and Great Massingham in 1836. The second area was around Thetford and extended from Brettenham and Snarehill in Norfolk probably as far south as Mildenhall in Suffolk. An egg was taken from a nest between Thetford and Brandon in 1819, but the last breeding record is of a successful brood hatched from a nest in a field of rye near the rabbit warren at Thetford a little later. The third area was around Newmarket in Suffolk and extended into Cambridgeshire. The last egg was taken in Cambridgeshire from near Shefford in 1831. In Yorkshire the chief and last breeding area was on the wolds of the east of the county. Extinction followed the ploughing up of the wolds and the species last bred in the south of the area in 1816 or 1817 near North Dalton and in the north in 1825. Breeding probably last took place on the Lincolnshire Wolds about 1825.

Individuals, possibly lingering on from the old populations, continued to be recorded up to around 1840 in East Anglia and further accidental birds were recorded sporadically elsewhere over the region throughout the century. Efforts to reintroduce the Great Bustard into Norfolk in 1900 were unsuccessful although breeding attempts were made in the following few years (Riviere 1930).

Black-winged Stilt

Himantopus himantopus

The Black-winged Stilt had been periodically recorded in Britain since at least the beginning of the 19th century. Some of the females shot before the middle of that century, upon dissection, were found to contain well-developed ovaries and, in light of the 20th century breeding records, it may be speculated that breeding may occasionally have taken place or would have done if the birds had not been killed.

In 1945, the first cases of proven breeding took place in Nottinghamshire when two pairs (possibly three) nested, one of which raised young (Staton 1945). In 1983 there was an unsuccessful breeding attempt in Cambridgeshire and a pair raised two young in Norfolk in 1987 (Batten *et al.* 1990).

Little Ringed Plover

Charadrius dubius

The Little Ringed Plover was considered a very rare vagrant to Britain during the 19th century; only eight examples were recorded. The first dated record was of one shot in the Isles of Scilly in October 1863; others were collected in Sussex (one of which may have been shot prior to 1850), Middlesex, the Isle of Wight and the Hampshire/Dorset border. The latest record that century was of one shot near Christchurch in April 1879. There were only seven further records in the 20th century, mainly from SE England, before the first breeding record occurred at Tring, Hertfordshire in 1938 where three young flew. In 1944 two pairs bred again at Tring and another in Middlesex and, from this point, the colonisation of Britain escalated—the rate of increase between 1948 and 1962 was about 15% per year. The colonisation has been facilitated by the expansion of building in Britain during the 20th century and the consequent rapid rise in the number of flooded gravel pits with their associated stony margins although other man-made sites (such as industrial tips and waste grounds, sewage farms, reservoirs and quarries) have been used, as, occasionally, have the more traditional shingle banks alongside rivers.

By the *68–72 Atlas* survey regular breeding was taking place in England as far west as the N Wales border and as far north as the Scottish border. In 1972, about 400 pairs were recorded summering in Britain. Before the *88–91 Atlas* survey the Little Ringed Plover had spread into Wales. In 1991 it was estimated that the population there was some 60 pairs and, interestingly, 50 of those bred in natural sites on river shingle. The population in Britain was estimated, based on the *88–91 Atlas* results, at between 825 and 1,070 pairs.

Temminck's Stint

Calidris temminckii

Temminck's Stint had never been suspected of breeding in Britain during the 19th century and was a rare but regular spring and autumn visitor. It was most frequently taken on the E and S coasts of England from the R Humber to the Isles of Scilly, especially so in Norfolk. North of the Humber it was rarely seen and, up to 1895, was only once recorded in Scotland.

Prior to the *68–72 Atlas* survey breeding was proven in Britain on only four occasions when eggs of the Temminck's Stint were found in Inverness-shire in 1934, 1936 and 1956 (adults of this species were also present in 1935 and 1947 but no nests were found) and in 1951 in Yorkshire. All of these attempts, however, were unsuccessful. During 1969–74 one or two pairs were present each year at one site in Scotland and the first known successful breeding attempt in Britain took place there in 1971. The number of adults seen in Scotland increased to a maximum of nine between 1978 and 1980 but then subsequently declined and only five adults were recorded on a single site in 1989.

Purple Sandpiper

Calidris maritima

Saxby (1874) noted that the Purple Sandpiper was the commonest of all the sandpipers in Shetland from October to May. This probably refers mainly to Unst as did his notes of clutches of eggs of this species, which were brought to him by the islanders. These eggs bore a strong resemblance to authentic specimens obtained from the Purple Sandpiper's Scandinavian breeding grounds, also in Saxby's collection.

To the present day Purple Sandpipers have spent the summer in Orkney and Shetland, and occasionally on the mainland coasts. In 1978 breeding was first proven at an undisclosed site in Scotland. That year a pair hatched three young and raised at least one juvenile, and breeding has been proven or suspected in every year since. In recent years two or three nests have been found annually at the site (Dennis 1983). Apparently suitable breeding sites exist in many places in Scotland and the species is probably much overlooked—it may have been pure chance that the breeding site was discovered in an area well-frequented by birdwatchers (J. Sharrock in litt).

Green Sandpiper

Tringa ochropus

Although the male's song has been noted on a number of occasions in England and Wales during the 19th century and, especially, in Scotland during the 20th century (particularly from the 1930s to the 1950s, Nethersole-Thompson and Nethersole-Thompson 1986) there have been only two cases of proven breeding of the Green Sandpiper in Britain. The first was at Levens in Westmorland in 1917 when adult birds were seen regularly from June onwards and, in August, they were seen in the company of two downy young. A pair was seen with a single chick on Speyside, Inverness-shire in 1959 (coincidently the same year that the Wood Sandpiper was proven breeding for the first time in Britain, in Sutherland).

Wood Sandpiper

Tringa glareola

It seems likely that the Wood Sandpiper was far more common on passage in E England and Scotland during the early years of the 19th century than later. The continuous drainage of the Dutch coastal marshes, and the consequent severe decline in the numbers of Wood Sandpipers breeding there, was blamed for the decline in the species seen in Britain (Stevenson 1866–90). The early breeding records in Britain probably concerned individuals from this Dutch stock.

An account of a young bird 'not having entirely lost its down' shot, together with an adult female, in a marsh in summer near Beechamwell, Norfolk, was published in *The Zoologist* of 1846. It was believed that it was 'not sufficiently feathered to have crossed the sea' and led to the belief that it had been bred near to the place that it was shot.

There were a number of records of suspected breeding in Northumberland during the 19th century, based either on the time of year in which birds in breeding or juvenile plumage were obtained or on the, apparently, suitable breeding habitat they inhabited. One well-authenticated case of breeding does exist, however. John Hancock spent much time searching for a nest on Prestwick Carr and was finally rewarded when he found one containing eggs in June 1853. The male was shot to complete his identification. A number of Wood Sandpipers had been shot at that place in preceding years and, so, they may have bred there before the nest was found. The drainage of Prestwick Carr was begun in 1854 and completed in 1857 and almost all of the site was destroyed at that time. In May 1857, at Gosforth Lake, Hancock watched the display flight of a male Wood Sandpiper that suggested an intention to nest there, but breeding was not proven. A record of eggs taken in Elgin prior to 1865 was discounted by later authors (Hartert et al. 1912).

It was not until 1959 that another pair was proved to breed when two unfledged birds were seen in a Sutherland marsh. Breeding occurred at the same site for the next three years and then, although not always proven, at least into the 1970s. Subsequently the Wood Sandpiper has bred in a number of locations in Scotland. The best years have been 1968 (ten pairs, three proven breeding), 1978 (7–8 pairs, four recorded breeding), and 1980 (8–10 pairs, six recorded breeding) (Batten et al. 1990).

Spotted Sandpiper

Actitis macularia

The Spotted Sandpiper, an abundant inhabitant of eastern North America, has been recorded on 108 occasions in

Britain and Ireland up to the end of 1993; 102 of the observations have occurred since the end of 1957 (J. Sharrock in litt). Its second occurrence in Scotland in 1975 led to a pair attempting to breed on Skye. The attempt was unsuccessful; two of the clutch of four eggs were infertile and the nest was deserted, perhaps owing to trampling by cattle or as a result of heavy rain (Reed *et al.* 1983). This was the first recorded breeding of this species in Europe and the Palearctic region and, indeed, the first Nearctic species known to attempt to breed in Europe.

Mediterranean Gull

Larus melanocephalus

The Mediterranean Gull was considered a very rare visitor to Britain until the 1950s; in fact there were only four records prior to 1940, the last in 1909 (J. Sharrock in litt). Although improved knowledge of the species' characteristics and improved expertise in field identification may have played their parts, from that time records became more regular and coincided with an increase at Mediterranean Gull colonies around the Black Sea. Breeding was recorded in many W European countries for the first time after the establishment of a colony in Hungary in the 1950s and in Britain in 1968 a pair of Mediterranean Gulls was identified breeding in a colony of over 10,000 pairs of Black-headed Gulls in Hampshire. Over the next few years a number of individuals were noted paired with Black-headed Gulls and in 1976 the second pure Mediterranean pair bred in Britain. Since 1979 breeding has been annual with a maximum of 11 confirmed pairs in Britain in 1990 mainly in SE England.

Little Gull

Larus minutus

The Little Gull was recognised as an irregular autumn and winter visitor to Britain during the 19th and very early 20th centuries and was occasionally seen during spring and summer. It occurred almost annually along the east coast and was especially common there during the late 1860s. To 1909 it had been recorded on 11 occasions in Ireland, chiefly near Dublin and Belfast (Hartert *et al.* 1912). There was no suggestion that it had bred or attempted to do so. Opportunistic nesting of the Little Gull has taken place on four occasions in Britain following an increase in the numbers of birds seen on passage and summering since

about the 1950s. Single pairs laid eggs on the Cambridgeshire/Norfolk border in 1975, in Norfolk and N Yorkshire in 1978 and in Nottinghamshire in 1987. No young were hatched during any of the attempts (Batten *et al.* 1990).

Gull-billed Tern

Gelochelidon nilotica

From about 1925 it became clear that the Gull-billed Tern was increasing in numbers on autumn passage along the Dutch coast. It was first recorded nesting in The Netherlands in 1931 and, from 1947, small numbers evidently bred regularly and may have spread from an undiscovered colony in one of the neighbouring countries. This spread may have led to the first known breeding in Britain of a pair of Gull-billed Terns in 1949 and 1950.

A pair of large, black-billed terns mobbed two birdwatchers in July 1949 at Abberton Reservoir in Essex. They appeared with Common Terns from a new islet upon which Little Terns and Black-headed Gulls were also nesting,but their identification remained a mystery until the following July when a nestling, subsequenty identified as a Gull-billed Tern was ringed (Pyman and Wainwnght 1952). There are no other records of its breeding in Britain or Ireland.

Great Auk (Garefowl)

Pinguinus impennis

The flightless Great Auk had inhabited many sites around the N Atlantic but persecution for meat and eggs and finally by collectors caused its extinction during the early years of the 19th century. In Europe it was encountered in the waters of Iceland, the Faeroe Islands and along the Norwegian coast but, apparently, it was only infrequently noted outside Arctic waters. Archaeological evidence in parts of Scotland, Durham and Ireland attests to its distribution in these islands but folklore accounts of breeding in the Isle of Man and on Lundy are doubtful. There appear to have been no confirmed reports of breeding in Britain or Ireland but the inhabitants of the Western Isles and Orkney convinced some early naturalists that breeding did, in fact, take place in those islands. Without direct evidence, however, these beliefs have to be recounted with care as the Great Auk was often recorded far out to sea, many miles from its breeding sites (especially off the Newfoundland coast), and it might have occasionally occurred in the seas off Britain and Ireland without breeding locally.

The last Great Auks seen around Orkney were killed in 1812 and 1813. William Bullock was informed that the female of a pair had been killed shortly before his second tour of the islands during the late autumn of 1812 but he located and chased a male for several hours in a six-oared boat. The chase took place around Papa Westray and was unsuccessful. A Great Auk, said to have been the same individual, was killed about a fortnight later, after Bullock had left the islands, and was sent to him. It eventually found its way into the collection of the British Museum (Montagu 1813). One was caught alive at St Kilda, Western Isles, in the winter of 1822 and another in 1829. This latter was examined by Dr Fleming, a noted British naturalist of the time, but it later escaped. Macgillivray recounted the assertion by the St Kildan natives that the Great Auk bred in the islands (Yarrell 1837–43). One, said to have been caught on Stac an Armin in St Kilda in about 1840, was later killed as a witch and was probably the last of the British Great Auks (Harvie-Brown and Buckley 1888). One was taken alive on the Waterford coast in 1834 (Yarrell 1837–43).

The last Great Auks ever seen alive were a pair bludgeoned to death on Eldey Rock, Iceland by three Icelandic fishermen in 1844 (although Morris (1851–57) appears to record the date as 1846). An egg was also taken but was smashed (Zonfrillo 1994).

Collared Dove

Streptopelia decaocto

Until about 1930, when an explosive expansion of its range began, the Collared Dove was confined, in Europe, to Turkey and parts of the Balkans. It reached Hungary in 1932, Czechoslovakia in 1936, Austria in 1938, Germany in 1943, the Netherlands in 1947, Denmark in 1948, Sweden and Switzerland in 1949, France in 1950 and Belgium and Norway in 1952—it spread over 1,600km in less than 20 years (Fisher 1953). In 1952 it is possible that the first wild Collared Dove was seen in Britain. It was identified at Manton near Lincolnshire but some uncertainty concerning its provenance resulted from the discovery that a dealer in Pontefract, Yorkshire had recently sold several birds in the area.

At least two pairs were present in a small garden in N Norfolk in 1955 but only one pair bred, raising two young. In 1956 16 individuals inhabited the area and in the following year breeding was proven in three new counties— Kent, Lincolnshire and Moray. The jump of about 600km to Scotland was characteristic of the mode of the Collared Dove's range expansion in Europe and was in the usual northwesterly direction (Bannerman 1953–63). Up to the mid 1960s the species' range expanded in Britain and Ireland at the rate of about 100% per annum (Hudson 1972). As optimum habitat became fully exploited the rate of increase slowed—by 1970 it had fallen to between 25% and 50% (Sharrock 1976). After the *68–72 Atlas* survey little evidence of further increase or expansion of range has been apparent except at the fringes of its British distribution (Gibbons *et al.* 1993).

Ring-necked Parakeet

Psittacula krameri

Many species of cockatoos, parakeets and lovebirds have been kept in semi-confinement in Britain since the 19th century and there have been numerous records of escaped parrots living at large for many years. Most of these groups and individuals gradually died out either during periods of hard weather or in the absence of supplementary or artificial feeding. Feral Ring-necked Parakeets were reported breeding in Northreps, Norfolk in 1855 (Lever 1977), in Essex in 1930 and in Northamptonshire in 1931 (Low 1992). Since about 1970, however, it became clear that groups of Ring-necked Parakeets in SE England were capable of independent existence (although they are heavily dependent on food on bird tables and ornamental garden plant species). Breeding was suspected in Kent in 1969 and was confirmed at two sites near S London in 1971 (Lever 1987). Since then, perhaps assisted initially by mild winter weather, it has increased substantially and the total British population (still mainly in Kent and the Thames valley) was estimated at around 1,000 (Lack 1986) or 'several thousands' (Gibbons *et al.* 1993). These figures may, however, be over-optimistic (Morgan 1993).

Snowy Owl

Nyctea scandiaca

The first Snowy Owl reported in Britain was a male shot in Unst by Edmondston in 1808 or 1811. He had heard rumours of large white owls in Shetland for some years from the local inhabitants of the islands and had spent much effort in confirming the reports. At this time it was clear that Snowy Owls could be found on Unst in almost every month of the year and evidently were seen then far more frequently than later (say, after 1850). This led to the belief that the species bred in the islands. Edmonston received a report that a pair of adults had been seen with two other individuals in August prior to 1822. One of the other owls was shot and was described as similar in size and shape to the Snowy Owl but much darker in colour. He also received information that a nest containing three well-fledged young, 'of a brown colour, sprinkled with grey', was found on a rocky ledge near Baltasound, Unst some years later. These records cannot now be confirmed—they were treated with scepticism by Evans and Buckley (1899) and ignored by Baxter and Rintoul (1953) and Thom (1986). A nest was finally found on Fetlar in June 1967 containing seven eggs (Tulloch 1968). Five young were raised to flying that year and in the following eight years 16 further young were raised, probably by the same pair (although since 1972 an additional female laid eggs), before the male disappeared. Females have continued to inhabit Fetlar but, apart from a failed effort to introduce a male to the island in 1989, no mates have been present and eggs laid have all been infertile (Thom 1986).

Bee-eater

Merops apiaster

Although noted as a very rare visitor to Britain since, at least, 1668 (Saunders 1889) there were no breeding records of Bee-eaters until the 20th century. Four pairs of Bee-eaters have bred, or attempted to breed, in Britain on two occasions and a further pair has bred in the Channel Islands. In 1920 a pair was watched visiting a hole in a sand bank on the western side of the R Esk at Musselburgh. They apparently showed every sign of intending to breed but in June the female was found in an exhausted or injured condition and died after laying an egg; the male disappeared on the same day (Baxter and Rintoul 1953). In 1955 three pairs nested in Streat sandpit near Plumpton in Sussex. Two of these were successful and seven young were raised (Shrubb 1976). In the following year a pair bred on Alderney in the Channel Islands (Batten *et al.* 1990). Since 1981 the number of Bee-eaters seen in Britain in summer has increased substantially (some in small groups) and, coupled with increases in other parts of Europe, has led to the hope that breeding may become more regular in the future.

Shore Lark

Eremophila alpestris

The Shore Lark was first noticed in Britain in Norfolk in 1830 and was first recorded from Scotland in East Lothian in 1859. It was recorded very sporadically in winter on the south and east coasts until 1879 when a considerable invasion occurred. After that year it became an annual autumn to spring visitor to the English eastern counties. An adult male in song in 1972 in the Highlands was the first summer record. In the following year a pair in the same area was suspected of having bred and single birds were seen there in 1975 and 1976. After an exceptional passage in the winter of 1976/77, there was the discovery of two singing males at the same site in 1977, a nest and eggs were found there in June that year and a juvenile was seen later. A second site held a singing male that year but there have been no further summer records there (Thom 1986).

Bluethroat

Luscinia svecica

The Bluethroat is a scarce passage visitor to Britain occurring annually in very variable numbers; about 275 were recorded in Scotland in 1981 and over 100 were seen on the Isle of May in May 1985 (Thom 1986). Throughout much of the 19th century it was, similarly, recorded regularly, mainly along the E coast of Britain (Hartert *et al.* 1912). At the Insh Marshes in Inverness-shire in 1968 a female was found incubating a clutch of six eggs but no male was seen and breeding was unsuccessful (Greenwood 1968). A male in song was found in the Spey valley on one day in June 1980 but was not seen again and, in 1985, a pair raised two young in Scotland (Murray 1987).

Black Redstart

Phoenicurus ochruros

The Black Redstart was evidently a very rare visitor to S England during the first half of the 19th century. After about 1860, however, the number of records began to increase and, from about 1880, Black Redstarts were recorded almost annually. It is not now clear whether the increase in records was due to an increase in the number of birds or whether it was the result of an increase in the number of observers and their competency (Borrer 1891, Ticehurst 1909). The authors of the time felt that the latter was probably the most likely but, in light of the subsequent breeding records, it is possible that an increase in the number of winter visitors eventually led to the Black Redstart's colonisation of Britain.

There was one very early Black Redstart breeding record: in 1845 a nest and a single egg were collected and both adults shot in a garden in Durham (Hancock 1874); although Witherby *et al.* (1938–41), and other writers, had ignored it, the nest and egg were authenticated in 1946 (Temperley 1946).

The next record (reported by Cooke in 1948) was of a pair that raised a brood in an old sheep hut at Pett Level in Sussex in 1909. This was a very short distance from two pairs that were found by Cooke to be breeding on the coastal cliffs in 1923 (and generally considered to have been the first for Britain). Sporadic breeding continued in SE England and regularly in Cornwall for a few years following. The first London breeding record was in 1926 on the derelict site of the previous year's Wembley Exhibition. Breeding continued there regularly until its desertion in 1942 and records came from other parts of London. The bombing in the city during the 1939–45 war created many new sites and a regular breeding population was established. Numbers in Britain have fluctuated since from about ten pairs in the early 1960s (Fitter 1965, 1971) to a peak of 118 reported pairs in 1988. Between the *68–72* and *88–91 Atlases* there has been evidence that the population in London and the SE England counties has declined as reclamation of derelict land has continued and that the main British population has shifted to areas of the Midlands and East Anglia.

Fieldfare

Turdus pilaris

The first record of breeding Fieldfares in Britain eventually followed a century of range expansion on mainland Europe. Formerly breeding only as far west as Poland and E Germany the species spread into W Germany in the second half of the 19th century. It spread into Switzerland in 1923, the French Jura in 1953 and, at about the same time, the Netherlands, and it bred for the first time in Denmark in 1965. In 1967, the same year that the Fieldfare colonised Belgium, Britain's first nest was found in Orkney (Balfour 1968) and breeding possibly took place in Durham (a pair and three juveniles were seen in mid July). Thereafter breeding became annual in Shetland with up to three pairs breeding each year and has been recorded in several central and E Scottish mainland counties (Sharrock 1976). The highest number of pairs confirmed breeding in Britain in any one year was five (in 1990), with other recent peaks in 1977 (four) and 1989 (three). Even making allowance for undetected pairs in remote areas, the current British breeding population has been estimated at under 25 pairs (Gibbons *et al.* 1993).

Redwing

Turdus iliacus

The first known case of the Redwing breeding in Scotland took place in Sutherland in 1925. Breeding was recorded sporadically, and not annually, in Scotland (and one pair in Co. Kerry in 1951) until 1967 when seven pairs were located. The discovery, during the first year of the *68–72 Atlas* survey, of 20 pairs in West Ross alone suggested that the Redwing had established a firm foothold in Scotland (Sharrock 1976). The main population is now established in the Highlands north of the Great Glen and probably consists of between 40 and 80 breeding pairs annually, though the numbers actually found are very dependent upon the activities of a few enthusiastic field workers. Since 1975 a few nests have been found in SE England, most notably in Kent. During 1981–91, numbers proved breeding in Britain varied from four (1981) to 30 (1982) and the maximum possible number (including every observation as a breeding pair) from 11 in 1981 to 68 in 1983 (J. Sharrock in litt).

Cetti's Warbler

Cettia cetti

Cetti's Warbler was not known in Britain prior to the 20th century; until the turn of the century it was hardly known at all away from the Mediterranean. The first acceptable British record of this species came in 1961 (Ferguson-Lees 1964) and, since 1967, increasing numbers were identified as a range expansion across Europe approached the English Channel (Bonham and Robertson 1975). The first proven case of breeding in Britain took place in Kent in 1972 when an adult was seen carrying food. The subsequent increase in breeding numbers was very rapid. Cetti's Warblers appeared at six or seven sites in Kent and others held territories in Suffolk and Norfolk in 1973. A bird ringed at the main breeding site in Belgium and found in Norwich gave the only indication of the origin of the British colonists (Sharrock 1976). Proof of breeding is very difficult to obtain (Sharrock 1976) but numbers of singing males give an indication of the size of the breeding population. Peaks were reached during 1983–84 of about 300 singing males distributed throughout S England and parts of SW Wales and 1990 when 350 males were recorded—both peaks followed mild winters (*88–91 Atlas*). The 'centre of gravity' of the British population has now shifted from Kent (where winters can be relatively severe) to SW England which is generally milder (J. Sharrock in litt).

Savi's Warbler

Locustella luscinioides

The history of the Savi's Warbler as a British breeding bird from its discovery to extinction is one of the shortest on record, lasting just 16 years. Published details of its complete status were scant and so the complete record can be recorded here.

It was first distinguished from its near relatives by Savi from specimens obtained in Tuscany in 1824. Savi's Warbler was first recognised as an inhabitant of Britain from specimens collected in the Cambridgeshire fens (perhaps near Duxford) in the spring of 1840 by Baker, the details of which were recorded in the *Annals of Natural History* of the same year. Subsequently it became clear that an earlier example had been misidentified. A specimen collected in May at Limpenhoe, Norfolk was submitted to Temminck in 1819 who attributed it to a variety of the Reed Warbler and then, later, to Cetti's Warbler. Re-examination of the specimen, following the recognition of the 1840 individuals, identified it as the first Savi's Warbler collected in Britain. Another was collected at Strumpshaw on behalf of Brown shortly afterwards and he reported that others were heard between Hoveton and Wroxham broads. It had been well known to the sedge cutters of Cambridgeshire for many years who knew it as the Brown, Red or Night Reeler distinct from the Reeler proper, the Grasshopper Warbler. They had also come across extraordinary nests, comprised almost entirely of the broad leaves of sweetgrass, during the course of their work. A pair of Savi's Warblers was obtained by Clarke in the summer of 1841 or 1842 from the same fen as the 1840 example but it was not until 1845 that a fresh nest and eggs were collected by the marshmen from Backsbite in the parish of Milton in Cambridgeshire. This example was purchased by Bond and the eggs were distributed to other collectors. Bond obtained in all two sets of eggs and six birds. Savi's Warbler disappeared from the Cambridgeshire fens around 1850. It was stated that it bred in the Huntingdonshire fens at this time but no dated examples appear to have been recorded. Newton's assertion in Yarrell (1871–85) that it bred in Suffolk was based on the supposition that records from the Suffolk border with both Cambridgeshire and Norfolk made it very likely. No birds were recorded collected from Suffolk marshes.

Following the collection of the early Cambridgeshire birds and the recognition of the 1819 example, collectors became anxious to obtain British specimens of Savi's Warbler and the fensmen of Norfolk were offered large sums of money to procure samples. In 1843 a pair of Savi's Warblers was shot at South Walsham, one of which was presented by Gurney to the Norwich Museum, the other to Heysham of Carlisle. Others were apparently observed and collected from South Walsham at around the same time and more specimens from the early 19th century, prior to Savi's description, were recalled by Frere. A nest in the collection of Newcome of Feltwell may have been of this species and was said to have come from the vicinity of Great Yarmouth. Apart from the very rare occurrence of migrants (birds thought to have been of this species were seen in the Humber district in 1897 and in Buckinghamshire and Suffolk) the last record of Savi's Warbler in breeding habitat in Britain was of a specimen shot for Stevenson by a man who was engaged in collecting Grasshopper Warblers for him. This was collected on 7th June 1856 near Surlingham, Norfolk.

The drainage of the Cambridge/Huntingdonshire fens was blamed for the extinction of the Savi's Warbler there. This was probably also true of the Norfolk population, as the numbers of collected birds were unlikely to have had a significant effect.

Savi's Warblers remained a scarce migrant until, in 1954, a male sang at Wicken Fen, Cambridgeshire throughout the summer. Then, in 1960, breeding was recorded for the first time since 1845 in a large reed bed in Kent although it may have taken place for several years previously (Pitt 1967). Since then breeding has been recorded regularly in Kent, Suffolk and Norfolk and sporadically in a number of counties of S and E England and Lancashire. Numbers peaked during 1977–80 at 30 singing males reported at up to 15 sites but since then have declined. In 1988 there were 13 records from only ten sites. The recolonisation of Britain by Savi's Warblers has coincided with an expansion of the species in NW Europe. Apart from the management of the marsh vegetation in the reserve breeding sites, the future of the tiny population in Britain is probably out of our control (Batten *et al.* 1990).

Moustached Warbler

Acrocephalus melanopogon

Apart from records of this Mediterranean, E European and SW Asian species in Hampshire (two together in 1951), one in Kent in 1952 and another in Buckinghamshire in 1965 there is one other, the very first for Britain, at the sewage farm at Milton, Cambridgeshire in 1946 (Hinde and Thom 1947). This latter record, of a pair that bred and raised young, has been much discussed, but, despite considerable scrutiny on many occasions of the evidence of identification (Sharrock 1981), it remains substantiated (Bircham 1989).

Firecrest (Fire-crested Wren)

Regulus ignicapillus

The Ibis of 1927 contained an account of a pair of nesting Firecrests in Lancashire, the first claimed for Britain. The evidence was examined in detail by ornithologists of the day and the weight of opinion decided that, as it was a sight record, it was prudent to reject it (Bannerman 1953–63).

In 1962, following the northward and westward spread of the species in Europe, the first satisfactory Firecrest breeding record took place in the Hampshire New Forest. Fledged young were located there following the discovery of three singing males during the spring of the previous year and a small, regular population became established. From the late 1960s, the location of singing males in the southern counties of Hertfordshire, Kent and Dorset suggested a more widespread distribution was developing. By 1972, a wood in Buckinghamshire held 23 singing males (Batten 1973) and over the next few years the population grew there and in adjacent woods (Sharrock 1976). Since the *68–72 Atlas* the Firecrest has continued its range expansion and numbers reached a peak during 1983 when 175 singing males held territory at 75 localities.

Short-toed Treecreeper

Certhia brachydactyla

The Short-toed Treecreeper replaces the Treecreeper in the Channel Islands and inhabits all of the main islands. It has been recognised there for many years—when Smith (1879) investigated the avifauna of the islands he recorded that it was a resident of Guernsey and Sark and that it bred not uncommonly in both. Dobson (1952) believed that it had been overlooked in the past but it had been recorded since 1919 on Jersey and was a common species on that island. Although the remains of an old nest had been found on Alderney in 1946 Dobson believed that there was none on the island that year. It remains, to the present day, a regular inhabitant of the steep-sided wooded valleys characteristic of many parts of the island group.

Woodchat Shrike (Woodchat)

Lanius senator

Shortly after the Woodchat Shrike was ascertained to be a visitor to Britain (Yarrell 1837–43) it was described breeding in the Isle of Wight. This record has weak provenance and confusing subsequent treatment. More (1865) recounted the assertion of one of his Hampshire correspondents, a Mr H. Rogers, that he had twice taken a nest of this species at Freshwater, Isle of Wight and identification was confirmed by a Frederick Bond. An adult was said by Rogers to have been seen in the neighbourhood of the nest site and Bond said that he had shot a young bird of the year in September 1856, again near the nest site. Bond was later described as 'a sportsman and a naturalist' (Harting 1866) but he appears to have had no special knowledge of the breeding of this species. The record was repeated later by Kelsall and Munn (1905) and mentioned by Yarrell (1871–85), Saunders (1889) and Witherby *et al.* (1938–41). Bannerman (1953–63) repeated the record and felt that it was doubtful but Cohen (1963) missed the reference in Kelsall and Munn (1905) completely. Whether the Woodchat Shrike has ever nested in Britain is a question that must remain unsatisfactorily answered—no other claim of breeding has been made although it continues to visit Britain annually in small numbers during migration, averaging seven adults per spring and three adults and four immatures per autumn (J. Sharrock in litt).

Brambling (Mountain Finch)

Fringilla montifringilla

Booth recorded a nest of this species in Glen Lyon, Perthshire in 1866. Although a number of other assertions of breeding had been made since, in East and West Ross and Inverness-shire, Booth's remains the only dated record from the 19th century. In the light of the unreliability of others of Booth's breeding records (Baxter and Rintoul 1953) his Brambling record must be treated with great caution. Baxter and Rintoul noted two other, undated, records.

The first confirmed breeding record took place in Sutherland in a Scots pine in 1920. The birds were watched nest building and on the 31st May the tree was climbed and seven eggs were taken (Baxter and Rintoul 1953). No further breeding record took place until a nest and three deserted eggs were found in Grampian in 1979. The first successful breeding was in 1982 in Inverness-shire when at least one young flew. Between the 1982 record and the *88–91 Atlas* survey a handful of pairs have been confirmed breeding and up to 35 recorded possibly breeding throughout Scotland and E England. Three pairs were recorded with breeding evidence during the *68–72 Atlas* and two during the survey period of the *88–91 Atlas*.

Serin

Serinus serinus

The Serin was recognised as a very rare vagrant to Britain in the 19th century and was first noted here in 1852. Prior to 1912 it had been recorded on just 20 occasions in England, ten of them on the Sussex coast resulting from the extensive netting operations carried out there. Some caution was attached to these records as the Serin was not uncommonly kept as a caged bird and it does seem striking that almost all of the Sussex records came from the vicinity of Brighton. However, most showed little sign of prior captivity and, on one occasion, a small flock was seen (Borrer 1891, Hartert *et al.* 1912). Other counties in which the Serin had been recorded were Kent, Norfolk, Hampshire, Somerset and Devonshire and one or two had been taken near London. Less convincing were those seen in Yorkshire and Oxfordshire. Two were taken in Dublin, one of them in the winter of 1893, and one was taken near Edinburgh in 1911 (Hartert *et al.* 1912).

Until 1958 the grand total of records numbered about 70 but, after 1960, there was a notable upsurge in records—there were 136 between 1958 and 1974. This period also saw the first breeding records in Britain: a pair bred in Dorset in 1967 and another in Sussex in 1969 after large autumn influxes in 1966–68 (Sharrock and Sharrock 1976). A northward and western range expansion of this species has been taking place from its Mediterranean homeland since before the 19th century and led to the prediction that the Serin would colonise Britain (Olsson 1971). The 1960s' breeding records were not unexpected, therefore. Although the number of breeding records has increased, especially in Devonshire since 1978, no more than two pairs are proven to breed in Britain each year and it has been suggested that the English Channel is a barrier that inhibits a definite movement in to the country (Batten *et al.* 1990, Gibbons *et al.* 1993).

Parrot Crossbill

Loxia pytyopsittacus

The Parrot Crossbill is a vagrant to Britain during irruptive movements from the Continent. Following one such in the autumn of 1982 over 100 were recorded in Britain (probably related to the failure of the cone crop in N Scandinavia) and single pairs bred in Norfolk in 1984 and 1985 raising two broods in each year (Catley and Hursthouse 1985). Incubation began in February and the nests were located in mature Corsican pine. Nests were built in other areas at that time but were not used; at another location in East Anglia newly fledged young were seen. A pair nested and reared four young in Highland Scotland in 1991, following another irruption in autumn 1990 when 159 individuals of this species were confirmed (Ogilvie 1994).

Scarlet Rosefinch (Scarlet Grosbeak, Common Rosefinch)

Carpodacus erythrinus

The Scarlet Rosefinch had been recorded on nine occasions in Britain prior to 1912 (Hartert *et al.* 1912). All autumn records, four had been taken in England (three in southeastern counties) and Wales and five in Scotland (four of which were recorded from the Isle of May from 1907 to 1910). There had been no suggestion that it had bred or attempted to breed.

Since about 1900 the Scarlet Rosefinch has extended its range in Europe. This expansion accelerated from 1930; many European countries were colonised from the 1970s. Breeding in Britain had been expected for many years and,

hence, there was little surprise when a nest and eggs were found (of a pair seen throughout the summer) in the Highlands in June 1982 (Mullins 1984). Since then singing males have been located in Scotland and one in Devonshire in 1986, but breeding was not confirmed again until a series of records were on the E coast of England in 1992. Breeding took place at two or three localities in Suffolk and 3–5 pairs were located in Yorkshire (J. Sharrock in litt).

Lapland Bunting

Calcarius lapponicus

From the late 19th century it was recognised that the Lapland Bunting was a regular visitor to Britain on autumn passage, particularly to the counties of the east coast. The numbers that pass through vary but it is generally much scarcer in Britain during the spring. In 1977 there were twice as many spring reports than was usual in Scotland and in that year breeding was confirmed for the first time. This was preceded in April 1968 by a male seen near Kingussie, in June 1974 by a report of a male in full breeding plumage in Caithness and, in 1977, by the presence, following a cold late spring, of up to 16 pairs occupying five sites. Breeding was confirmed when two broods of four young each were seen in July that year. In 1978 up to six pairs occupied three sites and two pairs were proved to have bred, and the following year 11 pairs, of a total of 14 occupying five sites, were proved to have bred. The colonisation was not maintained. In 1980, at the main site, only one pair bred and in 1981 only a single bird was present. The hoped-for colonisation of Britain seemed to have fizzled out but slender hopes of a revival were rekindled eight years later, in 1989, when a lone female was seen in late July (J. Sharrock in litt.).

Appendix A: Some small island avifaunas

The scale of the maps in the main accounts do not allow many of the smaller islands surrounding the coasts of Britain to be clearly delineated. Many of these islands hold internationally important colonies of, mainly, seabirds and the history of the populations of these birds is interesting. For these reasons, the avifauna of some of these islands are treated in more detail here.

In some cases, the breeding status of the birds is not clear from the text reproduced below. The names of those species known to have bred are highlighted in bold, those that probably bred are highlighted in italics and the names of those of uncertain status and those that had become extinct prior to 1875 are printed in roman type.

Isles of Scilly

James Clark and Francis R. Rodd contributed *The Birds of Scilly* in three parts to *The Zoologist* of 1906. F. R. Rodd was a nephew of E. H. Rodd, the author of *The Birds of Cornwall* and contributed some notes about the birds of Scilly to that work. *The Birds of Scilly* drew from many sources both published and unpublished from the 1840s and from protracted shooting and collecting trips to the islands by both writers.

Manx Shearwater—bred in prodigious numbers on Annett and a small colony existed near the Piper's Hole, Tresco.

Storm Petrel—numbers had decreased substantially since 1863 but it still bred on the Western Isles and on Annett since at least 1900.

Cormorant—nested in considerable numbers on the outer rocky islets.

Shag—bred more abundantly than the Cormorant.

Mute Swan—'tame' swans were kept on the pools on Tresco.

Mallard—bred sparingly on a number of islands.

Kestrel—a few pairs bred.

Peregrine—one, and sometimes two, pairs had bred annually for many years.

Partridges—both Grey and Red-legged had been unsuccessfully introduced on many occasions since the middle of the 19th century.

Quail—had been recorded breeding twice on Tresco and once on St Mary's.

Pheasant—was successfully introduced on Tresco a few years before 1856.

Corncrake—a few bred annually.

Moorhen—had become common on the islands since the 1860s particularly on the Abbey pools.

Coot—following a large influx in 1859 two or three pairs had bred on the Abbey pools.

Oystercatcher—bred in considerable numbers.

Ringed Plover—bred in considerable numbers.

Black-headed Gull—two nests were found in 1841 and another in 1845.

Lesser Black-backed Gull—bred in considerable numbers on most of the uninhabited islands.

Herring Gull—bred in considerable numbers on most of the uninhabited islands.

Great Black-backed Gull—bred in limited numbers on the highest rocks; 11 pairs bred in the islands in 1903.

Kittiwake—bred in large numbers on Menavawr in 1852. Soon after, they moved to Gorregan but declined from the 1870s. In 1900 there were just three nests there.

Sandwich Tern—over 100 pairs bred in 1841. By the end of the century only one or two pairs bred and those probably not annually.

Roseate Tern—considerable numbers bred in 1840 but had declined to one or two pairs in 1854. A few were noted in the autumn on their former breeding area in 1867 but had not been seen since.

Common Tern—declined markedly but a few still bred.

Arctic Tern—declined markedly but a few still bred.

Guillemot—formerly had bred in great profusion but numbers had decreased substantially.

Razorbill—bred in extraordinary numbers.

Puffin—bred in their thousands on Annett. Nests were also recorded on Mincarlo, the Scilly rock, Menavawr, Rosevear, Meledgan, Castle Bryher, Round Island, Innisvouls, Menewethan and Great Ganinnick .

Woodpigeon—since the first nest on Tresco in 1873 it had greatly increased throughout the islands.

Turtle Dove—had nested at least once in the islands on Tresco.

Cuckoo—was much more common in Scilly than on the Cornish mainland.

Skylark—bred in small numbers on many islands.

Swallow—common.

Meadow Pipit—an abundant resident.

Rock Pipit—an abundant resident and bred in considerable numbers on all suitable islands.

Pied Wagtail—nested commonly on all of the larger islands.

Wren—an abundant resident and bred on every island.

Dunnock—common.

Robin—bred on all inhabited islands.

Stonechat—common in all of the furze-breaks and on most of the wasteland. In 1903 about 30 pairs bred on St Helen's.

Wheatear—bred sparingly and had evidently decreased.

Blackbird—more common on Scilly than elsewhere in Cornwall.

Song Thrush—a common resident on all of the inhabited islands.

Sedge Warbler—a common summer migrant that bred freely, especially on Tresco.

Spotted Flycatcher—the first nest was found on Bryher in 1903.

Jackdaw—a nest and eggs found on Annett Head were probably of this species.

Rook—had attempted to breed on a number of occasions since the 1850s following autumn invasions. An introduction in 1865 was unsuccessful.

Carrion Crow—bred on all the outer uninhabited islands.

Raven—extinct. Bred on Gorregan in 1840 and may have done so in 1893.

House Sparrow—a common resident on the inhabited islands.

Linnet—bred in small numbers. In 1903 and 1904 nests were found on St Mary's, St Martin's and Tresco.

Corn Bunting—nested in small numbers.

Lundy, Devonshire

Although host to a small permanent human population and regularly visited by naturalists and sportsmen the published information on Lundy birds is scant and often suspected of being inaccurate in some of its detail by later writers. The following list has been assembled from the notes on the birds of Lundy in the *Birds of Devonshire* (D'Urban and Mathew 1892), a paper by F. L. Blathwayt (1900) and *A List of the Birds of Lundy* (Davis 1954). The latter was written by the warden on the island between 1951 and 1954 and included a review of all of the relevant literature published up to that time; one of the most important sources was the diaries of the Reverend Heaven who lived on the island for many years up to the 1870s and wrote many notes about the birds he saw.

Manx Shearwater—was suspected of breeding for many years during the 19th century and when it was finally confirmed doing so it was discovered to breed 'very numerously'.

Gannet—the colony was of ancient origin but, partly owing to severe persecution and, perhaps, the establishment of the colony on Grassholm, declined rapidly during the second half of the 19th century. About 70 pairs nested in 1890 but for a number of years all of the chicks were killed. There were about 30 pairs in 1893 and 1894 but by 1900 just three or four pairs were left. They became extinct on the island a few years later.

Cormorant—a large colony bred on the Gannet Rock. Occasionally pairs nested elsewhere, for example on the southwest point in 1875.

Shag—many nested around the island.

White-tailed Eagle—the islanders asserted that it had once bred.

Buzzard—nested in fluctuating numbers and, in 1900, one pair probably bred.

Osprey—an eyrie was recorded occupied until 1838.

Kestrel—was recorded as a fairly common species in 1900; however, no more than a pair or two have been recorded since.

Peregrine—the famous 'white-chested race' of Lundy Peregrines had been recorded for many centuries. In 1900 one pair definitely bred and another may have bred at the opposite end of the island near the Shutter Rock.

Red Grouse—there had been a number of unsuccessful introductions.

Grey Partridge—there had been a number of unsuccessful introductions.

Quail—bred in fluctuating numbers. In 1870 Heaven recorded 13 or 14 nests.

Corncrake—bred regularly.

Oystercatcher—bred.

Lapwing—bred occasionally. The only dated record was of a nest found in 1888.

Lesser Black-backed Gull—bred numerously in colonies around the island.

Herring Gull—second in number to the Kittiwake and bred in colonies all around the island.

Great Black-backed Gull—evidently declining although six or seven pairs still bred in 1900.

Kittiwake—was the most numerous of the gulls on Lundy and bred chiefly amongst the Guillemots and Razorbills in the north of the island. The trade in Kittiwake wings for the adornment of ladies' hats caused the destruction of many Kittiwakes on Lundy—9,000 were said to have been killed in two weeks during the 1880s.

Guillemot—was said to breed in enormous numbers; the chief breeding colony was located on the northern half of the western shore.

Razorbill—was said to breed in enormous numbers; the chief breeding colony was among the Guillemots on the western shore.

Great Auk—the tradition of a bird picked up dead on the island and of a very large egg found in 1838 or 1839 has been dismissed by a number of later writers. The supporting accounts, however, are tantalising in their detail and offer the possibility, at least, that the Great Auk once bred on Lundy many miles further south than its normal range.

Puffin—huge numbers were said to breed mainly in a colony at the north end of the island.

Rock Dove—Lundy was the 'chief Devonshire resort' of this species in 1837 but there were no further records.

Cuckoo—apparently parasitised the Meadow Pipits on the island.

Nightjar—there is conflicting evidence concerning this species' status on the island. It was recorded as 'common' in 1876; however, Heaven recorded it only once.

Skylark—one of the commonest breeding passerines.

Sand Martin—was recorded breeding in the 1840s.

Swallow—may have bred more commonly in the 19th century than later.

Meadow Pipit—one of the commonest breeding passerines.

Rock Pipit—bred commonly.

Yellow Wagtail—bred.

Wren—bred commonly.

Dunnock—bred.

Robin—bred commonly in the 19th century but may have declined since.

Stonechat—perhaps up to 28 pairs bred.

Wheatear—one of the commonest breeding passerines.

Blackbird—perhaps no more than 15 pairs bred.

Song Thrush—perhaps no more than nine pairs bred.

Whitethroat—bred.

Chough—formerly bred commonly on Lundy but became extinct there in about 1890.

Carrion Crow—a few pairs bred. The presence of hybrid crows on the island in 1900 indicates that the **Hooded Crows** that arrived in the 1890s probably bred.

Raven—one or two pairs bred.

Starling—probably colonised the island around the turn of the 19th century and perhaps a couple of pairs bred there in 1900.

House Sparrow—bred in fluctuating numbers but, in 1900, a flourishing colony existed in the buildings around the Manor Farm.

Chaffinch—recorded as one of the commonest breeding species on the island by D'Urban and Mathew but omitted by Blathwayt.

Goldfinch—may have occasionally bred.

Linnet—one of the commonest breeding passerines.

Yellowhammer—bred.

The Pembrokeshire Islands

In 1894, the Rev. Murray A. Mathew published *The Birds of Pembrokeshire and its Islands* after spending the years 1880–88 recuperating from an illness in the north of the county. His accounts of the birds of the Pembrokeshire islands owe much to the assistance of correspondents, especially the Proberts of St Davids.

Manx Shearwater—Ramsey: possibly bred as birds had been seen flying over Ramsey Sound. Skomer: myriads bred and was 'probably the largest colony in Britain'. Skokholm: numerous. Caldy: earlier in the century bred and possibly may still have done so during the 1880s. St Margarets: four or five were once flushed from crevices in the cliff.

Storm Petrel—Skomer: bred in an old wall above the cliff. Probably bred on other islands.

Gannet—Grassholm: the main colony at the top of the cliff and two or three other small colonies in the northwest of the island totalled about 250 breeding pairs.

Cormorant—Ramsey: nested on Ynys-y-bery in similar numbers to the Shags. Skomer: bred. Probably bred on other islands.

Shag—Ramsey: bred on the cliffs of Allt-felyn-fawr and Allt-felyn-fach. Skomer: bred. Caldy: a few bred on the south side. St Margarets: a few pairs bred.

Buzzard—Ramsey: a pair bred. Skomer: formerly bred.

Kestrel—Ramsey: may have bred.

Peregrine—Ramsey: a pair bred on the cliffs of Allt-felyn-fawr and Allt-felyn-fach. Skomer: a pair bred.

Grey Partridge—Skomer: stocked and thrived well.

Oystercatcher—Ramsey: a few bred. Skomer: a few bred.

Lapwing—Skomer: a few bred.

Whimbrel—Skomer: a bird flushed performed a distraction display.

Curlew—Skomer: a few bred.

Lesser Black-backed Gull—Ramsey: bred on the slopes at the top of the cliff. Grassholm: not numerous. Skomer: a colony on the cliff at Wick Haven.

Herring Gull—Ramsey: bred on the cliffs of Allt-felyn-fawr and Allt-felyn-fach. Grassholm: not numerous. Skomer: bred. Caldy: bred on the south side. St Margarets: 40–50 pairs bred.

Great Black-backed Gull—Ramsey: an occasional pair nested on the top of Ynys-y-bery and eggs were taken from a nest on one of the Bishop's Rocks. Grassholm: not numerous. St Margarets: an occasional pair.

Kittiwake—Ramsey: bred numerously on the cliffs of Allt-felyn-fawr and Allt-felyn-fach. Grassholm: largest colony was between the top of the cliff and the island summit with other large colonies located around the island. Skomer: bred in 'countless numbers' on the cliff at Wick Haven.

Roseate Tern—Skokholm: a pair or two may have bred on Skokholm Stack earlier in the century.

Common Tern—Skokholm: a small colony bred on Skokholm Stack.

Guillemot—Ramsey: bred in 'extraordinary' numbers on the cliffs above the bay at Dillyn and the cliffs of Allt-felyn-fawr and Allt-felyn-fach. Grassholm: very great numbers bred close to the Gannet colony. Skomer: bred in immense numbers on the cliffs at Wick Haven. Skokholm: bred. Caldy: bred on the south side. St Margarets: numerous.

Razorbill—Ramsey: bred numerously on the cliffs above the bay at Dillyn and the cliffs of Allt-felyn-fawr and Allt-felyn-fach. Grassholm: large numbers bred near to the Gannet colony. Skomer: bred on the cliffs at Wick Haven. Skokholm: bred. Caldy: bred on south side. St Margarets: numerous.

Puffin—Ramsey: colony on the north side of the island. Grassholm: countless numbers bred on the east side.

Skomer: countless numbers all over the island. Skokholm: bred. Caldy: bred on the south side. St Margarets: a few bred on the cliff summit.

Pigeons—Ramsey: a mixture of Stock, Feral and, possibly, Rock Doves bred in the caves at the north end.

Barn Owl—Skomer: numerous.

Short-eared Owl—Skomer: had bred occasionally.

Meadow Pipit—Ramsey: bred. Skomer: bred.

Rock Pipit—Ramsey: bred. Skomer: bred.

Stonechat—Ramsey: bred.

Wheatear—Skomer: bred.

Blackbird—Ramsey: birds seen.

Chough—Ramsey: bred in the caves of the north end of the island. Skomer: probably bred. Caldy: a pair bred in 1888 or 1889 and may have done for a few years subsequently.

Jackdaw—Ramsey: bred in countless numbers on the cliffs of Allt-felyn-fawr and Allt-felyn-fach. Skomer: bred.

Carrion Crow—Skomer: bred.

Raven—Ramsey: bred on the cliffs of Allt-felyn-fawr and Allt-felyn-fach. Skomer: birds present and probably bred.

Bardsey, Caernarvonshire

The following list was published in *The Zoologist* in 1902 and was written by O. V. Aplin (the author of *The Birds of Oxfordshire*, 1889) following his visit to the island in May 1901. The visit was short and, the author felt, some species may have been overlooked.

Manx Shearwater—considerable colony.

Cormorant—seen at sea.

Shag—a few may have bred on the eastern side of the island.

Peregrine—a single pair was believed to have bred.

Corncrake—common. Aplin heard three calling at the same time.

Oystercatcher—fairly common.

Lapwing—a few seen.

Curlew—one or two seen.

Common Sandpiper—one seen that may have been breeding.

Herring Gull—bred in considerable numbers.

Great Black-backed Gull—one pair was located breeding.

Guillemot—20 seen and probably bred.

Razorbill—two or three seen and was said to breed.

Cuckoo—several seen and heard.

Swallow—a good many seen.

Meadow Pipit—some bred.

Rock Pipit—fairly common.

Dunnock—pretty common.

Wheatear—fairly common.

Blackbird—very common.

Sedge Warbler—one or two heard.

Whitethroat—fairly numerous.

Willow Warbler—a few located.

Spotted Flycatcher—several evidently bred.

Chough—one or two pairs probably bred.

Jackdaw—common.

Carrion Crow—one pair seen.

Starling—abundant.

House Sparrow—a fair number.

Chaffinch—fairly common.

Goldfinch—at least one pair, probably more.

Linnet—several seen.

Corn Bunting—common.

The Farne Islands, Northumberland

On the 26th May, 1896, the Rev. P. Morres, at the invitation of a relative, visited the Farne Islands to study the breeding birds there. Four wardens were employed, at that time, to protect the islands from collectors and sportsmen. They were employed by the Northumbrian County Society and were resident on the islands, two on the inner islands and two on the outer. This list was published by Morres in 1896; other records are those of Bolam (1912).

Cormorant—bred in large numbers only on the Megstone, although one or two were seen on the Crumstone that may have been breeding.

Shag—bred in the 1870s with the Cormorants on the Megstone and again in 1902. Was already rare on The Pinnacles by 1836.

Eider—bred throughout the islands in numbers. At least 100 pairs bred on Knox's Reef and had increased since the practice of taking Lesser Black-backed Gull's eggs to control the gull's numbers had begun.

Oystercatcher—a few pairs bred on most of the islands.

Ringed Plover—a few pairs bred on most of the islands.

Lesser Black-backed Gull—the most ubiquitous bird of the islands, found breeding on all except the Islestone Shad. The largest colony was on Knox's Reef.

Herring Gull—bred on most of the islands but in far fewer numbers than the Lesser Black-backed Gull.

Kittiwake—bred only on the sides of The Pinnacles.

Sandwich Tern—bred on the Islestone Shad in countless numbers.

Roseate Tern—bred during the first half of the 19th century in large numbers on the Brownsman and one of the Wawmses. Declined later and from the 1870s only up to three pairs bred annually on Knox's Reef.

Common Tern—bred on Knox's Reef.

Arctic Tern—bred on Knox's Reef.

Guillemot—bred in large numbers on The Pinnacles, although it occasionally bred on the opposite ledges of the main island when numbers were high.

Razorbill—fewer than ten pairs bred (in some years they may not have bred at all) amongst the Guillemots.

Puffin—'scores' bred on Knox's Reef.

Isle of May

When scientific interest in migration developed in the late 19th century the Isle of May, at the entrance to the Firth of Forth, quickly gained a reputation as an important point from which to observe the passage of birds; its interest was generated from the work of Gaetke on Heligoland. Many early accounts recorded the migration passage over the island and in 1888 Harvie-Brown published an account entitled *The Isle of May: Its Faunal Position and Bird Life* in the *Proceedings of the Royal Physical Society of Edinburgh* that included a list of the birds that bred there up to 1884.

Cormorant—a few pairs bred.

Shag—bred commonly.

Eider—bred annually but in decreasing numbers because of the persecution they endured from tourists and egg collectors.

Kittiwake—common at the southwest end of the island and on the cave sides.

Roseate Tern—was said to have bred in the past (at least prior to 1870).

Guillemot—was described as 'fairly abundant' and nested on every available ledge.

Razorbill—a few bred annually although were said to breed 'in hundreds' in some years.

Black Guillemot—bred commonly in the past and ceased doing so by 1880.

Puffin—none bred in 1880 but 20 pairs were counted breeding in 1884.

Meadow Pipit—bred regularly and not uncommonly.

Rock Pipit—bred commonly and was probably the most abundant species on the island at all seasons.

Pied Wagtail—four or five pairs bred annually.

Dunnock—the first record of breeding was in 1884 when two broods were reared.

Wheatear—about 50 pairs bred annually.

Blackbird—bred regularly, but in small numbers, throughout the island and some were apparently resident throughout the year. Was scarce after the severe winter of 1878/79.

Song Thrush—was an occasional breeder up to 1882; thereafter three or four pairs bred each year.

Starling—had recently commenced breeding on the island and was increasing annually.

Linnet—a few pairs bred annually and had apparently increased in 1884.

Island of Bute

The first complete list of the birds of the Island of Bute was published by John Robertson in *The Annals of Scottish Natural History* in July 1903. He had visited the island several times during the previous seven years and the following list is the product of his own observations and his research into the birds of the island of the previous 30 years. He recorded 138 species of birds of which 'about 90' had nested.

Little Grebe—bred on most of the lochs on the island.

Grey Heron—there were heronries near Mount Stuart and in a glen in the north of the island.

Shelduck—was regarded as quite common in the west of the island.

Teal—not numerous.

Mallard—common.

Red-breasted Merganser—common.

Sparrowhawk—a few bred.

Kestrel—fairly common.

Merlin—bred sometime during the 1870s.

Red Grouse—common.

Black Grouse—common.

Grey Partridge—common.

Pheasant—common.

Corncrake—common.

Moorhen—common.

Coot—common.

Oystercatcher—common.

Ringed Plover—abundant.

Golden Plover—a few bred in N Bute.

Lapwing—common.

Dunlin—a few bred.

Snipe—a few nested.

Woodcock—some were believed to breed annually.

Curlew—common in some parts of the island.

Redshank—many bred, especially on the W coast.

Common Sandpiper—common.

Common Gull—fairly common. A few pairs bred on the island at Inchmarnock.

Common Tern—many nested in the Kyles of Bute.

Stock Dove—not common.

Woodpigeon—common.

Cuckoo—common.

Nightjar—frequent.
Swift—common about Rothesay.
Skylark—common.
Sand Martin—one small colony.
Swallow—common.
House Martin—locally common.
Tree Pipit—uncommon.
Meadow Pipit—common.
Rock Pipit—common.
Grey Wagtail—rare; nests were found near Mount Stuart.
Pied Wagtail—not uncommon.
Dipper—a few pairs may have bred.
Wren—common.
Dunnock—common.
Robin—abundant.
Redstart—occasional.
Whinchat—scarce.
Stonechat—a few pairs bred.
Wheatear—fairly common.
Ring Ouzel—occasional.
Blackbird—abundant.
Song Thrush—common.
Mistle Thrush—common.
Sedge Warbler—fairly common.
Whitethroat—common.
Garden Warbler—a few pairs bred.
Wood Warbler—a few bred about Mount Stuart.
Chiffchaff—a few pairs.
Willow Warbler—abundant.
Goldcrest—common.
Spotted Flycatcher—common.
Long-tailed Tit—a fair number were found.
Coal Tit—common.
Blue Tit—common.
Great Tit—common.
Treecreeper—a pair or two were located in suitable localities.
Magpie—persecuted to extinction; formerly very common.
Jackdaw—common.
Rook—common.
Carrion Crow—numerous.
Hooded Crow—not numerous.
Starling—abundant.
House Sparrow—abundant.
Chaffinch—very common.
Greenfinch—common.
Goldfinch—rare but had declined.
Linnet—common.
Twite—a few nested.
Redpoll—very common.
Bullfinch—occasional.
Yellowhammer—common.
Reed Bunting—not numerous.
Corn Bunting—pretty common near the sea.

Tiree, Inner Hebrides

Following 12 years of residence on the island, Peter Anderson published his *On Birds Observed in the Island of Tiree* in *The Annals of Scottish Natural History* in July 1898. The absence of trees and bushes made the island unsuitable for many species both on passage and during the breeding season.
Storm Petrel—may have bred at Kennavara Head.
Shag—very common; bred in caves at Kennavara Head.
Shelduck—bred.

Teal—numerous.
Mallard—numerous.
Shoveler—a few pairs bred.
Pochard—a few bred.
Tufted Duck—a few pairs began breeding during the 1890s.
Eider—abundant.
Common Scoter—a pair bred in 1897.
Red-breasted Merganser—abundant.
Kestrel—a pair bred in 1896 on Kennavara Head.
Merlin—a pair bred in 1897.
Peregrine—one pair on Kennavara Head.
Partridge species—'English and Hungarian Partridges have been introduced'.
Water Rail—a few remained in summer.
Corncrake—abundant.
Moorhen—bred.
Coot—abundant.
Oystercatcher—bred.
Ringed Plover—abundant.
Lapwing—numerous.
Dunlin—bred all over the island.
Snipe—numerous.
Greenshank—one breeding record.
Common Sandpiper—regular in small numbers.
Arctic Skua—bred irregularly.
Black-headed Gull—a few pairs bred.
Common Gull—numerous.
Lesser Black-backed Gull—common.
Herring Gull—common.
Kittiwake—numerous.
Common Tern—numerous.
Arctic Tern—abundant.
Little Tern—several colonies.
Guillemot—not as numerous as the Razorbill but formerly was more so.
Razorbill—bred on Kennavara Head.
Black Guillemot—a few pairs bred.
Rock Dove—bred.
Cuckoo—occurred sparingly.
Swift—occasional.
Skylark—abundant.
Sand Martin—bred up to 1886.
Meadow Pipit—abundant; nested in the old turf walls.
Rock Pipit—numerous.
Wheatear—abundant. Bred mostly in old walls.
Hooded Crow—common. Bred on the cliffs.
Raven—one pair bred every year on the cliffs of Kennavara Head.
Starling—'superabundant'
House Sparrow—became common over recent years.
Tree Sparrow—numerous and was becoming more so; bred in the old churches of Kirkapol.
Twite—abundant.
Corn Bunting—common.

Raasay, Inverness-shire

Charles Collier published his *The Birds of the Island of Raasay* in *The Ibis* in 1904 following seven years of residence on the island, which lies off the E coast of Skye in the Sound between the latter island and the mainland. He recorded 140 species of birds of which 79 were confirmed breeding.
Little Grebe—two pairs bred regularly.
Cormorant—was not as numerous as the Shag.

Shag—a considerable colony existed.

Grey Heron—one small heronry was located.

Teal—very few bred.

Mallard—nearly every loch held a pair.

Eider—a few bred and may have been increasing.

Red-breasted Merganser—nested in 'numbers'.

Hen Harrier—formerly common.

Sparrowhawk—common.

Buzzard—a pair or two bred.

Kestrel—plentiful.

Merlin—one or two pairs bred.

Peregrine—one pair nested.

Red Grouse—fairly numerous.

Black Grouse—was decreasing.

Grey Partridge—occasionally introduced but did not thrive.

Pheasant—introduced, 'does well'.

Corncrake—bred in considerable numbers.

Moorhen—two pairs bred.

Oystercatcher—generally distributed on the shore.

Ringed Plover—nested wherever there was shingle.

Golden Plover—a few nested.

Lapwing—about 12–15 pairs bred.

Dunlin—bred sparingly.

Snipe—bred 'in all places suitable to it'.

Woodcock—20–25 nests were found per year.

Curlew—bred on the lower ground.

Redshank—one pair.

Common Sandpiper—extremely abundant.

Common Gull—scattered nests, small numbers bred.

Lesser Black-backed Gull—numbers bred.

Herring Gull—hundreds bred on the west coast.

Great Black-backed Gull—one nesting place.

Kittiwake—about six nests were found annually on a cliff in the east of the island.

Common Tern—one colony of six to eight pairs existed and a few scattered pairs bred elsewhere.

Arctic Tern—very common; several small colonies were known.

Black Guillemot—common.

Rock Dove—'quantities' inhabited the caves.

Woodpigeon—common.

Cuckoo—very plentiful.

Tawny Owl—rare.

Long-eared Owl—one pair bred.

Short-eared Owl—formerly bred.

Nightjar—sparse.

Skylark—a few pairs, not numerous.

Swallow—five or six pairs.

Tree Pipit—not common.

Meadow Pipit—distributed over the whole island.

Rock Pipit—plentiful.

Yellow Wagtail—rare.

Grey Wagtail—nearly every stream had a pair of birds.

Pied Wagtail—observed in suitable breeding habitat.

Wren—scattered over the whole island.

Dunnock—scattered pairs.

Robin—scattered, not very numerous.

Redstart—a few.

Whinchat—very scarce.

Stonechat—quite common.

Wheatear—in numbers.

Ring Ouzel—quite common.

Blackbird—common on the south end of the island.

Song Thrush—large numbers bred.

Mistle Thrush—not common. A few pairs bred.

Sedge Warbler—one breeding record in 1899.

Willow Warbler—a great many bred.

Goldcrest—fairly plentiful.

Spotted Flycatcher—regular.

Long-tailed Tit—common.

Coal Tit—commonest tit. Large numbers nested.

Blue Tit—many bred.

Great Tit—a few pairs.

Treecreeper—very numerous in one wood.

Raven—three pairs nested.

Hooded Crow—very common.

Rook—a large rookery was destroyed by 1902.

Jackdaw—a few.

Starling—not very plentiful.

House Sparrow—very numerous.

Tree Sparrow—nested regularly.

Chaffinch—very common.

Greenfinch—rare.

Goldfinch—rare.

Linnet—about six pairs nested in one spot.

Twite—sparse.

Redpoll—common.

Bullfinch—a few scattered pairs.

Crossbill—rare.

Yellowhammer—not plentiful.

Reed Bunting—uncommon.

Corn Bunting—extremely abundant.

Priest Island, Ross-shire

Harvie-Brown and five others rowed over to the island from Gruinard Bay on 4th July, 1884. Harvie-Brown spent two hours on the island and then rowed around it. He published a record of the birds he observed in the *Transactions of the Norfolk and Norwich Naturalists' Society* in 1887. His list is reproduced broadly as he wrote it.

Cormorant—a colony of about 130 pairs was noted.

Shag—'say, three to four hundred pairs' bred.

Greylag Goose—one caught at sea and another was seen on Glaskeir Bheag [Glaskeir Bheag lies to the north of, and close to, Priest Island].

Mallard—a drake was seen in moult on one of the smaller lakes.

Peregrine Falcon—one pair 'evidently at home'.

Oystercatcher—common.

Common Sandpiper—one observed.

Lesser Black-backed Gull—common.

Herring Gull—common.

Great Black-backed Gull—common.

Razorbill—a few were seen in one crevice on the east cliff.

Black Guillemot—common.

Rock Dove—one seen; more abundant in NW Ross-shire.

Meadow Pipit—observed in suitable breeding habitat.

Rock Pipit—common.

Wheatear—a few.

Song Thrush—rare; one or two seen.

Starling—a few.

St Kilda, Western Isles

Several visits were made by naturalists to the islands of St Kilda at the end of the 19th century. Some records of the breeding birds have been gleaned from the accounts of Harvie-Brown and Buckley (1888), Elliott (1895), Heathcote (1900) and Harris and Murray (1978). The main source, however, for this list is that of Wiglesworth (1903) who spent three weeks on the islands in the summer of 1902 and delivered a lecture to the Liverpool Biological Society about his expedition.

Fulmar—until 1878 the only British breeding site. In 1899 the population was estimated at 20,000 pairs in colonies on Hirta, Dun, Boreray, many of the stacks and, especially, Soay.

Manx Shearwater—most abundant on Soay and bred on all of the islands. Decreasing, possibly because of competition for nesting holes from the increasing Puffin.

Storm Petrel—plentiful on Soay and may have bred in very small numbers on other islands.

Leach's Petrel—most abundant on Boreray, plentiful on Soay and fairly frequent on Dun. It bred sparingly on Hirta and there was a small colony on Levenish. Numbers on Dun and Hirta were much reduced owing to the number of eggs taken by the local people for sale to tourists and collectors.

Gannet—bred in one locality in three sites. The densest concentration was on Stac Lee although the other groups on Stac an Armin and the adjacent Boreray coast were only slightly less impressive. Wiglesworth estimated that there were 3,500–4,000 nests on Stac Lee, 3,000 on Stac an Armin and about 8,000 on the cliffs of Boreray. If non-breeding birds were included in the total, he guessed that *ca* 30,000 individuals were present.

Cormorant—probably bred up to the first half of the 19th century.

Shag—fairly plentiful. Bred on Hirta and Soay.

Eider—holding its own with difficulty as the adults and eggs were taken by the islanders. Bred on Hirta and Dun in small numbers and possibly on the other islands.

Red-breasted Merganser—said by Seebohm to have bred in the 19th century.

White-tailed Eagle—apparently bred in the 17th, 18th and, possibly, the early 19th centuries.

Kestrel—probably bred in the early 19th century.

Peregrine—one or two pairs on Dun, one on each of Soay and Hirta.

Corncrake—probably bred in the first half of the 19th century.

Oystercatcher—not numerous; several pairs bred around the coast.

Dunlin—breeding suspected on several occasions during the 19th century.

Snipe—the first record of breeding was of eggs taken in 1900 on Hirta. Two nests were found there in 1902.

Curlew—two pairs were thought to have bred in 1884.

Common Gull—possibly bred in the first half of the 19th century.

Herring Gull—fairly plentiful on all the islands.

Great Black-backed Gull—fairly plentiful; many eggs and young were taken by the native islanders.

Kittiwake—very plentiful in scattered colonies on all the islands.

Guillemot—exceedingly abundant on all of the islands and stacks; from the numbers of eggs taken, and nests that were unreachable, an estimate of 12,000 nests was made.

Razorbill—very numerous, although less so than the Guillemot. The largest colony on Hirta was near Miana Stac. It bred plentifully on Soay, more so on Dun and the largest colony in the islands was on Stac an Armin.

Great Auk—bred in the 17th century. The last British example was caught on Stac an Armin in July 1840.

Black Guillemot—Wiglesworth saw only one colony, that in rocks in the Dun passage.

Puffin—huge numbers bred on all islands. The largest colonies were on Boreray and Soay.

Rock Dove—almost certainly bred in 1884 but very quickly became extinct. None was recorded until 1930.

Rock Pipit—bred plentifully around the coasts of all of the islands.

Wren—bred commonly on all of the islands but was mercilessly collected, especially on Hirta, and nearly became extinct.

Wheatear—fairly plentiful throughout the islands.

Song Thrush—probably bred 1840 and 1847.

Hooded Crow—very abundant.

Raven—one pair on each of Hirta, Dun and Soay and two pairs on Boreray.

Starling—plentiful and bred in the stone walls and cleits.

Tree Sparrow—fairly plentiful, breeding in the stone walls and cleits (small, stone storage houses) of the village on Hirta.

Twite—fairly plentiful. Wiglesworth saw courting birds on Hirta but breeding was not recorded until 1931.

Corn Bunting—probably bred 1840, 1879 and 1896.

North Rona, Western Isles

North Rona is one of the most remote islands off NW Britain. The island was inhabited more or less continuously until 1844 and at its height was home to 30 people. These people carried out limited agriculture and managed sheep and they supplemented their income by supplying birds and feathers to Lewis. This list is based on the records of visits made to the island by J. Swinburne (1885) in 1883, J. A. Harvie-Brown (1888a) in 1885 and 1887, R. M. Barrington in 1886 (Harvie-Brown 1888a) and H. L. Popham in 1894 (in Fisher 1952).

Fulmar—first recorded in 1886 and Harvie-Brown saw one on a cliff shelf in 1887. The first egg was found in 1894.

Storm Petrel—in 1885 two females were dug out from cavities in the walls of the abandoned village. Another large colony was found in 1886.

Leach's Petrel—23 nests were dug out from the village ruins in 1883, the second colony discovered in Britain. In 1885, 24 nests were dug out and in 1887 eggs were taken from the same colony.

Shag—described as 'innumerable' in 1887 and nesting around much of the coast in loose rocks of caves.

Eider—described as 'very plentiful' and common.

Peregrine—pairs present in 1883 and 1887.

Oystercatcher—bred very commonly.

Ringed Plover—a pair was seen in the middle of June 1885 on a limited, but suitable patch of sand and gravel.

Dunlin—seen in 1887.

Whimbrel—a pair exhibiting distraction behaviour was seen in June 1885 but no attempt was made to find a nest or young. A male was shot in 1886.

Curlew—five or six pairs were present in 1883 and a single pair in 1886.

Lesser Black-backed Gull—seen on several occasions.

Herring Gull—fluctuating numbers.

Great Black-backed Gull—the colony on the SW promontory was described as large in 1883.

Kittiwake—many bred in several areas around the island.

Arctic Tern—found breeding on the northern peninsula

449

in 1885 but had moved to another site on the SW promontory by 1887. About 30 pairs bred in 1886.

Guillemot—large numbers bred in several colonies.

Razorbill—large numbers bred around the island.

Black Guillemot—bred during the period, sometimes in the ruins of the village.

Puffin—large numbers bred throughout the island in 1883 and during Harvie-Brown's visits they were abundant.

Meadow Pipit—small numbers bred.

Rock Pipit—described as breeding in 'a few' or 'scarce' numbers around the coast.

Wheatear—generally no more than five pairs bred under rocks in the cairns built by the old shepherds.

Sula Sgeir, Western Isles

Sula Sgeir is a small, desolate island off the NW coast of Scotland and is just west of North Rona. The only regular human interaction with Sula Sgeir up to the 19th century had been the centuries-old tradition of the harvesting of the eggs and young Gannets carried out by the men of Ness on Lewis. J. A. Harvie-Brown (1888a) and others visited the island in 1887 following an earlier, and very short, landing by J. Swinburne (1885) in 1883.

Fulmar—seen in 1887.

Gannet—7,000 pairs were estimated to have been breeding in 1883.

Shag—small numbers bred.

Eider—a nest with four fresh eggs was found in 1883.

Kittiwake—bred in large numbers.

Guillemot—bred plentifully.

Razorbill—bred plentifully.

Puffin—the colonies were considered similar in size to those on North Rona.

Flannan Islands, Western Isles

The Flannan Islands are situated in the Atlantic between Lewis in the Outer Hebrides and the St Kilda group. Other than the latter group the Flannans are amongst the most isolated islands of Britain and take the form of two groups. The eastern group consists of four islands and includes Eilean Mor (upon which was built a lighthouse in 1899) and Eilean Tigh. The western group, *ca* 3km further out, consists of three islands and, in addition, several smaller islets and skerries surrounded the groups. Clarke contributed an account of the birds of the islands to the *Annals of Scottish Natural History* of 1905 (Clarke 1905) that was based on a visit Harvie-Brown had made to the islands in 1882 (he landed briefly on Eilean Tigh and studied the cliffs of many of the other islands from his boat), from the returns made by the lighthouse keepers from 1899 and a visit Clarke made to the islands during the autumn of 1904 in the company of T. G. Laidlaw. Clarke's main interest in the birds of the islands concerned the passage of migrants during spring and autumn; nevertheless, the breeding birds were also recorded.

Fulmar—a few pairs had bred on some of the outer isles of the group for many years.

Storm Petrel—bred numerously throughout the islands, especially on Eilean Mor.

Leach's Petrel—was considered to have been the chief breeding place of this species at the time; a large colony bred on Eilean Mor.

Cormorant—was not noted breeding on Eilean Mor, but was believed to breed on the outer isles.

Shag—bred 'in considerable numbers' on all of the islands of the group.

Eider—was said to nest 'commonly on some of the islands'.

Peregrine—a pair bred regularly on one of the outer isles.

Oystercatcher—was considered a common summer visitor. Several pairs bred on Eilean Mor.

Whimbrel—bred regularly on Eilean Mor until they were disturbed by the building operations of the lighthouse from 1899.

Lesser Black-backed Gull—a colony of this species was noted on Eilean Tigh in 1881.

Herring Gull—bred numerously on all of the islands but was less frequent on Eilean Mor, where about six pairs bred.

Great Black-backed Gull—two pairs bred on Eilean Mor and a few more on the other islands.

Kittiwake—this was the commonest breeding gull in the islands and bred numerously.

Guillemot—was said that 'vast numbers breed'.

Razorbill—'thousands' were said to breed.

Black Guillemot—pairs were seen during the breeding season under the cliffs of Eilean Mor and were suspected of breeding.

Puffin—this was regarded as the commonest breeding species on Eilean Mor. 'Thousands' were said to breed on the top of the island and were suspected of nesting on the other islands.

Rock Pipit—was regarded as 'extremely abundant'.

Wheatear—four pairs were counted breeding on Eilean Mor.

Hooded Crow—a pair was seen regularly but the nest was not found.

Raven—a single pair inhabited the islands and bred on one of the outer isles.

Twite—a 'few' were noted in the islands during the summer and two pairs were recorded breeding on Eilean Mor.

Fair Isle, Shetland

By the early years of the 20th century the human inhabitants of Fair Isle had declined to a little over 100, following a shift in emphasis in the agriculture of the island from arable to sheep farming, when the mainland no longer needed to import grain from the island. Fair Isle was said by Clarke to have been among the least visited inhabited islands in Britain. Little was known of its flora and fauna before Clarke and his companion, N. B. Kinnear, spent five weeks on the island in 1905. Many examples of the birds, mammals and insects of the island were collected and, in due course, reported upon. The account of the birds was published in the *Annals of Scottish Natural History* in 1906 (Clarke 1906) and was collated from information collected by Clarke and Kinnear directly during their visit, from the observations of Tulloch, one of the lighthouse keepers, and of Wilson and Stout, two Fair Isle natives. Clarke and Kinnear spent many more weeks on the island in subsequent years and Clarke continued to report his findings in the 'Annals' until 1910 (Clarke 1907-10).

Fulmar—the island was colonised, probably, in 1903 after birds were seen prospecting in 1902.

Manx Shearwater—was believed to breed but nests were not found.

Storm Petrel—a number nested at the north end of the

island.

Cormorant—was considered very common and great numbers bred.

Shag—nested in greater numbers than the Cormorant.

Eider—was considered to breed abundantly on the island.

White-tailed Eagle—a pair had bred on Sheep Craig until some point between 1825 and 1840 although it is possible that two pairs had bred on the island before that time.

Quail—a nest was found in 1905.

Corncrake—was an annual summer visitor and breeding species.

Oystercatcher—nested in limited numbers.

Lapwing—the nests of a few pairs were found irregularly.

Arctic Skua—had formerly bred in some numbers but only a single pair remained during the first few years of the 20th century.

Great Skua—had bred in the past but had ceased to do so at some point after 1806.

Herring Gull—bred commonly on the island.

Great Black-backed Gull—bred in some numbers on the island.

Kittiwake—was the most abundant breeding gull species on the island; its main colony was on Sheep Craig.

Tern species—an unidentified species of tern had bred on the island during the early decades of the 19th century.

Guillemot—'great numbers' bred on the cliffs and stacks.

Razorbill—bred abundantly.

Black Guillemot—bred commonly.

Puffin—was the most abundant of the Fair Isle breeding birds.

Rock Dove—last bred on the island in about 1895. It was suggested that a decline in the amount of arable farming carried out during the agricultural depression and a bad winter in 1854/5 had contributed to the species' extinction on the island.

Skylark—was a resident species and bred commonly, but was confined to what little cultivated land remained.

Meadow Pipit—was a common breeding summer visitor.

Rock Pipit—was an abundant resident in all parts of the island.

White Wagtail—was first recorded breeding in 1909.

Wren—was regarded as a fairly common breeding species. Its nests were found on the cliffs, in stone walls and on the sides of the island's burns.

Song Thrush—the first breeding record was of recently fledged young in 1905.

Hooded Crow—five or six pairs bred on the cliffs.

Raven—in 1896 six pairs bred but the islanders had destroyed a number of the individuals because of the Raven's depredations on the island's sheep. By 1905 only two pairs remained.

Starling—was regarded as an extremely abundant resident breeding in the cliffs and buildings.

House Sparrow—was an abundant resident mainly near the houses.

Twite—the population on the island was reckoned to be numbered in 'thousands' but the author did not make it clear whether this was a breeding population.

Corn Bunting—was regarded as 'far from common' and resident on the crofts.

Appendix B: Names of plants mentioned in the text

Vernacular names are listed alphabetically; both scientific and vernacular names follow current usage.

ALDER *Alnus glutinosa*
ASH *Fraxinus excelsior*

BIRCH *Betulapendul/pubescens*
BRACKEN *Pteridium aquilinum*
BRAMBLE *Rubus fruticosus* agg.
BROOM *Cytisus scoparius*

CHERRY *Prunus padus/avium*
CLOVER *Trifolium* spp.

ELM *Ulmus glabra/procera*

FERN *Pteridophyta*
FIR *Abies* spp.
FURZE See Gorse

GORSE *Ulex europaeus/gallii*
GRASS *Gramineae*

HAWTHORN *Crataegus monogyna*
HEATHER Ericaceae/*Calluna vulgaris*
HOLLY *Ilex aquifolium*
HOP *Humulus lupulus*

KELP Laminariales

LARCH *Larix* spp.

MUSTARD *Brassica nigra*

NETTLE *Urtica dioica*

OAK *Quercus* spp.
OATS *Avena sativa*
OSIER *Salix viminalis*

PINE
    CORSICAN *Pinus nigra*
    SCOTS *P. sylvestris*
POTATO *Solanum tuberosum*

RAPE, OIL SEED *Brassica napus* ssp. *oleifera*
REED, COMMON *Phragmites australis*
RHODODENDRON *Rhododendron* spp.
ROSE, WILD *Rosa* spp.
RYE *Secale cereale*

SEDGE *Carex* spp.
SPRUCE *Picea* spp.
STRAWBERRY *Fragaria vesca*

SWEET-GRASS *Glyceria maxima*
SYCAMORE *Acer pseudoplatanus*

THISTLE *Carduus/Cirsium* spp.
TURNIP *Brassica rapa*

WHEAT *Triticum vulgare*
WHIN See Gorse
WILLOW *Salix* spp.

Appendix C: Names of birds mentioned in the text

Vernacular names are listed alphabetically and follow current usage. Scientific names were taken from British Ornithologists' Union (1992).

ARCTIC SKUA *Stercorarius parasiticus*
ARCTIC TERN *Sterna paradisaea*
AVOCET *Recurvirostra avosetta*

BAILLON'S CRAKE *Porzana pusilla*
BARNACLE GOOSE *Branta leucopsis*
BARN OWL *Tyto alba*
BAR-TAILED GODWIT *Limosa lapponica*
BEARDED TIT *Panurus biarmicus*
BEE-EATER *Merops apiaster*
BITTERN *Botaurus stellaris*
BLACKBIRD *Turdus merula*
BLACKCAP *Sylvia atricapilla*
BLACK GROUSE *Tetrao tetrix*
BLACK GUILLEMOT *Cepphus grylle*
BLACK-HEADED GULL *Larus ridibundus*
BLACK-NECKED GREBE *Podiceps nigricollis*
BLACK REDSTART *Phoenicurus ochruros*
BLACK-TAILED GODWIT *Limosa limosa*
BLACK TERN *Chlidonias niger*
BLACK-THROATED DIVER *Gavia arctica*
BLACK-WINGED STILT *Himantopus himantopus*
BLACK WOODPECKER *Dryocopus martius*
BLUE-HEADED WAGTAIL *Motacilla flava flava*
BLUETHROAT *Luscinia svecica*
BLUE TIT *Parus caeruleus*
BOBWHITE QUAIL *Colinus virginianus*
BRAMBLING *Fringilla montifringilla*
BULLFINCH *Pyrrhula pyrrhula*
BUZZARD *Buteo buteo*

CANADA GOOSE *Branta canadensis*
CAPERCAILLE *Tetrao urogallus*
CARRION CROW *Corvus corone corone*
CETTI'S WARBLER *Cettia cetti*
CHAFFINCH *Fringilla coelebs*
CHIFFCHAFF *Phylloscopus collybita*
CHINESE RING-NECKED PHEASANT *Phasianus colchicus mongolicus*
CHOUGH *Pyrrhocorax pyrrhocorax*
CHUKAR *Alectoris chukar*
CIRL BUNTING *Emberiza cirlus*
COAL TIT *Parus ater*
COLLARED DOVE *Streptopelia decaocto*
COMMON CROSSBILL *Loxia curvirostra*
COMMON GULL *Larus canus*
COMMON SANDPIPER *Actitis hypoleucos*
COMMON SCOTER *Melanitta nigra*
COMMON TERN *Sterna hirundo*
COOT *Fulica atra*

CORMORANT *Phalacrocorax carbo*
CORN BUNTING *Miliaria calandra*
CORNCRAKE *Crex crex*
CRANE *Grus grus*
CRESTED TIT *Parus cristatus*
CUCKOO *Cuculus canorus*
CURLEW *Numenius arquata*

DARTFORD WARBLER *Sylvia undata*
DIPPER *Cinclus cinclus*
DOTTEREL *Charadrius morinellus*
DUNLIN *Calidris alpina*
DUNNOCK *Prunella modularis*

EGYPTIAN GOOSE *Alopochen aegyptiacus*
EIDER *Somateria mollissima*

FIELDFARE *Turdus pilaris*
FIRECREST *Regulus ignicapillus*
FULMAR *Fulmarus glacialis*

GADWALL *Anas strepera*
GANNET *Morus bassanus*
GARDEN WARBLER *Sylvia borin*
GARGANEY *Anas querquedula*
GOLDCREST *Regulus regulus*
GOLDEN EAGLE *Aquila chrysaetos*
GOLDENEYE *Bucephula clangula*
GOLDEN ORIOLE *Oriolus oriolus*
GOLDEN PHEASANT *Chrysolophus pictus*
GOLDEN PLOVER *Pluvialis apricaria*
GOLDFINCH *Carduelis carduelis*
GOOSANDER *Mergus merganser*
GOSHAWK *Accipiter gentilis*
GRASSHOPPER WARBLER *Locustella naevia*
GREAT AUK *Pinguinis impennis*
GREAT BLACK-BACKED GULL *Larus marinus*
GREAT BUSTARD *Otis tarda*
GREAT CRESTED GREBE *Podiceps cristatus*
GREAT NORTHERN DIVER *Gavia immer*
GREAT REED WARBLER *Acrocephalus arundinaceus*
GREAT SKUA *Catharacta skua*
GREAT SPOTTED WOODPECKER *Dendrocopos major*
GREAT TIT *Parus major*
GREENFINCH *Carduelis chloris*
GREEN SANDPIPER *Tringa ochropus*
GREENSHANK *Tringa nebularia*
GREEN WOODPECKER *Picus viridis*
GREY HERON *Ardea cinerea*
GREYLAG GOOSE *Anser anser*
GREY PARTRIDGE *Perdix perdix*
GREY WAGTAIL *Motacilla cinerea*
GUILLEMOT *Uria aalge*
GULL-BILLED TERN *Gelochelidon nilotica*

HAWFINCH *Coccothraustes coccothraustes*
HEN HARRIER *Circus cyaneus*
HERRING GULL *Larus argentatus*
HOBBY *Falco subbuteo*
HONEY BUZZARD *Pernis apivorus*
HOODED CROW *Corvus c. cornix*
HOOPOE *Upupa epops*
HOUSE MARTIN *Delichon urbica*
HOUSE SPARROW *Passer domesticus*

HYBRID CROW *Corvus c. corone* ✕ *C. c. cornix*

JACKDAW *Corvus monedula*
JAY *Garrulus glandarius*

KENTISH PLOVER *Charadrius alexandrinus*
KESTREL *Falco tinnunculus*
KINGFISHER *Alcedo athis*
KITTIWAKE *Rissa tridactyla*

LADY AMHERST'S PHEASANT *Chrysolophus amherstiae*
LAPLAND BUNTING *Calcarius lapponicus*
LAPWING *Vanellus vanellus*
LEACH'S PETREL *Oceanodroma leucorhoa*
LESSER BLACK-BACKED GULL *Larus fuscus*
LESSER SPOTTED WOODPECKER *Dendrocopos minor*
LESSER WHITETHROAT *Sylvia curruca*
LINNET *Carduelis cannabina*
LITTLE BITTERN *Ixobrychus minutus*
LITTLE CRAKE *Porzana parva*
LITTLE GREBE *Tachybaptus ruficollis*
LITTLE GULL *Larus minutus*
LITTLE OWL *Athene noctua*
LITTLE RINGED PLOVER *Charadrius dubius*
LITTLE TERN *Sterna albifrons*
LONG-EARED OWL *Asio otus*
LONG-TAILED DUCK *Clangula hyemalis*
LONG-TAILED TIT *Aegithalos caudatus*

MAGPIE *Pica pica*
MALLARD *Anas platyrhynchos*
MANDARIN DUCK *Aix galericulata*
MANX SHEARWATER *Puffinus puffinus*
MARSH HARRIER *Circus aeruginosus*
MARSH TIT *Parus palustris*
MARSH WARBLER *Acrocephalis palustris*
MEADOW PIPIT *Anthus pratensis*
MEDITERRANEAN GULL *Larus melanocephalus*
MERLIN *Falco columbarius*
MISTLE THRUSH *Turdus viscivorus*
MONTAGU'S HARRIER *Circus pygargus*
MOUSTACHED WARBLER *Acrocephalus melanopogon*
MOORHEN *Gallinula chloropus*
MUTE SWAN *Cygnus olor*

NIGHTINGALE *Luscinia megarhynchos*
NIGHTJAR *Caprimulgus europaeus*
NUTHATCH *Sitta europaea*

OSPREY *Pandion haliaetus*
OYSTERCATCHER *Haematopus ostralegus*

PALLAS'S SANDGROUSE *Syrrhaptes paradoxus*
PARROT CROSSBILL *Loxia pytyopsittacus*
PEREGRINE *Falco peregrinus*
PHEASANT *Phasianus colchicus*
PIED FLYCATCHER *Ficedula hypoleuca*
PIED WAGTAIL *Motacilla alba yarrelli*
PINTAIL *Anas acuta*
POCHARD *Aythya ferina*
PTARMIGAN *Lagopus mutus*
PUFFIN *Fratercula arctica*

PURPLE SANDPIPER *Calidris maritima*

QUAIL *Coturnix coturnix*

RAVEN *Corvus corax*
RAZORBILL *Alca torda*
RED-BACKED SHRIKE *Lanius collurio*
RED-BREASTED MERGANSER *Mergus serrator*
RED-CRESTED POCHARD *Netta rufina*
RED GROUSE *Lagopus lagopus*
RED KITE *Milvus milvus*
RED-LEGGED PARTRIDGE *Alectoris rufa*
RED-NECKED GREBE *Podiceps grisegena*
RED-NECKED PHALAROPE *Phalaropus lobatus*
REDPOLL *Carduelis flammea*
REDSHANK *Tringa totanus*
REDSTART *Phoenicurus phoenicurus*
RED-THROATED DIVER *Gavia stellata*
REDWING *Turdus iliacus*
REED BUNTING *Emberiza schoeniclus*
REED WARBLER *Acrocephalus scirpaceus*
REEVES'S PHEASANT *Syrmaticus reevesi*
RINGED PLOVER *Charadrius hiaticula*
RING-NECKED PARAKEET *Psittacula krameri*
RING OUZEL *Turdus torquatus*
ROBIN *Erithacus rubecula*
ROCK DOVE/FERAL PIGEON *Columba livia*
ROCK PIPIT *Anthus petrosus*
ROOK *Corvus frugilegus*
ROSEATE TERN *Sterna dougallii*
RUDDY DUCK *Oxyura jamaicensis*
RUFF *Philomachus pugnax*

SAND MARTIN *Riparia riparia*
SANDWICH TERN *Sterna sandvicensis*
SAVI'S WARBLER *Locustella luscinioides*
SCARLET ROSEFINCH *Carpodacus erythrinus*
SCAUP *Aythya marila*
SCOTTISH CROSSBILL *Loxia scotica*
SEDGE WARBLER *Acrocephalus schoenobaenus*
SEA EAGLE *Haliaeetus albicilla*
SERIN *Serinus serinus*
SHAG *Phalacrocorax aristotelis*
SHELDUCK *Tadorna tadorna*
SHORE LARK *Eremophila alpestris*
SHORT-EARED OWL *Asio flammeus*
SHORT-TOED TREECREEPER *Certhia brachydactyla*
SHOVELER *Anas clypeata*
SISKIN *Carduelis spinus*
SKYLARK *Alauda arvensis*
SLAVONIAN GREBE *Podiceps auritus*
SNIPE *Gallinago gallinago*
SNOW BUNTING *Plectrophenax nivalis*
SNOWY OWL *Nyctea scandiaca*
SONG THRUSH *Turdus philomelos*
SPARROWHAWK *Accipiter nisus*
SPOTTED CRAKE *Porzana porzana*
SPOTTED FLYCATCHER *Muscicapa striata*
SPOTTED REDSHANK *Tringa erythropus*
SPOTTED SANDPIPER *Actitis macularia*
STARLING *Sturnus vulgaris*
STOCK DOVE *Columba oenas*
STONECHAT *Saxicola torquata*
STONE CURLEW *Burhinus oedicnemus*
STORM PETREL *Hydrobates pelagicus*

SURF SCOTER *Melanitta perspicillata*
SWALLOW *Hirundo rustica*
SWIFT *Apus apus*

TAWNY OWL *Strix aluco*
TEAL *Anas crecca*
TEMMINCK'S STINT *Calidris temminckii*
TREECREEPER *Certhia familiaris*
TREE PIPIT *Anthus trivialis*
TREE SPARROW *Passer montanus*
TUFTED DUCK *Aythya fuligula*
TURKEY *Meleagris galloparva*
TURTLE DOVE *Streptopelia turtur*
TWITE *Carduelis flavirostris*

WATER RAIL *Rallus aquaticus*
WHEATEAR *Oenanthe oenanthe*
WHIMBREL *Numenius phaeopus*
WHINCHAT *Saxicola rubetra*
WHITE-HEADED DUCK *Oxyura leucocephala*
WHITE-TAILED EAGLE *Haliaeetus albicilla*
WHITETHOAT *Sylvia communis*
WHITE WAGTAIL *Motacilla alba alba*
WHOOPER SWAN *Cygnus cygnus*
WIGEON *Anas penelope*
WILLOW TIT *Parus montanus*
WILLOW WARBLER *Phylloscopus trochilus*
WOODCHAT SHRIKE *Lanius senator*
WOODCOCK *Scolopax rusticola*
WOOD DUCK *Aix sponsa*
WOODLARK *Lullula arborea*
WOODPIGEON *Columba palumbus*
WOOD SANDPIPER *Tringa glareola*
WOOD WARBLER *Phylloscopus sibilatrix*
WREN *Troglodytes troglodytes*
WRYNECK *Jynx torquilla*

YELLOWHAMMER *Emberiza citrinella*
YELLOW WAGTAIL *Motacilla flava flavissima*

Appendix D:
Names of animals mentioned in the text

Vernacular names are listed alphabetically; both scienfic and vernacular names follow current usage.

ADDER *Vipera berus*
ANT *Formicidae*
      MEADOW *Lasius flavus*
      WOOD *Formica rufa*
BEETLE Coleoptera
CADDIS Trichoptera
CAT *Felis catus*
CATTLE *Bos taurus*
CATERPILLAR Lepidoptera (larva)
COCKROACH Blattodea
COD *Gadus morrhua*
DEER Cervidae
FOX *Vulpes vulpes*
HADDOCK *Gadus aeglefinus*
HALIBUT *Hippoglossus vulgaris*
HARE *Lepus* spp.
HERRING *Clupea harengus*
HORSE *Equus caballus*
KANGAROO *Macropus* spp.
MACKEREL *Scomber scombrus*
MARTEN, PINE *Martes martes*
MAYFLY Ephemeroptera
MINK, AMERICAN *Mustela vison*
MOUSE *Mus musculus*
MUSSEL Lammelli branchia
ZEBRA *Dreissena polymorpha*
OAK MOTH *Lasiocampa quercus*
RABBIT *Oryctolagus cuniculus*
RAT, COMMON (BROWN) *Rattus norvegicus*
SALMON *Salmo salar*
SANDEEL, COMMON *Hyperophus lanceolatus*
      LESSER Ammodytes tobianus
SHEEP Ovis ammon
SQUIRREL, RED *Sciurus vulgaris*
      GREY S. *carolinensis*
STOAT *Mustela erminea*
TROUT *Salmo* spp.
VOLE *Clethrionomys/Microtus* spp.
WEASEL *Mustela nivalis*
WIREWORM Coleoptera, Elateridae (larva)

BIBLIOGRAPHY

ALDRIDGE, W. 1885. *A Gossip about the Wild Birds of Norwood and Crystal Palace District.* Burdett and Co., London.

ALEXANDER, B. 1908. Birds. In *Victoria History of the County of Kent.* Dawsons of Pall Mall, London.

ALEXANDER, H.T. 1929. The birds of the Lickey Hills and Bittell Reservoirs. *Proc. Birmingham Nat. Hist. Phil. Soc.* **15**: 197–212.

ALEXANDER, W.B. 1945–47. The Woodcock in the British Isles. *The Ibis* **87**: 512–550, **88**: 1–24, 159–179, 271–286, 427–444, **89**: 1–28.

ALEXANDER, W.B. 1947. *A Revised List of the Birds of Oxfordshire.* Oxford Ornithological Society, Oxford.

ALEXANDER, W.B. and D. LACK. 1944. Changes in status among British breeding birds. *Brit. Birds* **38**: 42–45, 62–69, 82–88.

ANDERSON, P. 1898. On birds observed in the Island of Tiree. *Annls Scot. Nat. Hist.* **27**: 153–161.

ANDREWS, I.J. 1986. *The Birds of the Lothians.* Scottish Ornithologists' Club, Edinburgh.

ANDREWS, J. and S. CARTER. 1993. *Britain's Birds in 1990–91: the Conservation and Monitoring Review.* BTO/JNCC, Thetford.

ANGUS, S. 1983. *Sutherland Birds.* The Northern Times Ltd., Golspie.

APLIN, O.V. 1890–91. On the distribution and sojourn in the British Islands of the Spotted Crake. *The Zoologist* **1890**: 401–407, **1891**: 88–96.

APLIN, O.V. 1889. *The Birds of Oxfordshire.* Oxford University Press, London.

APLIN, O.V. 1892. On the Distribution of the Cirl Bunting in Great Britain. *The Zoologist.* **16**: 121–128.

APLIN, O.V. 1902. The birds of Bardsey Island, with additional notes on the birds of Lleyn, 2 parts. *The Zoologist.* **5**: 8–17, 107–110.

APLIN, O.V. 1910. Summer in Lleyn with some notes on the birds of the district. *The Zoologist.* **10**: 41–50, 99–108.

ARMITT, M. 1897. *Studies of Lakeland Birds,* 1st Series. George Middleton, Ambleside.

ARMITT, M. 1901. *Studies of Lakeland Birds,* 2nd Series. George Middleton, Ambleside.

ARNOLD, E.C. 1936. *Birds of Eastbourne.* Baskerville Press, Eastbourne.

ASPDEN, W. 1933. Notes on Puffin Island. *Trans. Anglesey Antiq. Soc.*

AVERY, M.I. and A. DEL NEVO. 1991. Action for Roseate Terns. *RSPB Conserv. Rev.* **5**: 54–59.

AVERY, M. and R. LESLIE. 1990. *Birds and Forestry.* Poyser, London.

BABINGTON, Rev. C. 1884–86. *Catalogue of the Birds of Suffolk.* Van Voorst, London.

BAIKIE, W.B. and R. HEDDLE. 1848. *Historia Naturalis Orcadensis.*

BAILLIE, S.R. 1990. Integrated population monitoring of breeding birds in Britain and Ireland. *Ibis.* **132**: 151–166.

BAILLIE, S.R. and H. MILNE. 1989. Movements of Eiders *Somateria mollissima* on the east coast of Britain. *Ibis.* **131**: 321–135.

BALFOUR, E. 1968. Breeding Birds of Orkney. *Scottish Birds.* **5**: 89–104.

BALFOUR, E. 1972. *Orkney Birds—status and guide.* Senior, Stromness.

BALSTON, R.J., C.W. SHEPHERD and E. BARTLETT. 1907. *Notes on the Birds of Kent.* R.H. Porter, London.

BANNERMAN, D.A. 1953–63. *The Birds of the British Islands.* Oliver and Boyd, Edinburgh.

BARKER, T.W. 1905. *Handbook to the Natural History of Carmarthenshire.* Private publication, Carmarthen.

BARRETT, J.H. 1959. The Birds of the Parish of Dale, including Skokholm. *Field Studies* Vol. 1 No. 1. Field Studies Council, London.

BARRINGTON, R.M. 1915. The last(?) Irish Golden Eagle. *Irish Nat.* **24**: 63.

BATTEN, L.A. 1973. The colonisation of England by the Firecrest. *Brit. Birds.* **66**: 159–166.

BATTEN, L.A., C.J. BIBBY, P. CLEMENT, G.D. ELLIOTT and R.F. PORTER. 1990. *Red Data Birds in Britain.* Poyser, London.

BAXTER, E.V. and RINTOUL, L.J. 1922. *Some Scottish Breeding Duck—their arrival and dispersal.* Oliver and Boyd, Edinburgh.

BAXTER, E.V. and L.J. RINTOUL. 1928. *The Geographical Distribution and Status of Birds in Scotland.* Oliver and Boyd, Edinburgh.

BAXTER, E.V. and L.J. RINTOUL. 1953. *The Birds of Scotland.* Oliver and Boyd, Edinburgh.

BECKWITH, W.E. 1879. Birds of Shropshire. *Trans. Shropshire Archaeol. and Nat. Hist. Soc.* **2**: 365-395.

BECKWITH, W.E. 1881. Birds of Shropshire continued. *Trans. of the Shropshire Archaeol. and Nat. Hist. Soc.* **4**: 326–328.

BECKWITH, W.E.. 1887–1893. Notes on Shropshire Birds. *Trans. Shropshire Archaeol. Nat. Hist. Soc.* **10**: 383–398, **11**: 223–238, 387–402, second series **1**: 201–216, **2**: 1–16, **3**: 313–328, **4**: 183–198, **5**: 31–48.

BELL, T.H. 1962. *The Birds of Cheshire.* Sherratt and Son, Altrincham.

BELL, T.H. 1967. *A Supplement to "The Birds of Cheshire".* Sherratt and Son, Altrincham.

BELT, A. 1888. List of the Birds of the Ealing District. *Ann. Rep. for 1887–88 Ealing Microscop. and Nat. Hist. Soc.* 12–8.

BERRY, J. 1939. *International Wildfowl Enquiry: The Status and Distribution of Wild Geese and Wild Duck in Scotland.* Cambridge University Press, Cambridge.

BETTS, M. 1992. *Birds of Skokholm.* BioLine, Cardiff.

BEWICK, T. 1797–1804. *History of British Birds.* Bewick, Newcastle.

BEWICK, T. 1847. *History of British Birds,* 8th edition. Bewick, Newcastle.

BIDWELL, E. 1886. A Visit to the Isles of Scilly during the Nesting Season. *Trans. Norfolk and Norwich Nat. Soc.* **IV**, pt. II: 201–214.

BIRCH, J.E., R.R. BIRCH, J.M. BIRTWELL, C. DONE, E.J. STOKES and G.F. WALTON. 1968. *The Birds of Flintshire.* Privately published, Chester.

BIRCHAM, P.M.M. 1989. *The Birds of Cambridgeshire.* Cambridge University Press, Cambridge.

BIRCHAM, P.M.M., J.C.A. RATHMELL and W.J. JORDAN. 1994. *An Atlas of the Breeding Birds of Cambridgeshire.* The Cambridge Bird Club, Cambridge.

BIRKHEAD, M. and C. PERRINS. 1986. *The Mute*

Swan. Croom Helm, London.

BLACKBURN, H. 1895. *Birds from Moidart and Elsewhere*. David Douglas, Edinburgh.

BLAKER, G.B. 1934. The Barn Owl in England and Wales. *RSPB*, London.

BLATHWAYT, Rev. F.L. 1900. A Visit to Lundy. *The Zoologist*. 4: 375–380.

BLATHWAYT, Rev. F.L. 1902. The Roseate Tern on the Farne Islands. The Zoologist 5: 53–54.

BLATHWAYT, Rev. F.L. 1906. Birds. In *Victoria History of the County of Somerset*. Dawsons of Pall Mall, London.

BLATHWAYT, Rev. F.L. 1915. The Birds of Lincolnshire. *Lincolnshire Nat. Union, Trans. 1914*. 178–211.

BLATHWAYT, Rev. F.L. 1933. A Revised List of the Birds of Dorset. *Proc. Dorset Nat. Hist. Archaeol. Soc.* **55**: 165–209.

BLATHWAYT, Rev. F.L. 1945. A Revised List of the Birds of Dorset. *Proc. Dorset Nat. Hist. Archaeol. Soc.* **67**: 95–126.

BLEZARD, E. 1946. Lakeland Natural History. *Carlisle Nat. Hist. Soc.*, Arbroath.

BLEZARD, E. (ed.), M. GARNETT, R. GRAHAM and T.L. JOHNSTON. 1943. Birds of Lakeland. *Carlisle Nat. Hist. Soc.*, Arbroath.

BOLAM, G. 1912. *The Birds of Northumberland and the Eastern Borders*. Henry Hunter Blair, Alnwick.

BOLAM, G. 1932. A Catalogue of the Birds of Northumberland. *Trans. Nat. Hist. Soc. of Northumberland, Durham & Newcastle-upon-Tyne*, 8: 1–165.

BONHAM. P.F. and J.C.M. ROBERTSON. 1975. The spread of the Cetti's Warbler in north-west Europe. *Brit. Birds* 68: 393–408.

BOOTH, E.T. 1881–87. *Rough Notes on the Birds observed during Twenty-five Years' Shooting and Collecting in the British Islands*. Porter, London.

BOOTH, C.J., M. CUTHBERT and P. REYNOLDS. 1984. *The Birds of Orkney*. The Orkney Press, Stromness.

BORASTON, J.M. 1905. *Nature- Tones and Undertones*. Sherratt and Hughes, London.

BORRER, W. 1891. *The Birds of Sussex*. R.H. Porter, London.

BOYS, J.V. 1972. *A Checklist of the Birds of Dorset*. Dorset Natural History and Archaeological Society, Poole.

BRIGGS, A. 1893. Bird Notes from North Ronaldsay. *Annls. Scot. Nat. Hist.* 2: 154–178.

BRITISH ORNITHOLOGISTS' UNION. 1992. *Checklist of Birds of Britain and Ireland*. 6th edition. British Ornithologists' Union, Tring.

BROECKER, W.S. 1975. Camp Century Ice Cores. *Science* 189: 460–463.

BROOKE, M. 1990. *The Manx Shearwater*. Poyser, London.

BROOKE, M. de L. and N.B. DAVIES. 1987. Recent changes in host usage by Cuckoos *Cuculus canorus* in Britain. *J. Anim. Ecol.* 56: 873–883.

BROWNE, M. 1889. *Vertebrate Animals of Leicestershire and Rutland*. Private publication, Birmingham.

BROWNE, M. 1907. Birds. In *Victoria History of the County of Leicestershire*. Dawsons of Pall Mall, London.

BRUCE, G. 1895. *The Land Birds about St. Andrews*. John Leng, Dundee.

BUCHANAN, J.H. 1882. History of the Chough in Scotland. *Proc. Roy. Phys. Soc. Edinburgh*. **12**: 94–101.

BUCKLAND, S.T., M.V. BELL and N. PICOZZI. 1990. *The Birds of North-East Scotland*. North-East Scotland Bird Club, Aberdeen.

BUCKLEY, T.E. and J. A. HARVIE-BROWN. 1891. *A Vertebrate Fauna of the Orkney Islands*. David Douglas, Edinburgh.

BUCKNILL, J.A.S. 1900. *The Birds of Surrey*. R.H. Porter, London.

BUCKNILL, J.A.S. 1902. Birds. In *Victoria History of the County of Surrey*. Dawsons of Pall Mall, London.

BULL, H.G. 1888. *Notes on the Birds of Herefordshire*. Jakeman and Carver, London.

BULLOCK, I.D, D.R. DREWETT and S.P. MICKLEBURGH. 1985. The Chough in Wales. *Nature in Wales*. **4**: 46–57.

BUND, J.W.W. 1891. *A List of the Birds of Worcestershire and the Adjoining Counties*. Private publication, Worcester.

BUNN, D.S., A.B. WARBURTON and R.D.S. WILSON. 1982. *The Barn Owl*. Poyser, Calton.

BURTON, J.F. 1995. *Birds and Climate Change*. Christopher Helm, London.

BUTLER, A.G. 1886. *British Birds Eggs—a Handbook of British Oology*. Janson, London.

BUXTON, J. (ed.). 1981. *The Birds of Wiltshire*. Wiltshire Library and Museum Service, Trowbridge.

CAMPBELL, B. 1953. A comparison of bird populations upon "industrial" and "rural" farmland in South Wales. *Trans. Cardiff Nat. Soc.* **81**: 4–65.

CAMPBELL, B. and FERGUSON-LEES, I.J. 1972. *A Field Guide to Birds' Nests*. Constable, London.

CAMPBELL, J.M. 1904. *Notes on the Natural History of the Bell Rock*. David Douglas, Edinburgh.

CANDLER, C. 1888. Observations on the Birds. In F.W. Galpin, *Plants and Birds of Harleston*. Bartlett and Co., London.

CARDIFF NATURALISTS' SOCIETY. 1900. The Birds of Glamorgan. *Trans. Cardiff Nat. Soc.* **31**: 1–37.

CARDIFF NATURALISTS' SOCIETY. 1925. Birds of Glamorgan. *Trans. Cardiff Nat. Soc.* **58**: 39–84.

CARLISLE NATURAL HISTORY SOCIETY. 1954. Lakeland Ornithology. *Trans. Carlisle Nat. Hist. Soc.*, Arbroath.

CARTER, S.P. (ed). 1995. *Britain's Birds in 1991–92: the conservation and monitoring review*. BTO/JNCC, Thetford.

CATLEY, G.P. and D. HURSTHOUSE. 1985. Parrot Crossbills in Britain. *Brit. Birds*. **78**: 482–505.

CAWKELL, H.A.R. 1969. A discussion of the Hastings Rarities. *Hastings and E. Sussex Nat.* **X**: 165–172

CHANCE, E.P. 1922. *The Cuckoo's Secret*. Sidgewick and Jackson, London.

CHANCE, E.P. 1940. *The Truth About the Cuckoo*. Country Life, London.

CHAPMAN, A. 1889. *Bird-Life of the Borders*. Gurney and Jackson, London.

CHAPMAN, A. 1907. *Bird-Life of the Borders, on Moorland and Sea*. Gurney and Jackson, London.

CHASE, R.W. 1886. Birds. In *British Association Handbook of Birmingham*. British Association, Birmingham.

CHISLETT, R. 1923. The Whimbrel in Shetland. *Brit. Birds*. **17**: 150–154.

CHISLETT, R. 1953. *Yorkshire Birds*. A. Brown and Sons Ltd., London.

CHRISTY, R.M. 1890. *The Birds of Essex*. Simkin Marshall Hamilton, Chelmsford.

CHRISTY, R.M. 1903. Birds. In *Victoria History of the County of Essex*. Dawsons of Pall Mall, London.

CLARK, F. and D.A.C. McNEIL. 1980. Cliff-nesting colonies of House Martins *Delichon urbica* in Great Britain. *Ibis* 122: 27–42.

CLARK, J. 1906. Birds. In *Victoria History of the County of Cornwall*. Dawsons of Pall Mall, London.

CLARK, J. and F.R. RODD. 1906. The Birds of Scilly. *The Zoologist*. 10: 240–252, 295–306, 335–346.

CLARK, J.M. 1984. *Birds of the Hants/Surrey Border*. Hobby Books, Aldershot.

CLARKE, W.E. 1905. Birds of the Flannan Islands. *Annls Scot. Nat. Hist.* 9: 8–19, 80–86.

CLARKE, W.E. 1906–10. The Birds of Fair Isle. *Annls of Scot. Nat. Hist.* 10: 4–21, 69–80; 11: 66–80, 246; 12: 72–85; 13: 69–75; 14: 65–67.

CLARKE, W.E. 1912. *Studies in Bird Migration*. Gurney and Jackson, London.

CLARKE, W.E. and W.D. ROEBUCK. 1881. *A Handbook of the Vertebrate Fauna of Yorkshire*. Lovell Reeve and Co., London.

COHEN, E. 1963. *Birds of Hampshire and the Isle of Wight*. Oliver and Boyd, Edinburgh.

COHEN, E. and J. TAVERNER. 1972. *A Revised List of Hampshire and Isle of Wight Birds*. Oxford Illustrated Press, Oxford.

COLE, A. 1993. *In Search of the Cirl Bunting*. Privately published, Stroud.

COLLIER, C. 1904. The Birds of the Island of Raasay. *The Ibis* series VIII, vol. 4: 490–512.

CONDER, P. 1989. *The Wheatear*. Christopher Helm, London.

COOK, A. 1975. Changes in the Carrion/Hooded Crow hybrid zone and the possible importance of climate. *Bird Study* 22: 165–168.

COOK, M. 1992. *The Birds of Moray and Nairn*. The Mercat Press, Edinburgh.

COOKE, A.S. 1979. Population declines of the Magpie *Pica pica* in Huntingdonshire and other parts of eastern England. *Biol. Conserv.* 15: 317–324.

COOKE, R. 1946. Black Terns breeding in Sussex. *Brit. Birds*. 39: 71–72.

COOKE, R. 1948. Black Redstarts on Pett Level, East Sussex. *British Birds* XLI: 46–48.

COOMBS, F. 1978. *The Crows*. B.T. Batsford Ltd., London.

CORDEAUX, J. 1866–82. Ornithological notes from North Lincolnshire. *The Zoologist*. 1: 73–76, 129–132, 215–17, 258–60, 293–5; 2: 546–8, 589–93, 690–2, 807–11, 943–6; 3: 1029–31, 1123–5, 1250–2, 1283–6, 1411–3, 1476–8; 4: 1543–4, 1666–70, 1736–41, 1840–1841, 1905–8; 5: 1976–9, 2053–5, 2077–81, 2153–5, 2285–9, 2335–8, 2389–92; 6: 2469–72, 2495–6, 2594–6, 2653–6, 2782–4, 2859–61; 7: 2928–32, 3014–16, 3095–8, 3165–6, 3320–3; 8: 3400–2, 3464–5, 3556–8, 3684–7, 3781–2; 9: 3856–9, 3942–3, 4029–31, 4059–63, 4224–6; 10: 4294–6, 4361–6,. 4488–90, 4617–8, 4669–70, 4709–10; 11: 4778–80, 4897–9, 4982–5, 5031, 5062; 3: 371–5; 4: 6–15; 6: 84–90.

CORDEAUX, J. 1872. *Birds of the Humber District*. Van Voorst, London.

CORDEAUX, J. 1879–89. *Report on the Migration of Birds etc*. West, Newman, London.

CORDEAUX, J. 1899. *A List of the British Birds belonging to the Humber District*. R.H. Porter, London.

COULSON, J.C. 1963. The status of the Kittiwake in the British Isles. *Bird Study* 10: 147–179.

COULSON, J.C. 1974. Kittiwake *Rissa tridactyla*. In Cramp, S., W.R.P. Bourne and D. Saunders *The Seabirds of Britain and Ireland*. Collins, London.

COWARD, T.A. 1910. *A Vertebrate Fauna of Cheshire and Liverpool Bay*. Witherby, London.

COWARD, T.A. and C. OLDHAM. 1900. *The Birds of Cheshire*. Sherratt and Hughes, Manchester.

COWARD, T.A. and C. OLDHAM. 1902. Notes on the Birds of Anglesea. *The Zoologist* 6: 401–415.

COX, S. 1984. *A New Guide to The Birds of Essex* Essex Bird Watching and Preservation Society, Southend-on-Sea.

CRAMP, S. (ed.) 1977–94. *Handbook of the Birds of Europe, the Middle East and North Africa: the birds of the Western Palearctic*. Oxford University Press, Oxford.

CRAMP, S., W.R.P. BOURNE and D. SAUNDERS. 1974. *The Seabirds of Britain and Ireland*. Collins, London.

CROOKE, C., R. DENNIS, M. HARVEY and R. SUMMERS. 1993. Population size and breeding success of Slavonian Grebes in Scotland. In Andrews, J. and S. Carer (eds), *Britain's Birds in 1990–91: the conservation and monitoring review*. BTO/JNCC, Thetford.

CROSSMAN, A.F. 1896–1901. Notes on Birds observed in Hertfordshire during the years 1895–1900. *Trans. Hertfordshire Nat. Hist. Soc. Field Club*. 9: 73–84, 148–162; 10: 33–43, 84–102, 136–142, 180–184; 11: 47–52.

CROSSMAN, A.F. 1899. List of the Birds of Hertfordshire. *Trans. Hertfordshire Nat. Hist. Soc.* 10: 84–102.

CROSSMAN, A.F. 1902. Birds. In *Victoria History of the County of Hertfordshire*. Dawsons of Pall Mall, London.

CULLEN, J.P. and P.P. JENNINGS. 1986. *Birds of the Isle of Man*. Bridgeen Publications, Douglas.

CULLEN, J.P. and D.J. SLINN. 1975. *The Birds of the Isle of Man—A List with Notes*. 3rd revised edition. The Manx Museum and National Trust, Douglas.

DALGLEISH, J.J. 1883. The Distribution of the Tree Sparrow in Scotland. *Proc. Roy. Phys. Soc. Edinburgh* 13: 196–202.

DANDY, J.E. 1969. *Watsonian Vice-Counties of Great Britain*. The Ray Society, London.

DANIEL, R.B. Rev. 1807–13. *Rural Sports and Supplement*. Longman, London.

DAVIES, P. 1954. *A List of the Birds of Lundy*. Lundy Field Society, Exeter.

DAVIS, P. 1993. The Red Kite in Wales: setting the record straight. *Brit. Birds* 86: 295–298.

DAY, J.C.U. 1984. Population and breeding biology of Marsh Harriers in Britain since 1900. *J. Appl. Ecol.* 21: 773–787.

DAZLEY, R.A. and P. TRODD. 1994. *The Breeding Birds of Bedfordshire*. Bedfordshire Natural History Society, Bedford.

DEAN, T. 1990. *The Natural History of Walney Island*. Faust Publications, Burnley.

DEANE, C.D. 1954. *Handbook of the Birds of Northern Ireland*. Belfast Museum and Art Gallery, Belfast.

DEANS, P., J. SANKEY, L. SMITH, J. TUCKER, C. WHITTLES and C. WRIGHT. 1992. *An Atlas of the*

Breeding Birds of Shropshire. Shropshire Ornithological Society, Shrewsbury.

DELANEY, S. 1993. Introduced and escaped Geese in Britain in summer 1991. *Brit. Birds* 86: 591–599.

DENNIS, R.H. 1983. Purple Sandpipers breeding in Scotland. *Brit. Birds* 76: 563–566.

DENNIS, R.H. 1984. *A Status and Guide to the Birds of Badenoch and Strathspey*. Roy Dennis Enterprises, Inverness.

DENNIS, R.H. 1987. Boxes for Goldeneyes: a success story. *RSPB Conserv. Rev.* 1: 85–87.

DENNIS, R.H., P.M. ELLIS, R.A. BROAD and D.R. LANGSLOW. 1984. The status of the Golden Eagle in Britain. *Brit. Birds* 77: 592–607.

DEPARTMENT OF THE ENVIRONMENT. 1991. *Digest of Environmental Protection and Water Statistics*. HMSO, London.

DES FORGES, G. and D.D. HARBER. 1963. *A Guide to the Birds of Sussex*. Oliver and Boyd, Edinburgh.

DEWAR, G.A.B. 1899. *Wildlife in Hampshire Highlands*. Dent, London.

DICKSON, R.C. 1992. *Birds in Wigtownshire*. G.C. Book Publishers Ltd., Wigtown.

DIGBY-PIGGOTT, T. 1892. *London Birds and Other Sketches*. R.H. Porter, London.

DIMBLEBY, G.W. 1984. Anthropogenic changes from Neolithic through Medieval times. *New Phytol.* 98: 57–72.

DIXON, C. 1888. *Our Rarer Birds*. Chapman & Hall, London.

DIXON, C. 1893. *The Game Birds and Wild Fowl of the British Islands*. Chapman & Hall, London.

DIXON, C. 1895. *The Gamebirds and Wildfowl of the British Islands etc.*, reissue. Chapman & Hall, London.

DIXON, C. 1899. *Bird-life in a Southern County*. Walter Scott Ltd., London.

DIXON, C. 1909. *The Bird Life of London*. William Heinemann, London.

DOBBS, A. (ed.). 1975. *The Birds of Nottinghamshire*. David and Charles, Newton Abbot.

DOBIE, W.H. 1898. Birds of West Cheshire, Denbighshire and Flintshire. *Proc. Chester Soc. Nat Sci. Lit.* 4: 282–351.

DOBINSON, H.M. and A.J. RICHARDS. 1964. The effects of the severe winter of 1962/63 on birds in Britain. *Brit. Birds* 57: 373–434.

DOBSON, R. 1952. *Birds of the Channel Islands*. Staples Press Ltd., London.

DONALD, P.F., J.D. WILSON and M. SHEPHERD. 1994. The decline of the Corn Bunting. *Brit. Birds* 87: 106–132.

DONOVAN, J. and G. REES. 1994. *Birds of Pembrokeshire*. Dyfed Wildlife Trust, Haverford west.

DRANE, R. and T.W. PROGER. 1891. The Rarer Birds of the Cardiff District in James I. (ed.), *British Association Handbook for Cardiff and District*. British Association, Cardiff. pp. 154–163.

DUNN, R. 1837. *The Ornithologist's Guide to the Islands of Orkney and Shetland*. Privately published, Hull.

D'URBAN, W.S.M.. 1906. Bird. In *Victoria History of the County of Devon*. Dawsons of Pall Mall, London.

D'URBAN, W.S.M. and Rev. M.A. MATHEW. 1892. *The Birds of Devon*. R.H. Porter, London.

D'URBAN, W.S.M. and Rev. M.A. MATHEW. 1895a. *Supplement to the Birds of Devon. R.H. Porter, London*.

D'URBAN, W.S.M. and Rev. M.A. MATHEW. 1895b. *The Birds of Devon, including Supplement*. 2nd edition. R.H. Porter, London.

DYMOND, J.N. 1980. *The Birds of Lundy*. The Devon Birdwatching and Preservation Society, Totnes.

DYMOND, J.N. 1991. *The Birds of Fair Isle*. Privately published.

EASTERBROOK, T.G. 1983. *Birds of the Banbury Area 1972–1981*. Banbury Ornithological Society, Banbury.

EDLIN, H.L. 1956. *Trees, Woods and Man*. Collins, London.

EGGLING, W.J. 1960. *The Isle of May*. Oliver and Boyd, Edinburgh.

ELKINS, N. 1983. *Weather and Bird Behaviour*. Poyser, Calton.

ELLIOTT, J.S. 1895. Observations on the fauna of St Kilda. *Zoologist* 19: 281–286.

EVANS, A.D. 1992. The numbers and distribution of Cirl Buntings *Emberiza cirlus* breeding in Britain in 1989. *Bird Study* 39: 17–22.

EVANS, A.D. and K.W. Smith. 1994. Habitat selection of Cirl Buntings *Emberiza cirlus* wintering in Britain. *Bird Study* 41: 81–87.

EVANS, A.H. 1904. The Birds of Cambridgeshire in Marr, J.E. and A.E. Shipley, *Handbook to the Natural History of Cambridgeshire*. Cambridge University Press, Cambridge.

EVANS, A.H. 1911. *A Fauna of the Tweed Area*. David Douglas, Edinburgh.

EVANS, A.H. and T.E. BUCKLEY. 1899. *A Vertebrate Fauna of the Shetland Islands*. David Douglas, Edinburgh.

EVERETT, M.J. 1971. Breeding status of Red-necked Phalaropes in Britain and Ireland. *Brit. Birds* 64: 293–302.

EYTON, T.C. 1838–39. An attempt to ascertain the fauna of Shropshire and North Wales. *Annls Nat. Hist.* I: 285–292, II: 52–56.

FAWCETT, J.W. 1890. *The Birds of Durham*. Privately published, Consett.

FEA, J. 1775. *The Present State of the Orkney Islands considered; etc.*, Privately published, Edinburgh.

FEARE, C.J. 1994. Changes in the numbers of common Starling and farming practice in Lincolnshire. *Brit. Birds* 87: 200–204.

FERGUSON-LEES, I.J. 1951. The Peregrine population of Britain, parts I & II. *Bird Notes* 24: 200–205, 309–314.

FERGUSON-LEES, I.J. 1964. Studies of less familiar birds. 129. Cetti's Warbler. *Brit. Birds* 57: 357–359.

FERNS, P.N., H.W. HAMAR, P.N. HUMPHREYS, F.D. KELSEY, E.T. SARSON, W.A. VENABLES and I.R. WALKER (eds.). 1977. *The Birds of Gwent*. Gwent Ornithological Society, Pontypool.

FISHER, J. 1952. *The Fulmar*. Collins, London.

FISHER, J. 1953. The Collared Turtle Dove in Europe. *Brit. Birds* 46: 153–181.

FITTER, R.S.R. 1959. *The Ark in our Midst*. Collins, London.

FITTER, R.S.R. 1965. The breeding status of the Black Redstart in Britain. *Brit. Birds* 58: 481–492.

FITTER, R.S.R. 1971. Black Redstarts breeding in Britain in 1964–68. *Brit. Birds* 64: 117–124.

FLEMING, Rev. J. 1828. *A History of British Animals, etc*. Privately published, Edinburgh.

FORBES, A.C. 1904. *English Estate Forestry*. Arnold, London.

FORBES, H.O. 1906. Birds. In *Victoria History of the County of Lancashire*. Dawsons of Pall Mall, London.

FORREST, H.E. 1899. *The Fauna of Shropshire*. Wilding, Shrewsbury.

FORREST, H.E. 1907. *The Vertebrate Fauna of North Wales*. Witherby, London.

FORREST, H.E. 1908. Birds. In *Victoria History of the County of Shropshire*. Dawsons of Pall Mall, London.

FORREST, H.E. 1919. *A Handlist to the Fauna of North Wales*. Witherby, London.

FOX, R.H. 1909. Birds. In F. Morey, *A Guide to the Natural History of the Isle of Wight*. The Country Press, Newport.

FROST, R. 1978. *The Birds of Derbyshire*. Moorland Publishing Co., Buxton.

FRYER, G. 1987. Evidence for the former breeding of the Golden Eagle in Yorkshire. *Naturalist* **112**: 3–7.

FULLER, R.J. 1982. *Bird Habitats in Britain*. Poyser, Calton.

FULLER, R.J., J.K. BAKER, R.A. MORGAN, R. SCROGGS and M. WRIGHT. 1985. Breeding populations of the Hobby *Falco subbuteo* on farmland in the southern Midlands of Britain. *Ibis* **127**: 510–516.

FURNESS, R.W. 1987. *The Skuas*. Poyser, Calton.

GALBRAITH, H., S. MURRAY, S. RAE, D.P. WHITFIELD and D.B.A. THOMPSON. 1993. Numbers and breeding distribution of the Dotterel *Charadrius morinellus* in Great Britain. *Bird Study* **40**: 161–169.

GARRIOCK, J. 1879. Fulmar Petrel breeding in the Isle of Foula. *The Zoologist* **3**: 380.

GIBBONS, D.W. 1987. Juvenile helping in the Moorhen *Gallinula chloropus*. *Anim. Behav.* **35**: 170–181.

GIBBONS, D.W., J.B. REID and R.A. CHAPMAN. 1993. *The New Atlas of Breeding Birds of Britain and Ireland: 1988–91*. Poyser, London.

GIBSON, C. 1956. *Birds of Tayside*. Dundee Museum and Art Gallery, Dundee.

GIBSON, J.A. 1970. *An Atlas of Renfrewshire Vertebrates*. Renfrewshire Natural History Society, Glasgow.

GILBERT, H.A. and C.W. WALKER. 1941. *Herefordshire Birds*. Woolhope Naturalists' Field Club, Hereford.

GILBERT, H.A. and C.W. Walker. 1954. *Herefordshire Birds*. Woolhope Naturalists' Field Club, Hereford.

GINN, H.B. 1969. The use of annual ringing and nest record card totals as indicators of bird population levels. *Bird Study* **16**: 210–248.

GLADSTONE, H.S. 1910. *The Birds of Dumfriesshire*. Witherby, London.

GLADSTONE, H.S. 1911. *Addenda and Corrigenda to the Birds of Dumfriesshire*. Council of the Dumfriesshire and Galloway Natural History and Antiquarian Society, Dumfries and Maxwelltown.

GLADSTONE, H.S. 1923. *Notes on the Birds of Dumfriesshire*. Council of the Dumfriesshire and Galloway Natural History and Antiquarian Society, Dumfries and Maxwelltown.

GLADSTONE, H.S. 1924. Notes on the Birds of Dumfriesshire. *Dumfriesshire & Galloway Nat. Hist. and Antiq. Soc.* **9**: 10–117.

GLEGG, W.E. 1929. *A History of the Birds of Essex*. Witherby, London.

GLUE, D.E. and D. SCOTT. 1980. Breeding biology of the Little Owl. *Brit. Birds* **73**: 167–180.

GOULD, J. 1832–37. *The Birds of Europe*. Privately published, London.

GRABHAM, O. 1907. Birds. In *Victoria History of the County of Yorkshire*. Dawsons of Pall Mall, London.

GRAHAM, H.D. 1890. *The Birds of Iona and Mull*. David Douglas, Edinburgh.

GRANT, M.C. 1991. Nesting densities, productivity and survival of breeding Whimbrel *Numenius phaeopus* in Shetland. *Bird Study* **38**: 160–169.

GRAY, R. 1871. *The Birds of the West of Scotland*. Murray, Glasgow.

GRAY, R. and T. ANDERSON. 1869. *Birds of Ayrshire and Wigtownshire*. Murray, Glasgow.

GREAVES, W. 1911. Birds of Todmorden in Stansfield, A. and J. Nowell (eds.), *Flora of Todmorden*. Privately published, Stansfield, pp 1a–10a.

GREEN, R.E. 1978. Factors affecting the diet of farmland Skylarks *Alauda arvensis*. *J. Anim. Ecol.* **47**: 913–928.

GREEN, R.E. 1995a. Diagnosing causes of bird population declines. *Ibis (Supplement)* **137**: S47–55.

GREEN, R.E. 1995b. Monitoring of Stone Curlews and breeding success. In Carter, S.P. (ed.). *Britain's Birds in 1991–92: the conservation and monitoring review*. BTO/JNCC, Thetford, pp 138–141.

GREEN, R.E. and G.H. GRIFFITHS. 1994. Use of preferred nesting habitat by Stone Curlews *Burhinus oedicnemus* in relation to vegetation structure. *J. Zool.* **233**: 457–471.

GREEN, R.E. and T.J. STOWE. 1993. The decline of the Corncrake in Britain and Ireland in relation to habitat change. *J. Appl. Ecol.* **30**: 689–695.

GREEN, R.E. and G. WILLIAMS. 1994. The ecology of the Corncrake *Crex crex* and action for its conservation in Britain and Ireland. Pp 69–74 in Bignal, E., D.I. McCracken and D.J. Curtis (eds.). *Nature Conservation and Pastoralism in Europe*.

GREENWOOD, J.J. 1968. Bluethroat nesting in Scotland *Brit. Birds* **61**: 524–525.

GRENFELL, H.E. and D.K. THOMAS. 1982. *A Guide to Gower Birds*. Gwent Ornithological Society and Glamorgan Naturalists' Trust, Glamorgan.

GRIBBLE, F.C. 1983. Nightjars in Britain and Ireland in 1981. *Bird Study* **30**: 167–176.

GRIEVE, S. 1885. *The Great Auk, or Garefowl (Alca impennis, Linn). Its History, Archaeology and Remains*. Oliver and Boyd, London and Edinburgh.

GRIGG, D. 1989. *English Agriculture—an historical perspective*. Blackwell, London.

GROUNDWATER, W. 1974. *Birds and Mammals of Orkney*. Kirkwall Press, Kirkwall.

GUEST, J.P., D. ELPHICK, J.S.A. HUNTER and D. NORMAN. 1992. *Breeding Birds Atlas of Cheshire & Wirral*. Cheshire and Wirral Ornithological Society, Chester.

GURNEY, J.H. 1899. The Bearded Titmouse, *Panurus biarmicus*, Linn. *Trans. of Norfolk and Norwich Nat. Soc.* **VI**: 429–438.

GURNEY, J.H. 1913. *The Gannet*. Witherby, London.

GURNEY, J.H. and T. SOUTHWELL. 1886–1904. Fauna and Flora of Norfolk, part xi, List of Norfolk Birds. *Trans. Norfolk and Norwich Nat. Soc.* **4**: 259–286, 397–431; **5**: 642–649; **7**: 733–740.

HAINES, C.R. 1907. *Notes on the Birds of Rutland*. R.H. Porter, London.

HAINES, C.R. 1908. Birds. In *Victoria History of the County of Rutland*. Dawsons of Pall Mall, London.

HANCOCK, J. 1874. *A Catalogue of the Birds of Northumberland and Durham*. Williams and Norgate, London.

HARDY, E. 1941. *Birds of the Liverpool Area*. Buncle, Arbroath.

HARRADINE, J. 1985. Duck shooting in the United Kingdom. *Wildfowl* **36**: 81–94.

HARRIS, M.P. 1984. *The Puffin*. Poyser, London.

HARRIS, M.P. and S. MURRAY. 1978. *Birds of St. Kilda*. HMSO, London.

HARRISON, C. 1982. *An Atlas of the Birds of the Western Palearctic*. Collins, London.

HARRISON, C. 1988. *A History of the Birds of Britain*. Collins, London.

HARRISON, C.J.P. 1980. A re-examination of British Devensian and early Holocene bird bones in the British Museum (Natural History). *J. Archaeol. Sci.* **7**: 53–68.

HARRISON, G.R., A.R. DEAN, A.J. RICHARDS and D. SMALLSHIRE. 1982. *The Birds of the West Midlands*. Collins, London.

HARRISON, J.M. 1942. *A Handbook of the Birds of Sevenoaks or the Western District of Kent*, Witherby, London.

HARRISON, J.M. 1953. *The Birds of Kent*. Witherby, London.

HARRISON, J.M. 1968. *Bristow and the Hastings Rarities Affair*. Privately published.

HARRISSON, T.H. and P.A.D. HOLLOM. 1931–33. The Great-crested Grebe enquiry. *Brit. Birds* **24**: 249; **26**: 62, 102, 142, 174; [Scotland] **26**: 286.

HARTERT, E.J.O. and F.C.R. JOURDAIN. 1920. The Birds of Buckinghamshire and Tring Reservoirs. *Novitate Zoologicae* **27**: 171–259.

HARTERT, E.J.O., F.C.R. JOURDAIN, N.F. TICEHURST and H.F. WITHERBY. 1912. *A Handlist of British Birds*. Witherby, London.

HARTERT, E.J.O. and Hon. W. ROTHSCHILD. 1905. Birds. In *Victoria History of the County of Buckinghamshire*. Dawsons of Pall Mall, London.

HARTHAN, A.J. 1946. *The Birds of Worcestershire*. Littlebury and Co. Ltd., Worcester.

HARTING, J.E. 1864. The Birds of Walney Island. *The Zoologist* **22**: 9156–9165

HARTING, J.E. 1866. *The Birds of Middlesex*. Van Voorst, London.

HARTING, J.E. 1872. British Heronries. *The Zoologist* **7**: 3261–3272.

HARTING, J.E. 1873. Appendix to British Heronries. *The Zoologist* **8**: 3404–3407.

HARTING, J.E. 1901. *A Handbook of British Birds etc.*, new and revised edition, Nimmo, London.

HARVIE-BROWN, J.A. 1878. On the Capercaillie in Scotland. *Proc. Nat. Hist. Glasgow* **III**: 348–349.

HARVIE-BROWN, J.A. and BARTHOLOMEW, J.G. 1893. *Naturalist's Map of Scotland*. David Douglas, Edinburgh.

HARVIE-BROWN, J.A. 1879. *The Capercaillie in Scotland*. David Douglas, Edinburgh.

HARVIE-BROWN, J.A. 1880a. On the decrease in Scotland of the Greater Spotted Woodpecker. *Proc. N.H. Soc. Glasgow*, **4**: 6.

HARVIE-BROWN, J.A. 1880b. The Capercaillie in Scotland. *Scot. Nat.* **5**: 289–294.

HARVIE-BROWN, J.A. 1886. The Snow Bunting breeding in Scotland. *The Zoologist* **10**: 43.

HARVIE-BROWN, J.A. 1887. Priest Island and its birdlife. *Trans. Norfolk and Norwich Nat. Soc.* **IV**: 310–315.

HARVIE-BROWN, J.A. 1888a. Further notes on North Rona, being an appendix to John Swinburne's paper on that island in the 'Proceedings' of this Society, 1883–1884. *Proc. Royal Phys. Soc. Edinburgh* **9**: 284–299.

HARVIE-BROWN, J.A. 1888b. The Isle of May: its faunal position and bird life. *Proc. Roy. Phys. Soc. of Edinburgh* **9**: 303–325.

HARVIE-BROWN, J.A. 1892. The Great Spotted Woodpecker in Scotland. *Annls of Scot. Nat. Hist.* **1**: 4–17.

HARVIE-BROWN, J.A. 1895. The Starling in Scotland, its increase and distribution. *Annls Scot. Nat. Hist.* **4**: 2–22.

HARVIE-BROWN, J.A. 1896. The Tufted Duck in Scotland: its increase and distribution. *Annls of Scot. Nat. Hist.* **5**: 3–23.

HARVIE-BROWN, J.A. 1906. *A Fauna of the Tay Basin and Strathmore*. David Douglas, Edinburgh.

HARVIE-BROWN, J.A. 1908. The Great Spotted Woodpecker's resuscitation in Scotland since 1841 or 1851. *Annls Scot. Nat. Hist.* **12**: 210–216.

HARVIE-BROWN, J.A. 1912. The Fulmar. *Scot. Nat.* **1**: 97–102, 121–132.

HARVIE-BROWN, J.A. and T.E. BUCKLEY. 1887. *A Vertebrate Fauna of Sutherland, Caithness and West Cromarty*. David Douglas, Edinburgh.

HARVIE-BROWN, J.A. and T.E. BUCKLEY. 1888. *A Vertebrate Fauna of the Outer Hebrides*. David Douglas, Edinburgh.

HARVIE-BROWN, J.A. and T.E. BUCKLEY. 1891. *A Vertebrate Fauna of the Orkney Islands*. David Douglas, Edinburgh.

HARVIE-BROWN, J.A. and T.E. BUCKLEY. 1892. *A Vertebrate Fauna of Argyll and the Inner Hebrides*. David Douglas, Edinburgh.

HARVIE-BROWN, J.A. and T.E. BUCKLEY. 1895. *A Fauna of the Moray Basin*. David Douglas, Edinburgh.

HARVIE-BROWN, J.A. and Rev. H.A. MACPHERSON. 1904. *A Fauna of the North-West Highlands and Skye*. David Douglas, Edinburgh.

HAWKES, B. 1979. Ring-necked Parakeet enquiry. *BTO News* **102**: 5.

HEATHCOTE, A., H. MORREY SALMON and D. GRIFFIN. 1967. *The Birds of Glamorgan*. The Cardiff Naturalists' Society, Cardiff.

HEATHCOTE, N. 1900. *St. Kilda*. Longmans, Green and Co., London.

HEPBURN, A. 1851. Notes on the Mammalia and Birds found at St. Abbs Head. *Hist. and Proc. Berwickshire Nat. Club* **III**: 70–77, 1850–1856.

HEWITSON, W.C. 1831–38. *British Oology etc.* Privately published, Newcastle Upon Tyne.

HEYSHAM, J. 1794. List of Cumberland Birds, in J. Hutchinson's *History of Cumberland*. **1**: 4–23; **2**: 393–398. Carlisle.

HIBBERT-WARE, A. 1938. *Report of the Little Owl Food Enquiry*. Witherby, London.

HICKLING, R. 1978. *Birds in Leicestershire and Rutland*. Leicestershire and Rutland Ornithological Society, Leicester.

HINDE, R.A. and A.S. THOM. 1947. The breeding of the Moustached Warbler in Cambridgeshire. *Brit. Birds* **40**: 98.

HOLLAND, P., I. SPENCE and T. SUTTON. 1984. *Breeding Birds in Greater Manchester*. Manchester Ornithological Society, Manchester.

HOLLAND, P.K. and D.W. YALDEN. 1991. Population dynamics of Common Sandpipers *Actitis hypoleucos* breeding along an upland river system. *Bird Study* **38**: 151–159.

HOLLAND, P.K. and D.W. YALDEN. 1994. An estimate of lifetime reproductive success for the Common Sandpiper *Actitis hypoleucos*. *Bird Study* **41**: 110–119.

HOLLOM, P.A.D. 1940. Report on the 1938 survey of Black-headed Gull colonies. *Brit. Birds* **33**: 202, 230.

HOPE-JONES, P. 1974. *The Birds of Merioneth*. Cambrian Ornithological Society, Glan Conwy.

HOPE-JONES, P. and P. DARE. 1976. *The Birds of Caernarvonshire*. Cambrian Ornithological Society, Glan Conwy.

HOPE-JONES, P. and J.L. ROBERTS. 1982. Birds of Denbighshire. *Nature in Wales* **1**: 56–65.

HOWARD, H.E. 1902. The Birds of Sark. *The Zoologist* **71**: 416–422.

HOWARD, H.E. 1907–14. *The British Warblers*. R.H. Porter, London.

HUDSON, P.J. 1989. Black Grouse in Britain. *Game Conserv. Ann. Rev.* **20**: 119–124.

HUDSON, P. 1992. *Grouse in Space and Time: the population biology of a managed gamebird*. The Game Conservancy, Fordingbridge.

HUDSON, R. 1972. Collared Doves in Britain and Ireland during 1965–1970. *Brit. Birds* **65**: 139–155.

HUDSON. R. and G.A. PYMAN. 1968. *A Guide to the Birds of Essex*. Essex Birdwatching and Preservation Society, Southend-on-Sea.

HUDSON, W.H. 1898. *Birds in London*. Longmans, Green and Co., London.

HUDSON, W.H. 1903. *Hampshire Days*. Longmans, Green and Co., London.

HUNT, J. 1829. *A General History of the County of Norfolk*. Stacy, Norwich.

HUNTER, E.N. 1970. Great Northern Diver breeding in Scotland. *Scot. Birds* **6**: 195.

HUNTER, E.N. and R.H. DENNIS. 1972. Hybrid Great Northern Diver **x** Black-throated Diver in Wester Ross. *Scot. Birds* **7**: 89–91.

HUSTINGS, F. 1988. *European Monitoring Studies of Breeding Birds*. Beek, The Netherlands.

HUTCHINSON, C.D. 1989. *Birds in Ireland*. Poyser, Calton.

HUTCHINSON, T. 1900. Birds of Herefordshire. *Trans. Woolhope Nat. Field Club*. Transactions for 1899: 190–243.

IM THURN, Sir E.F. 1870. *Birds of Marlborough*. Perkins, Marlborough.

INGRAM, G.C.S. and H. MORREY SALMON. 1939. The Birds of Monmouthshire. *Trans. Cardiff Nat. Society*. **70**: 93–127.

INGRAM, G.C.S. and H. MORREY SALMON. 1954. *A Handlist of the Birds of Carmarthenshire*. West Wales Naturalists' Trust, Haverfordwest..

INGRAM, G.C.S. and H. MORREY SALMON. 1955. *A Handlist of the Birds of Radnorshire*. Herefordshire Ornithological Club, Kington.

INGRAM, G.C.S. and H. MORREY SALMON. 1957. The Birds of Brecknock. *Brycheiniog*. **3**: 182–259.

INGRAM, G.C.S. and H. MORREY SALMON. 1963. Humphreys (rev. ed.), *The Birds of Monmouthshire*. Newport Museum, Newport.

INGRAM, G.C.S., H. MORREY SALMON and W.M.

CONDRY. 1966. *The Birds of Cardiganshire*. The West Wales Naturalists' Trust, Haverfordwest.

IRBY, L.H.L. 1899. Observations on the birds of the islands of Tiree and Coll. *Annls Scot. Nat. Hist.* **8**: 206–210.

IRWIN, R. 1951. *British Bird Books: An Index to British Ornithology*. Grafton, London.

JACKSON, E.E. 1966. The Birds of Foula. *Scot. Birds* **4**: Special Supplement, 1–50.

JACKSON, H.R. 1937. The Birds of Atholl. *Trans. Perthshire Soc. Nat. Sci.* **9**: 173–181.

JENKINS, A.R. 1958. *The Birds of the Letchworth Region*. Letchworth Naturalists' Society, Letchworth.

JENKINS, A.R. 1960. Birds. In *The Coventry District—A Naturalists Guide*. Coventry and District Natural History and Scientific Society, Coventry. pp. 102–110.

JENYNS, Rev. L. 1835. *A Manual of Vertebrated Animals; etc*. Privately published, Cambridge.

JOURDAIN, F.C.R. 1905. Birds. In *Victoria History of the County of Derbyshire*. Dawsons of Pall Mall, London.

JOURDAIN, F.C.R. 1926. Ornithology in J.J. Walker, *The Natural History of the Oxford District*. Oxford University Press, Oxford. pp. 128–160.

KALELA, O. 1949. Changes in geographic ranges in the avifauna of northern and central Europe in relation to recent changes in climate. *Bird Banding* **20**: 77–103.

KELLY, G. 1986. *The Norfolk Bird Atlas*. Norfolk and Norwich Naturalists' Society, Hunstanton.

KELSALL, J.E. 1909. Nesting records of the Kittiwake in the Isle of Wight. *Brit. Birds* **2**: 262–264.

KELSALL, Rev. J.E. and P.W. Munn. 1905. *The Birds of Hampshire and the Isle of Wight*. Witherby, London.

KENNEDY, A.W.M. CLARK. 1868. *The Birds of Berkshire and Buckinghamshire*. Private publication, Eton.

KENNEDY, P.G., R.F. RUTTLEDGE and C.F. SCROOPE. 1954. *The Birds of Ireland*. Oliver and Boyd, Edinburgh.

KENNEDY, P.J. 1961. *A List of the Birds of Ireland*. National Museum of Ireland. Stationery Office, Dublin.

KIRKMAN, F.B. (ed.). 1910–13. *The British Birds Book*. Jack, London.

KNOX, A.E. 1849. *Ornithological Rambles in Sussex*. Van Voorst, London.

LACK, D. 1934. *The Birds of Cambridgeshire*. Cambridge Bird Club, Cambridge.

LACK, P. 1986. *The Atlas of Wintering Birds in Britain and Ireland*. Poyser, Calton.

LACK, P. and D. FERGUSON. 1993. *The Birds of Buckinghamshire*. Buckinghamshire Bird Club, High Wycombe.

LAMB, H.H. 1963. What can we find out about the trend of our climate? *Weather* **18**: 194–216.

LATHAM, J. 1785. *A General Synopsis of Birds, volume III*. Leigh and Sotheby, London.

LATHAM, J. 1821–28. *A General History of Birds*. Privately published, Winchester.

LEVER, C. 1977. *The Naturalized Animals of the British Isles*. Hutchinson, London.

LEVER, C. 1987. *Naturalised Birds of the World*. Longman, London.

LEWIS, S. 1953. *The Breeding Birds of Somerset and their Eggs*. Privately published, Stockwell.

LILFORD, Lord. 1895. *Notes on the Birds of Northamptonshire and Neighbourhood*. R.H. Porter, London.

LITTLEBOY, J.E. 1880. The Birds of Our District. *Trans.*

Watford Nat. Hist. Soc. and Hertfordshire Field Club. **2:** 17–32.

LLOYD, C., M.L. TASKER and K. PARTRIDGE. 1991. *The Status of Seabirds in Britain and Ireland.* Poyser, London.

LLOYD, L.C. 1938. Migratory birds in Shropshire. *Tran. Caradoc and Severn Valley Field Club.* **10:** 214–236.

LOCKLEY, R.M., G.C.S. INGRAM and H.M. SALMON. 1949. *The Birds of Pembrokeshire.* The West Wales Field Society, Haverfordwest.

LOCKIE, J.D. 1955. The breeding habits and food of Short-eared Owls after a vole plague. *Bird Study* **2:** 53–69.

LONDON NATURAL HISTORY SOCIETY. 1964. *Birds of the London Area,* Revised edition. Rupert Hart-Davies, London.

LORD, J. and D.J. MUNNS. 1970. *Atlas of Breeding Birds of West Midlands.* Published for the West Midlands Bird Club by Collins, London.

LOVE, J.A. 1983. *The Return of the Sea Eagle.* Cambridge University Press, Cambridge.

LOVEGROVE, R., G. WILLIAMS and I. WILLIAMS. 1994. *Birds in Wales.* Poyser, London.

LOW, Rev. G. 1813. *Fauna Orcadensis: or The Natural History, etc. of Orkney and Shetland.* Published and edited by Lench, Edinburgh.

LOW, Rev. G. 1879. *A Tour through the Islands of Orkney and Shetland etc.* Kirkwall.

LOW, R. 1992. *Parrots. Their Breeding and Care.* 3rd (rev.) edn. Blandford, Poole.

LOYD, L.R.W. 1929. *The Birds of South East Devon.* Witherby, London.

LUBBOCK, Rev. R. 1845. *Observations on the Fauna of Norfolk.* Longmans, London.

LUBBOCK, Rev. R. 1879. T. Southwell (ed.), *Observations on the Fauna of Norfolk.* New edition. Jarrold, Norwich.

McALDOWIE, A.M. 1893. *The Birds of Staffordshire (reprinted from the Transactions of the North Staffordshire Field Club).* Privately published, Stoke-on-Trent.

MACAULAY, K. 1764. *The History of St.Kilda etc.* Beckett and De Hondt, London.

MACGILLIVRAY, W. 1837–1852. *History of British Birds.* Scott, Webster and Geary, London.

MACGILLIVRAY, W. 1840–42. *A Manual of British Ornithology.* Scott, Webster and Geary, London.

MACGILLIVRAY, W. 1855. *The Natural History of Deeside and Braemar.* Scott, London.

MACKENZIE, N. 1905. Notes on the Birds of St. Kilda. *Annls Scot. Nat. Hist.* **14:** 75–80, 141–153.

MACPHERSON, Rev. H.A. 1892. *A Vertebrate Fauna of Lakeland.* David Douglas, Edinburgh.

MACPHERSON, Rev. H.A. 1901. Bird. In *Victoria History of the County of Cumberland.* Dawsons of Pall Mall, London.

MACPHERSON, Rev. H.A. and W. DUCKWORTH. 1886. *The Birds of Cumberland, critically studied, including some notes on the Birds of Westmorland.* Thurnam and Sons, Carlisle.

MACRURY, J. 1894. The Birds of the Island of Barra. *Annls Scot. Nat. Hist.* **3:** 140–145, 203–214.

MACRURY, J. 1896. Additional Notes on the Birds of the Island of Barra. *Annls of Scot. Nat. Hist.* **3:** 22–24.

MACRURY, J. 1898. The Birds of the Island of Barra—additions and notes. *Annls of Scot. Nat. Hist.* **7:** 75–77.

McWILLIAM, J.M. 1927. *The Birds of the Island of Bute.* Witherby, London.

McWILLIAM, J.M. 1936. *The Birds of the Firth of Clyde.* Witherby, London.

MANSELL-PLEYDELL, J.C. 1888. *The Birds of Dorsetshire.* R.H. Porter, London.

MARCHANT, J.H., R. HUDSON, S.P. CARTER and P. WHITTINGTON. 1990. *Population Trends in British Breeding Birds.* BTO, Tring.

MARQUISS, M. 1981. The Goshawk in Britain—its provenance and present status. In Kenwood, R.E. and M. Lindsey (eds.), *Understanding the Goshawk.* International Association for Falconry, Oxford. pp. 43–55.

MARQUISS, M. 1989. Grey Herons *Ardea cinerea* breeding in Scotland: numbers, distribution and census techniques. *Bird Study* **36:** 181–191.

MARTIN, M. 1698. *A Late Voyage to St. Kilda, etc.* Brown and Goodwin, London.

MASEFIELD, J.R.B. 1908. Birds. In *Victoria History of the County of Staffordshire.* Dawsons of Pall Mall, London.

MASSEY, M.E. 1976. *Birds of Breconshire.* Brecknock Naturalists' Trust, Brecon.

MATHEW, Rev. M.A. 1894. *The Birds of Pembrokeshire and its Islands.* R.H. Porter, London.

MEAD, C.J. and D.J. PEARSON, 1974. Bearded Reedling populations in England and Holland. *Bird Study* **21:** 211–214.

MEAD, C. J. and K. SMITH. 1982. *Hertfordshire Breeding Bird Atlas.* Tring.

MEADE-WALDO, E.G.B. 1900. Birds. In *Victoria History of the County of Hampshire.* Dawsons of Pall Mall, London.

MEEK, E.R. and B. LITTLE. 1977. The spread of the Goosander in Britain and Ireland. *Brit. Birds* **70:** 229–237.

MELLERSH, W.L. 1902. *A Treatise on the Birds of Gloucestershire.* Bellows, Gloucester.

MIKKOLA, H. 1983. *Owls of Europe.* Poyser, Calton.

MILLAIS, J.G. 1902. *The Natural History of the British Surface Feeding Ducks.* Longmans, London.

MILLAIS, J.G. 1905. Birds. In *Victoria History of the County of Sussex.* Dawsons of Pall Mall, London.

MILLAIS, J.G. 1913. *British Diving Ducks.* Longmans, London.

MINISTRY OF AGRICULTURE, FISHERIES AND FOOD. 1993. *Agriculture in the UK.* HMSO, London.

MITCHAM, T. 1992. *Rutland Breeding Bird Atlas.* Spiegl Press, Stamford.

MITCHELL, F.S. 1885. *The Birds of Lancashire.* Van Voorst, London.

MITCHELL, F.S. 1892. *The Birds of Lancashire.* 2nd edition revised by H. Saunders. Gurney and Jackson, London.

MONAGHAN, P. and J.C. COULSON. 1977. The status of large gulls nesting on buildings. *Bird Study* **24:** 89–104.

MONTAGU, G. 1802, 1813. *Ornithological Dictionary, and Supplement.* White, London.

MONTAGU, G. 1833. *Ornithological Dictionary of British Birds,* 2nd. edition, reissue. Rennie, London.

MOORE, N.W. 1957. The past and present status of the Buzzard in the British Isles. *Brit. Birds* **50:** 173–197.

MOORE, R. 1969. *The Birds of Devon.* David and Charles, Newton Abbot.

MORE, A.G. 1865. On the distribution of birds in Great Britain during the nesting season. *The Ibis.* **1:** 1–27,

119–142, 425–458.

MORE, A.G. 1890. *A List of Irish Birds*. HMSO, Dublin.

MOREAU, R.E. 1927. Quail. *Bull. Zool. Soc. Egypt*. **1**: 6–13.

MOREAU, R.E. 1951. The British status of the Quail and some problems of its biology. *Brit. Birds* **44**: 257–276.

MORGAN, D.H.W. 1993. Feral Rose-ringed Parakeets in Britain. *Brit. Birds* **86**: 561–564.

MORLEY, A. 1934. *Bird Life on the Clifton Downs*. J. Baker and Son, Clifton.

MORRES, A.P. 1896. *Amongst the Birds of the Farne Islands*. Brown and Co., Salisbury.

MORREY SALMON, H. *A Supplement to The Birds of Glamorgan 1967*. The Cardiff Naturalists' Society, Cardiff.

MORRIS, A., D. BURGES, R.F. FULLER, A.D. EVANS and K.W. SMITH. 1994. The status and distribution of Nightjars *Caprimulgus europaeus* in Britain in 1992. *Bird Study* **41**: 181–191.

MORRIS, B.R. 1855. *British Gamebirds and Wildfowl*. Groombridge, London.

MORRIS, Rev. F.O. 1851–57. *A History of British Birds*. Groombridge and Son, London.

MOUNTFORT, G. 1957. *The Hawfinch*. Collins, London.

MOXON, J.H.H. 1882. *The Birds of the Fens*. Cambridge University Press, Cambridge.

MUDIE, R. 1834. *The Feathered Tribes of the British Islands*. Whittaker and Son, London.

MUIRHEAD, G. 1889–1895. *The Birds of Berwickshire*. David Douglas, Edinburgh.

MULLENS, W.H. and H.K. SWANN. 1917. *A Bibliography of British Ornithology*. Macmillan and Co., London.

MULLENS, W.H. and H.K. SWANN. 1919–1920. *A Geographical Bibliography of British Ornithology*. Witherby, London.

MULLINS, J.R. 1984. Scarlet Rosefinch breeding in Scotland. *Brit. Birds* **77**: 133–135.

MURRAY, R.D. 1987. Bluethroats in Scotland during 1985. *Scot. Birds* **14**: 168–174.

NASH, J.K. 1935. *The Birds of Midlothian*. Witherby, London.

NELSON, B. 1978. *The Gannet*. Poyser, Berkhamsted.

NELSON, T.H., W.E. CLARKE, and F. BOYES, 1907. *The Birds of Yorkshire*. Brown and Sons, London.

NETHERSOLE-THOMPSON, D. 1931. Field habits and nesting of the Hobby. *Brit. Birds* **25**: 142–150.

NETHERSOLE-THOMPSON, D. 1951. *The Greenshank*. Collins, London.

NETHERSOLE-THOMPSON, D. 1966. *The Snow Bunting*. Oliver and Boyd, Edinburgh.

NETHERSOLE-THOMPSON, D. 1973. *The Dotterel*. Collins, London.

NETHERSOLE-THOMPSON, D. 1975. *Pine Crossbills*. Poyser, Berkhamsted.

NETHERSOLE-THOMPSON, D. 1993. *The Snow Bunting*, New edition. Peregrine Books, Leeds.

NETHERSOLE-THOMPSON, D. and M. NETHERSOLE-THOMPSON. 1979. *Greenshanks*. Poyser, Berkhamsted.

NETHERSOLE-THOMPSON, D. and M. NETHERSOLE THOMPSON. 1986. *Waders: their Breeding, Haunts and Watchers*. Poyser, Calton.

New Statistical Account of Scotland. 1834–45. Edinburgh.

NEWTON, A. and H. GADOW. 1893–96. *A Dictionary of Birds, etc.* A. and C. Black, London.

NEWTON, I. 1967. The feeding ecology of the Bullfinch (*Pyrrhula pyrrhula* L.) in southern England. *Journal of Animal Ecology*. **36**: 721–744a.

NEWTON, I. 1986. *The Sparrowhawk*. Poyser, Calton.

NEWTON, I. 1987. The adaptive radiation and feeding ecology of some British finches. *Ibis* **109**: 33–98.

NEWTON, I. 1993. Studies of West Palearctic birds. 192. Bullfinch. *Brit. Birds* **86**: 638–648.

NEWTON, I. and M.B. HAAS. 1984. The Return of the Sparrowhawk. *Brit. Birds* **77**: 47–70.

NICHOLSON, E.M. (ed.) 1929. Index of the Heron Population. *Brit. Birds* **22**: 106–118.

NICHOLSON, E.M. 1951. *Birds and Men*. Collins, London.

NICHOLSON, E.M., and I.J. FERGUSON-LEES. 1962. The Hastings Rarities. *Brit. Birds* **55**: 345–351.

NOBLE, H. 1898. *A List of European Birds*. R.H. Porter, London.

NOBLE, H. 1899. Letter on the breeding of the Scaup Duck in Sutherlandshire. *Bull. Brit. Orn. Club* **8**: 44–47.

NOBLE, H. 1906. Birds. In *Victoria History of the County of Berkshire*. Dawsons of Pall Mall, London.

NORRIS, C.A. 1945. Summary of a report on the distribution and status of the Corncrake (*Crex crex*). *Brit. Birds* **38**: 142–148, 162–168.

NORRIS, C.A. 1947a. *Notes on the Birds of Warwickshire*. Cornish Brothers Ltd., Birmingham.

NORRIS, C.A. 1947b. Report on the distribution and status of the Corncrake. *Brit. Birds* **40**: 226–244.

NORRIS, C.A. 1951a. *West Midlands Bird Distribution Survey, 1946–50*. Privately published, Birmingham.

NORRIS, C.A. 1951b. The Birds of Warwickshire, Worcestershire and Staffordshire. *RSPB Occasional Publications* No. 17, London.

NORRIS, C.A. 1960. The breeding distribution of thirty bird species in 1952. *Bird Study* **7**: 129.

NORTHERN IRELAND BIRDWATCHERS' ASSOCIATION. 1992. *Northern Ireland Bird Report 1986–90*.

O'CONNOR, R.J. and M. SHRUBB. 1986. *Farming and Birds*. Cambridge University Press, Cambridge.

OAKES, C. 1953. *The Birds of Lancashire*. Oliver and Boyd, Edinburgh.

OAKES, C. and E. BATTERSBY. 1939. *The Birds of East Lancashire*. Privately published, Burnley.

OGILVIE, M.A. 1994. Rare breeding birds in the United Kingdom in 1991. Parrot Crossbill. *Brit. Birds* **87**: 366–393.

OLSSON, V. 1971. Studies of less familiar birds. 165. Serin. *Brit. Birds* **64**: 213–223.

ORDNANCE SURVEY. 1987. *Gazetteer of Great Britain*. Ordnance Survey, London.

ORMEROD, S.J. and S.J. TYLER. 1987. Dippers, *Cinclus cinclus* and Grey Wagtails *Motacilla cinerea* as indicators of stream acidity in upland Wales. *ICBP Technical Publication* No.6.

OWEN, M., G.L. ATKINSON-WILLES, and D.G. SALMON 1986. *Wildfowl in Great Britain*. 2nd edn. Cambridge University Press, Cambridge.

OWEN, D.A.L. 1988. Factors affecting the status of the Chough in England and Wales; 1780–1980. In E. Bignal and D.J. Curtis (eds) *Choughs and Land-use in Europe, the Proceedings of an International Workshop on the Conservation of the Chough*, Pyrrhocorax pyrrhocorax, *in the E.C. 11–14 November 1988*. Scottish Chough Study Group, Tarbert. pp 72–80.

PAGE, G.W., L.E. STENZEL, D.W. WINKLER and C.W. SWARTH. 1983. Spacing out at Mono Lake: breeding success, nest density, and predation in the Snowy Plover. *Auk* **100**: 13–24.

PALMER, E.M. and D.K. BALLANCE. 1968. *The Birds of Somerset*. Longmans, London.

PALMER, M.G. (ed.). 1946. *The Fauna and Flora of the Ilfracombe District of North Devon*. Ilfracombe Field Club.

PARR, D. (ed.). 1972. *Birds in Surrey, 1900–1970*. Batsford, London.

PARR, R. 1992. The decline and extinction of a population of Golden Plover in north-east Scotland. *Ornis Scand.* **23**: 152–158.

PARR, S.J. 1991. Occupation of new conifer plantations by Merlins in Wales. *Bird Study* **38**: 103–111.

PARR, S.J. 1994. Population changes of breeding Hobbies *Falco subbuteo* in Britain. *Bird Study* **41**: 131–135.

PARSLOW, J.L.F. 1973. *Breeding Birds of Britain and Ireland*. Poyser, Berkhamsted.

PASHBY, B.S. 1985. *John Cordeaux—Ornithologist*. Spurn Bird Observatory, Grimsby.

PATERSON, J. 1901. Birds. In *Fauna, Flora and Geology of the Clyde Area, A Handbook Prepared for the Meeting of the British Association at Glasgow*, Glasgow. pp. 160–170.

PATERSON, J. 1927. The British Willow-Titmouse in the Clyde Area. *Scot. Nat.* **16**: 17–23.

PATON, E.R. 1925. *The Birds of Hareshawmuir*. The 'Standard' Office, Kilmarnock.

PATON, E.R. and O.G. PIKE. 1929. *The Birds of Ayrshire*. Witherby, London.

PATTERSON, A.H. 1905. *Nature in Eastern Norfolk*. Methuen, London.

PATTERSON, R.L. 1880. *Birds, Fish and Cetacea of Belfast Lough*. Chapman & Hall, London and Belfast.

PAYN, W.H. 1962. *The Birds of Suffolk*. Barrie and Rockliff, London.

PEAL, R.E.F. 1968. The distribution of the Wryneck in the British Isles, 1964-1966. *Bird Study* **15**: 111–126.

PEARSON, C. 1904. Twite breeding in North Devonshire. *Bull. Brit. Orn. Club XIV*.

PEERS, M. 1985. *The Birds of Radnorshire and Mid-Powys*. Privately published, Llandrindod Wells.

PEERS, M. and M. SHRUBB. 1990. *Birds of Breconshire*. Brecknock Wildlife Trust.

PEIRSON, L.G. 1939. Handlist of the Birds of Marlborough District. *Marlborough College Nat. Hist. Soc. Rep.*, No. 88.

PEIRSON, L.G. 1959. *Wiltshire Birds*. The Wiltshire Archaeological and Natural History Society, Devizes.

PENHALLURICK, R. 1978. *The Birds of Cornwall and the Isles of Scilly*. Headland Publications.

PENNANT, T. 1771. *A Tour in Scotland*. Privately published, Chester.

PENNANT, T. 1772. Supplement to *A Tour of Scotland*. Privately published, Chester.

PENNANT, T. 1776. *A Tour in Scotland*. 4th edn. White, London.

PENNANT, T. 1778. *A Tour in Wales*. Privately published, London.

PENNIE, I.D. 1951. The history and distribution of the Capercaillie in Scotland. *Scot. Nat.* **62**: 65–87 and **63**: 4–17, 135.

PERRY, R. 1948. *Shetland Sanctuary*. Faber and Faber, London.

PETTY, S.J. 1989. Goshawks: their status, requirements and management. *Forestry Commission Bulletin* 81. HMSO, London.

PHILIPS, J.C. 1923–26. *Natural History of the Ducks*. Publisher unknown, Boston, USA.

PHILLIPS, E.C. 1899. *The Birds of Breconshire*. Edwin Davies, Brecon.

PHILLIPS, E.C. 1908. Birds. In *Victoria History of the County of Herefordshire*. Dawsons of Pall Mall, London.

PHILLIPS, W.N. 1948. *The Birds of Breconshire*. Privately published, Brecon.

PIDSLEY, W.E.H. 1891. *The Birds of Devonshire*. Gibbings, London.

PIERSMA, T. 1986. Breeding waders in Europe: a review of population size estimates and a bibliography of information sources. *Wader Study Group Bulletin, Supplement*. **48**: 1–116.

PITT, R.G. 1967. Savi's Warbler breeding in Kent. *Brit. Birds* **60**: 349–355.

POTTS, G.R. 1969. The influence of eruptive movements, age, population size and other factors on the survival of the Shag *Phalacrocorax aristotelis*. *J. Anim. Ecol.* **38**: 53–102.

POTTS, G.R. 1970. Recent changes in the farmland fauna with special reference to the decline of the Grey Partridge. *Bird Study*. **17**: 145–660.

POTTS, G.R. 1986. *The Partridge: Pesticides, Predation and Conservation*. Collins, London.

POTTS, G. R. and N.J. AEBISCHER. 1995. *Ibis*, in press.

POWER, F.D. 1910. *Ornithological Notes from a South London Suburb*. Glaisher, London.

PRENDERGAST, E.D.V. and J.V. BOYS. 1983. *The Birds of Dorset*. David and Charles, Newton Abbot.

PRENTIS, W. 1894. *Notes on the Birds of Rainham*. Gurney and Jackson, London.

PRESTT, I. 1965. An enquiry into the recent breeding status of some of the smaller birds of prey and crows in Britain. *Bird Study* **12**: 196–221.

PYMAN, G.A. 1959. The status of the Red-crested Pochard in the British Isles. *Brit. Birds* **52**: 42–56.

PYMAN, G.A. and C.B. WAINWRIGHT. 1952. The Breeding of the Gull-billed Tern in Essex. *Brit. Birds* **45**: 337–339.

RACKHAM, O. 1986. *The History of the Countryside*. Dent, London.

RADFORD, M.C. 1966. *The Birds of Berkshire and Oxfordshire*. Longmans, London.

RALFE, P.G. 1906. *The Birds of the Isle of Man*. David Douglas, Edinburgh.

RATCLIFFE, D. 1980. *The Peregrine Falcon*. Poyser, Calton.

REED, T.M., A. CURRIE and J.A. LOVE. 1983. The Birds of the Inner Hebrides. *Proc. Roy. Soc. Edinburgh* **84B**: 449–472.

RICHARDSON, M.G. 1990. The distribution and status of the Whimbrel *Numenius p. phaeopus* in Shetland and Britain. *Bird Study* **37**: 61–68.

RINTOUL, L.J. and E.V. BAXTER. 1935. *A Vertebrate Fauna of Forth*. Oliver and Boyd, Edinburgh.

RIVIERE, B.B. 1930. *A History of the Birds of Norfolk*. Witherby, London.

ROBERTS, P. 1985. *The Birds of Bardsey*. The Bardsey Bird and Field Observatory.

ROBERTSON, J. 1903. A List of the Birds of the Island of Bute. *Annls Scot. Nat. Hist.* **47**: 135–144.

ROBERTSON, P. and M. WOODBURN. 1993. *The*

Pheasant. The New Fur, Feather and Fin, volume 1.

RODD, E.H. 1880. *The Birds of Cornwall and the Scilly Islands*. Trübner and Co., London.

ROWAN, W. 1915. The Blakeney Point Ternery. *Brit. Birds*. 8: 250–266.

RUFFER, J.G. 1977. *The Big Shots; Edwardian Shooting Parties*. Quiller Press, London.

RUTTER, E.M., F.C. GRIBBLE and T.W. PEMBERTON. 1964. *A Handlist of the Birds of Shropshire*. The Shropshire Ornithological Society, Shrewsbury.

RUTTLEDGE, R.F. 1966. *Ireland's Birds*. Witherby, London.

RYVES, B.H. 1948. *Bird Life in Cornwall*. Collins, London.

RYVES, B.H and H.M. QUICK. 1946. A survey of the status of birds breeding in Cornwall and Scilly since 1906. *Brit. Birds* 39: 3, 34.

SAGE, B.L. 1959. *A History of the Birds of Hertfordshire*. Barrie and Rockliff, London.

ST JOHN, C.W.G. 1848. *A Sportsman and Naturalist's Tour in Sutherlandshire*. Murray, London.

St JOHN, C.W.G. 1863. *Natural History and Sport in Moray*, David Douglas, Edinburgh.

SALTER, J.H. 1895–1904. Observations on Birds in Mid-Wales. The Zoologist.(3) **19**: 179; (3) **20**: 24–26; (4) **8**: 66–71.

SALTER, J.H. 1900. *List of the Birds of Aberystwyth and Neighbourhood*. University College of Wales Scientific Society, Aberystwyth.

SALTER, J.H. 1928. The Kite in South Wales. *Trans. Cardiff Nat. Soc.* **61**: 77–85.

SANDS, J. 1877. *Out of the World; or life in St. Kilda*, 2nd edition. MacLachlan and Stewart, Edinburgh.

SAUNDERS, D.R. 1962. Storm Petrels on Skokholm. *Nature in Wales* **8**: 59–60.

SAUNDERS, H. 1889. *Illustrated Manual of British Birds*. Van Voorst, London.

SAUNDERS, H and W. EAGLE CLARKE. 1927. *An Illustrated Manual of British Birds*. 3rd. edition. Gurney and Jackson, London.

SAXBY, H.L. 1874. *The Birds of Shetland*. MacLachlan and Stewart, Edinburgh.

SCHLAPFER, A. 1988. Populationsokologie der Feldlerche *Alauda arvensis* in der intensiv genutzen Agrarlandschaft. *Orn. Beob.* **85**: 309–371.

SEAGO, M.J. 1967. *The Birds of Norfolk*. Jarrolds, London.

SEALY, A.F. 1859. Baillon's Crake nesting in Cambridgeshire. *The Zoologist* (1) **17**: 6329.

SEEBOHM, H. 1883–85. *A History of British Birds*. R.H. Porter, London.

SEEBOHM, H. 1884. On a new species of British Wren. *The Zoologist* **8**: 333–335.

SEEBOHM, H. 1890. *Classification of Birds*. R.H. Porter, London.

SEEBOHM, H. and J.A. HARVIE-BROWN. 1901. *The Birds of Siberia*. Murray, London.

SELBY, P.J. 1821. *Illustrations of British Ornothology*. Constable, London.

SELBY, P.J. 1833. Illustrations of British Ornithology, Longman, Rees, Orme, Brown, Green and Longman, London.

SELBY, P.J. 1834. Observations on the Birds observed in the Neighbourhood of Coldbrandspath in April, and these at St Abbs' Head in July 1832, and June 1833, *History and Proceedings of the Berwickshire Naturalists' Club* **1**: 18–20, 20–22.

SELBY, P.J. 1835. On the birds inhabiting the County of Sutherland, etc. *Trans. Nat. Hist. Soc. of Northumberland and Durham*. **I**: 288.

SELBY, P.J. 1841. Report on the Ornithology of Berwickshire and District. *Hist. and Proc. Berwickshire Nat. Club* I: 250-62.

SELLERS, R.M. 1991. Breeding and wintering status of the Cormorant in the British Isles. *Proc. Workshop 1989 on Cormorants* Phalacrocorax carbo. Rijkswaterstaat Directorate Flevoland, Lelystad: 30–35.

SERVICE, R. 1902. The Vertebrate Zoology of Kirkcudbrightshire. In Maxwell. *Guide Book to the Stewartry of Kirkcudbright*. 7th. edition. Privately published, Castle Douglas. pp. 193–215.

SERVICE, R. 1906. The Waders of Solway. *Proc. Nat. Hist. Soc. of Glasgow*. **8**: 46-60

SHARROCK, J.T.R. 1976. *The Atlas of Breeding Birds in Britain and Ireland*. Poyser, Calton.

SHARROCK, J.T.R. 1981. *Birds New to Britain and Ireland*. Poyser, Calton.

SHARROCK, J.T.R. and E.M. SHARROCK, 1976. *Rare Birds in Britain and Ireland*. Poyser, Berkhamsted.

SHEPPARD, R. and R.E. GREEN. 1994. Status of the Corncrake in Ireland in 1993. *Irish Birds* **5**: 125–138.

SHEPPARD, Rev. R. and Rev. W. WHITEAR. 1826. A Catalogue of the Norfolk and Suffolk Birds, with remarks. *Trans. Linnean Soc.* **36**: 14–34.

SHIRREFF, J. 1814. *General View of the Agriculture of the Orkney Islands*. Edinburgh.

SHRUBB, M. 1976. *The Birds of Sussex – their present status*. Phillimore and Co., Chichester.

SIM, G. 1903. *The Vertebrate Fauna of Dee*. Wyllie and Son, Aberdeen.

SINCLAIR, J. 1791–99. *The Statistical Account of Scotland*. W. Creech, Edinburgh.

SITTERS, H.P. 1982. The decline of the Cirl Bunting in Britain, 1968-80. *British Birds* **75**: 105-108.

SITTERS, H.P. 1985. Cirl Buntings in Britain in 1982. *Bird Study* **32**: 1–10.

SITTERS, H.P. 1988. *Tetrad Atlas of the Breeding Birds of Devon*. Devon Birdwatching and Preservation Society, Yelverton.

SKIRVING, R.S. 1878. The Birds of Islay. *Proc. Roy Phys. Soc. of Edinburgh*. **10**: 35–43.

SLATER, Rev. H.H. 1902. Birds. In *Victoria History of the County of Northamptonshire*. Dawsons of Pall Mall, London.

SMITH, Rev. A.C. 1887. *The Birds of Wiltshire*. R.H. Porter, London.

SMITH, A.E. and R.K. CORNWALLIS. 1955. The Birds of Lincolnshire. *Lincolnshire Nat. Hist. Brochure* No.2

SMITH, Cecil. 1869. *The Birds of Somersetshire*. Van Voorst, London.

SMITH, Cecil. 1879. *The Birds of Guernsey and the Neighbouring Islands*. Van Voorst, London.

SMITH, Charles. 1750. *The Antient and Present State of the County and City of Cork etc.* Privately published, Dublin.

SMITH, H. 1974. *Birds of the Sheffield Area*. Sheffield City Museums and Sorby Natural History Society, Sheffield.

SMITH, R.D. 1993. The population dynamics of Snow Buntings in the Cairngorms. *Report to Scottish Natural Heritage*, Edinburgh.

SMITH, R.D., M. MARQUISS, D.P. WHITFIELD and D.B.A. THOMPSON. In press. Snow Buntings in Scotland: an update.

SMITH, S. 1950. *The Yellow Wagtail.* Collins, London.

SMITH, T. 1930–38. The Birds of Staffordshire. *Trans. North Staffordshire Field Club.* Appendices 1–9 in Vol. 64–72.

SMOUT, A-M. 1986. *The Birds of Fife – an outline of their status and distribution.* John Donald, Edinburgh.

SOUTHWELL, T. 1901. Birds. In *Victoria History of the County of Norfolk.* Dawsons of Pall Mall, London.

SPENCER, K.G. 1973. *Status and Distribution of Birds in Lancashire.* Privately published.

STATON, J. 1945. The breeding of Black-winged Stilts in Nottinghamshire in 1945. *Brit. Birds* 38: 322–328.

STEELE-ELLIOTT, J. 1895. Observations on the fauna of St. Kilda. *The Zoologist* 19: 282–286.

STEELE-ELLIOTT, J. 1897–1901. *The Vertebrate Fauna of Bedfordshire.* Privately published, Birmingham.

STEELE-ELLIOTT, J. 1904. Birds. In *Victoria History of the County of Bedfordshire.* Dawsons of Pall Mall, London.

STENZEL, L.E., J.C. WARRINER, J.S. WARRINER, K.S. WILSON, F.C. BIDSTRUP and G.W. PAGE. 1994. Long-distance breeding dispersal of Snowy Plovers in western North America. *J. Anim. Ecol.* 63: 887–902.

STEVEN, H.M. and A. CARLISLE, 1959. *The Native Pinewoods of Scotland.* Oliver and Boyd, Edinburgh.

STERLAND, W.J. 1869. *The Birds of Sherwood Forest.* Reeve and Co., London.

STERLAND, W.J. and J. WHITAKER. 1879. *A Descriptive List of the Birds of Nottinghamshire.* Privately published, Mansfield.

STEVENSON, H. 1866–90. *The Birds of Norfolk.* Van Voorst, London.

STROUD, D.A. and D. GLUE. 1991. *Britain's Birds in 1989–90: the conservation and monitoring review.* BTO/NCC, Thetford.

STROUD, D.A., T.M. REED, M.W. PIENKOWSKI and R.A. LINDSAY. 1987. *Birds, Bogs and Forestry. The Peatlands of Caithness and Sutherland.* NCC, Peterborough.

SUMMERS-SMITH, J.D. 1989. A history of the status of the Tree Sparrow *Passer montanus* in the British Isles. *Bird Study* 36: 23–31.

SWAINE, C.M. 1982. *The Birds of Gloucestershire.* Alan Sutton, Gloucester.

SWANN, H.K. 1893. *Birds of London.* Swan Sonnenschien, London.

SWANN, H.K. 1923. *A Chronological List of British Birds, a supplement to A Bibliography of British Ornithology.* Wheldon and Wesley, London.

SWEET, R. 1823–32. *The British Warblers.* Private publication, London.

SWENNEN, C. 1977. (Population structure and food of the Eider *Somateris m. mollissima* in the Dutch Wadden Sea.) Dutch with English summary. *Ardea* 64: 311–371.

SWINBURNE, J. 1885. Notes on the islands of Sula Sgeir, or North Barra and North Rona, with a list of birds inhabiting them. *Proc. Roy. Phys. Soc. Edinburgh* 8: 51–67.

SZÉKELY, T. and C.M. LESSELLS. 1993. Mate change by Kentish Plovers *Charadrius alexandrinus.* *Ornis Scand* 24: 317–322.

TAPPER, S. 1992. *Game Heritage: An Ecological Review from Shooting and Gamekeeping Records.* Game Conservancy, Fordingbridge.

TATE, P. 1985. *A Century of Bird Books.* Witherby, London.

TATNER, P. 1983. The diet of urban Magpies *Pica pica.* *Ibis* 125: 90–107.

TAYLOR, D.W., D.L. DAVENPORT and J.M.M. FLEGG. 1984. *The Birds of Kent.* Kent Ornithological Society, Tonbridge.

TEGETMEIER, W.G. 1911. *Pheasants, their Natural History and Practical Management.* Cox, London.

TEMPERLEY, G.W. 1946. Breeding of the Black Redstart in Britain: a century-old record. *Brit. Birds* 39: 110.

TEMPERLEY, G.W. 1951. A History of the Birds of Durham. *Trans. Nat. Hist. Soc. Northumberland, Durham and Newcastle Upon Tyne.* Vol. 10: 1–296.

THOM, V.M. 1986. *Birds in Scotland.* Poyser, Calton.

THOMAS, D.K. 1992. *An Atlas of Breeding Birds in West Glamorgan.* The Gower Ornithological Society, Llanmorlais.

THOMPSON, D.B.A. and A. BROWN. 1992. Biodiversity in montane Britain: habitat variation, vegetation diversity and objectives for conservation. *Biodiv. and Conserv.* 1: 179–208.

THOMPSON, D.B.A., A.H. HUSTER and M.B. USHER (eds.). 1994. *Heaths and Moorlands: cultural landscapes.*

THOMPSON, P.S. and W.G. HALE. 1993. Adult survival and numbers in a coastal breeding population of Redshank *Tringa totanus* in north-west England. *Ibis* 135: 61–69.

THOMPSON, W. 1849–1856. *The Natural History of Ireland.* Reeve, Benham.

THORNTON, Colonel T. 1804. *A Sporting Tour through the Northern Parts of England and the great part of the Highlands of Scotland etc..*, London.

TICEHURST, C.B. 1932. *The Birds of Suffolk.* Gurney and Jackson, London.

TICEHURST, N.F. 1909. *A History of the Birds of Kent.* Witherby, London.

TICEHURST, N.F. 1957. *The Mute Swan in England.* Cleaver-Hume, London.

TICEHURST, N.F. and F.C.R. JOURDAIN. 1911. On the distribution of the Nightingale during the breeding season in Great Britain. *Brit. Birds.* 5: 2–21.

TOMES, R.F. 1901. Birds. In *Victoria History of the County of Worcestershire.* Dawsons of Pall Mall, London.

TOMES, R.F. 1904. Birds. In *Victoria History of the County of Warwickshire.* Dawsons of Pall Mall, London.

TRISTAM, Rev. H.B. 1905. Birds. In *Victoria History of the County of Durham.* Dawsons of Pall Mall, London.

TRODD, P. and D. KRAMER. 1991. *Birds of Bedfordshire.* Castlemead, Welwyn Garden City.

TUBBS, C.R. 1963. The significance of the New Forest to the status of the Dartford Warbler in England. *Brit. Birds* 56: 41–48.

TUBBS, C.R. 1967. Numbers of Dartford Warblers in England during 1962–66. *Brit. Birds* 60: 87–89.

TUCK, Rev. J.G. 1891. *The Ornithology of Suffolk.* Privately published, Sheffield.

TUCK, Rev. J.G. 1911. Birds. In *Victoria History of the County of Suffolk.* Dawsons of Pall Mall, London.

TUCKER, G.M., S.M. DAVIES and R.J. FULLER. 1994. The ecology and conservation of Lapwings *Vanellus vanellus.* UK Nature Conservation No. 9.

TULLOCH, R.J. 1968. Snowy Owl breeding in Shetland in 1967. *Brit. Birds* 61: 119–132.

TURNBULL, W.C. 1867. *Birds of East Lothian and a por-*

tion of the adjoining counties. Privately published, Glasgow.

TURNER, A. and C. ROSE. 1989. *Swallows and Martins – an identification guide and handbook*. Houghton Mifflin, Boston.

TURNER, E.S. 1964. *All Heaven in a Rage*. Michael Joseph, London.

TYLER, S. and S. ORMEROD. 1994. *The Dippers*. Poyser, London.

USSHER, R.J. and R. WARREN. 1900. *The Birds of Ireland*. Gurney and Jackson, London.

VENABLES, L.S.V. and U.M. VENABLES. 1955. *Birds and Mammals of Shetland*. Oliver and Boyd, Edinburgh.

VILLAGE, A. 1990. *The Kestrel*. Poyser, London.

VINICOMBE, K., J. MARCHANT and A. KNOX. 1993. Review of status and categorisation of feral birds on the British List. *Brit. Birds* 86: 605–614.

VOOUS, K.H. 1960. *Atlas of European Birds*. Nelson, Amsterdam.

WALPOLE-BOND, J.A. 1903. *Bird Life in Wild Wales*. Fisher Unwin, London.

WALPOLE-BOND, J.A. 1914. *Field Studies of Some Rarer British Birds*. Witherby, London.

WALPOLE-BOND, J.A. 1938. *A History of Sussex Birds*. Witherby, London.

WALSH, P.M., J. SEARS and M. HEUBECK. 1991. Seabird numbers and breeding success in 1990. *NCC Chief Scientist Directorate Report* No. 1235.

WARDE-FOWLER, W. 1906. The Marsh Warbler: a breeding record of 14 years. *The Zoologist* 10: 401–409.

WARING, M. and S. DAVIS, 1983. Rediscovery of Leach's Petrels breeding in Ireland. *Irish Birds* 2: 360–363.

WATSON, A. and R.D. SMITH. 1991. Scottish Snow Bunting numbers in summer 1970–87. *Scot. Birds* 16: 53–56.

WATSON, D. 1977. *The Hen Harrier*. Poyser, Berkhamsted.

WATSON, H.C. 1847–59. *Cybele Britannica*. London.

WATSON, H.C. 1873–74. *Topographical Botany*. Quaritch, London.

WHITAKER, J. 1906. Bird. In *Victoria History of the County of Nottinghamshire*. Dawsons of Pall Mall, London.

WHITAKER, J. 1907. *Notes on the Birds of Nottinghamshire*. Walter Black and Co., Ltd., Nottingham.

WHITE, F.B. 1872. Insecta Scotica – introduction. *Scottish Naturalist* 1: 161–162.

WHITE, G. 1789. *The Natural History and Antiquities of Selbourne, etc.* B. White and Son, London.

WHITE, W.W. 1931. *Bird Life in Devon*. Cape, London.

WHITLOCK, F.B. 1893. *The Birds of Derbyshire*. Bemrose and Sons Ltd., London.

WHITTAKER, I. 1932. *The Birds of Heywood District*. Robert Howe Ltd., Heywood.

WIGLESWORTH, J. 1903. St Kilda and its Birds. Reprinted from the *Liverpool Biological Society*.

WILLIAMS, J. 1957. Changed status of birds observed on survey of St. Tudwal's Island, North Wales, 1956. *Merseyside Naturalists' Association Bird Report 1955–57*.

WILLIAMSON, K. 1964. A census of breeding land birds on Hirta, St. Kilda, in summer 1963. *Bird Study* 11: 153–167.

WILLIAMSON, K. 1965. *Fair Isle and its Birds*. Oliver and Boyd, Edinburgh.

WILMORE, A., A.N. WILMORE, W. GRAVESON, R. MORSE and W. BICKERTON. 1925. *The Natural History of Hertfordshire*. G. Bell and Sons Ltd., London.

WILSON, J.D. and S.J. BROWNE. 1993. Habitat selection and breeding success of Skylarks *Alauda arvensis* on organic and conventional farmland. BTO *Research Report* 129, Thetford.

WILSON, J.O. 1933. *Birds of Westmorland and the Northern Pennines*. Hutchinson and Co., London.

WISE, J.R. 1862. *The New Forest: its history and scenery*. London.

WITCHELL, C.A. and W.B. STRUGNELL. 1892. *The Fauna and Flora of Gloucestershire*. James, Stroud.

WITHERBY, H.F. and N.F. TICEHURST. 1908. The spread of the Little Owl from the chief centres of its introduction. *Brit. Birds* 1: 335–342.

WITHERBY, H.F., F.C.R. JOURDAIN, N.F. TICEHURST and B.W. TUCKER. 1938–41. *The Handbook of British Birds*. Witherby, London.

WOLLEY, J. 1864–1907. *Ootheca Wolleyana*. R.H. Porter, London.

WOOD, N.A. 1974. The breeding behaviour and biology of the Moorhen. *Brit. Birds* 67: 104–158.

YALDEN, D.W. 1992. The influence of recreational disturbance on Common Sandpipers *Actitis hypoleucos* breeding by an upland reservoir. *Biol. Conserv.* 61: 41–49.

YAPP, W.B. 1983. Game-birds in medieval England. *Ibis* 125: 218–221.

YARRELL, W. 1837–1843. *A History of British Birds*. Van Voorst, London.

YARRELL, W. 1871–1885. *History of British Birds*, 4th revised edition. Van Voorst, London.

YOUNG, A. 1804. *A General Review of the Agriculture of Norfolk*. Board of Agriculture, London.

ZONFRILLO, B. 1994 Garefowl or Great Auk *Pinguinus impennis*. *Brit. Birds* 87: 269–270.

ACKNOWLEDGEMENTS

A great many people have been instrumental in ensuring that this project has finally come to fruition and that it is as accurate as I can possibly make it. I have received help in a number of ways from a variety of people. Without the assistance of some, the book would never have been either started or completed. Without others, it would not have achieved, as I believe, a reasonable level of authority and accuracy. Stephen Bainbridge first kindled my interest in the Victorian avifaunas and later, as the concept of the book germinated, Tony Cross and Caroline Moscrop, with great patience, enthusiasm and tolerance, helped me turn an embryonic idea into something that would be both possible and worthwhile. Peter Rathbone and J.T.R. Sharrock lent their enthusiasm to the project and introduced me to Andrew Richford at T. & A.D. Poyser. With the support of friends, especially Pat Woodhead, my family, Andrew Richford and David Gibbons, I eventually swallowed hard and threw in a good job in industry to settle down to put the results of my reading of hundreds of dusty but evocative Victorian ornithological accounts onto paper. Without these people the book may never have come to have been written. But others have also helped. Without the following the book may never have achieved the authority that I hope it has. All have reviewed the accounts of the bird species of which they have special knowledge and suggested sources that I had missed, different interpretations of what I had found and the most up-to-date thoughts on recent changes in those species' fortunes: Dr. Mark Avery, Dr Stephen Baillie, Dr. Colin Bibby, Dr. Mike Brooke, Dr. David Bryant, Dr. James Cadbury, John Callion, Dr. Lennox Campbell, Dr. Steve Carter, Dr. John Cayford, Peter Davies, John Day, Roy Dennis, Paul Donald, Dr. Andy Evans, Dr. Chris Feare, Dr. Jim Flegg, Dr. Tony Fox, Dr. Rob Fuller, Dr. Robert Furness, Dr. Ernest Garcia, Dr. David Gibbons, David Glue, Dr. Andy Gosler, Murray Grant, Dr. Rhys Green, Dr. David Harper, Dr. Mike Harris, Andrew Henderson, Dr. David Hill, Dr. David Houston, Dr. Peter Hudson, David Jardine, Dr. Martin Kelsey, Jeff Kirby, Dr. Alan Knox, Dr. Kate Lessells, Sir Christopher Lever, John Love, Dr. Mick Marquiss, Chris Mead, Dr. Pat Monaghan, Eric Bignall, Dr. Dorian Moss, Dr. Ian Newton, Dr. Mark O'Brien, Dr. Malcolm Ogilvie, Steve Parr, Dr. Ian Patterson, Dr. Chris Perrins, Dr. Dick Potts, Tony Prater, Dr. Stan da Prato, Dr. Robert Prys-Jones, Dr. Derek Ratcliffe, Dr. Jim Reid, Dr. Peter Robertson, Dr. Janet Sears, Dr. J.T.R. Sharrock, Mike Shrubb, Dr. Ken Smith, Dr. David Snow, Dr. Denis Summers-Smith, Dr. Mark Tasker, Dr. Des Thompson, Dr. Patrick Thompson, Dr. Colin Tubbs, Dr. Stephanie Tyler, Dr. Paul Walsh, Dr. Sarah Wanless, Dr. Jeff Watson, Dr. Jeremy Wilson, Dr Derek Yalden.

I am grateful to the British Trust for Ornithology for allowing use of the distribution maps from *The Atlas of Breeding Birds in Britain and Ireland* as comparative companions to my own.

Above all, Pauline provided support, care and cups of tea through all of my work and without her the thing would never have happened.

Index of bird names

Main entry in **bold type**.